Edwin Pa posite School

D1179703

SCIENCE 30

Science 30
Alberta Education
ISBN 978-0-7741-2891-9
Reprint 2015

SCIENCE 30 PROJECT TEAM

Project Managers

Stephen Gallagher, Teacher
W. P. Wagner School of Science and Technology
Edmonton, Alberta

Dan Leskiw, Teacher
Victoria Composite School for the Performing Arts
Edmonton, Alberta

Authors and Field-Test Teachers

Stan Bissell, Teacher
W. P. Wagner School of Science and Technology
Edmonton, Alberta

Jon Carstensen-Sinha, Teacher
M. E. LaZerte Composite High School
Edmonton, Alberta

Mark Haak, Teacher
W. P. Wagner School of Science and Technology
Edmonton, Alberta

Cliff Sosnowski, Department Head of Science
Louis St. Laurent High School
Edmonton, Alberta

Program Consultants

John Drader, Science Examination Manager
Learner Assessment Branch, Alberta Education
Learning and Teaching Resources Branch, Alberta Education

Caroline Nixon, Program Manager
K–12 Science, Curriculum Branch, Alberta Education

Vic Romanyshyn, Resource Manager
K–12 Science
Learning and Teaching Resources Branch, Alberta Education

Stella Shrum, Assistant Director
K–12 Core Programs, Curriculum Branch, Alberta Education

Content Reviewers

Bryan Clintberg, Teacher
Archbishop O'Leary High School
Edmonton, Alberta

John Drader, Science Examination Manager
Learner Assessment Branch, Alberta Education

Jack Edwards, Examination Manager
Learner Assessment Branch, Alberta Education

Caroline Nixon, Program Manager
K–12 Science, Curriculum Branch, Alberta Education

John Pachkowski, Science Teacher
Alberta Distance Learning Centre

Vic Romanyshyn, Resource Manager
K–12 Science
Learning and Teaching Resources Branch, Alberta Education

Wade Strass, Teacher
Spruce Grove Composite High School
Spruce Grove, Alberta

Greg Voigt, Teacher
Archbishop Oscar Romero High School
Edmonton, Alberta

Elizabeth Goodwin, Teacher
Archbishop O'Leary High School
Edmonton, Alberta

Production

Instructional Designer
Maureen Stanley
Resource Sector, Alberta Education

Developed by Distributed Learning Resources Branch Alberta Education, Barrhead

Director
Hélène Fournier

Editing Coordinator
Lori Ristoff

Editors
Suzanne Babiuk, Dave Quick,
& Jerritt Sabiston

Publishing Coordinator
Lance Gerhardt

Desktop Publishers
Roxanne Goerz & Christine Scarlett

Graphic Designer
Dave Bell

Multimedia Coordinator
Phil Christiansen

Multimedia Production
Alison Jones & Yin Maung

Copyright Coordinator
Leslie Peppler

Copyright Officer
Hal Welke

Library Services
Barbara Thomas

Distributed Learning Contributor
Eldon Krikke

Production Support
Marlene Greig
Peter Livermore
Marguerite Reynolds

Contracted Services

Social Considerations Reviewer
Patricia Milligan, Certified Recognizing Diversity
and Promoting Respect Analyst

Indexing
Judy Dunlop Information Services

Editorial Review
Jim and Janice Ackroyd, Acrotech Education Services

Video Production
Frame 30 Productions Ltd., Edmonton, Alberta

Multimedia Production
SWUR.com Corporation, Edmonton, Alberta

Printing by Program Resources Branch Alberta Education, Barrhead

Production Manager
Mike Emery

Bindery Supervisor
Fred Thistle

The authors and Alberta Education would like to thank the students and teachers
who participated in the field tests, photography sessions, and video productions.

WELCOME TO Science 30

Units

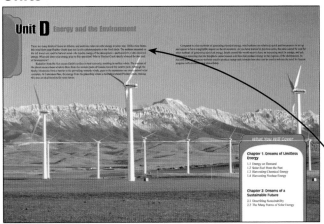

Science 30 provides an opportunity for you to explore connections among societal issues, technologies, and science. Science 30 organizes these explorations into four units. They are Unit A: Maintaining Health; Unit B: Chemistry and the Environment; Unit C: Electromagnetic Energy; and Unit D: Energy and the Environment. Each unit opens with an introduction that establishes the theme. In the case of Energy and the Environment, the theme is balancing the need for human progress with environmental stewardship.

> The introduction includes key questions that encourage you to begin to think about the main ideas to be explored in that unit.

Chapters

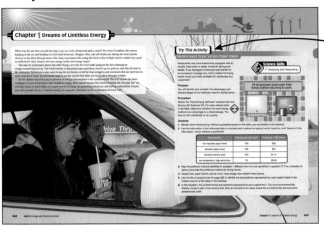

> Each chapter begins with an activity. This is a hands-on learning activity that provides immediate contact with the science concepts developed in the chapter.

Each of the chapters within a unit focuses on one aspect of the theme for that unit. Chapter 1 of Unit D begins by considering how most people in the modern world use energy. Patterns of energy consumption are investigated by considering the energy technologies that are used to make energy available for everyday activities.

Lessons

> The opening of a lesson often begins by making links to things you have learned in other chapters or in previous courses.

Each lesson within a chapter focuses on a key science concept that links to the chapter's story line and the unit's overall theme. Throughout each lesson, a concept is presented in a story that weaves the science knowledge and skills, societal issues, and technological applications.

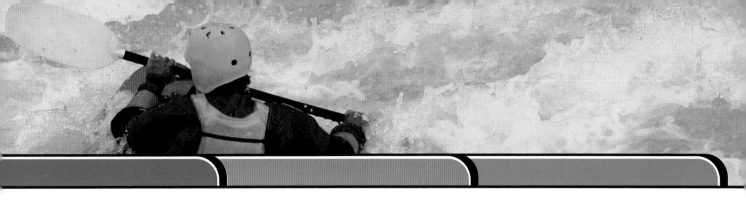

Learning with Technology

Science 30 Textbook CDs

Many activities require the use of a computer. In many cases, this means that you will have to access information on the Science 30 Textbook CDs, which are attached to the back cover of the textbook. The information may be in the form of an applet, a computer simulation, a video, a spreadsheet, or a handout needed to complete an activity.

LearnAlberta.ca

LearnAlberta.ca is a protected digital learning environment for Albertans. This Alberta Education portal, found at http://www.learnalberta.ca, is a place where you can support your learning by accessing resources for projects, homework, help, review, or study.

For example, LearnAlberta.ca contains a large Online Reference Centre that includes multimedia encyclopedias, journals, newspapers, transcripts, images, maps, and more. The National Geographic site contains many current video clips that have been indexed for Alberta Programs of Study. The content is organized by grade level, subject, and curriculum objective. Use the search engine to quickly find key concepts. Check this site often as new interactive multimedia segments are being added all the time.

If you find that a password is required, contact your teacher or school to get one. No fee is required.

Alternative Learning Environments and Distributed Learning

Although many students who enrol in Science 30 will be in a traditional classroom with a teacher, an increasing number of students will find themselves in alternative learning environments. The options include online or virtual schools, home education, outreach programs, and alternative programs.

Distributed learning students can find customized resources on the Science 30 Textbook CDs in the folder called Distributed Learning Student Guide.

Visual Cues

Visual cues are provided throughout the textbook to help remind you about the special requirements of a particular learning activity.

Technology indicates that you will be using specialized computer software to complete the learning activity. The software could be designed for developing spreadsheets, multimedia presentations, or documents.

Internet Search is a cue reminding you that the activity requires you to complete a search to gather specific topic information. The activity will provide focusing questions that will help direct your searching.

Science 30 Textbook CD is a cue reminding you to access information on either CD. The information could be in the form of an applet, a data table, a spreadsheet, or some form of a handout.

Safety

Many learning activities in this course require you to be especially cautious because you will be dealing with potentially hazardous materials. The caution icon alerts you to the hazards and indicates helpful procedures and techniques.

CAUTION!
Use gloves, safety glasses, and a lab apron for this activity.

Science Skills

The specific skills that you will be practising in an investigation or in an activity are indicated by a visual cue. Some activities may require you to use only one skill, while others may require you to practise all of them.

Science Skills
- ✓ Initiating and Planning
- ✓ Performing and Recording
- ✓ Analyzing and Interpreting
- ✓ Communication and Teamwork

Special Learning Activities

Investigations

Investigations are opportunities to practise the inquiry skills of science.

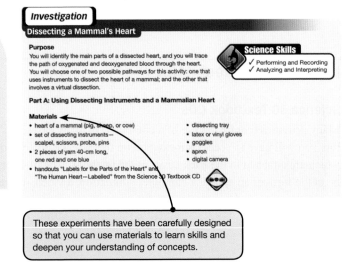

These experiments have been carefully designed so that you can use materials to learn skills and deepen your understanding of concepts.

Utilizing Technology

Utilizing Technology activities require the use of a computer.

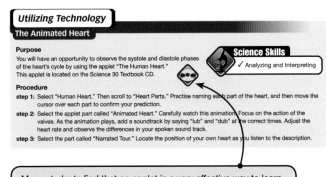

Many students find that an applet is a very effective way to learn about an abstract concept because the learning process is highly visual and the pace of the activity is determined by the learner.

Try This Activity

A Try This Activity is a hands-on demonstration or exploration completed with simple equipment.

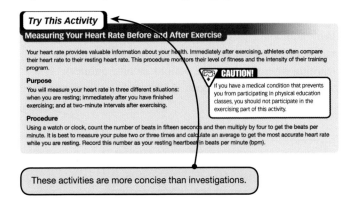

These activities are more concise than investigations.

Special Features

Did You Know?

The Did You Know? feature identifies interesting information that relates to the concepts.

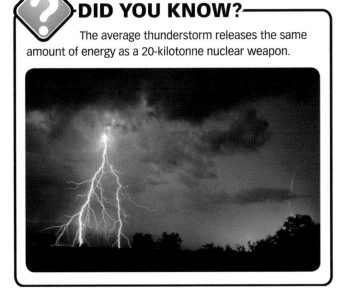

DID YOU KNOW?

The average thunderstorm releases the same amount of energy as a 20-kilotonne nuclear weapon.

Health File

This feature, found only in Unit A, identifies opportunities for you to add to your personal health file throughout the unit.

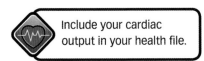

Include your cardiac output in your health file.

Career Profile

Each unit ends with a career profile about how one individual established a science career.

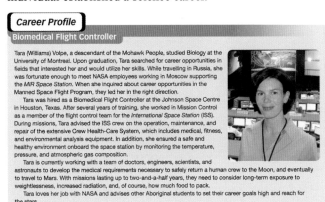

Career Profile

Biomedical Flight Controller

Tara (Williams) Volpe, a descendant of the Mohawk People, studied Biology at the University of Montreal. Upon graduation, Tara searched for career opportunities in fields that interested her and would utilize her skills. While travelling in Russia, she was fortunate enough to meet NASA employees working in Moscow supporting the *MIR Space Station*. When she inquired about career opportunities in the Manned Space Flight Program, they led her in the right direction.

Tara was hired as a Biomedical Flight Controller at the Johnson Space Centre in Houston, Texas. After several years of training, she worked in Mission Control as a member of the flight control team for the *International Space Station* (ISS). During missions, Tara advised the ISS crew on the operation, maintenance, and repair of the extensive Crew Health-Care System, which includes medical, fitness, and environmental analysis equipment. In addition, she ensured a safe and healthy environment onboard the space station by monitoring the temperature, pressure, and atmospheric gas composition.

Tara is currently working with a team of doctors, engineers, scientists, and astronauts to develop the medical requirements necessary to safely return a human crew to the Moon, and eventually to travel to Mars. With missions lasting up to two-and-a-half years, they need to consider long-term exposure to weightlessness, increased radiation, and, of course, how much food to pack.

Tara loves her job with NASA and advises other Aboriginal students to set their career goals high and reach for the stars.

Science Links

This advanced organizer identifies connections to related topics in the other units.

Science Links

Many scientists suspect that skin cancers caused by exposure to UV light could become more of a problem in the future because a key component of the atmosphere that protects people from this radiation is being depleted. Most of the UV photons emitted by the Sun are absorbed by ozone in the stratosphere. As described in Unit B, human activities release compounds, such as CFCs, that reduce the concentration of ozone in the stratosphere.

Summarize Your Learning

At the end of each chapter you will have the opportunity to summarize the key ideas in a number of ways.

Summarize Your Learning

In this chapter you learned a number of new biological terms, processes, and theories. It will be much easier for you to recall and apply the information you have learned if you organize it into patterns.

Since the patterns have to be meaningful to you, there are some options about how you can create this summary. Each of the following options is described in "Summarize Your Learning Activities" in the Reference section. Choose one of these options to create a summary of the key concepts and important terms in Chapter 2.

Option 1: Draw a concept map or a web diagram.	Option 2: Create a point-form summary.	Option 3: Write a story using key terms and concepts.	Option 4: Create a colourful poster.	Option 5: Build a model.	Option 6: Write a script for a skit (a mock news report).

Features at the Back of the Textbook

Reference

The Reference section at the back of this textbook contains helpful information that you will need to refer to throughout the course. In addition to tables and charts, you can find information related to safety and to a variety of learning strategies.

Glossary

As you read the textbook, important terms are identified with a bold font. These terms are defined close to where they occur in the lesson, and they are also defined in the Glossary at the back of this textbook.

Lesson Answers

Short answers to questions asked within lessons can be found in the Lesson Answers section. This includes answers to practice questions and lesson review questions. Answers to investigations, chapter review questions, and unit review questions must be obtained from your teacher.

Assessment

Example Problems

When you first encounter a new type of problem that applies a concept to the unit's theme, an example problem will give you the essential coaching needed for success. When you reach the end of a chapter or a unit, use example problems as a tool for studying. If you cover up the solution and then re-attempt the problem, you can then compare your answer with the detailed solution.

Example Problem 1.7

A balloon is given a charge of -4.5 nC.

a. Determine the electric field strength 30 cm from the centre of the balloon.

b. Sketch a diagram of the electric field lines around the balloon.

Solution

a. $q_{source} = -4.5$ nC
$$= -4.5 \times 10^{-9} \text{ C}$$

$$d = 30 \text{ cm} \times \frac{1 \text{ m}}{100 \text{ cm}}$$

$$= 0.30 \text{ m}$$

$$|E| = ?$$

Solutions to example problems include a list of data and any unit conversions.

$$|E| = \frac{kq_{source}}{r^2}$$

The negative sign is not used in the equation. The negative sign is used to determine direction in part b.

$$= \frac{\left(8.99 \times 10^9 \text{ N} \cdot \text{m}^2/\text{C}^2\right)\left(4.5 \times 10^{-9} \text{ C}\right)}{(0.30 \text{ m})^2}$$

$$= 4.5 \times 10^2 \text{ N/C}$$

The electric field strength 30 cm from the balloon's centre is 4.5×10^2 N/C.

Helpful hints and reminders are included to keep the solution clear.

b. Since the direction of the electric field is determined by the force on a positive test body, the electric field lines are directed toward the negatively charged balloon.

Each step is clearly shown.

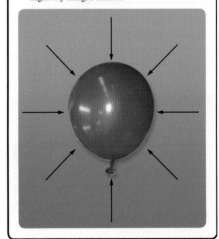

Practice Questions

Practice questions can be found throughout the lessons of each chapter. These questions are in the context of the lesson and are designed to check your understanding of the concepts.

> ### Practice
>
> **33.** Evaluate the categories used in the Toxic Substances List by indicating both good and bad points about the categories.
>
> **34.** DDT is a substance on the Toxic Substances List and is not permitted for use in Canada. Use the Internet to identify the evidence used to place DDT on the list. Use this evidence to determine under which categories DDT would appear.

Lesson Review Questions

Each lesson ends with review questions. These questions check your knowledge of important terms, your understanding of key concepts, and your ability to relate this learning to real-world applications.

Chapter Review Questions

Chapter review questions provide an opportunity for you to apply knowledge, skills, and concepts from all lessons within a chapter. To answer one question, you will often be required to apply what you have learned in several lessons to a new situation.

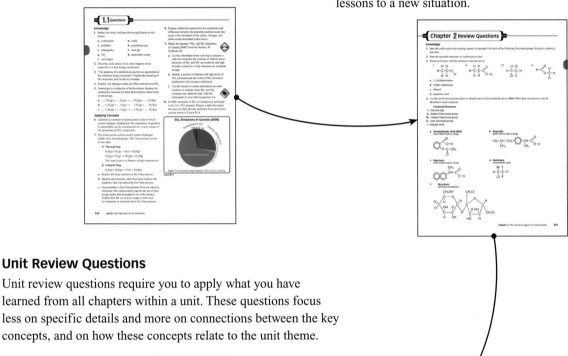

Unit Review Questions

Unit review questions require you to apply what you have learned from all chapters within a unit. These questions focus less on specific details and more on connections between the key concepts, and on how these concepts relate to the unit theme.

Unit A Contents

MAINTAINING HEALTH

Unit B Contents

CHEMISTRY AND THE ENVIRONMENT

Unit C Contents

ELECTROMAGNETIC ENERGY

Unit D Contents

ENERGY AND THE ENVIRONMENT

Unit A Maintaining Health

How would you spend a warm summer day in the mountains? For this family, hiking seemed like the best idea. Since the trail was not far from their campsite, they were able to start hiking by mid-morning.

The family in the photo enjoys these sorts of activities, and they look forward to many more years together of this kind of exploring. Their passion for hiking is just one of the many characteristics that they share: they all seem to enjoy high levels of fitness; they rarely get colds or the flu; and the children are frequently told that they strongly resemble each other and their parents. Which of these characteristics relate to lifestyle choices? Which ones are inherited? When you think about your own health and the characteristics that you share with your family members, which traits are due to the choices your family makes regarding diet and exercise, and which ones are inherited?

In this unit you will examine how the circulatory and immune systems work together to keep you healthy. You will study the major components of these two systems and consider factors that can affect how they function. In the second part of Unit A, you will look at the major principles of genetics and use these concepts to explain how some traits can be passed on from one generation to the next. Throughout the unit you will investigate and evaluate technologies used to explore, maintain, repair, and assist our bodies.

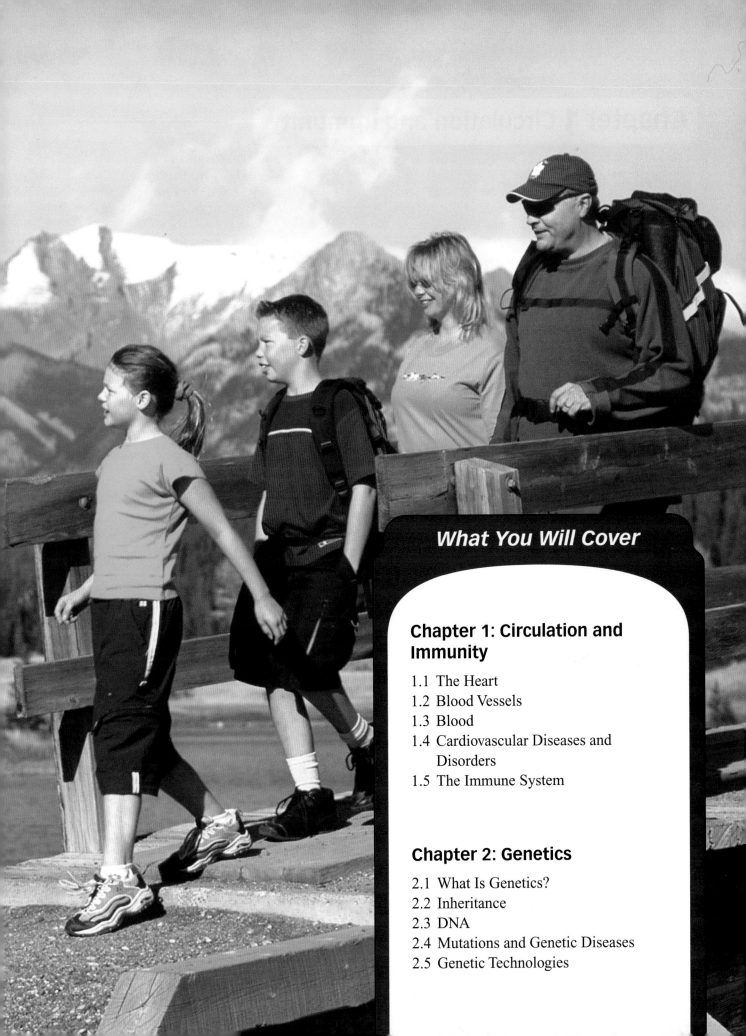

What You Will Cover

Chapter 1: Circulation and Immunity

Chapter 2: Genetics

Chapter 1 Circulation and Immunity

When was the last time you spent a hot summer's day on the water with your friends? Although kayaking requires some specialized equipment, tubing is wonderfully low tech—all you need is an inner tube and the right setting. Tubing down a river can be especially fun. Some businesses take advantage of places where a river naturally makes a C-shaped turn—this allows both the entry point and the exit point to be close together. In this way when a passenger reaches the exit point, it's a short walk uphill to start all over again. Places that rent inner tubes often employ lifeguards to make sure that the riders are safe. These businesses also employ security personnel to ensure that only paying customers use the facility's inner tubes. There is also a maintenance staff to replace worn-out tubes. Through local patterns of evaporation and precipitation, the water cycle provides the water pump for the river system.

The function and parts of the human circulatory system are comparable to tubing down the river. The circulatory system has a muscular pump that cycles blood. Some blood cells are shaped like the tubes so they can easily move through the bloodstream, but these cells transport dissolved gases instead of human riders. Like blood vessels, the river's banks direct the flow of fluid. Human blood has cells that act like the security guards, the lifeguards, and even the maintenance crews.

Try This Activity

Measuring Your Heart Rate Before and After Exercise

Your heart rate provides valuable information about your health. Immediately after exercising, athletes often compare their heart rate to their resting heart rate. This procedure monitors their level of fitness and the intensity of their training program.

Purpose

You will measure your heart rate in three different situations: when you are resting; immediately after you have finished exercising; and at two-minute intervals after exercising.

Procedure

Using a watch or clock, count the number of beats in fifteen seconds and then multiply by four to get the beats per minute. It is best to measure your pulse two or three times and calculate an average to get the most accurate heart rate while you are resting. Record this number as your resting heartbeat in beats per minute (bpm).

step 1: Make sure you are seated and rested before beginning this activity. Locate your pulse or the pulse of a partner by using both your index finger and your middle finger. The pulse is most easily found by pressing these two fingers against the inside of your wrist or against the carotid artery, which runs up your neck on either side of your throat. Each beat of your pulse corresponds to a beat of your heart. Using your thumb may interfere with counting since the thumb contains its own pulsing artery.

step 2: Most members of your class will engage in four minutes of the **same** physical activity at a moderate level. Physical activities to choose from include jumping jacks, running on the spot, or, while seated, repeatedly lifting two textbooks from your shoulder to above your head. At the instant the activity ends, take your pulse. In beats per minute, record your pulse immediately after exercising.

step 3: Continue recording your pulse rate every minute for the next five minutes or until your pulse returns to its resting rate.

step 4: Record your average values for both your resting heart rate and your recovery time. Share this information with your teacher so that you and your classmates can calculate average values for your class.

> ### CAUTION!
> If you have a medical condition that prevents you from participating in physical education classes, you should not participate in the exercising part of this activity.

Analysis

1. Compare your resting heart rate with the class average. Should a difference between heart rates alarm you?

2. List some factors that might contribute to the difference in resting heart rates among class members.

3. Describe how your heart rate changed during exercising, and relate how it was altered after you stopped.

4. How long did it take for your heart rate to return to its resting rate? Compare your time to recover with that of other people.

5. Explain why it is necessary for each class member to perform the same exercise for the same length of time.

6. Include in your health file your resting heart rate, your heart rate during exercise, and your recovery time.

 As you learn about the circulatory system, immune system, and genetics, you will be collecting information about yourself similar to the information that a doctor might collect about you. Throughout Unit A you will compile this information into a health record for yourself. When you see the health file visual cue, add information to your file. In addition to recording valuable data about yourself, your health file will be a valuable study guide.

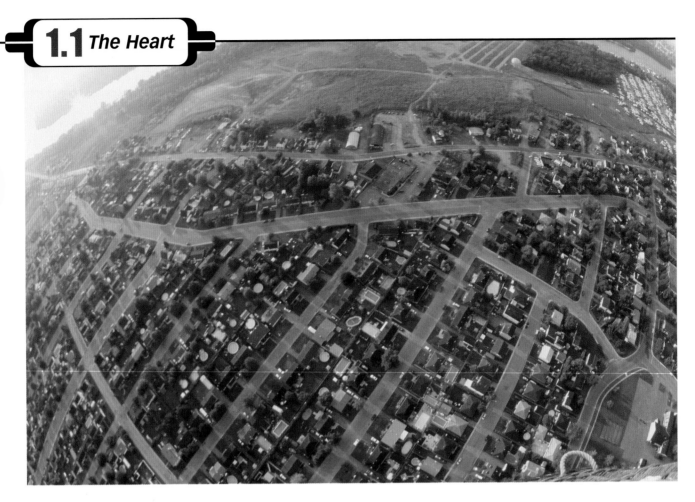

Transportation Systems

The human body is made up of trillions of cells closely packed together. These cells are similar to the closely packed houses that make up a city. Each house's inhabitants generate wastes that must be regularly removed, and each house requires a constant supply of water and energy (such as electricity and natural gas). The houses are often far from the source of the needed supply or the waste disposal site. Like houses, cells generate wastes and require constant supplies. An efficient network for transporting materials is required to keep both cells and houses functioning properly. Blood vessels in the human body function very much like highways, roads, and pipes that serve cities and towns. Notice that no home in the photo is far from a road. In your body, no cell is more than two or three cells away from a blood vessel. Like roadways, there are one-way blood vessels, major and minor blood highways, and even the occasional traffic jam as blood vessels break or clog.

The Body's Internal Transportation System

Microscopic organisms and even some larger invertebrates do not need to have an extensive internal transportation system. This is because their cells are in direct contact with the environment, and gases and materials can move to each of the organism's cells through simple diffusion. Similarly, as cities grow larger, a greater number of roadways and services and more complicated networks for transportation are required. The larger and more complex the organism, the greater the need for a more extensive internal transportation network that effectively transports materials to all specialized cells. This internal transportation network is called the **circulatory system** or the **cardiovascular system**.

▶ **circulatory system or cardiovascular system:**
the system consisting of the heart, blood vessels, and blood that circulates through the body

The human circulatory system performs four key functions. It

- transports and delivers oxygen and nutrients (e.g., minerals, vitamins, and glucose) to the body's cells in exchange for carbon dioxide and wastes
- transports and delivers chemical messengers—such as hormones—throughout the body
- distributes body heat
- defends against disease

The heart, blood vessels, and blood are the circulatory system's major components. Many people use the term *cardiovascular system* because this name includes the key parts of

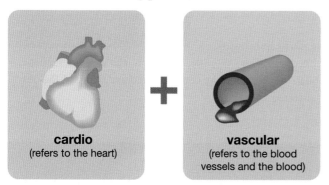

cardio
(refers to the heart)

+

vascular
(refers to the blood vessels and the blood)

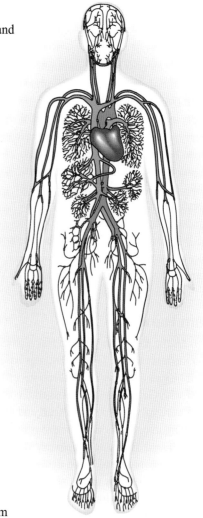

By the end of Chapter 1, you will be able to describe the structure and function of the circulatory system and its major parts and examine how the circulatory system facilitates interactions between the human body's blood cells and the external environment. You will also investigate substances that harm the circulatory system and study disorders of the system.

Ideas About the Heart

Some historical ideas about how the heart and circulatory system work may seem strange to some. The ancient Egyptians believed that a person's emotions, wisdom, and personality originated in the heart rather than in the brain. When someone died they believed that the dog-headed god, Anubis, weighed that person's heart to determine his or her fate in the afterlife. Even today, people still use this Egyptian idea of the heart causing emotions by using metaphors like "suffering from a broken heart," "stealing someone's heart," or "speaking from the heart."

In the second century CE, a Greek physician named Galen became very influential as a personal physician to the Roman emperor. He was very interested in observing the functioning of biological systems. Since studying human dissections was not considered acceptable, many of Galen's ideas were based on his studies of animal dissections. This led him to develop misconceptions about human anatomy, including that the heart was split into two chambers, that food was turned into blood by the liver and then used up by the body, and that blood sloshed back and forth like the ocean's tides. Galen also believed that the heart sucked blood in from the veins rather than acting like a pump. Galen's ideas were widely accepted and his misguided teaching influenced beliefs that lasted for an incredible 1500 years!

Figure A1.1: Galen

Leonardo da Vinci

In the late fifteenth century, Leonardo da Vinci, the famous Renaissance artist, inventor, and scientist began examining many human cadavers and made accurate and detailed drawings of the heart and circulatory system. Da Vinci made careful records of his observations, often comparing the human body to a machine. One of his drawings compares the human heart, with its chambers, to a furnace. Experimentation and investigation on human cadavers was discouraged at the time and some of da Vinci's findings contradicted the beliefs and teachings of that era. To keep his work secret and to prevent other people from stealing his ideas, he used his own special shorthand mirror image writing. Perhaps if circumstances had permitted Leonardo da Vinci to share and publish his work, a more complete understanding of the heart and its functions would have been available to Renaissance-era physicians.

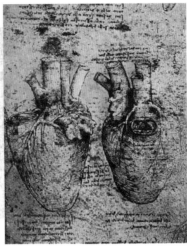

William Harvey

In the 1600s the physician William Harvey began to seriously question the teachings of Galen. Findings based on Harvey's studies of human anatomy and dissections of human cadavers disagreed with Galen's well-established theories. Harvey found that there were valves in both the heart and the veins that kept blood moving in one direction—not sloshing like ocean tides as Galen believed. By using simple mathematical calculations, Harvey took the volume of blood that the heart could hold and multiplied that volume by the number of times the heart beat per minute. This calculation resulted in a value far greater than the amount of fluid the body could hold. Harvey concluded that the heart must be re-pumping the same blood. This experiment contradicted Galen's idea that the liver was turning food into new blood to be used up by the body. Because Harvey was not able to explain how blood got from the arteries to the veins, his theory was not immediately accepted.

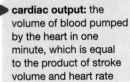

cardiac output: the volume of blood pumped by the heart in one minute, which is equal to the product of stroke volume and heart rate

Figure A1.2: William Harvey

A few years after Harvey's death, Marcello Malpighi used a microscope to discover the tiny hair-like capillaries that connect arteries to veins. This confirmed Harvey's theory that a small volume of blood was constantly circulated to all parts of the body and that the heart, arteries, and veins were connected in a circulatory system.

At the centre of Harvey's work were simple calculations relating to the volume of blood and the heartbeat. Today, similar calculations can reveal amazing information about the effectiveness of the heart as a pump. The heart of a typical adult human male pumps out 70 mL of blood per beat. This is called stroke volume. The stroke volume for a typical adult human female is about 60 mL per beat. The average resting heart rate for men and women is around 72 beats per minute. So, if you know the volume of blood pumped in each beat and the number of beats that occur in a minute, you can determine the volume of blood pumped by the heart in one minute. This value is called the **cardiac output**.

A typical human male has a stroke volume of 70 mL per beat and a resting heart rate of 72 beats per minute.

a. Calculate the cardiac output. Express your answer in litres per minute.

b. Calculate the volume of blood that would be pumped in one day based upon the cardiac output.

Solution

a. stroke volume = 70 mL/beat

$$= 70 \text{ mL/beat} \times \frac{1 \text{ L}}{1000 \text{ mL}}$$

$$= 0.070 \text{ L/beat}$$

heart rate = 72 beats/minute

cardiac output = ?

The cardiac output is 5.0 L/min.

$$\text{cardiac ouput} = (\text{stroke volume}) \times (\text{heart rate})$$

$$= \frac{(0.070 \text{ L})}{\text{beat}} \times \frac{72 \text{ (beats)}}{\text{min}}$$

$$= 5.04 \text{ L/min}$$

$$= 5.0 \text{ L/min}$$

Note: It is often best to handle the conversion of units when listing the data. The final answer is rounded to two significant digits since the given values are expressed to two significant digits.

b. $$\text{volume pumped in one day} = \frac{(5.04 \text{ L})}{\text{min}} \times \frac{(60 \text{ min})}{1 \text{ h}} \times \frac{(24 \text{ h})}{1 \text{ d}} = \frac{7257.6 \text{ L}}{\text{d}} = 7.3 \times 10^3 \text{ L/d}$$

Note: The unrounded value from a. is used in the follow-up calculation in part b. Since the original given values were expressed to two significant digits, the final answer should be rounded to two significant digits. In this case, scientific notation is required, unless the answer is expressed in kL.

1. Copy and complete this table. In the middle column, summarize each person's different historical theories about the heart and circulatory system. Each of the three listed individuals contributed at the time to the understanding of the heart and circulatory system. In the right column, describe the limitations of each theory or contribution.

HEART THEORIES

Person	Theory About the Heart	Limitations of the Theory
Galen		
Leonardo da Vinci		
William Harvey		

2. A female Science 30 student has a resting heart rate of 68 beats per minute. Determine her cardiac output in litres per minute.

3. Refer to your answer from question 2. How much blood would this student's heart pump in one year if it maintained the resting heart rate?

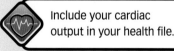 Include your cardiac output in your health file.

4. The average human has approximately 5 L of blood. How long does it take the heart to pump this volume?

5. If a male raised his heart rate to 180 beats per minute through intensive exercise, such as running on a treadmill, how much blood would his heart pump per minute? Assume that the stroke volume remains at 70 mL per beat.

6. A rain barrel holds approximately 213 L of water. This same volume could fill more than 100, 2-L pop bottles.

    a. Determine your resting heart rate using the techniques from "Try This Activity: Measuring Your Heart Rate Before and After Exercise." Use this value to calculate your cardiac output.

    b. If you had a pump working at the same rate as your cardiac output, how long would it take to fill a 213-L barrel?

    c. Suppose your heart rate doubled its resting value because you were exercising. How long would it take your pumping heart to fill the same barrel under these circumstances? Assume the stroke volume remains constant for all parts of this problem.

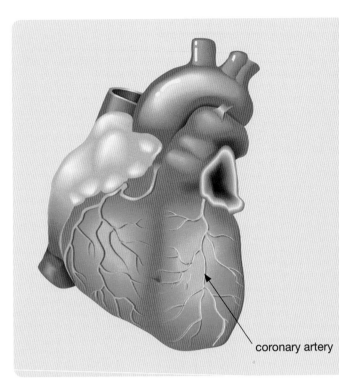

The Heart: An Amazing Pump

Clench your hand into a fist. The size of your closed hand corresponds approximately to the size of your heart. Now squeeze your hand and relax it. Imagine doing that action about every second. That would add up to over 80 000 times per day and 2.5 billion times in an average lifetime! This squeezing—called contracting—and relaxing is exactly what your heart does every day.

Like any other muscle that is contracting, the heart needs a constant supply of oxygen and other nutrients. Since the entire body depends upon the heart, the first organ that the heart supplies with oxygen-rich blood is itself. The blood vessels that supply the heart are called the **coronary arteries**.

coronary artery

▶ **coronary arteries:** the vessels that supply the heart muscle with oxygen-rich blood

⯈ DID YOU KNOW?

The pacemaker is a small region of specialized muscle tissue that sets the tempo of the heartbeat. The pacemaker generates electrical signals that cause the muscle fibres in the heart to simultaneously contract in a co-ordinated manner. If one muscle fibre of a heart chamber is stimulated to contract, all the fibres of that chamber contract in unison. This en masse contraction makes the heart muscle unique.

If the heart's pacemaker cells are unable to regulate a steady heartbeat, then an artificial pacemaker can be surgically implanted.

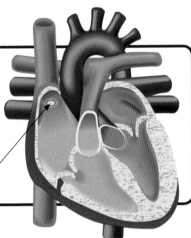

pacemaker

Science Links

An artificial pacemaker is a small battery-operated machine that sends electrical signals to the heart through tiny wires. This little computer "listens" to the heart and supplements its normal rhythm. Adjustments to the pacemaker can be made without further surgery by using radio-wave signals. These signals are sent through the skin and other tissues to the artificial pacemaker from a control wand outside of the body.

In Unit C you'll learn more about radio waves as well as devices that both produce and transmit electrical energy.

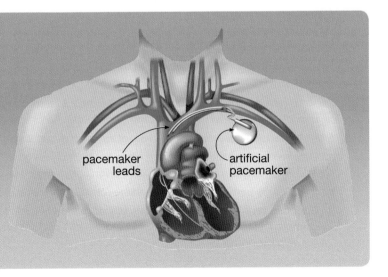

pacemaker leads

artificial pacemaker

Your heart is a muscular pump that has been beating without rest since you were a developing embryo, and it will continue to push blood to every part of your body until the end of your life. All the blood in your body is in constant motion. With each powerful heartbeat, life-giving blood is sent to every one of your approximately 60 trillion cells. Without the work of your heart, you would be dead in a matter of minutes.

When you imagine a heart you might think of the familiar shape that children learn to draw in preschool, but the shape of the human heart is really more like an upside-down pear with four open spaces, or chambers, inside. Since the heart is a muscle, its look and texture is like that of the red meat you would see in a raw steak. Contrary to the popular belief that the heart is found on the left side of the chest, the heart is actually located almost in the centre of the chest where it is protected by the hard sternum (or breastbone). During a medical checkup, the doctor listens on the left side with a stethoscope because the heart is pointed slightly to the left, and sounds produced by parts of the heart are easier to hear there.

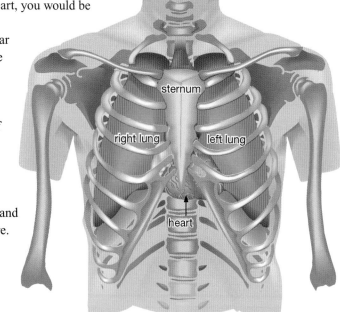

Anatomy of the Heart

Study the labelled diagram of the human heart in Figure A1.3. Note that the areas containing oxygen-rich blood are shaded red and the areas containing oxygen-poor blood are blue.

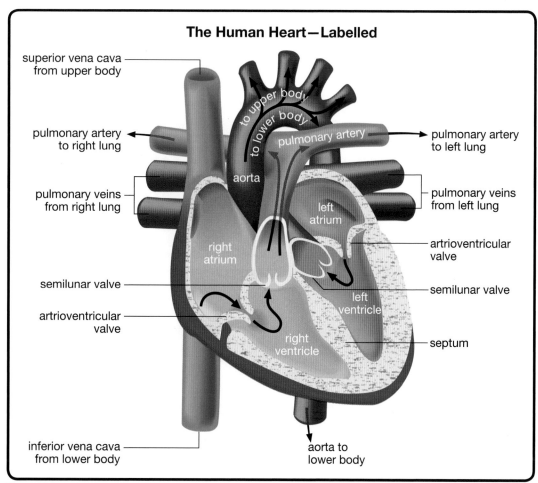

The Human Heart—Labelled

- superior vena cava from upper body
- to upper body
- to lower body
- pulmonary artery to right lung
- pulmonary artery
- pulmonary artery to left lung
- aorta
- pulmonary veins from right lung
- left atrium
- pulmonary veins from left lung
- right atrium
- artrioventricular valve
- semilunar valve
- semilunar valve
- artrioventricular valve
- left ventricle
- right ventricle
- septum
- inferior vena cava from lower body
- aorta to lower body

Figure A1.3

Do you notice that the human heart in Figure A1.3 seems to have the left and right mixed up? That's because heart diagrams are labelled from the point of view of the person who has the heart. If this heart was in the person who was facing you, this is how this person would label left and right.

You probably also noticed that the heart is unevenly split into four chambers. The right and left sides of the organ are partitioned by a thick wall called the **septum**. The smaller top two chambers are the left **atrium** and right atrium, together called atria. The bottom two pointed chambers are the left **ventricle** and right ventricle. The left ventricle is slightly bigger in size because its job is to pump oxygen-rich blood to most of the body. The four chambers are divided by **heart valves** that ensure blood will travel in only one direction through the heart. The valves between the atria and the ventricles are held in place by string-like tendons that act like the ropes on a drawbridge. These tendons help ensure the proper alignment of the valves when they are closed.

▶ **septum:** a thick wall of muscle that divides the left and right sides of the heart

▶ **atrium:** the smaller upper chamber that receives blood returning to the heart

▶ **ventricle:** the larger v-shaped bottom chamber that pumps blood from the heart

▶ **heart valves:** thin flaps of tissue in the heart that open and close to ensure the proper direction for blood flow

Blood Flow Through the Heart

Since blood circulates constantly through the body, you could begin to trace the flow of blood at any point. In Figure A1.4, blood's path is traced in a step-by-step manner starting with the place where blood first enters the heart on its way back from the body.

Figure A1.4

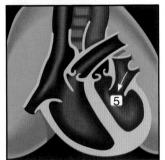

1. The vena cavae are large veins that collect oxygen-poor and carbon dioxide-rich blood from the upper body and lower body. The blood enters the heart and collects in the right atrium from both the superior and inferior vena cavae.

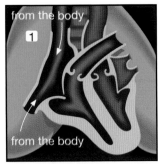

2. The contraction of the right atrium forces blood into the right ventricle.

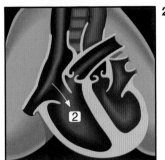

3. The right ventricle contracts and forces the blood to flow out of the heart into the pulmonary arteries. The pulmonary arteries move the blood away from the heart toward the right and left lungs. At the lungs, the blood undergoes gas exchange by receiving oxygen and releasing carbon dioxide, a waste product of cell activity.

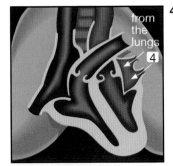

4. The oxygen-rich blood is then sent back toward the heart through the pulmonary veins to the left atrium.

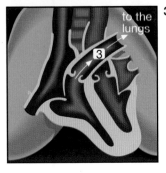

5. The contraction of the left atrium forces the blood into the left ventricle, the heart's most muscular chamber.

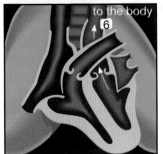

6. The contraction of the left ventricle forces the blood into the aorta. The aorta is the largest artery in the body and through its many branches, directs oxygen-rich blood to the entire body.

7. Obtain the handout "The Human Heart" from the Science 30 Textbook CD. Attempt to answer the following questions without referring to Figure A1.3. After you have completed as much as you can, use the diagrams in the textbook to complete and/or correct your work.

    a. Add a label for each of the areas identified on this diagram.

    b. Add red shading to the areas that deal with oxygenated blood and blue shading to the areas that deal with deoxygenated blood.

    c. Add arrows to indicate the direction of blood flow through each of the chambers and major blood vessels.

    d. Add the numbers *1* through *6* to outline the sequence for the path of a blood cell as it travels through each of the heart chambers. Begin with number 1 representing the place where blood first enters the heart on its way back from the body.

Heartbeat

You have so far traced the step-by-step flow of blood through the heart, but the action of the heart does not work in steps. Blood does not move through one chamber while the other chambers lay empty waiting for their turn to move the blood on; instead, the two sides of the heart fill at the same time and act together like parallel pumps. Once filled with blood, both atria contract at the same time, followed by the simultaneous contraction of both ventricles. Before the contraction of the ventricles occurs, they are relaxed and the valves between the atria and ventricles are open. This allows blood to flow in and fill the ventricular chambers. This relaxation part of the cycle is called the **diastole**. In the first step of a two-step contraction, the atria contract together to push the blood down into the ventricles. In the second step, the two ventricles contract to force the blood out of the heart. This two-part contraction of the heart cycle is called the **systole**. The "lub-dub" heart sound that a doctor listens for through a stethoscope is due to the heart valves functioning during diastole and systole.

    One complete contraction (systole) and one complete relaxation (diastole) combine to make a heartbeat—one cycle of the heart's activity.

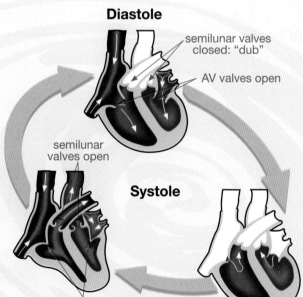

Diastole

semilunar valves closed: "dub"

AV valves open

▶ **diastole:** the phase of the heart's cycle where a chamber of the heart, either an atrium or a ventricle, relaxes and fills with blood

▶ **systole:** the phase of the heart's cycle when the ventricles contract to eject blood from within the chamber

semilunar valves open

Systole

AV valves closed: "lub"

The two ventricles contract (ventricular systole) to force blood out of the heart.

The high pressure forces the artrioventricular valves to close. A "lub" sound is made.

The semilunar valves are forced open by the high-pressure blood leaving the ventricles.

The atria and ventricles relax, (atrial and ventricular diastole) filling with blood.

The artrioventricular valves open due to the lower pressure of the blood within the ventricles.

Blood outside the heart is under higher pressure, so the semilunar valves are forced to close. A "dub" sound is made.

When the atria contract—called atrial systole—the blood is forced from the atria into the ventricles.

The artrioventricular valves remain open.

The semilunar valves remain closed.

The Animated Heart

Science Skills

✓ Analyzing and Interpreting

Purpose

You will have an opportunity to observe the systole and diastole phases of the heart's cycle by using the applet "The Human Heart." This applet is located on the Science 30 Textbook CD.

Procedure

step 1: Select "Human Heart." Then scroll to "Heart Parts." Practise naming each part of the heart, and then move the cursor over each part to confirm your prediction.

step 2: Select the applet part called "Animated Heart." Carefully watch this animation. Focus on the action of the valves. As the animation plays, add a soundtrack by saying "lub" and "dub" at the correct times. Adjust the heart rate and observe the differences in your spoken sound track.

step 3: Select the part called "Narrated Tour." Locate the position of your own heart as you listen to the description.

Analysis

Computer animations can demonstrate complex processes in ways that are clear and easy to understand. However, compromises are made in terms of which details are included and which ones are omitted. Watch the computer animation again as you answer the following questions.

1. Which details of the systole part of the heart's cycle are included? Which are omitted?

2. Which details of the diastole part of the heart's cycle are included? Which are omitted?

3. If a person has a heart rate of 72 beats/min, then one heartbeat lasts 0.83 s. In other words, the entire heart cycle of diastole, atrial systole, and ventricular systole occurs in just 0.83 s. On average the diastole lasts for 0.4 s and the ventricular systole lasts for 0.3 s, which only leaves about 0.1 seconds for the atrial systole.

Use this information to suggest an explanation for the trends you identified in your answers to questions 1 and 2.

DID YOU KNOW?

When a doctor listens to a patient's heart with a stethoscope, sometimes swishing or whooshing sounds—called *heart murmurs*—are heard in addition to the standard "lub-dub" of the heartbeat. Heart murmurs result from the turbulent flow of blood through the heart—this is why they can sound like water rushing through the end of a garden hose.

Pediatricians classify most heart murmurs they hear as *innocent*, because they are not associated with a heart disease or abnormality. Most children will have a heart murmur at some time, but these innocent murmurs usually disappear by the time they become adults.

The doctor may decide that the characteristics of a particular heart murmur require additional testing to determine if there is an underlying problem with blood flow through the heart. In these cases, the murmur is usually due to the abnormal functioning of a heart valve. A valve may not be closing tightly—it may be too narrow or too stiff. A treatment plan is then designed to address the specific condition.

Factors Affecting Heart Rate

Many factors can affect your heart rate. From your own experiences you know that emotions, such as fear or excitement, quickly increase the heart rate. At one time, you have probably been so scared that it felt like your heart was going to jump out of your chest. Changes in external temperature also can cause your heart rate to change. For example, if you sit in a hot tub, the external temperature of your body increases greatly and the heart must work harder to pump blood around in an attempt to dissipate body heat through the skin.

If training with weights can make a muscle like your bicep larger, can other forms of exercise make your heart larger?

Exercise that improves your heart's ability to provide working muscles with oxygen is called cardiovascular training, or aerobic exercise. Examples include swimming, running, or cycling. In each case, the exercise is done non-stop at a moderate rate for at least 20 minutes. These activities are commonly called cardio workouts because they increase the demand of the body's muscles for oxygen. Cardio workouts, therefore, cause the heart to increase the volume of blood it pumps every minute, elevating the heart rate above its resting value.

The effect of a lifestyle that includes cardiovascular exercise is that the heart and surrounding blood vessels do not become larger; but, instead, these tissues improve in their stretching ability. If the heart muscles are more elastic they have a greater capacity to expand, thus increasing the amount of blood pumped during each heartbeat. These improvements to elasticity translate to an increased stroke volume both when the heart is put under peak demand and when it is resting. This is why people who engage in a lot of cardiovascular exercise develop hearts that need to beat less often to circulate the same amount of blood. A stronger heart is not a larger heart, but is instead a more elastic one. Athletes tend to have a lower-than-average resting heart rate—often only 45 to 50 beats per minute.

Utilizing Technology

Heart Rate Monitoring

Athletes often record their heart rates immediately after waking and record this data for an extended period of time. This technique gives them more accurate resting-heart-rate data because there are probably fewer external variables first thing in the morning—such as diet, caffeine, or exercise—that could affect the heart rate. Increases in the morning resting heart rate could indicate the onset of illness or a lack of recovery from overtraining.

Science Skills

✓ Performing and Recording
✓ Analyzing and Interpreting
✓ Communication and Teamwork

Purpose

For two weeks you will record your resting heart rate and the minutes spent in physical activity every day.

Procedure

step 1: For two weeks you will record your resting heart rate before you get out of bed, and you will also note the approximate minutes spent in physical activity for each day. Physical activity could include walking, participation in sports, dancing, or movement associated with chores or a job such as carrying or lifting.

step 2: Organize your data using a spreadsheet. Use the spreadsheet to create graphs that summarize your results.

Analysis

1. Did you notice any significant changes within the resting-heart-rate data? Were these changes related to the onset of an illness or to a sudden change in the level of physical activity?

2. Compare your findings with those of other students. Is there evidence to support the idea that individuals who regularly participate in cardiovascular exercise tend to have a lower resting heart rate? Why is this question difficult to answer?

Target Heart Rate for Exercise

A chest-strap heart-rate monitor is often used to help ensure that the wearer is exercising at a desired level. Once your heart exceeds approximately 85% of its maximum heart rate, your body burns less fat and produces more lactic acid, which causes muscle soreness. One way to estimate your maximum heart rate is to subtract your age from 220.

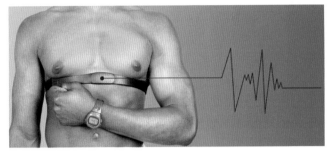

It is important to realize that this method of determining your maximum heart rate is just a guideline. Some medications, especially those related to the heart, require a lower maximum heart rate be used than the one provided by this guideline. If you have a chronic medical condition or have any doubts about whether a medication you are taking affects your maximum heart rate, contact your physician to determine your maximum heart rate.

Target Heart Rates	
Personal Health Goal	**Percentage of Maximum Heart Rate**
maintain fitness level	50 to 60%
increase fat burning or weight loss	60 to 70%
increase cardiovascular endurance	70 to 80%

The maximum heart rate is an important value because it helps provide a guide for goals that you may have for either maintaining or improving your health. A common mistake that people make is that they begin a new exercise program with activities that cause their heart rate to be too high. The best approach is to pace yourself by beginning with activities that will only push you to about 50% of your maximum rate. This is especially important if you have had an inactive lifestyle. You can then gradually increase the intensity of your workouts over the first months of your program. It is always a good idea to consult with your physician if you are just starting a new exercise program or if you have questions about health or fitness.

8. Determine your maximum heart rate by subtracting your age from 220.

9. Use your answer from question 8 to complete the following table.

Your Target Heart Rate	
Personal Health Goal	**Heart Rate**
maintain fitness level	
increase fat burning or weight loss	
increase cardiovascular endurance	

10. Describe how your answers to question 9 will change as you get older.

 Add your maximum heart rate and your target heart rate for different health goals to your health file.

DID YOU KNOW?

The most effective cardiovascular fitness programs involve activities that are done for at least twenty minutes four or five times a week at moderate activity levels. If you make walking your primary means of transportation, you can build a fitness routine into your day without having to join either a gym or a health club. As is the case with any fitness programs, the best approach is to build regular walking into your weekly routine, to gradually increase the intensity, and to include warm-up and cool-down stretches.

Investigation

Dissecting a Mammal's Heart

Purpose

You will identify the main parts of a dissected heart, and you will trace the path of oxygenated and deoxygenated blood through the heart. You will choose one of two possible pathways for this activity: one that uses instruments to dissect the heart of a mammal; and the other that involves a virtual dissection.

Science Skills

✓ Performing and Recording
✓ Analyzing and Interpreting

Part A: Using Dissecting Instruments and a Mammalian Heart

Materials

- heart of a mammal (pig, sheep, or cow)
- set of dissecting instruments— scalpel, scissors, probe, pins
- 2 pieces of yarn 40-cm long, one red and one blue
- handouts "Labels for the Parts of the Heart" and "The Human Heart—Labelled" from the Science 30 Textbook CD

- dissecting tray
- latex or vinyl gloves
- goggles
- apron
- digital camera

Procedure

step 1: Place the heart in front of you with the largest blood vessel—the aorta—at the top of the heart and facing the bottom of the dissecting tray. Notice the presence of a diagonal line of blood vessels, going from the upper left to the lower right on the outside of the heart. These are the coronary arteries that supply the heart itself with blood. These vessels are often surrounded by some fatty tissue.

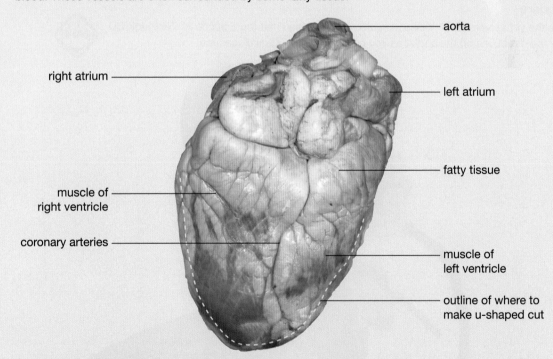

Confirm that you have the heart oriented properly by feeling each half of the heart on either side of the coronary artery with your hand. The heart's left side should feel thicker and more muscular than the heart's right side. **Remember:** The heart's left side is on your right as you look at the heart.

step 2: Begin by making a u-shaped cut around the sides of the heart to make a "flip-top" heart. Carefully hold the scalpel parallel to the table top as you cut. Be sure not to completely cut the heart into two separate sections. You should end up with a "flip-top" heart. This allows the interior of the heart to be observed and also to be put back together for later in this activity.

step 3: Lift the upper side of the heart away to reveal its inner chambers. Identify the side of the heart with the thicker-walled chambers. This is the heart's left side. Orientate the heart so the heart's left side is on your right.

step 4: Using your finger or a dissecting probe, locate where the blood enters the right atrium (vena cava). Blue yarn can be used to simulate the pathway in which deoxygenated blood flows. Thread a piece of blue yarn through the vena cava into the right atrium and then through the atrioventricular valve into the right ventricle.

step 5: Use your finger or probe around to find out where the blood must exit the right ventricle through the semilunar valve into the pulmonary artery. Remember that the blood cannot go back through the one-way valve or across the septum, which forms a barrier between the heart's right and left sides. Thread the blue yarn from the right ventricle to the pulmonary artery.

step 6: Tie a piece of red yarn to the blue yarn to simulate that the blood has become oxygenated in the lungs. Use the red string to trace the pathway that oxygenated blood flows through the pulmonary veins, to the heart's left side, and out through the aorta.

step 7: Obtain the handout "Labels for the Parts of the Heart" from the Science 30 Textbook CD. Cut out each of the labels and use dissection pins to attach the labels to the corresponding parts of the heart. If you are uncertain, use the "The Human Heart—Labelled" handout to help you identify the major parts of your dissected heart.

step 8: Have your teacher check your labelled heart.

step 9: Take a digital photograph of your dissected heart, complete with all the labels pinned in place.

Part B: Using a Computer Applet

Procedure

Locate the virtual version of "Dissecting a Mammal's Heart" on the Science 30 Textbook CD. Follow the directions on the applet as you complete your virtual dissection.

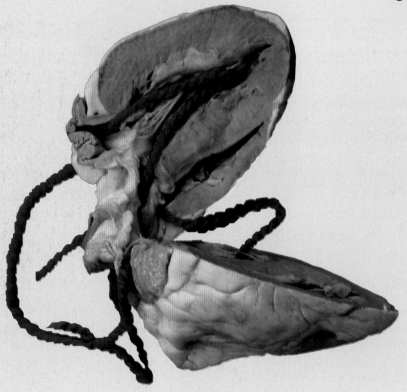

Beliefs about the heart and the circulatory system have changed over time. William Harvey was the first person to prove that blood circulated around the body in a closed system of vessels. The pump that drives the circulatory system is the heart. The output of blood from the heart depends on how many times the heart contracts and how much blood it moves with each contraction. The atria contract simultaneously, followed by the simultaneous contraction of the two ventricles. This two-part contraction creates a "lub-dub" sound due to the functioning of the heart's valves.

The heart rate is affected by emotion, temperature, exercise, fitness level, sleep, hormones, chemicals, drugs, and alcohol. By monitoring the heart rate during exercise programs, appropriate levels of exertion can be ensured. Heart rate is a key indicator of cardiovascular fitness.

⊫❪ **1.1** *Questions* ❫⊨

Knowledge

1. Beginning with the vena cava, indicate the order of the following structures of the cardiovascular system through which blood flows: left atrium, right ventricle, lungs, body, right atrium, left ventricle, aorta.

2. Refer to Figure A1.5. Match the numbered structures on the heart to the part of the heart that

   a. receives oxygenated blood from the lungs

   b. sends oxygenated blood to the body

   c. prevents the backflow of blood in the heart

   d. separates the right and left halves of the heart

   e. collects deoxygenated blood from the body

Applying Concepts

3. a. If an Olympic athlete has an increased stroke volume of 100 mL, calculate his cardiac output at rest (50 bpm), with light exercise (115 bpm), and with high-intensity exercise (180 bpm). Assume the stroke volume remains constant.

   b. Explain why you expect the athlete to have a lower resting heart rate than a person with an inactive lifestyle.

4. Why are the walls of the heart's right ventricle thinner than the walls of the heart's left ventricle?

5. Compare the systole and diastole portions of the heart cycle.

6. Describe the purposes of a chest strap or other type of heart-rate monitor when a person is exercising.

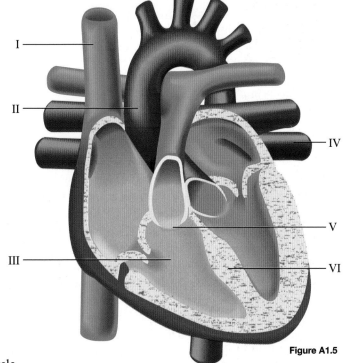

Figure A1.5

Figure A1.6: Glacial meltwater flows into the Bow River, which supplies about one million people with drinking water in southern Alberta.

The water that most Albertans drink begins as melt water high in the Rocky Mountains. Rivers then carry this water to communities throughout the province where it is pumped to water purification facilities and reservoirs before moving to people's homes. Each dwelling requires two piping systems: one to bring in the clean water and another to remove the waste water.

Because both systems transport fluids, the circulatory system of the human body can be compared to the water delivery system in a city or town. The cells in people's bodies have similar needs to the residents of a home. Every cell in your body, from the cells that make up the pumping muscles of the heart to the faraway cells in the tips of your toes, must be constantly supplied with blood. The sewage waste water collected at each home must be quickly removed and wastes must not be allowed to mix with the clean water coming from the pumping station, so wastes are transported in separate pipes. The blood that leaves the heart through the aorta is rich in oxygen and nutrients. This blood must be pumped in separate vessels from the blood that is full of carbon dioxide and wastes.

Just as cities and towns must have a fast and efficient way of transporting clean water to residents and of removing waste water, the body's circulatory system must also work to quickly and efficiently transport blood to and from the cells.

Human Circulatory System

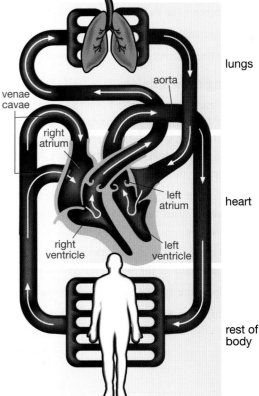

lungs

aorta

venae cavae

right atrium

left atrium — heart

right ventricle

left ventricle

rest of body

Water Delivery System

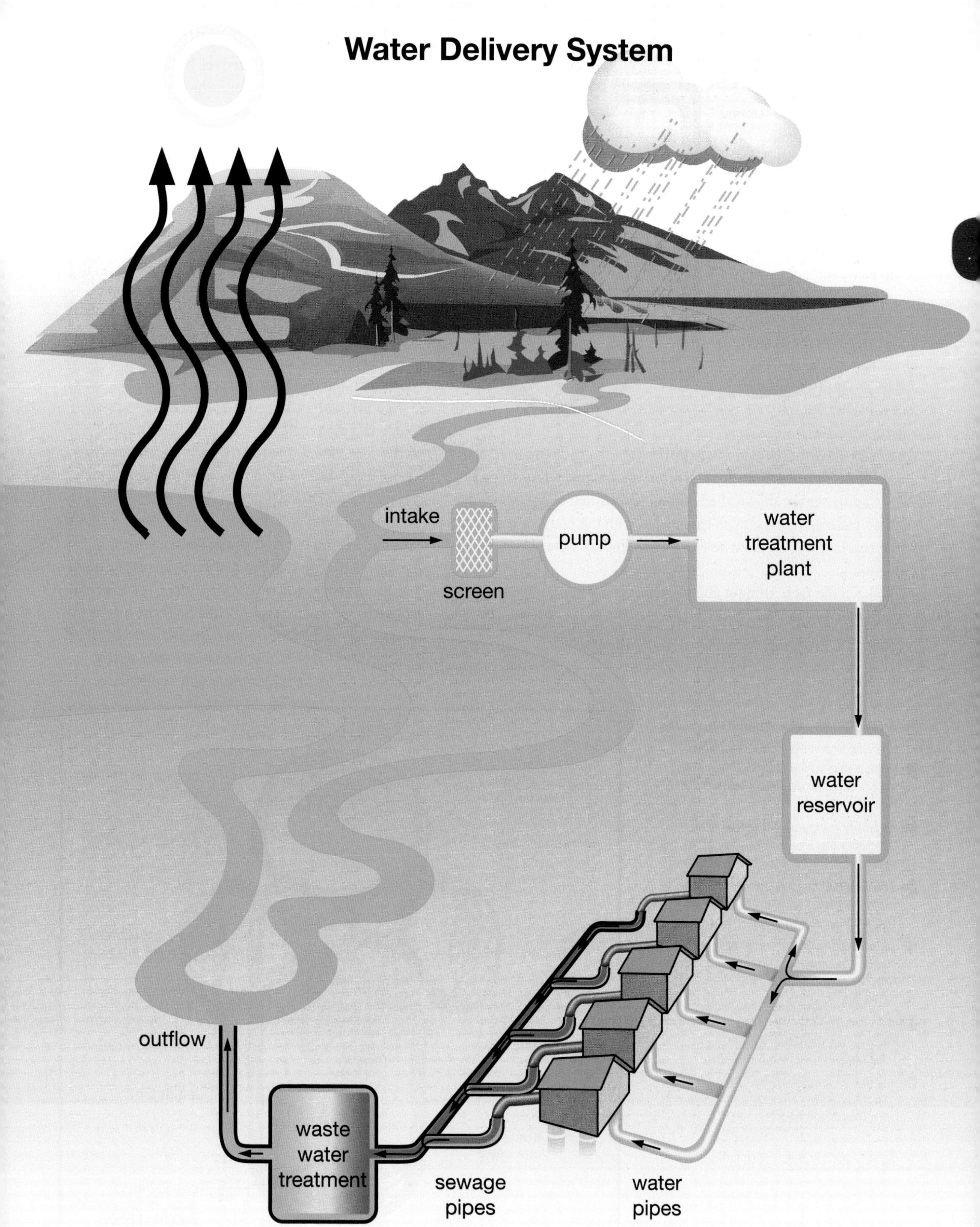

intake

screen

pump

water treatment plant

water reservoir

outflow

waste water treatment

sewage pipes

water pipes

The Pathway of Blood

As you saw in Lesson 1.1, the basic components of the human circulatory system are the heart, which pumps the blood; the blood vessels that transport the blood to all parts of the body; and the blood.

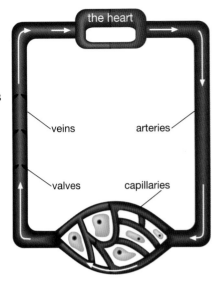

Three types of blood vessels transport the blood. A blood vessel that carries blood away from the heart is called an **artery**, while a blood vessel that transports blood toward the heart is called a **vein**. Both arteries and veins branch into smaller vessels to effectively reach every part of the body. A **capillary** is a microscopic tube that connects the smallest branch of an artery to the tiniest branch of a vein. Capillaries are thin-walled porous vessels that allow materials, such as gases and fluids, to be exchanged with the body's cells. Every living cell in the body must be close to a capillary to remain alive and functioning.

To keep the facts straight about arteries and veins, many students use this memory device:

<u>A</u>rteries carry blood <u>A</u>way from the heart.

Major Arteries and Veins

The deoxygenated blood arrives back to the heart from the body's major veins, which flow into the **venae cavae**, the largest veins in the body. The blood from each vena cava is carried to the heart's right side where it is pumped to the lungs through the **pulmonary arteries**. Within the capillaries of the lungs, the blood exchanges carbon dioxide for oxygen. The oxygen-rich blood then returns to the heart's left side through the **pulmonary veins**. The word *pulmonary* means "having to do with the lungs" because it comes from *pulmo*, the Latin word for lungs. This is why the movement of blood into and out of the lungs is called pulmonary circulation.

Except for the pulmonary vein, blood that flows through the veins is low in oxygen. Whereas oxygen-rich blood is red in colour, oxygen-poor blood is a darker shade of red. In diagrams, the difference in blood colour is emphasized by using completely different colours—red for oxygen-rich blood and blue for oxygen-poor blood.

Oxygen-rich blood leaves the heart by travelling through the largest artery in the body, known as the **aorta**. Recall that the first branches of the aorta are the coronary arteries, which supply oxygen and nutrients to the heart muscle itself. These arteries appear on the surface of the right and left ventricles. The aorta divides further into other arteries that carry blood to the major organs and body tissues.

- **artery:** a thick-walled blood vessel that carries blood away from the heart
- **vein:** a thin-walled blood vessel with valves that carries blood toward the heart
- **capillary:** a tiny blood vessel that connects the smallest branch of an artery to the smallest branch of a vein
- **vena cavae:** the largest veins in the body that carry oxygen-poor blood to the heart
- **pulmonary artery:** the large blood vessel that carries oxygen-poor blood from the heart's right ventricle to the lungs
- **pulmonary vein:** the large blood vessel that carries oxygenated blood from the lungs to the heart's left atrium
- **aorta:** the largest artery in the body; carries oxygen-rich blood from the left ventricle of the heart

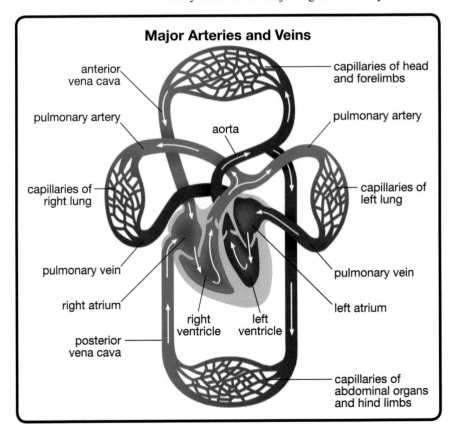

Major Arteries and Veins

11. The body's circulatory system can be compared to a community's water system.

   a. Identify the parts of the body's circulatory system that correspond to the community's water pipes, sewage pipes, pump, and water.

   b. Describe at least two limitations of the comparison between a community's water system and the body's circulatory system.

12. Identify the major artery or vein that best matches each description.

   a. carries oxygen-poor blood from the heart to the lungs

   b. the body's largest artery

   c. carries oxygen-rich blood from the aorta to nourish heart tissues

   d. carries oxygen-rich blood to the heart

   e. carries oxygen-poor blood to the heart from the body's tissues

13. It is a common misconception that arteries always carry oxygen-rich blood and veins always carry oxygen-poor blood. Explain why this concept is not true in the case of pulmonary circulation.

14. A capillary is a microscopic structure. Its walls are comprised of only one layer of very thin cells.

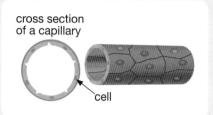

cross section of a capillary

cell

Explain why it is important for the walls of capillaries to be thin.

The Specialization of Blood Vessels

The blood vessels of the circulatory system are specialized for their specific functions. Arteries have thick elastic walls to withstand the pressure of the pumping heart. Except in the case of the pulmonary artery, the blood that flows in the arteries is oxygen-rich. This oxygenated blood is bright red in colour, and arteries other than the pulmonary artery are usually coloured red in circulatory system diagrams. As the arteries get farther away from the heart and aorta, they branch out and get smaller in diameter and lower in pressure. These smaller branched arteries are called **arterioles**.

▶ **arteriole:** a small artery that joins a larger artery to a capillary

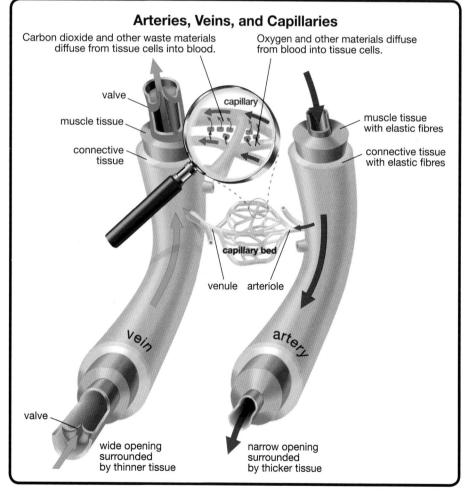

Arteries, Veins, and Capillaries

Carbon dioxide and other waste materials diffuse from tissue cells into blood.

Oxygen and other materials diffuse from blood into tissue cells.

valve

muscle tissue

connective tissue

capillary

muscle tissue with elastic fibres

connective tissue with elastic fibres

capillary bed

venule arteriole

vein

artery

valve

wide opening surrounded by thinner tissue

narrow opening surrounded by thicker tissue

Arterioles are attached to the very thin-walled capillaries. The capillary is the place where needed nutrients, like oxygen and glucose, are exchanged for wastes—like carbon dioxide. The capillary walls are only one-cell thick because they need to be thin enough for the exchange of gases to take place by diffusion. Capillaries exist in a **capillary bed**, which is a web of capillaries surrounding the cells of body tissues. There are thousands of kilometres of capillaries in a human body. If you lined up all of the blood vessels end to end, they would wrap around Earth's equator at least four times!

After the blood—depleted of oxygen and nutrients—leaves the capillary, it flows into the branches of veins called **venules**. The blood in venules and the larger veins has a much lower pressure than the blood pressure in an artery, so the walls of veins do not need to be as thick and elastic as the walls of arteries. The low-pressure blood has to get back to the heart against the pull of gravity. This is accomplished with the help of one-way valves in veins that prevent a backflow of blood, and also by the action of contracting body muscles.

▶ **capillary bed:** a network of capillaries in a particular area or organ of the body

▶ **venule:** a small vein that joins a larger vein to a capillary

▶ **varicose vein:** an enlarged, twisted vein near the surface of the skin resulting from poorly functioning valves

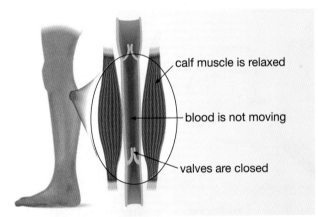

calf muscle is relaxed

blood is not moving

valves are closed

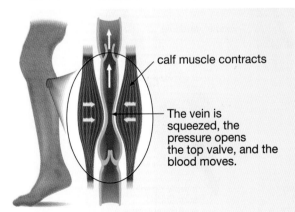

calf muscle contracts

The vein is squeezed, the pressure opens the top valve, and the blood moves.

Varicose Veins

As a person moves, the moving muscles push on blood in the veins while one-way venous valves prevent a backflow of blood and direct the blood back toward the heart. If the veins become stretched and the valves are damaged, blood in the veins pools and the veins become raised in a condition called **varicose veins**. People who spend much of their day standing have a greater tendency to develop varicose veins.

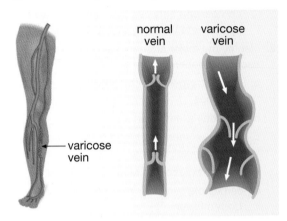

normal vein

varicose vein

varicose vein

Practice

15. A blood cell travels through different blood vessels as it passes through the circulatory system after leaving the heart. The blood vessels involved include the following terms: capillary, vein, venule, artery, and arteriole.

    Read each of the following descriptions and match each blood vessel term with a description.

    a. Large one-way valves in this vessel help direct blood back to the heart.

    b. These vessels are so small that blood cells must pass in single file.

    c. Capillaries converge into this vessel before entering a vein.

    d. This vessel is the pathway for oxygen-rich blood to enter capillaries.

    e. This vessel has thick walls with elastic fibres.

16. Consider the numbered list of blood vessels you used in question 15. Beginning with oxygen-rich blood that leaves the heart, place these terms in the order in which they are encountered by a blood cell.

17. Explain why circulatory problems often occur with people who are bedridden or with inactive people who seldom use their muscles.

18. Why do varicose veins most often occur in the lower legs?

19. Why should people who spend much of their workday standing up ensure that they elevate their feet at the end of the day?

Science Skills

✓ Performing and Recording
✓ Analyzing and Interpreting

British scientist William Harvey helped prove that blood circulates in a closed system of blood vessels rather than swishing back and forth like tides, as was previously believed. Part of his investigation looked at the role of valves of the veins.

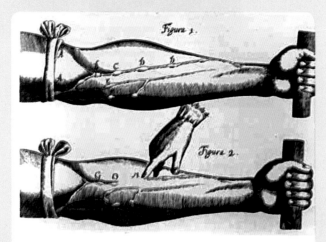

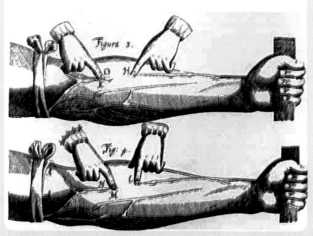

Purpose

You will observe the action of the valves working within the veins in the back of your hand.

Procedure

step 1: Lay your hand flat on a table so that you can see the veins on the top of your hand. Note that these photographs show the procedure using veins on your left hand.

step 2: Describe the appearance of the veins. Do the veins branch out or are they straight? Do the veins bulge more in certain areas? Record your observations.

step 3: Locate a straight section of a prominent vein. Firmly place the middle finger of your other hand on the end of this straight section of veins closest to your fingers.

step 4: While continuing to push down with your middle finger, take the index finger of your other hand and push down close to the middle finger on the same vein.

step 5: Continue to apply pressure with both fingers, and slide your index finger toward your wrist until you reach the end of the vein's straight section.

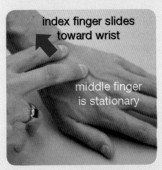

index finger slides toward wrist

middle finger is stationary

step 6: While continuing to apply pressure with your middle finger, release your index finger.

step 7: Carefully observe the straight section of the vein that used to be between the two fingers. Does blood flow back into the vein? Is there observable evidence of a valve's presence?

step 8: Repeat the process described in steps 3 to 7 with the following modifications:

- Place the index finger at the end of the straight section of vein closest to the wrist.

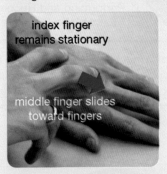

index finger remains stationary

middle finger slides toward fingers

- Then place the middle finger next to the index finger. Slide the middle finger toward the fingers, away from the wrist.
- Release the middle finger and see if the blood flows back into the veins.

Observations

1. Describe your observations from steps 2, 7, and 8.

Analysis

2. State whether it was easier or more difficult to push blood in the veins away from the heart than it was to push blood toward the heart.

3. Use your observations to sketch the veins in your hand. Indicate the location of the valves.

Conclusion

4. Write a concluding statement about the direction of blood flow. Refer to the valves in the veins of your hand.

Blood Pressure

During your last visit to a doctor, you may have noticed an apparatus for measuring **blood pressure** hanging on the wall. The gauge may resemble a thermometer; but instead of measuring temperature, this gauge is designed to measure pressure in terms of the height that a column of mercury can be raised. The greater the pressure, the higher the column of mercury rises in the tube. This is the origin of **millimetres of mercury**, the traditional unit for measuring blood pressure. The symbol for this unit is **mmHg**.

> **blood pressure:** the pressure exerted by blood against the walls of blood vessels such as arteries
>
> **millimetres of mercury:** a unit for measuring pressure in terms of the height of a column of mercury that can be supported by that pressure
>
> **mmHg:** the symbol for millimetres of mercury

The term *blood pressure* usually refers to the pressure exerted by blood on the walls of a major artery. As shown in Figure A1.7, this is an indirect measurement in which the arterial blood pressure is equal to the pressure of the air in an inflatable cuff around the patient's arm, which is then equal to the pressure exerted by a column of mercury.

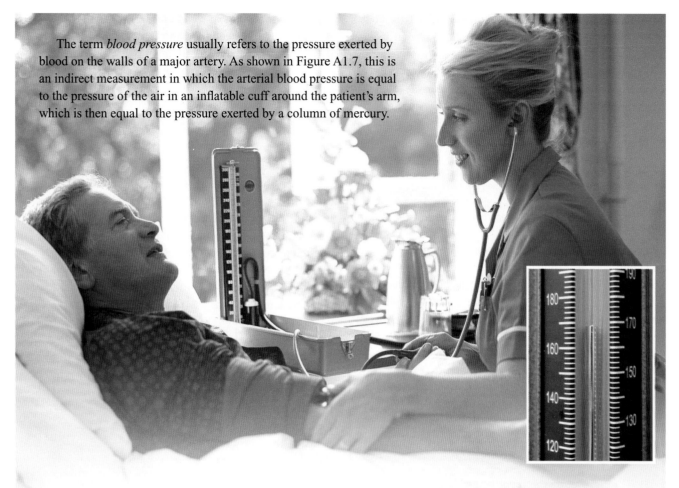

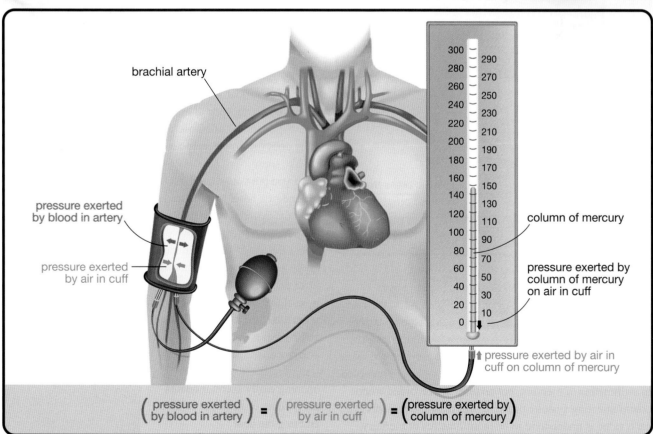

brachial artery

pressure exerted
by blood in artery

pressure exerted
by air in cuff

column of mercury

pressure exerted by
column of mercury
on air in cuff

pressure exerted by air in
cuff on column of mercury

$$\binom{\text{pressure exerted}}{\text{by blood in artery}} = \binom{\text{pressure exerted}}{\text{by air in cuff}} = \binom{\text{pressure exerted by}}{\text{column of mercury}}$$

Figure A1.7: The pressure in the column of mercury is equal to the pressure of the blood in the artery.

Blood pressure forces the blood to flow through the body's vessels. Since the heartbeat has a cycle of contraction and relaxation, two pressures are measured with blood pressure.

The first number in a blood pressure reading is the larger **systolic pressure**, which represents pressure in the arteries when the heart's ventricles are contracting. The elastic fibres surrounding the arteries stretch slightly in response to this pressure.

> ▶ **systolic pressure:** the pressure exerted on the artery walls when the heart's ventricles are contracting
> ▶ **diastolic pressure:** the residual pressure exerted on the artery walls when the heart's ventricles are relaxing

The second number, called **diastolic pressure**, is smaller and represents the residual pressure in the arteries when the heart's ventricles are relaxing and the chambers of the blood are refilling. This pressure is due to the elastic walls of the arteries attempting to return to their previous shape between ventricle contractions.

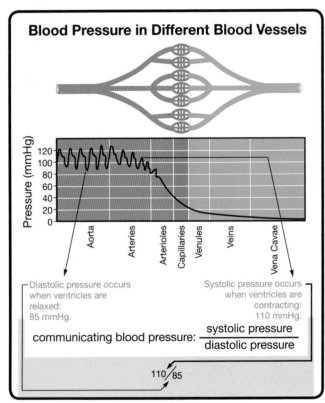

Blood Pressure in Different Blood Vessels

Diastolic pressure occurs when ventricles are relaxed: 85 mmHg.

Systolic pressure occurs when ventricles are contracting: 110 mmHg.

communicating blood pressure: $\dfrac{\text{systolic pressure}}{\text{diastolic pressure}}$

$110/85$

Figure A1.8

Blood pressure is written as systolic pressure over diastolic pressure. Using the values in Figure A1.8, the blood pressure would be 110/85. Even though this blood pressure value is read as *110 over 85*, this form of communication is not a fraction, so it should not be simplified or reduced. Note that the units for each individual pressure value are recorded in millimetres of mercury, but no units are recorded when communicating systolic pressure over diastolic pressure: each value is understood to be in millimetres of mercury.

The normal range of blood pressure for adults is a systolic pressure between 90 and 135 mmHg with a diastolic pressure between 50 and 90 mmHg. Blood pressure values in excess of 140/90 are considered to be high blood pressure or **hypertension**.

> ▶ **hypertension:** chronic, abnormally high blood pressure, characterized by values greater than 140/90

Note that by the time blood leaves the arterioles and then enters the capillaries, pressure is significantly reduced. Since the smallest capillaries only allow blood cells to pass in single file, there is more resistance to the blood flow. Therefore, there is a reduction in blood pressure. So, how does blood return to the heart? Recall that the skeletal muscles squeeze the veins during exercise. This is combined with the action of one-way valves within the veins to force blood back to the heart.

Pressure and Blood Flow

As water flows from an outside faucet through a garden hose to a sprinkler or a nozzle, pressure on the water drives it through the hose. If there are no leaks, then the number of litres per minute that leave the hose should equal the number of litres per minute that enter the hose. Although this appears to be stating the obvious, it explains the behaviour of water as it leaves the hose. As an example, consider what happens when you clamp your thumb over the open end of a hose. Why does the flow become a jet-like spray?

If you put your thumb over the end of a hose, you reduce the cross-sectional area of the opening. The small opening forces the water to leave much faster to balance the number of litres per minute that enter the hose at the faucet end. Similarly, if the attachment on the hose's end increases the cross-sectional area, then the speed of the water drops since the larger opening easily accommodates the number of litres per minute entering the hose.

How does this thinking apply to the flow of blood from arteries to capillaries? Even though each individual capillary has a very tiny cross-sectional area, the huge number of capillaries fed by an artery means that the total cross-sectional area is much greater. One result of this is that the speed of the blood drops dramatically as it passes through a capillary bed, as in Figure A1.9. Another result is that the increase in cross-sectional area also contributes to the drop in blood pressure as the blood flows through a capillary bed from the arteries and arterioles.

The fact that blood travels slowly through the capillary bed means that the exchange of substances through diffusion between cells of tissue and the blood is enhanced. As blood leaves the capillary beds, the total cross-sectional area of the vessels decreases. As a result, the blood flow speeds up. However, because blood pressure is so low by the time it leaves the capillary beds, the flow speed through veins is much less than the speed through arteries.

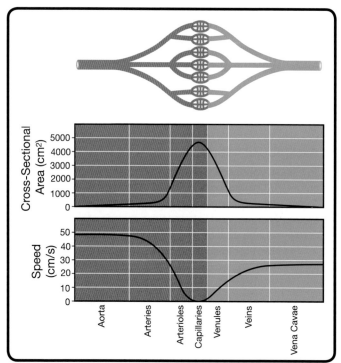

Figure A1.9

Practice

20. While waiting at a pharmacy to pick up a prescription, you decide to have your blood pressure tested using the automated machine available for customers. The machine says that your blood pressure is 138 over 96.

    a. Explain what the values of 138 and 96 measure. What is happening in your heart and arteries?

    b. Identify what unit could be included with each measurement you explained in question 20.a.

    c. Is 138 over 96 a cause for concern? What would you do with this information?

21. During diastole, the heart's ventricles are relaxing but there still is residual pressure in the arteries. Identify the source of this pressure.

22. Explain what causes the blood flow velocity to drop as it passes through the capillaries.

Measuring Blood Pressure

Blood pressure readings are often taken as part of a regular medical checkup. If blood pressure is too high, there is a risk of blood vessels bursting. This would be particularly dangerous if a vessel burst in your heart or brain. If blood pressure is too low, not enough blood can get to all the vital parts of your body. This may cause dizziness or fainting.

Your body has mechanisms to help control the amount of blood pressure. If your blood pressure is low, the blood vessels will be constricted or narrowed. If your blood pressure is high, the blood vessels will be dilated or widened. Many factors affect blood pressure. Readings can vary greatly between individuals due to the strength or rate of heart contractions or the elasticity of arteries. Higher blood pressure readings can also be attributed to anxiety level, exercise, a greater than normal amount of blood in the vessels, viscosity (thickness) of the blood, kidney disease, the presence of chemicals—including caffeine—in the body, or the narrowing of blood vessels due to a buildup of plaque along artery walls.

Measuring Blood Pressure

Purpose

You will measure your blood pressure while resting and immediately after exercise.

Background Information

To assess your health, a doctor or nurse may measure your blood pressure using either an automated digital machine or an older type of instrument called a **sphygmomanometer**. To use a sphygmomanometer, the person measuring your blood pressure inflates a cuff around your arm and listens to the sounds of your arteries with a stethoscope. The instant certain sounds change, the height of the column of mercury is noted for that moment.

The steps for measuring blood pressure are outlined in the following illustrations.

▶ **sphygmomanometer:**
an instrument for measuring blood pressure

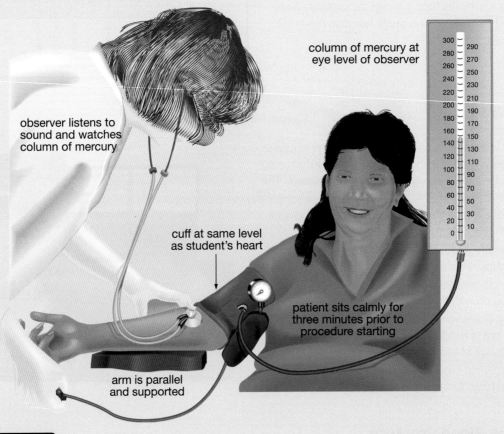

column of mercury at eye level of observer

observer listens to sound and watches column of mercury

cuff at same level as student's heart

patient sits calmly for three minutes prior to procedure starting

arm is parallel and supported

CAUTION!

- Prior to starting this investigation, be sure to carefully read the provided investigation instructions and those details included with the machine that you will be using.
- **Do not exceed 160 mmHg when inflating the cuff on the sphygmomanometer.**
- Remember that only a health-care professional, such as your doctor, can diagnose an abnormality in your blood pressure. A higher than average reading in this investigation is not necessarily an indication of high blood pressure.
- Mercury is a hazardous substance that can produce serious negative health effects. If a sphygmomanometer breaks and mercury spills into the open, the substance must be cleaned up immediately and thoroughly using proper procedures.
- If you have a medical condition that prevents you from participating in physical education classes, you should not participate in the exercising part of this investigation.

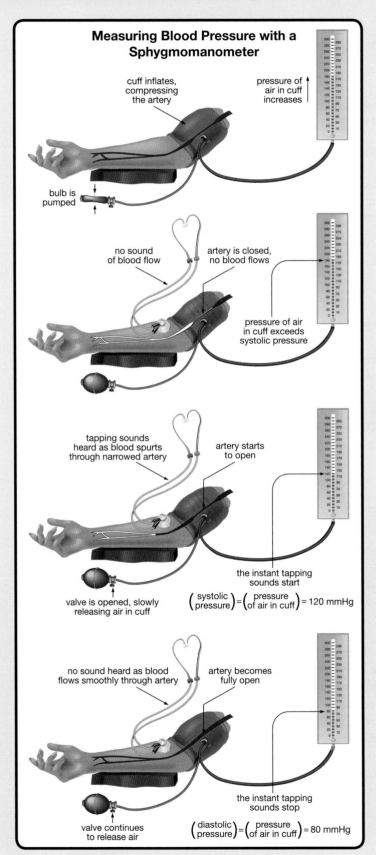

Measuring Blood Pressure with a Sphygmomanometer

cuff inflates, compressing the artery

pressure of air in cuff increases

bulb is pumped

no sound of blood flow

artery is closed, no blood flows

pressure of air in cuff exceeds systolic pressure

tapping sounds heard as blood spurts through narrowed artery

artery starts to open

valve is opened, slowly releasing air in cuff

the instant tapping sounds start

$$\left(\begin{array}{c}\text{systolic} \\ \text{pressure}\end{array}\right) = \left(\begin{array}{c}\text{pressure} \\ \text{of air in cuff}\end{array}\right) = 120 \text{ mmHg}$$

no sound heard as blood flows smoothly through artery

artery becomes fully open

valve continues to release air

the instant tapping sounds stop

$$\left(\begin{array}{c}\text{diastolic} \\ \text{pressure}\end{array}\right) = \left(\begin{array}{c}\text{pressure} \\ \text{of air in cuff}\end{array}\right) = 80 \text{ mmHg}$$

Procedure

step 1: You should be rested and sitting comfortably before beginning this activity. Using either a digital blood pressure machine or a sphygmomanometer and a stethoscope, have a classmate take your resting blood pressure. Record this number (in mmHg) as your resting blood pressure. If you use a digital machine for measuring blood pressure, follow the instructions provided with that machine. If you do not have access to a sphygmomanometer or a digital machine, measure your blood pressure by visiting a local pharmacy that has an automated blood pressure machine available for customer use.

step 2: Engage in four minutes of physical activity (jumping jacks, running on a spot, stepping up and down from a chair or stool) and have your blood pressure taken again at the end of the four minutes. Be sure that each class member performs the same exercise for the same amount of time for this activity.

Analysis

1. Obtain a class average for resting blood pressure. Compare the class average to the average adult blood pressure of 120 mmHg/ 80 mmHg. Describe how your own resting blood pressure compares to the average adult blood pressure.

2. Compare your blood pressure before and after exercising. Explain why your blood pressure changed after the exercise.

3. Compare the change in your systolic blood pressure reading after exercise to the change in your diastolic blood pressure reading after exercise. Did the readings change by the same amount? Can you account for the changes observed?

4. List some sources of error that may have affected the accuracy of the measurements made in this activity. Describe some improvements that could create more accurate measurements.

 In your health file, record your resting blood pressure level and your blood pressure level after exercise.

Blood Pressure and Heart Rate

Science Skills

✓ Initiating and Planning

Purpose

You will design an experiment to investigate a factor known to have an effect on blood pressure and heart rate.

Background Information

This investigation will allow you to apply what you have learned so far about blood pressure, heart rate, and the circulatory system. You have already been introduced to several factors known to have an effect on both blood pressures and heart rates.

Choose one of these factors. Then design an experiment that will allow you to test the effect of this factor on both blood pressure and heart rate.

You may decide to undertake some background research on the factor that will be the focus of your experiment. This will help you generate questions and identify what kind of data you will be collecting. It is also useful to research the importance of establishing a double-blind test when designing your experiment.

Process

The end product will be a detailed procedure for an investigation. You'll describe how to complete the necessary measurements and observations.

Procedure

step 1: Identify a specific question that needs to be investigated to determine the effects of the variable you have chosen to study.

step 2: Identify the manipulated variable, the responding variable, and the control group for your experiment. Based upon your background research, define a double-blind test and relate it to how the data will be collected in this experiment.

step 3: Determine what data needs to be collected to answer the question identified in step 1. Describe a means to collect that data, and list the tools required. Be sure to include any necessary safety precautions.

step 4: Design and construct data tables to ensure all the necessary observations are made and recorded.

1.2 Summary

The circulatory system's basic components are the heart, the blood vessels, and the blood. In this lesson you learned that vessels in the circulatory system are defined by their size and the direction in which they carry blood, relative to the heart. The vessels are specialized for their specific functions. Capillaries are uniquely designed for the exchange of nutrients between the body's cells and the circulatory system. Because matter exchange between capillaries occurs by diffusion, every cell in the body must be close to a capillary.

The pumping of the heart's ventricles exerts pressure on blood, and this pressure is then transferred to the artery walls. Blood pressure has two readings. The systolic reading is the artery pressure when the heart's ventricles are contracting. The diastolic reading is residual artery pressure when the heart's ventricles are relaxed. When listed separately, the units of millimetres of mercury are included with each of these pressure values. When communicated together, the units are usually omitted and the pressures are communicated as systolic pressure over diastolic pressure. An average blood pressure reading for adults is 120/80. Readings of 140/90 or greater are considered to be high blood pressure or hypertension.

Blood pressure is greatly reduced as the blood flow encounters resistance when passing single file through the many kilometres of tiny capillaries. By the time blood passes to the veins, blood pressure is so low that the blood is helped back to the heart by one-way valves and the contractions of skeletal muscles.

Knowledge

1. Copy and complete the following table to compare arteries, veins, and capillaries.

Characteristic	Arteries	Veins	Capillaries
description of vessel walls			
direction of vessel blood flow in relation to heart			
blood oxygen level in vessel			
colour in a circulatory system diagram			
blood pressure in vessel			
valves present			
pulse present			

Applying Concepts

2. People who have type 1 diabetes do not produce insulin—the sugar-regulating hormone—and they must have regular hypodermic insulin injections to regulate their blood sugar. Researchers are working on developing a dry powdered form of insulin that can be delivered by the same kind of inhaler used by people with asthma.

   a. Describe some possible benefits of the inhaler delivery system.

   b. Insulin is usually injected into fat underneath the skin. List the pathway that injected insulin takes from a capillary bed under the skin to a target cell in the liver.

   c. List the pathway that inhaled insulin would take from the lungs to a target cell in the liver.

   d. Which of the two delivery methods—injected or inhaled—would be faster at getting to target cells?

3. Identify some factors that can cause a person's blood pressure to increase.

4. Explain why it is more dangerous if an artery—rather than a vein—is cut in an accident.

5. Sketch a capillary bed. Include the artery, the arteriole, the vein, the venule, and the proper placement of valves. Include a few tissue cells being fed by the capillaries. Add arrows to your sketch that indicate the direction of blood flow, and add arrows that show what materials are being exchanged and the exchange direction.

6. Soldiers on guard are often required to stand in one place for long periods of time. While standing at attention some of the soldiers sway back and forth, slightly contracting and relaxing their calf muscles. Other soldiers exercise the muscles in their lower legs by slightly wiggling their toes in oversized boots. Soldiers who do not use strategies like these often faint after standing for a long time. Explain why contracting and relaxing the muscles in their lower legs helps prevent soldiers from fainting.

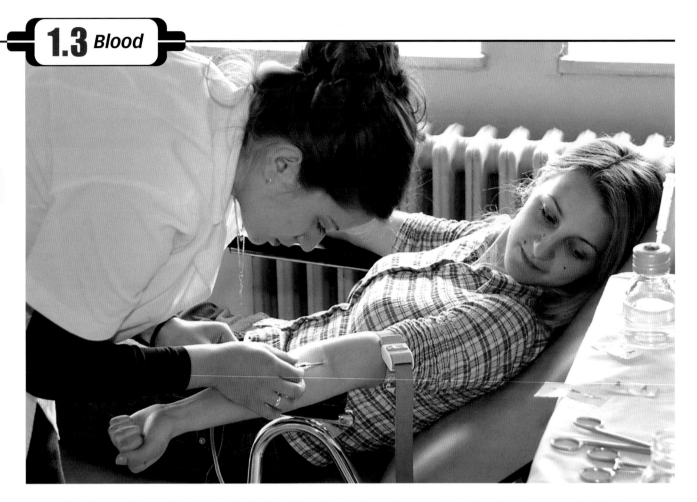

Your school is organizing a blood drive for the local blood bank. If you have not given blood before, you probably have questions about what will happen during the donation. Before blood is donated, potential donors—aged 17 or more—are asked a list of questions about their general health, their travel history, and their participation in certain activities. The answers determine if there is a risk that the donor's blood carries a disease that could be passed on to the person receiving the blood. In addition to medical concerns, some people are prohibited from donating blood or receiving transfusions for religious reasons.

If you are able to participate, a nurse will test your temperature and blood pressure to see if you are healthy enough to donate. The nurse will also take a drop of blood from your finger and time how long it takes for the blood to sink in a solution to examine the oxygen-carrying capacity of your red blood cells.

The nurse will then insert a sterile needle into a vein in your arm and take about 450 mL of blood. Your body contains about 5 L of blood, and this small donated volume of 450 mL will quickly be replaced by new blood cells formed in the spongy marrow inside your bones. Since the donated blood can become thick and clot quickly in the air, a chemical called an anticoagulant must be added to stop the collected sample from clumping.

The collected blood will then be taken to a lab where it will be tested to ensure it is free of dangerous diseases, such as hepatitis and HIV. Once this screening process is complete, the donated blood may be given to patients who have a need for the entire sample or some of its components.

It may be donated as whole blood, but later the individual parts of blood may be separated. Some patients require the portion that causes clotting, while others are given only the liquid part of blood to replace fluids they have lost in an accident or during major surgery. It is estimated that one blood donation is able to help three other people, and it quite often helps save lives.

Blood is the fluid of life. Because the jobs performed by blood are so important, people die if they lose too much of this vital fluid. Since the average adult only has about 5 L of blood, it must be quickly cycled by the circulatory system to efficiently carry out its jobs. In previous lessons you learned that blood is constantly circulated throughout the body so it can deliver oxygen and nutrients and remove wastes from cells as they carry out their functions—however, blood also transports other materials such as chemical messengers (called hormones), vitamins, and minerals. Blood also helps to protect people's bodies from disease and maintains water balance, temperature, and pH. Health-care workers examine blood samples from people who are not feeling well because irregularities in a blood sample can help diagnose an imbalance in the body.

So many images come to mind when we think about blood because we are aware of the vital importance of this fluid flowing within our bodies. Just the sight of lost blood makes some people uncomfortable. Blood is often used as a symbol of our spirit and can signify both life and death. Children are someone's "flesh and blood," murderers have "blood on their hands," something that you were meant to do is "in your blood," and hard work requires "blood, sweat, and tears."

Place the word *blood* within a small circle at the centre of a blank page. Draw a larger circle around the smaller one. Brainstorm all the different ideas, terms, metaphors, symbols, and sayings that come to mind with this word and write them within the larger circle. Draw a box around the large circle. Determine the sources for ideas and terms that you wrote within the larger circle, and write these terms within the box. As an alternative, this activity may be done in small groups or as a class, with many students contributing to the formation of one circle diagram.

Blood Components

Blood appears to be a liquid with a uniform red colour, but blood is actually a mixture of living cells and pieces of cells suspended in a broth-like liquid. If you let a blood sample sit for a while or spin a blood sample in a machine called a centrifuge, the blood separates into layers to reveal its different parts.

At the bottom of the centrifuge sample, the red blood cells are clearly visible. The pale yellow liquid that is seen to occupy the top half of the blood samples is called **plasma**.

Plasma is like the broth of a soup because it is mostly water with substances dissolved or floating in it. About 55% of blood volume is due to the watery plasma. In between the plasma and the red blood cells is a section of clear fluid containing the **white blood cells** and **platelets**. Platelets contribute the smallest amount to the volume of blood.

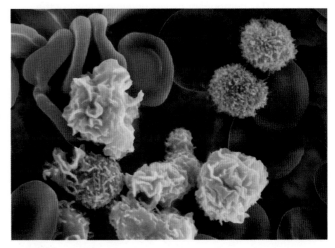

White blood cells are designed to protect the body from disease-causing organisms and other harmful materials. Sometimes these foreign substances enter the body through a cut in the skin. At the site of a cut, the platelets are tiny fragments of cells that play a key role in helping blood clot. The clot eventually hardens to form a scab that keeps the wound clean while new replacement skin grows. In this lesson you'll learn more about the roles played by plasma, red blood cells, white blood cells, and platelets.

plasma: the pale yellow fluid portion of blood where the cells are suspended

white blood cell: a colourless blood cell that acts to defend the body against diseases and other foreign invaders

platelet: a particle found in the bloodstream that begins the blood-clotting process at the site of a wound

Separation of Blood into Components

Obtain a copy of the handout "Separating Blood into Its Components" from the Science 30 Textbook CD. Use this handout to answer questions 23 and 24.

23. Add the following labels to this diagram: red blood cells; plasma; white blood cells; platelets; sample of blood prior to placement in centrifuge; sample of blood after removal from centrifuge; and centrifuge.

24. Identify the blood component(s) that best describes each of the following statements.

  a. This component comprises about 55% of blood volume.

  b. This component makes up almost 45% of the total volume of blood.

  c. Together, these components comprise less than 1% of the total volume of blood.

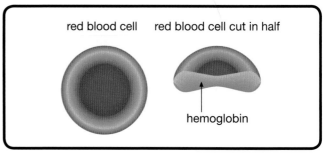

red blood cell   red blood cell cut in half

hemoglobin

A red blood cell's lifespan in the bloodstream is about 120 days. As red blood cells die, they are absorbed by the liver and are soon replaced with new cells produced in the bone marrow. The bone marrow produces millions of red blood cells every second. Each red blood cell takes about two days to develop. As the red blood cells mature and are released from the bone marrow, they lose their nucleus. Having no nucleus provides extra room to pack the cell full of the **hemoglobin** molecule.

Red Blood Cells

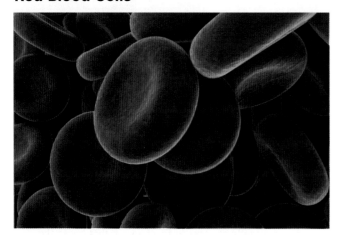

Red blood cells, also called **erythrocytes**, are the most numerous cell type in a blood sample. In one drop of blood there are about one million red blood cells. These cells are designed to transport oxygen. They are shaped like a covered inner tube, with a depression in the middle but not a hole. This distinctive shape—called **biconcave**—allows them to slide through the blood vessels with ease. If their shape were more square or jagged they might stick to each other or the vessel walls, which would result in a jam that slows or stops circulation in that vessel. The cream-filled, doughnut-like shape provides a large surface area to volume ratio for an efficient gas exchange.

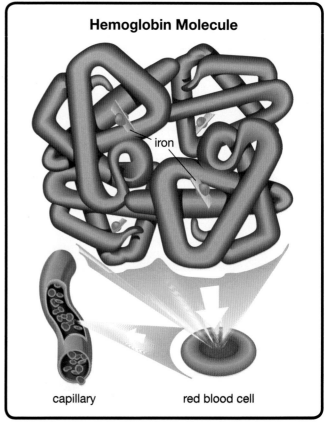

Hemoglobin Molecule

iron

capillary   red blood cell

Hemoglobin is a pigment that gives the red blood cells and whole blood their red colour. It contains iron which interacts with the oxygen present in the lungs. A hemoglobin called **oxyhemoglobin** is bound to oxygen and has a bright red colour.

▶ **erythrocyte:** a term for a red blood cell that contains hemoglobin and transports oxygen from the lungs to the body's cells

▶ **biconcave:** the distinctive shape of red blood cells where the cells are flat but dip inwards at the centre on both the top and bottom

▶ **hemoglobin:** an iron-containing pigment that binds oxygen to facilitate its movement in the circulatory system

▶ **oxyhemoglobin:** a hemoglobin bound with oxygen that appears bright red in colour

As red blood cells pass through the lungs, hemoglobin molecules pick up oxygen molecules to form oxyhemoglobin. The red blood cells are transported through arteries, arterioles, and eventually to capillary beds next to body tissues. As these cells slowly pass through capillaries near tissue cells, the reaction is reversed: the oxygen is released and the blood loses its bright red colour.

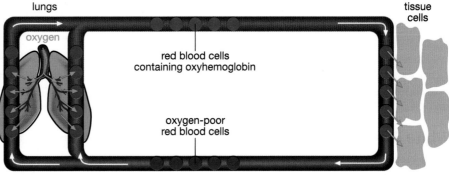

in the lungs:
hemoglobin + oxygen → oxyhemoglobin

in the capillaries beside tissue cells:
oxyhemoglobin → hemoglobin + oxygen

Investigation

Iron-Fortified Cereals

Background Information

New red blood cells are constantly being made to replace old red blood cells, and iron is needed for the production of the red blood cell's hemoglobin. Good sources of iron include foods such as meat, fish, poultry, beans, dried fruits, and whole grain breads. For people who don't receive enough iron through their regular diet, it is beneficial for them to supplement their iron supply by eating foods with added iron. Many cereal companies advertise that their product is "fortified with iron."

Purpose

You will separate the iron from breakfast cereal enriched with iron.

Materials

- 750 mL (3 cups) of iron-fortified cold breakfast cereal
- mortar and pestle or a rolling pin
- two 1000-mL beakers
- magnetic stirrer complete with magnetic stir bar and magnetic retrieval wand
- 700 mL of distilled water
- plastic rinse bottle with distilled water

Procedure

step 1: Crush the cereal with a rolling pin or a mortar and pestle until the cereal becomes a fine powder. Place the powdered cereal in one of the 1000-mL beakers.

step 2: Add 700 mL of distilled water to the other 1000-mL beaker.

step 3: Carefully add the stir bar to the beaker's bottom and place the beaker on the magnetic stirrer. If the magnetic stirrer is combined with a hot plate, do not turn on the hot plate.

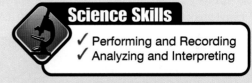

Science Skills

✓ Performing and Recording
✓ Analyzing and Interpreting

step 4: Turn on the magnetic stirrer at a moderate speed setting. While it is spinning, carefully add the powdered cereal. The rotation speed may have to be increased.

step 5: Stir for approximately 30 minutes.

step 6: Turn off the magnetic stirrer. Use the retrieval wand to carefully remove the stir bar. Gently rinse any cereal off the stir bar and then observe its surface.

Analysis

1. State the iron property that accounts for what you observed on the magnetic stir bar's surface.

2. People who don't get enough iron from their diets, or those people who suffer from chronic blood loss, have lowered red blood cell levels and can develop a blood condition called *anemia*. Based on your knowledge of red blood cell functions, what symptoms do you think people with anemia might have?

3. One test used to see if potential blood donors have anemia is to put a drop of a donor's blood in a vial of thick blue fluid. If the blood drop falls very slowly or does not sink at all, it could be a sign that the donor is anemic or low in red blood cells on that particular day. Explain why a sample of blood from someone who has anemia might fall less quickly than a sample of blood from a person who does not have anemia.

4. To stay healthy, men require about 10 mg of iron per day and women about 15 mg per day. Pregnant women daily need about 30 mg of iron. Explain why pregnant women might require double the mass of iron required by women who are not pregnant.

White Blood Cells

White blood cells, also called **leukocytes**, are much larger than red blood cells and are found in much lower numbers. In a healthy individual there is only about one white blood cell for every 600 to 700 red blood cells. Like red blood cells, leukocytes are made in a person's bone marrow. Unlike red blood cells, leukocytes keep their nucleus when they mature. Their shape is not uniform and they lack a colour pigment. In prepared slides and photographs, white blood cells are often stained so that they can be observed more clearly. The life span of a white blood cell is generally about 13 to 20 days.

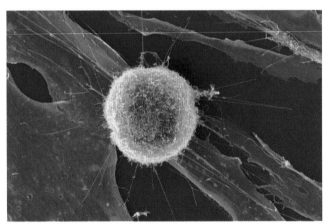

Figure A1.10: A human white blood cell attacks cancer cells.

When disease-causing organisms enter the body, the number of white blood cells increases by releasing stored white blood cells from the body or producing more in the bone marrow. A doctor will often request that a white blood cell count be performed in a blood sample. Elevated white blood cell counts usually signal an infection.

▶ **leukocytes:** a term for white blood cells

▶ **protein:** a large organic molecule consisting of a chain of amino acids; an essential building block of all cells that plays a key role in the functioning of body systems

▶ **fibrinogen:** a soluble protein present in blood plasma that converts to fibrin when blood clots

25. Cancer patients often experience extreme fatigue because the cells in their muscle tissues are oxygen depleted. This condition exists because the chemotherapy many patients undergo to treat their cancer has a side effect of reducing the number of blood cells.

    a. In these circumstances, identify what type of blood cells are especially needed by cancer patients.

    b. The type of blood cells in question 25.a. must be separated from whole blood. Describe a process that could separate whole blood into its components.

26. The body produces millions of red blood cells in the bone marrow every second. White blood cells are made in bone marrow at twice the rate of red blood cells. However, in a given sample of blood, nearly 45% of the blood consists of red blood cells and less than 1% is made of white blood cells.

    a. Suggest a reason for the lower volume of white blood cells in a sample of blood even though they are produced at twice the rate of red blood cells.

    b. Most agents that cause disease are outside the bloodstream and are found in the fluid spaces between tissue cells. Use this information to develop another reason for the lower volume of white blood cells in a sample of blood.

Platelets

Think back to the last time you had a small scrape or a minor cut to your skin and the tissues below your skin. The bleeding usually stops after a few minutes because **proteins** in your blood work to form a plug that seals the damaged blood vessels. A protein present in blood and capable of forming a plug is called **fibrinogen**. This protein remains inactive until called into action by the platelets.

Platelets rupture when they come into contact with a rough surface, and they trigger a complex series of chemical reactions. These reactions cause the dissolved fibrinogen protein to convert to its active form—a thread-like protein called **fibrin**. The fibrin threads become interwoven to produce a mesh that traps red blood cells. As more red blood cells get caught in the net of fibrin, the combination of these fibres and blood cells produce a thick red jellylike substance called a **blood clot**. When this mesh of threads and red blood cells hardens and dries, it is called a scab. The skin under the scab heals and the scab eventually falls off.

Many life-threatening medical conditions are related to blood clotting. A diet high in fat can make the walls of arteries become rough—this causes platelets to adhere and produce blood clots inside the vessel. A blood clot in these circumstances can lead to serious cardiovascular problems, including heart attacks or strokes.

Some people lack the ability to produce the necessary blood proteins that allow platelets to form a clot. For these individuals, even minor cuts and bruises bleed excessively and take much longer to heal. This condition is called **hemophilia**. To keep healthy, people with hemophilia often need transfusions of protein clotting factors and platelets.

> ▶ **fibrin:** a thread-like insoluble protein formed from fibrinogen
> The threads of fibrin mesh to form the fabric of a blood clot.
> ▶ **blood clot:** a jellylike, solid mass consisting mainly of red blood cells trapped in a net of fibrin fibres
> ▶ **hemophilia:** a blood disorder involving the blood's reduced ability to clot, which can lead to excessive bleeding

The Clotting Process

The skin is cut. Blood starts leaking out of the body to wash out dirt and germs from the cut.

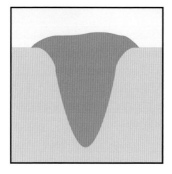

Platelets come into contact with the rough surface of the cut. The platelets rupture and release chemicals that convert fibrinogen into threads of fibrin.

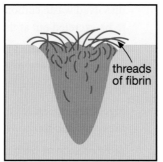

threads of fibrin

Red blood cells get caught in the fibrin net to form a blood clot.

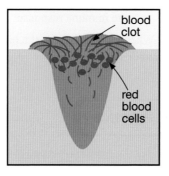

blood clot

red blood cells

The clot hardens to form a protective barrier known as a scab.

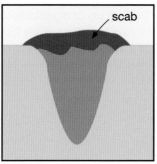

scab

❓ DID YOU KNOW?

Alexei Romanov, the son of Nicholas II—the last Tsar of Russia—had hemophilia. At the time, there was little understanding and no treatment for the disease. Alexei's mother, Alexandra, employed the help of a self-proclaimed healer named Rasputin to help Alexei. Some people believed that Rasputin was able to use hypnosis to help control Alexei's condition and slow his bleeding. Rasputin was hated by many Russians for his powerful influence with the royal family, and he was killed by his enemies in 1916.

Investigation

Observing a Prepared Blood Smear

Science Skills

✓ Performing and Recording
✓ Analyzing and Interpreting

Purpose

You will use prepared slides of human blood to observe the structure and abundance of the cellular components of blood.

Materials

- prepared human blood slides
- compound microscope
- blank unlined paper
- pencil

Procedure

step 1: Review basic microscope skills by reading the handout "Using a Microscope" from the Science 30 Textbook CD.

step 2: Obtain a prepared human blood slide and view the slide under high-power magnification.

step 3: Identify and draw to scale a red blood cell, two white blood cells, and platelets—perhaps these are only barely visible. Remember that the blood sample is most likely stained for better visibility and, therefore, the colours may not be representative. Label the three cellular components of blood on your drawing. Include a label for the white blood cell nucleus.

step 4: Count and record the number of red blood cells and white blood cells in the field of view.

Analysis

1. Describe two physical differences between the observed red blood cells and white blood cells.

2. The function of red blood cells is to transport oxygen. How is a red blood cell's shape and structure related to its function?

3. Compare the two white blood cells that you sketched in step 3. Describe how these two cells are similar. Describe how they are different.

4. State the ratio of red blood cells to white blood cells in the section of the prepared blood slide that you observed.

Plasma

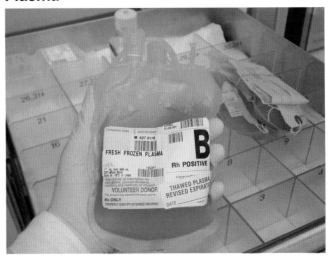

Plasma is a yellowish liquid that is like soup broth, because it is mostly water with substances dissolved or suspended in it. More than half of blood is composed of watery plasma. The plasma holds and transports such substances as the following:

- cells of the blood—red blood cells, white blood cells, and platelets

- dissolved waste carbon dioxide from the capillaries to be excreted out at the lungs

- urea, a waste product from the liver filtered by the kidneys to become urine

- hormones from glands

- digested nutrients such as glucose, amino acids, vitamins, and minerals from the digestive tract

- proteins such as fibrinogen that aid in blood clotting, as well as other proteins like antibodies involved in the immune response

When patients have lost a lot of blood due to an accident or major surgery, they may be given donated plasma to replace the lost fluid.

Practice

Use the following information to answer questions 27 to 30.

The majority of blood collected at a blood donation clinic is not left as whole blood. It is instead separated by a centrifuge into its components of red blood cells, plasma, and platelets. In this way, your single donation of one blood unit can help three other people.

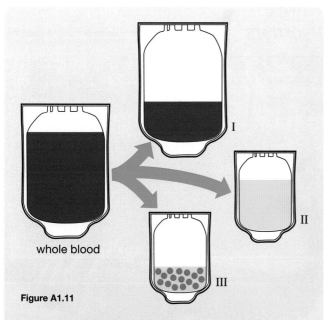

Figure A1.11

27. Refer to Figure A1.11. Identify the blood component that corresponds best to each of bags I, II, and III.

28. Burn victims suffer a significant loss of skin tissue and are, therefore, highly susceptible to deadly dehydration. What blood component best addresses this problem?

29. A cancer patient receiving radiation treatment is often unable to produce enough of a key blood component that prevents uncontrollable internal bleeding. Identify the blood component given to this patient in a transfusion.

30. Explain the following statement:

    "Every time you give blood you can save up to three lives."

1.3 Summary

The typical human body contains about 5 L of blood that transports materials around the body to help prevent disease. Blood is a mixture of living and non-living components: red blood cells, white blood cells, platelets, and plasma.

The disc-shaped red blood cells are full of a molecule called hemoglobin, which allows these blood cells to carry and transport oxygen to the body's cells. White blood cells are designed to help protect the body from disease-causing organisms. Platelets are the blood parts that make blood self-sealing. When there is a cut, platelets form a clot to stop the loss of blood—people with hemophilia lack key factors in their blood that help form clots. Plasma is a yellowish liquid that the blood cells and platelets float in. Many substances are dissolved in plasma, including glucose, urea, and hormones.

1.3 Questions

Knowledge

1. a. List the four components of blood in decreasing order of their relative volume in whole blood (from most abundant to least abundant).

    b. Sketch a scale diagram of each component of question 1.a.

2. Obtain a copy of the handout "Blood Smears" from the Science 30 Textbook CD. The first five blood smears on this handout come from a healthy patient. The sixth blood smear is from a patient with neutrophilia.

    a. Identify the major difference between the blood smears from the healthy patient shown in slides 3, 4, and 5 with the blood smear from the patient with neutrophilia on slide 6.

    b. Suggest a possible reason for the difference you identified in 2.a.

Applying Concepts

3. Carbon monoxide is a colourless, odourless gas produced during the combustion of fossil fuels, including gasoline. Carbon monoxide binds to the hemoglobin in red blood cells much faster and more strongly than does oxygen. Based on your knowledge of the role of red blood cells, explain why exposure to carbon monoxide can be so dangerous.

4. Leeches and vampire bats are both parasites that feed on animal blood. After they use their sharp teeth to cut the surface of the animal's skin, they release a blood-thinning chemical called an anticoagulant that not only stops blood from clotting but also allows greater blood flow by dilating blood vessels.

    Explain why an anticoagulant might be useful for treating circulatory system problems.

5. Leukemia is a type of cancer where the body produces large numbers of abnormal blood cells—particularly white blood cells—that do not function properly.

    a. How could having improperly functioning white blood cells affect people with leukemia?

    b. Why would doctors treat leukemia by giving patients a bone marrow transplant?

6. Do you meet the basic criteria to be a blood donor? Use the Internet to gather information about the basic eligibility criteria for donating blood in Canada.

The traditional diet of Inuit people living in coastal communities has centred on fish like arctic char and marine mammals including seals, walruses, and whales. These trends even extend to traditional snack food. Maktaaq, which is whale skin attached to a few centimetres of insulating fat, or blubber, is considered to be one of the finest delicacies in the traditional Inuit diet because it is so delicious. Sometimes maktaaq is consumed immediately after the kill as the whale is being brought ashore, while other times the maktaaq and other whale foods are allowed to freeze and are then buried in snow-covered food caches for later use.

Nutritionists and medical researchers began to collect data in the 1970s about the eating habits and the incidences of illness and disease in traditional Inuit communities. The results of these studies were surprising. Even though fat from marine mammals was a staple of a traditional Inuit diet, the incidence of **cardiovascular disease** in the population was very low. This data stands in sharp contrast to data gathered from communities outside of the Arctic where a high-fat diet coincided with higher rates of cardiovascular diseases.

▶ **cardiovascular disease:** one of many disorders—coronary heart disease, strokes, and varicose veins—that affect the heart and/or the blood vessels

Figure A1.12: Maktaaq is an Inuit delicacy.

If the Inuit diet is so high in fat, why is there such a low incidence of cardiovascular disease among Inuit who follow a traditional lifestyle?

The full answer is still under investigation, but as you will see in this lesson the preliminary findings are quite intriguing. To understand better the results of the early investigations, you will need to learn about the causes of some major cardiovascular diseases, the different types of fat that are part of your diet, and the **traditional ecological knowledge** of Canada's Inuit.

▶ **traditional ecological knowledge:** the accumulated observations and understanding of the people living within an area, acquired over many hundreds of years through direct contact with the environment

Incorporating traditional ecological knowledge involves developing an understanding of human interactions with the environment and focusing on the inseparable relationship among land, resources, and culture.

Practice

In the 1700s, many Europeans who came to the Arctic to explore or hunt whales began to get a disease called scurvy after spending many months in the far north. Scurvy is a connective-tissue disease that is thought to be the number one cause of deaths at sea in the age of sail. Scurvy symptoms include pale skin, sunken eyes, tender gums, tooth loss, internal bleeding, and a physical and mental deterioration of the body that frequently leads to death.

It was eventually discovered that having fresh fruit and vegetables aboard ships prevented scurvy. The nickname of *limey* for a British sailor comes from the use of limes on British ships to prevent scurvy. It was not until 1932 that medical science established the biochemical cause of scurvy.

Meanwhile, Inuit people who lived their entire lives in the Arctic environment did not have access to fresh fruit and vegetables, but they did not suffer from scurvy.

Use the Internet to gather information to help you answer the following questions.

31. Identify the essential nutrient linked to the cause of scurvy. Explain why it affected sailors, explorers, and whalers on long voyages during the 1700s.

32. How did maktaaq play a key role in preventing scurvy within the Inuit population?

33. Prior to the use of limes and other fresh fruit, explain how the traditional ecological knowledge of the Inuit could have helped the early European explorers of Canada's Arctic who suffered from scurvy.

Cardiovascular Diseases and Cholesterol

As the terms *cardio* + *vascular* suggest, cardiovascular diseases are disorders of the heart + blood vessels. As shown in Figure A1.13, cardiovascular diseases include a wide range of disorders.

Cardiovascular Disease	Description of Disorder	Heart Disease	Blood Vessel Disease
atherosclerosis	hardening of arteries due to accumulation of fatty deposits		✓
coronary heart disease	restricted blood flow through coronary arteries resulting in chest pain and heart attack	✓	
heart attack	clot in a coronary artery cuts off blood supply to heart muscle and tissue dies	✓	
stroke	sudden loss of brain function caused by an interruption in blood flow to brain		✓
aneurysm	bulging or weakness in wall of artery or vein		✓
valvular heart disease	diseases of heart valves leading to narrowing, leaking, or improper closing of valves	✓	
septal heart defects	opening within septum that allows blood to flow between left and right ventricles of heart	✓	

Figure A1.13

Read through the descriptions of these disorders in Figure A1.13. Note that an interruption of the blood flow through key arteries plays a major role in many of the diseases on this table. In many cases, arteries lose their effectiveness because the blood has too high a concentration of **cholesterol**. Cholesterol is a vital component of all cell membranes and is a key ingredient in the production of important hormones and vitamin D. This essential substance creates problems when its concentration in the bloodsteam becomes too high. Accumulated cholesterol deposits build up along with fat and other debris on the inside walls of arteries. Like the sticky film of bacteria that builds up on your teeth before brushing, these sticky deposits in arteries are also called **plaque**. As plaque accumulates, the affected artery starts to narrow. Since the outer layer of plaque can harden into a rough and rigid surface, the artery becomes stiff. The narrowed opening and rough interior makes it more difficult for blood to flow.

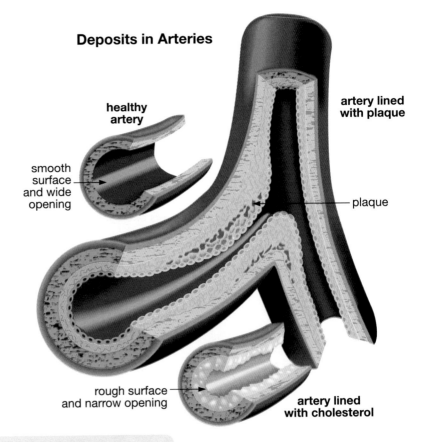

Deposits in Arteries

healthy artery

smooth surface and wide opening

artery lined with plaque

plaque

rough surface and narrow opening

artery lined with cholesterol

▶ **cholesterol:** a waxy, fat-like substance present in the cell membrane of every body cell and in food from animal sources

High levels of cholesterol can lead to cardiovascular disease.

▶ **plaque:** a semi-hardened accumulation of substances originally suspended in a fluid

Cholesterol and fat are transported by special blood proteins in plasma through the bloodstream. About two-thirds of all the cholesterol in your blood can be found in **low-density lipoprotein (LDL)**. LDL is responsible for carrying cholesterol in the bloodstream from the liver to cells of body tissues. This is the cholesterol that may find its way to the inside walls of blood vessels and lead to plaque. You can see why these particles are often referred to as "bad cholesterol."

Another blood protein, called **high-density lipoprotein (HDL)**, carries cholesterol to your liver so it can be excreted from your body. Since this protein scours the bloodstream to collect excess cholesterol, it is sometimes called "good cholesterol."

▶ **low-density lipoprotein (LDL):** a blood protein that carries cholesterol in the bloodstream from the liver to the rest of the body

Too much LDL in the blood leads to deposits on the walls of arteries, so this is referred to as "bad cholesterol."

▶ **high-density lipoprotein (HDL):** a blood protein that carries cholesterol in the bloodstream from the body cells to the liver

High levels of HDL in the blood means it is less likely that deposits will form on the walls of arteries, so this is referred to as "good cholesterol."

Practice

34. If you were told to make a sandwich that contained no cholesterol, would you choose butter, cheese, ham, peanut butter, or tuna as a filling?

35. The following results come back from two people who just got their blood cholesterol tested.

Person	Concentration of Cholesterol in the Bloodstream	
	Low-Density Lipoprotein (LDL)	High-Density Lipoprotein (HDL)
A	3.62 mmol/L	0.90 mmol/L
B	2.33 mmol/L	1.94 mmol/L

a. Explain what the unit mmol/L means.

b. Explain which one of these people has the healthier cholesterol levels.

Atherosclerosis and Coronary Heart Disease

Atherosclerosis is the process in which deposits of cholesterol and fatty substances build up on the inside lining of an artery. This buildup results in a loss of elasticity or a hardening of the vessel. This condition may occur in any of the major body arteries.

When atherosclerosis affects coronary arteries that supply the heart with blood, complications result that affect the heart muscle's functioning. In this case, the disease is called **coronary heart disease**. Under these conditions the body's inability to supply the heart with sufficient oxygen leads to a buildup of toxic wastes. This causes a cramping pain called **angina**, which may begin behind the breastbone and then radiate out to the neck and arms.

▶ **atherosclerosis:** a hardening of the arteries due to the accumulation of fatty deposits

▶ **coronary heart disease:** a disease in which blood flow through the coronary arteries is restricted, possibly resulting in chest pain and/or a heart attack

▶ **angina:** chest pain caused by a narrowing of vessels that supply blood to the heart tissue

Coronary Heart Disease

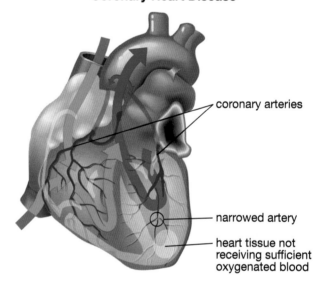

coronary arteries

narrowed artery

heart tissue not receiving sufficient oxygenated blood

Clots, Strokes, and Heart Attacks

If the plaque coating the artery becomes rough and cracked, platelets passing this area in the bloodstream can rupture and release chemicals that start the clotting process. Fibrinogen in the plasma is converted to thread-like fibrin, and red blood cells become trapped in the fibrin mesh to form a clot. The blood clot can completely block the flow of blood in an artery.

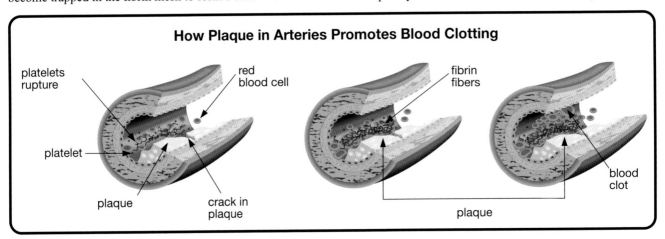

How Plaque in Arteries Promotes Blood Clotting

A blood clot in the coronary arteries, which supply the heart with blood, can damage the heart muscle and cause a **heart attack**. In this type of heart attack, cells of the heart muscle die because the clot prevents coronary arteries from supplying blood to those heart cells.

A blood clot in arteries supplying the brain with blood can cause a stroke. In a **stroke**, brain cells die. Memory loss, paralysis, or even death can result.

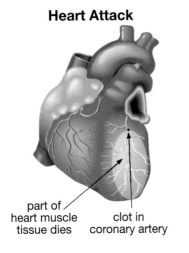

Heart Attack

part of heart muscle tissue dies — clot in coronary artery

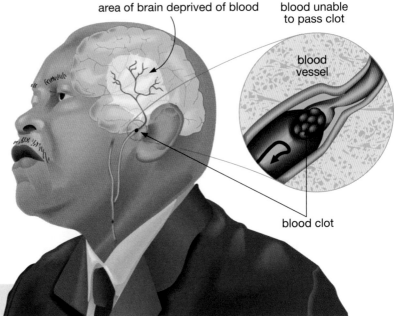

Stroke

area of brain deprived of blood — blood unable to pass clot

blood vessel

blood clot

Practice

36. Explain the following statement.

"Cardiovascular disease is a very broad term used to describe a collection of diseases and conditions. In some cases, one cardiovascular disease can cause another cardiovascular disease."

37. Earlier in this chapter you learned that a stronger heart is not a larger heart but a more elastic one. Elasticity—the ability to return to an initial form after being stretched—is a characteristic of a healthy heart. This same thinking also applies to healthy arteries.

  a. Describe how the buildup of plaque reduces the elasticity of arteries.

  b. Explain how the hardening and narrowing of arteries affects blood pressure.

38. Describe how the buildup of plaque on artery walls increases the likelihood of dangerous blood clots forming in the arteries.

> **heart attack:** the death of heart cells due to a blockage in the coronary arteries that supply oxygenated blood to the heart

> **stroke:** a sudden loss of brain function caused by an interruption in the blood flow to the brain

Fats and Cholesterol in the Bloodstream

Consider what you have learned so far in Lesson 1.4. Since the buildup of fat and cholesterol within arteries is one of the root causes of many cardiovascular diseases, you might be tempted to think that you should eat a low-fat, low-cholesterol diet. For many years this was considered sound advice for maintaining good health. However, if this were the whole story, how can you explain the fact that Inuit who eat their traditional diet have a very low incidence of cardiovascular disease, even though they obtain more than 50% of their calories from fat? Clearly there is more to this story.

Although food high in cholesterol can have an impact on the levels of cholesterol in your bloodstream, the typical person makes about 75% of the blood cholesterol in the liver, with only about 25% absorbed from food. Limiting the foods that contain cholesterol may not have a dramatic impact on lowering blood cholesterol levels. The real secret to lowering the levels of cholesterol in your bloodstream is to rethink the mix of fats in your diet.

The first distinction is between saturated fats and unsaturated fats. Recall from previous courses that saturated hydrocarbons contain only a single covalent bond between adjacent carbon atoms. Unsaturated hydrocarbons contain at least one double or triple covalent bond between carbon atoms. A saturated fat is made from long chains of fatty acids in which all the carbons are connected by single covalent bonds.

An unsaturated fat is made from long chains of fatty acids in which there is at least one double or triple bond. If there is only one double or triple bond, that fat is classified as monounsaturated. If there is more than one double or triple bond, it is classified as polyunsaturated. As shown in Figure A1.14, the presence of a double or triple bond in unsaturated fatty acids has a profound effect on the structure and, therefore, the properties of these molecules. Note that since the double bond occurs after the ninth carbon from the omega end, oleic acid is referred to as an omega-9 fatty acid.

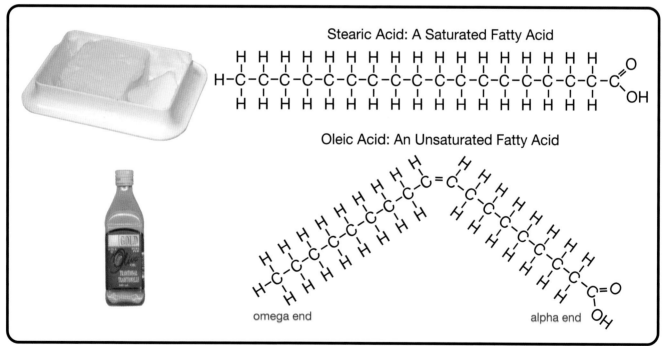

Figure A1.14: Butter is made of saturated fats, which contain saturated fatty acids. Olive oil is made of unsaturated fats, which contain unsaturated fatty acids.

So the types of fats and fatty acids you encounter at meal times can be categorized as either saturated or unsaturated. You may also encounter a third category of fats in the industrially produced trans fats. These compounds are created through an industrial process that involves bubbling hydrogen gas through hot vegetable oil under pressure in a special metal vat. In "Classifying Fats and Fatty Acids," trans fats are shown to be produced from vegetable oils, but they are organized under saturated fats because of the effects that trans fats have on cholesterol in the bloodstream.

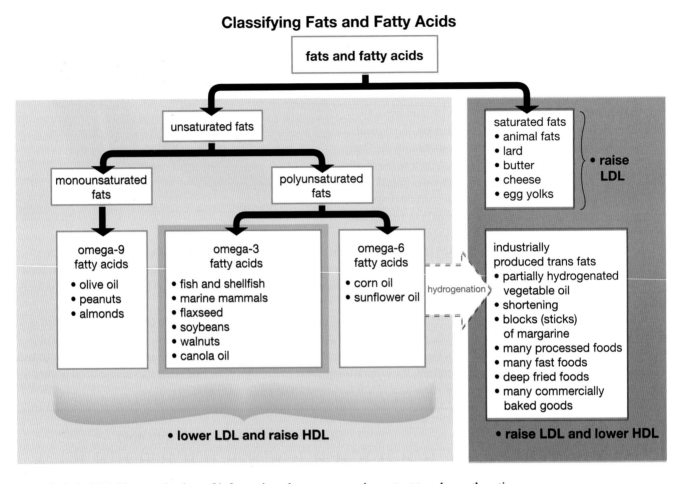

Classifying Fats and Fatty Acids

Although this table contains lots of information, there are some important trends worth noting:

- The fats on the right have negative effects on blood cholesterol levels.
- The fats and fatty acids on the left have positive effects on blood cholesterol levels.
- The staple foods in the traditional Inuit diet—marine mammals and fish—are rich sources of omega-3 fatty acids. These substances have a positive effect on blood cholesterol levels.

Essential Fatty Acids

The fats listed on the left side of "Classifying Fats and Fatty Acids" are not only better than those on the right-hand side, but these substances are, in fact, essential for good health. You need these nutrients to form healthy cell membranes, to properly develop the brain and nervous system, and to produce hormone-like substances that regulate body functions (e.g., blood pressure).

▶ **essential fatty acid:** a fatty acid that the body cannot synthesize itself and must be obtained from food

It is particularly important for you to eat foods with fats and oils that contain the **essential fatty acids** of omega-3 and omega-6. These substances cannot be produced from other substances within your body—you must obtain them from the foods you eat. Although most people have no trouble getting enough omega-6 fatty acids, many individuals find it challenging to obtain an adequate supply of omega-3 fatty acids.

39. Explain why limiting foods high in cholesterol can have only a limited effect on lowering blood cholesterol levels.

Use the information in "Classifying Fats and Fatty Acids" to answer questions 40 and 41.

40. In each part of this question you will be given a meal description. In each case, identify the dominant type of fat or fatty acid consumed and describe the likely effect on blood cholesterol levels.

    a. A day begins with a breakfast of bacon, eggs, and two pieces of buttered toast.

    b. A snack at a sporting event consists of a large order of deep-fried onion rings, a doughnut, and a large soft drink.

    c. A lunch at school consists of a tin of flaked tuna, along with a salad made up of fresh vegetables and homemade dressing created from olive oil and spices.

41. Suppose you decide to eliminate nearly all foods that contain fat. The only exception is that once in a while you treat yourself to a plate of fries with gravy from a local diner. Explain the negative impact of this eating pattern.

Heart Healthy Lifestyle

Males, individuals over 65 years of age, and people with a family history of cardiovascular disease are at the greatest risk for developing atherosclerosis and the potentially fatal circulatory problems that result from it. These risk factors cannot be controlled, but there are lifestyle choices that can affect your chances of getting atherosclerosis and related cardiovascular diseases.

If you routinely eat foods high in cholesterol, you may be negatively affecting your blood cholesterol levels. To maintain healthy cholesterol levels, keep in mind that the right mix of fats is actually more important than avoiding foods high in

cholesterol. Nutritionists recommend trying to eliminate foods from your diet that contain industrially produced trans fats and add that you should replace foods containing saturated fats with foods that contain unsaturated fats.

People who have high blood cholesterol levels, who are overweight, who engage in little physical activity, who have high blood pressure, or who smoke (or even those exposed to high levels of second-hand tobacco smoke) are at a greater risk of developing circulatory diseases. Stress and excessive alcohol use can also strain the heart and blood vessels to increase the chances of developing a circulatory disorder. Making good lifestyle choices can help to ensure that you reduce the influence of factors that can harm your circulatory system.

? DID YOU KNOW?

The number one cause of death in most developed countries is cardiovascular disease. Each year nearly 80 000 Canadians die from heart disease and strokes. This is the equivalent of the entire population of Red Deer.

Try This Activity

Analyzing Nutrition Fact Labels

Purpose

You will analyze nutrition fact labels to determine which foods are best for maintaining cardiovascular health.

Materials

You will need samples of nutrition fact labels from several brands of butter, margarine, and other spreads.

Procedure

step 1: Gather the nutrition fact labels from butter, margarine, and other types of spreads that you use most often in your home.

step 2: Create a chart to compare these products. The chart should include the product name, serving size, the food energy in calories, total fat, saturated fat, trans fats, cholesterol, fibre, and sodium.

Analysis

1. Rank the products in amount of cholesterol per gram of product and amount of saturated fat per gram of product. Identify which of the spreads would be best for someone trying to lower the blood cholesterol level.

2. A diet that includes lots of salty food causes sodium levels in the bloodstream to elevate. The body responds by adding more water to the bloodstream in an attempt to dilute the sodium concentration. Therefore, the volume of the blood increases.

   a. Explain why a diet that contains many salty foods leads to higher blood pressure levels.

   b. Identify which food items are best suited for someone diagnosed with high blood pressure.

3. Bile, mostly made of cholesterol, is a substance that helps to digest fat. Soluble fibre is found in foods like apples, brown rice, and beans. When soluble fibre passes through the digestive tract, it can help trap bile in the intestine—this allows bile to be excreted along with other wastes.

   a. Explain how soluble fibre helps to reduce blood cholesterol levels.

   b. Identify what food items contain significant amounts of fibre.

4. Other than differences in dietary content, list some factors that may influence consumer choice in terms of buying one of these products.

Omega-3 Fatty Acids and the Traditional Inuit Diet

Turn back to "Classifying Fats and Fatty Acids," which compared types of fats and fatty acids in terms of their effects on blood cholesterol levels. Note the location of fish and marine mammals on this table: these foods are rich sources of eicosapentaenoic acid (EPA), and docosahexaenoic acid (DHA). These particular omega-3 fatty acids can be derived only from marine sources—you cannot get them from plants or animals that live on land. These substances play a key role in allowing fish and marine mammals to survive in frigid environments. A good rule of thumb is that the colder the water, the greater the concentration of omega-3 fatty acids the fish and other animals can accumulate.

Figure A1.15: Salmon, along with mackerel and sardines, are coldwater fish and are all good sources of omega-3 fatty acids.

At the time this textbook was published, research on the benefits of a diet rich in omega-3 fatty acids from EPA and DHA marine sources was still underway. However, early findings indicate that these substances have a protective effect when it comes to cardiovascular diseases.

It is important to realize that this research is still in its early stages and that the extent of these possible protective effects is still being investigated. How these protective mechanisms actually work is not yet thoroughly understood. Nevertheless, it does appear that the traditional ecological knowledge of the Inuit and medical science both support the same notion: a diet that contains foods like coldwater fish can have some positive effects on health.

It is also worth noting that the presence of omega-3 fatty acids from marine sources is not the only factor to consider when explaining the low incidence of cardiovascular diseases for Inuit who follow a traditional lifestyle. Genetics may also play a role. In addition, a lot of exercise accompanies the harvesting of food sources in the traditional Inuit diet. As you learned earlier in this chapter, people who include cardiovascular exercise or aerobic training as a part of their daily lives have stronger hearts that don't need to beat as often to circulate the same amount of blood.

42. Assume for the purposes of this question that research establishes there will be significant improvements to the cardiovascular health of the general population if people include marine sources of omega-3 fatty acids as an important part of their diets.

    a. A theme you encountered in previous science courses and will continue to explore in Science 30 is the notion that a technological solution to a problem often creates an unintended set of new problems. Identify what problem is addressed by having people increase the marine sources of omega-3 fatty acids in their diets.

    b. List some unintended new problems that could arise from this technological solution.

    c. How might some of the unintended problems identified in 42.b. be solved?

43. Refer to question 42. Some people argue that many of the difficulties created by technological fixes to problems stem from the fact that science can sometimes be characterized as "knowing more and more about less and less." In other words, science and technology can become intensely focused on the minute details of an extremely narrow field of study, and sometimes the "big picture" gets lost in the details.

    a. Review the definition for traditional ecological knowledge. How does this point of view help keep the "big picture" in focus?

    b. Comment on the possible benefits of integrating scientific research with traditional ecological knowledge.

44. Obtain a copy of the handout "Cardiovascular Disease Risk Questionnaire" from the Science 30 Textbook CD. Complete the questionnaire.

> Add the completed questionnaire to your health file.

Other Cardiovascular Diseases

Not all cardiovascular diseases have their causes tightly linked to the effects of cholesterol and the types of fat present in a person's diet. Many cardiovascular diseases are due to injuries, conditions present at the time of birth, or a number of other factors.

Aneurysm

Have you ever turned on a garden hose and then bent the hose or pinched off the end of it so that the water couldn't come out? You might have noticed that pressure increased in the hose before the blockage. This extra pressure could cause the tough plastic surrounding the hose to weaken, bulge, and eventually tear. A stretched weakness in a blood vessel is called an **aneurysm**. An aneurysm can happen in any blood vessel, but it occurs most often in the aorta where blood pressure is highest. Sometimes an aneurysm is due to disease or injury, or it may be present from birth. Having an aneurysm is a dangerous condition because the stretched vessel wall is weak and could burst, causing internal bleeding. A ruptured aneurysm in the brain can cause a stroke or death. The development of an aneurysm can be caused by hypertension and atherosclerosis, but certain people have this condition at birth. An aneurysm is usually repaired by surgery, assuming the patient lives long enough to get surgery.

Aneurysm

artery wall   weakened fibres

> **aneurysm:** a widening or bulging of a blood vessel due to a weakening of the vessel wall

> **septal defect:** a condition where the opening between the left and right halves of the heart fails to close before birth, causing excess blood to be pumped to the lungs

Septal Defect

When a fetus is developing in the womb, its blood doesn't need to go to its lungs to be oxygenated because the baby gets its oxygen from the mother's umbilical cord. Blood circulation in the fetal heart bypasses the lungs through an opening in the septum at the two atria—the top heart chambers. Before the baby is born, the hole between the two heart halves closes up. Occasionally, a baby will be born with a "hole in its heart." This **septal defect** causes some blood to flow into the right side of the heart, and excess blood is pumped to the lungs. The baby's septal defect usually closes up on its own, but larger holes often need surgery to be properly sealed.

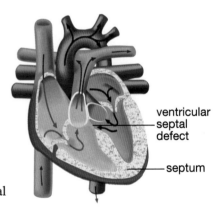

ventricular septal defect

septum

Valvular Heart Disease

Natural Heart Valves

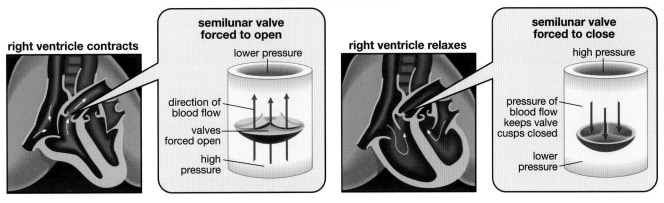

Heart valves are used to control the direction of the flow of blood. If the valves don't close properly, blood can *backwash* against the direction of blood flow. If the valves are too narrow, insufficient blood is passed between the chambers and the heart must work much harder to circulate the required amount of blood.

Replacement Heart Valves

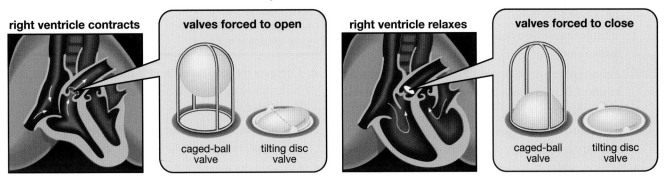

If a defective heart valve cannot be repaired, it is often replaced with an artificial valve or a valve made from human tissue or animal tissue. Artificial valves made from plastic or metal last for a long time but may cause blood clots. Recipients of artificial valves often have to take blood thinners for the rest of their lives. Valves made from human or animal tissue do not last as long as artificial replacements, but they pose less risk for the formation of blood clots.

1.4 Summary

Diseases or disorders of the heart and blood vessels that impair the functioning of the cardiovascular system are called cardiovascular diseases. Your risk for developing a cardiovascular disease may depend upon inherited genetic factors and lifestyle choices.

Atherosclerosis is a condition where a buildup of fatty substances, called plaque, coat the lining of arteries. This results in impaired circulation and heart pain (angina). Atherosclerosis can lead to the production of blood clots and even a vessel blockage. A blood clot in the coronary artery can cause a heart attack or, if it's located in the arteries leading to the brain, can cause a stroke.

Lifestyle factors that increase a person's risk of developing a circulatory disease include high blood cholesterol, high blood pressure, being overweight or inactive, smoking, high stress levels, and excessive alcohol use. Other cardiovascular diseases include aneurysms, valvular heart disease, and septal defect.

The traditional ecological knowledge of Inuit people has helped initiate scientific research. The fact that there is such a low incidence of cardiovascular disease among Inuit people who follow a traditional lifestyle—even though their diet is so high in fat—has acted as a trigger for current investigations. The importance of the types of fats and fatty acids in a person's diet is one of the major outcomes of this work.

Knowledge

1. Match each of the following terms with a description of its circulatory problem.

   - plaque
   - atherosclerosis
   - angina
   - heart attack
   - stroke
   - aneurysm
   - septal defect

   a. a chest pain during exertion due to constricted coronary arteries

   b. a death of brain cells due to a blood clot in an artery supplying the brain with blood

   c. a hole between the two halves of the heart that hasn't yet closed after birth

   d. a hardening of the arteries due to a buildup of plaque in the vessel

   e. a material with a rough, hard surface that forms on the inside of arteries due to the buildup of cholesterol and fatty substances

   f. a condition that is caused by a blockage in the coronary arteries

   g. a weakened bulge in a blood vessel that could rupture

Applying Concepts

2. A woman with a family history of heart and circulatory problems visits her doctor. List at least four things the doctor might ask about the patient's lifestyle, and describe changes the doctor might suggest to reduce the risk of the patient developing a circulatory disease.

3. Compare the analogy of a city's water delivery system to the human circulatory system. Explain what the following problems with a water delivery system can be compared to in the human circulatory system.

   a. Something is stuck in one of the pipes and has caused some homes to lose water service.

   b. The water pressure is so high that it is putting a strain on the pipes and causing them to leak.

   c. A valve in the water pump is faulty.

Use the following information to answer questions 4 to 10. First Nations people who live in northern Alberta have acquired traditional ecological knowledge by living in the boreal forest for thousands of years. One element within this vast body of knowledge is that moose is a valuable source of food because it keeps people healthy. After scientific research, nutritionists have concluded that moose meat is a healthy food. The data in this table compares the nutritional value of raw moose meat to raw beef.

Nutrient (Serving Size)	Raw Moose Meat (100 g)	Raw Beef (100 g)
energy	427 kJ	1163 kJ
protein	22.24 g	17.48 g
total fat	0.74 g	22.55 g
• saturated fatty acids	0.22 g	9.16 g
• omega-6 fatty acids	0.14 g	0.57 g
• omega-3 fatty acids	0.03 g	0.23 g

4. Compare the total fat content to the serving size for both moose meat and beef. Express your answers as a percentage.

5. Account for the difference in food energy between the serving of moose meat and the beef serving.

6. Compare the saturated fat content to the serving size for both moose meat and beef. Express your answers as percentages.

7. Refer to your answers for question 6. Explain the significance of these numbers in terms of the effects on blood cholesterol levels.

8. Compare the omega-6 and the omega-3 fatty acid content to the total fat content for both moose meat and beef. Express your answers as percentages.

9. Refer to your answer to question 8. Explain the significance of these numbers in terms of the effects on blood cholesterol levels.

10. Refer to your answers for questions 4 to 9 to explain why moose meat is a good food choice for reducing the risk factors associated with cardiovascular diseases.

During medieval times in Europe, people worked very hard to farm and to tend their agricultural lands to produce enough food for their survival. Land was so valuable that wars often erupted over good farmland. Invading armies would attempt to take the land that people worked so hard to tend, so great fortresses were built for protection. If an army invaded, people from the surrounding countryside could move inside the castle to be protected by the thick castle walls. Any damage to the walls would quickly be patched by stonemasons. The castle could only be entered through guarded gates and across moats that could drown enemies.

Castle guards were posted along the walls to spot invaders, while other sentries patrolled and attacked any invaders who managed to sneak in. Different invading armies would use unique approaches and techniques to try to get into castles. After repelling the attack of an invading army, the defenders would be better able to respond to the same enemy if they tried to invade again.

Think of your body as if it were a medieval fortress. Different parts of your body act to maintain an ideal environment for the growth, health, and functioning of your cells. The organs in your body constantly work to provide the cells with a continuous supply of nutrients and to create a comfortable temperature and chemical environment. Unfortunately, the internal environment that the body works hard to create and maintain is also an ideal environment for the growth of disease-causing agents. These substances, often called germs or **pathogens**, are microscopic and act like foreign armies because they are constantly trying to invade the fortress of the human body.

▶ **pathogen:** an agent, especially a virus or a bacterium, that causes disease

The human body has many ways to defend itself from pathogens:

- The skin covering the human body is a protective barrier, and it acts like the thick stone walls of a fortress. Skin is the first line of defence and prevents most disease organisms from getting inside the body.

- Because the sweat and oil secretions produced by the skin are acidic, bacterial growth is minimized.

- In Lesson 1.4 you learned about the role of platelets. These disks quickly create clots to repair damaged or broken skin to keep out foreign organisms. In a similar way, stonemasons repair damaged castle walls with replacement stones and mortar.

- The body has barriers that help defend these openings. For example, the nasal passage has hairs that work as filters, and mucous secretions trap most disease-causing organisms before they can reach the lungs. As well, the eyes are protected by an antiseptic liquid in your tears, and the stomach contains strong acid that kills most swallowed germs.

- The human body even has a defending army of white blood cells that act like soldiers—white blood cells attack pathogens that manage to break through the first line of defence to invade the body.

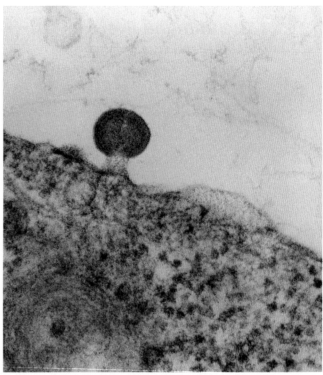

Figure A1.16: An HIV virus particle penetrates a cell membrane of human lymph tissue.

45. After reading the lesson introduction, copy and complete the following table that compares the roles and parts of a castle fortress to the parts of the immune system.

Part of Immune System	Role	Part of a Castle
		castle walls
cilia and mucous secretions		
	patch holes in protective barrier	
white blood cells		

Spreading Disease

If the body's natural defenses are not able to destroy or block a pathogen from entering it, the pathogen will begin to reproduce and spread. Even in the most sanitary living conditions, people regularly encounter microscopic substances that can get into their bodies, reproduce, and make them feel sick. These invading germ organisms can be passed along in several ways. When someone sneezes, coughs, or even talks, tiny droplets are expelled from the lungs. If this person's body has been infected by a disease-causing organism, like the influenza virus—which causes what is commonly referred to as the "flu"—or tuberculosis (TB), these expelled droplets will contain some of the pathogens. When other people breathe in these droplets, they can become infected by the pathogen.

? **DID YOU KNOW?**

In some cases, bacteria and viruses can survive for months on the surfaces of everyday objects. When you touch an object, like the handle on an escalator in a shopping mall, you can transfer these pathogens to your hands and from there to your eyes, nose, or mouth, allowing pathogens to enter the body.

Regularly washing your hands is one of the best ways to avoid getting sick. All you need is soap and water. Ideally, you should rub your hands together for at least 15 s and scrub all surfaces including your wrists, under your fingernails, between your fingers, and the backs of your hands.

Food Poisoning

Pathogens can enter the body through the digestive system if contaminated food or water is ingested. The acid environment of the stomach is normally able to kill disease organisms. Food poisoning—an intense disturbance of the digestive tract—occurs when food is not cooked thoroughly, is improperly stored, or when the food is prepared in unsanitary conditions. For example, one type of food poisoning is caused by eating food contaminated with salmonella bacteria. Other instances of food poisoning can be seen in the "Common Types of Bacterial Food Poisoning" table.

Cholera is a disease caused by a type of bacteria often found in dirty and untreated water. If the cholera bacteria are not killed by the low stomach pH, the bacteria can multiply in the intestine and infect the blood supply or release toxins that harm the body.

COMMON TYPES OF BACTERIAL FOOD POISONING

Bacterium	Habitat	Common Food Sources	Symptoms
salmonella	animal and human intestinal tracts	high protein foods like meat, poultry, fish, and eggs	diarrhea, vomiting, nausea, chills, and fever within 12 to 24 hours
clostridium botulinum (botulism)	soils, plants, marine sediments, and fish	improperly canned foods	blurred vision, respiratory distress, and possible death
listeria monocytogenes	soil, vegetation, and water— can survive for long periods in soil and plant materials	milk, soft cheeses, vegetables fertilized with manure	flu-like symptoms that mimic meningitis—elderly and babies most susceptible
E. coli (travellers' diarrhea)	feces of infected humans	meat and cheeses	diarrhea, abdominal cramps, no fever

Pathogens in the Bloodstream

HIV and the virus causing hepatitis C are examples of viruses transmitted through the bloodstream. When the skin is punctured or cut, pathogens can enter the bloodstream before platelets can seal up the breach. Cuts should be washed out and then covered with sterile bandages and dressings.

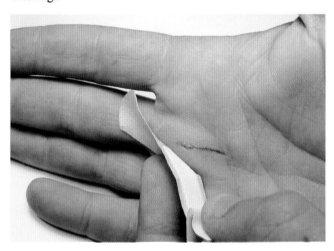

DID YOU KNOW?

During the 1300s, an outbreak of the bubonic plague, or Black Death, occurred in Europe. This disease was carried by the fleas that initially lived on rats. After the rats died, the fleas passed the disease on to humans. In just five years, the Black Death killed about 25 million people, or the equivalent of one-quarter of Europe's population at that time.

There are still scattered cases of bubonic plague as the disease is often passed by flea bites from infected wild rodents—such as ground squirrels—to humans. If detected early, the disease is curable with modern medicines.

Vectors

Organisms that carry pathogens from one person to another are called **vectors**. Mosquitoes are examples of organisms that can act as vectors. In hot climates, such as the areas shaded brown on the "Prevalance of Malaria" map, mosquitoes can transmit the potentially deadly malaria parasite. When a mosquito punctures the skin to draw blood, it pumps some of its saliva into the bite. The saliva contains a chemical, called an anticoagulant, which prevents clotting while blood is drawn. The malaria parasite is carried in the mosquito saliva and is transmitted during the bite. This mosquito-borne parasite is a leading worldwide cause of death and sickness.

Prevalance of Malaria

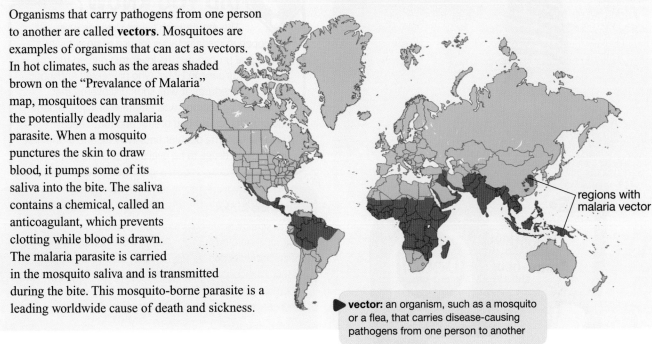

regions with malaria vector

▶ **vector:** an organism, such as a mosquito or a flea, that carries disease-causing pathogens from one person to another

Try This Activity

Preventing Infection Poster

Design a poster that could be used to educate primary school students (grades 1 to 3) about the importance of good hygiene and practices that can help prevent infection by disease-causing pathogens. The poster should be colourful and attractive enough to appeal to young students.

Alternatively, your teacher could arrange for you to make a presentation to a primary school class on this topic or invite a primary school class to choose their favourite poster.

Joseph Lister (1827–1912)

During the nineteenth century, people who survived a successful medical operation often died due to infections that occurred during the operation. Most often, the infected wounds developed into gangrene or sepsis. Gangrene usually occurs in the extremities when cell tissues die because circulation has been lost in that area. A bacterial infection can cause a loss of circulation and result in gangrene. Sepsis is an illness that develops from a bloodstream infection by toxin-producing bacteria. At the time, there was not a complete understanding of how disease-causing agents were transmitted.

Joseph Lister was a British surgeon who studied Louis Pasteur's work on micro-organisms. Lister believed that hospitals needed to be clean and that he needed to kill unseen micro-organisms that were getting into wounds from the air. He began spraying a solution of carbolic acid onto wounds during operations and soaking dressings used for bandaging wounds in carbolic acid. This practice prevented the wounds from becoming septic. Lister's work with **antiseptics** reduced post-operation infections and saved many lives.

▶ **antiseptic:** a solution or substance that prevents or inhibits the growth of micro-organisms

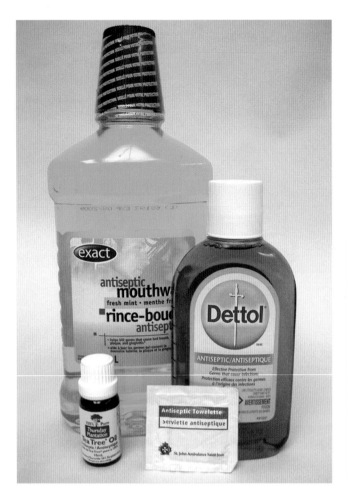

DID YOU KNOW?

The mouthwash called Listerine was developed in the late 1800s for use as an antiseptic for surgical procedures. Its inventors named the product after Joseph Lister, who pioneered antiseptic surgical procedures. It was soon discovered that the antiseptic solution was effective at killing mouth bacteria that cause bad breath and tooth decay. Listerine became popular and, in 1914, one of the first prescription drugs to be available over the counter.

Science Links

Carbolic acid is called *phenol* under the modern-day chemical naming system. Phenols are actually a group of compounds containing a ring of carbon atoms and an attached alcohol group. You will learn more about these chemical structures in Unit B. Phenols are still used as a component of commercial antiseptics.

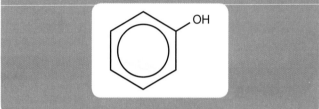

Comparing Microscopic Pathogens

Micro-organisms live unseen all around. They are in the food and water that people ingest and in the air that they breathe. Most micro-organisms are harmless or even beneficial, such as those that live in your large intestine and play a role in digestion. If certain species infect a body or grow to large numbers, their negative effects cause the symptoms of disease.

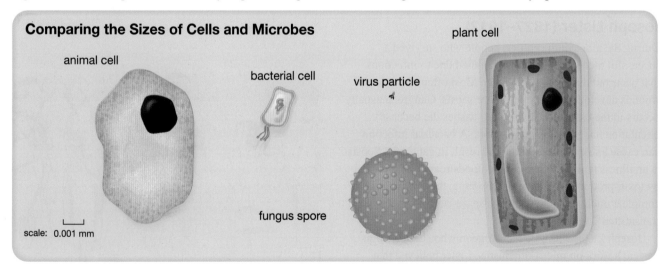

Comparing the Sizes of Cells and Microbes

animal cell

bacterial cell

virus particle

plant cell

fungus spore

scale: 0.001 mm

Protozoans

Malaria is caused by single-celled organisms called **protozoans**. Some protozoans live as parasites and require a host in which to reproduce. Because these protozoa exist with human cells, they are difficult to destroy without harming the host's cells. The protozoans that cause malaria are transmitted by a mosquito vector and infect human red blood cells.

> **protozoan:** a group of microscopic, single-celled organisms that each have a nucleus
>
> Many disease-causing protozoans can only divide within a host organism.

Figure A1.17: A red blood cell is infected with a malaria parasite.

Fungi

Mold, mushrooms, and yeast are all examples of **fungi**. Most fungi live off the remains of dead or decaying organisms, but some are parasitic. Athlete's foot is an example of a fungal infection.

> **fungi:** organisms that absorb food in solution directly through their cell walls and do not conduct photosynthesis; reproduction occurs through spores

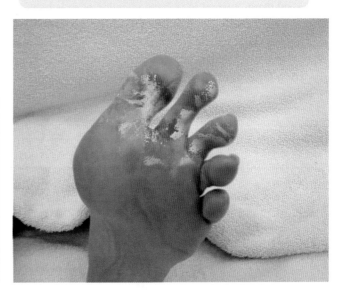

Bacteria

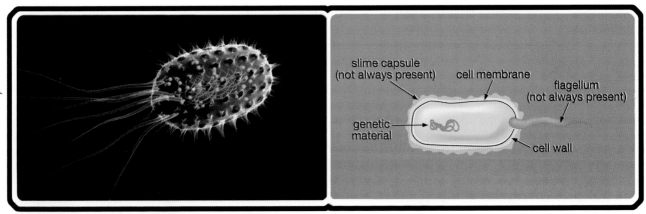

slime capsule (not always present)
cell membrane
flagellum (not always present)
genetic material
cell wall

Bacteria are small, single-celled organisms with a cell wall and cytoplasm. Unlike plant or animal cells, their genetic material is floating in cytoplasm and is not contained in a nucleus. Bacteria come in many different sizes and shapes including spiral-shaped, rod-shaped, or round. Some bacteria have a long whip-like tail—called a flagellum—or several flagella to help them move. Bacteria reproduce rapidly by simply splitting in two and can grow exponentially under ideal conditions. As disease-causing bacteria grow inside of you, their life processes damage your cells or they produce toxins that make you feel ill. **Antibiotics**, such as penicillin, are drugs that kill bacteria and, therefore, can be used to reduce or stop bacterial infections.

> **bacteria:** microscopic, single-celled organisms that lack a membrane-bound nucleus and membrane-bound organelles; reproduction is chiefly by cell division to produce identical daughter cells
>
> **antibiotic:** a drug that fights bacterial infections

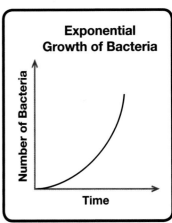

Exponential Growth of Bacteria

Number of Bacteria

Time

Viruses

Viruses are extremely tiny particles ($\frac{1}{100\text{th}}$ the size of a bacterium). Viruses do not grow, feed, or respire, so they are not considered to be cells. Scientists do not even consider them to be living organisms. They consist of a geometrically shaped protein coat and genetic material. Many viruses cause diseases. Viruses reproduce by infecting a host cell and injecting their genetic material into it, turning the host cell into a virus-making factory. Once new viruses are produced, the host cell ruptures and releases virus particles to infect more host cells. **Antiviral drugs** attempt to stop the infection of cells by viruses. These drugs also affect the development of new virus particles in the host cell.

Bacteria and viruses are the most common types of disease-causing agents that can make people feel sick. The illness symptoms are due to tissue damage caused by these disease agents and by how bodies respond to this tissue damage.

▶ **virus:** a non-cellular particle consisting of a protein coat surrounding genetic material that multiplies only within the cells of a living organism

▶ **antiviral drug:** a type of medication that controls or cures an infection from a virus

How a Virus Infects a Cell

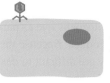
virus attaches to host cell

genetic material injected into host cell attacks nucleus

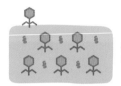
cell used to make new virus parts

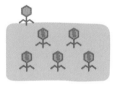
viruses assembled

new viruses free to infect other cells

cell bursts open

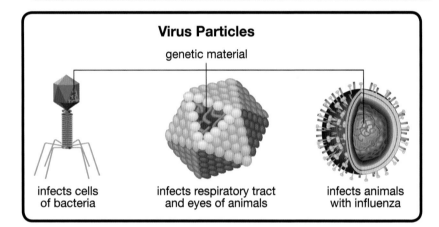

Virus Particles

genetic material

infects cells of bacteria

infects respiratory tract and eyes of animals

infects animals with influenza

Practice

46. Record and complete the following table in your notes.

MICROSCOPIC PATHOGENS

Type of Pathogen	Defining Characteristics	Example of a Disease Caused by This Type of Pathogen
protozoans		
fungi		
bacteria		
viruses		

47. In the late 1800s, scientists were struggling in their early attempts to isolate and identify viruses. Attempts to filter the particles responsible for viruses from infected plant fluids were unsuccessful, as were attempts to observe these particles in standard light microscopes. Identify the property of viruses that would account for these early difficulties.

Utilizing Technology

Informing the Public About an Infectious Disease

Purpose

You and your partners will develop a concise bulletin to inform the general public about an infectious disease. Your bulletin could take the form of a brochure, a poster, a multimedia presentation, or some other presentation to your class.

Background Information

You have been employed by a public health clinic to produce an informative bulletin about an infectious disease. Health-care professionals wish to use the brochure you create to help patients become more informed about diseases. Your teacher may assign you a disease topic or you may choose a topic. Remember that your bulletin must be about an infectious disease like meningitis, strep throat, SARS, chicken pox, or hantavirus, and not about hereditary or environmental diseases and disorders like cancer, Down syndrome, or atherosclerosis. Check with your teacher before beginning if you are unsure about your chosen topic.

Materials

You will need to assemble the materials necessary for the bulletin format that your group plans to develop. You will also need access to the Internet, school library, and other resources to research your topic and to produce a product that summarizes the information in your own words.

Procedure

Read through the entire procedure. Then decide how you will divide up the tasks among group members.

step 1: The first task for your group is research. You may use the Internet and/or other resources to determine answers to the following questions:

- What background information should the public know about the disease you have chosen?
- What are the signs and symptoms of the disease?
- How is this disease transmitted?
- How can the disease be prevented and/or treated?
- Who is at risk for getting this disease?
- What do current statistics reveal about the number of people infected?

step 2: Plan how you can clearly communicate the answers to the questions in step 1 by using the format you have chosen. Your bulletin should be concise and effective.

step 3: Carry out the plan you devised in step 2 by preparing your bulletin about the disease you chose.

step 4: Share your bulletin with other students.

step 5: View the bulletins of other students.

Evaluation

1. Ask your classmates for feedback on the bulletin your group produced. How effectively did your group's bulletin address the six key questions from step 1? What aspects of your bulletin could be improved?

2. What did you learn from the bulletins prepared by other groups? If you completed this activity again, what would you do differently?

Immune Response

The immune system is like an internal army that fights off disease-causing organisms able to invade the body's first lines of defence.

The descriptions that follow match the graphic titled "Overview of Immune Response."

(1) The first event that initiates the process occurs when an invading pathogen breaks through the body's protective layer of skin and enters body tissues or the bloodstream. Fighting an infection begins with the detection of the disease-causing organism. Your internal army is composed of white blood cells that constantly check the identity of every substance encountered in the bloodstream to distinguish between the parts of your body and potentially harmful foreign parts. Each organism or virus displays unique chemical structures—usually proteins—on its surface. These structures are called **antigens**. Antigens on the outer surface of pathogens act like fingerprints to allow cells of the immune system to recognize these substances as potentially harmful foreign pathogens and to eliminate them from the body.

(2) It is the job of a type of white blood cell called a **macrophage** (literally meaning big eater) to patrol the bloodstream and eat dead cells, cellular debris, foreign cells, and molecules from outside the body. When a macrophage engulfs and destroys a disease-causing agent, it does not destroy the foreign antigen.

(3) Instead, it presents the invader's antigen on the surface of its cell membrane.

(4) Another group of white blood cells, called **T-cells**, mature in the thymus gland, which is a tiny structure behind the sternum. One type of T-cell—called a **helper T-cell**—binds to and recognizes antigens presented on the surface of a macrophage. The helper T-cell then serves to co-ordinate the remaining components of the immune system to respond to the invading pathogen.

(5) The helper T-cells can be thought of as the internal army's reconnaissance unit that provides vital information to co-ordinate an attack. Once the helper T-cells have recognized an antigen on a macrophage, they send out chemical messages to other groups of white blood cells.

(6) Helper T-cells alert the **B-cells**, which mature in the bone marrow. When the B-cells receive this chemical message from helper T-cells, they begin to multiply.

(7) Some of the B-cells produce proteins called **antibodies**. The antibodies produced by the stimulated B-cells are specific for each antigen presented on the macrophage.

(8) The antibodies attach to the antigens and sometimes stick to more than one invader by creating clumps of pathogens more easily engulfed by macrophages.

(9) The antibodies act like handcuffs to immobilize and tag the invaders for easier destruction by the macrophages.

(10) Helper T-cells also send chemical messengers to stimulate **killer T-cells**. Killer T-cells regularly patrol the body looking for cells that have changed due to mutation and could become cancerous. Since viruses replicate within body cells, the killer T-cells also look for cells that have been infected with viruses. The T-cells destroy these body cells by releasing proteins that create large holes in the membranes of the target cells.

(11) During the immune response, **memory B-cells and memory T-cells** are created and remain after the invading pathogen has been destroyed. The memory cells act like military intelligence archives by keeping a blueprint of the encountered invader's antigen to make the immune response quicker the next time that particular antigen enters the body.

(12) Once the invading organisms have been destroyed, another type of T-cell called the **suppressor T-cell** ends the battle by signalling the immune system to return to its pre-infection state.

antigen: a complex molecule on the surface of an invading pathogen that triggers an immune response

It is short for antibody generator.

macrophage: a type of white blood cell that engulfs dead cells, cellular debris, and foreign cells

It presents pathogenic antigens to T-cells in the immune response.

T-cell: a type of white blood cell that matures in the thymus gland

It recognizes and destroys invaders or releases chemical messengers to co-ordinate the immune response.

helper T-cell: a type of T-cell that co-ordinates the actions of other cells involved in the immune response

It sends chemical messages to activate the antibody producing B-cells and killer T-cells.

B-cell: a type of white blood cell that produces antibody molecules when stimulated by helper T-cells

antibody: a protein molecule produced by a B-cell designed to bind to a specific antigen to facilitate its destruction

killer T-cell: a type of T-cell that recognizes and destroys body cells by releasing proteins that create large holes in the target cell's membrane

memory B-cell and memory T-cell: specialized white blood cells that persist in the bloodstream to provide future immunity to invaders bearing a specific antigen

suppressor T-cell: a type of T-cell that sends chemical messengers to stop the immune response to an antigen

Overview of Immune Response

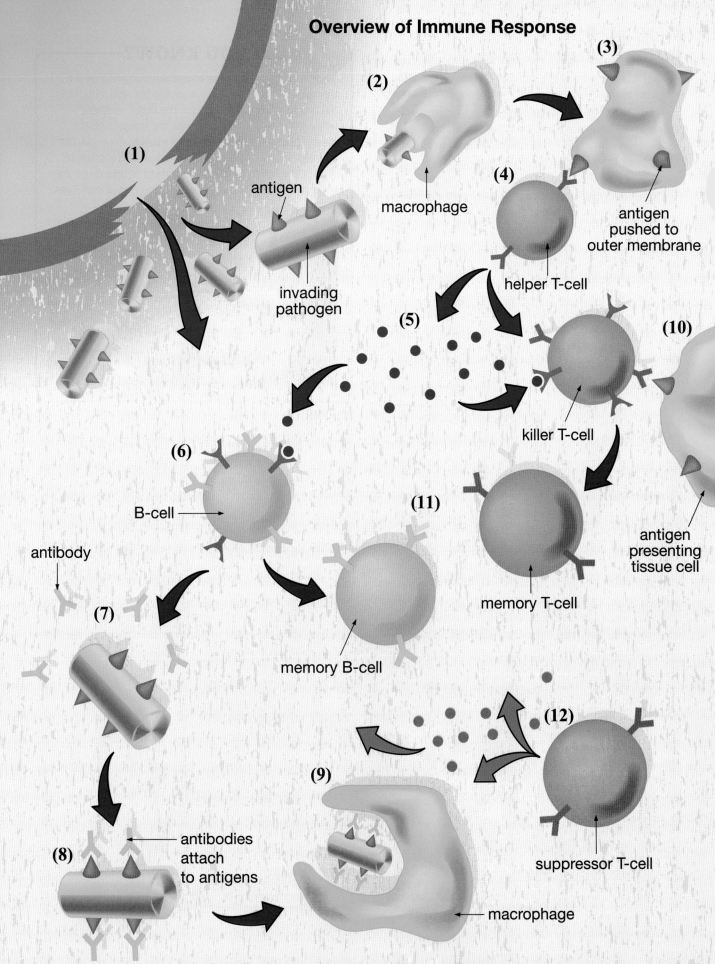

(1)

(2) macrophage

(3) antigen pushed to outer membrane

antigen

invading pathogen

(4) helper T-cell

(5)

(10) antigen presenting tissue cell

killer T-cell

(6) B-cell

antibody

(7)

(8) antibodies attach to antigens

memory B-cell

(11) memory T-cell

(9)

(12) suppressor T-cell

macrophage

48. Obtain a copy of the handout "Overview of Immune Response" from the Science 30 Textbook CD.

    a. Without looking at the labelled version of this illustration in the textbook, attempt to add the missing labels to this diagram.

    b. Once you have attempted 48.a., use the textbook illustration both to fill in labels that you were unable to complete and to check your work.

49. Obtain a copy of the handout "The Immune Response—Components and Roles" from the Science 30 Textbook CD.

    a. Without looking at information presented in the textbook, attempt to add the missing information to this table.

    b. Once you have attempted 49.a., use the information in the textbook both to complete and check your work.

? DID YOU KNOW?

The presence of antigens on organs that are transplanted from one person to another also stimulates the recipient's immune system. The organ recipient's white blood cells often recognize the antigens on the donated cells and attack them by treating the organ like a foreign invader. To prevent a rejection of transplanted organs, transplant recipients may need to take drugs that suppress their immune systems for the rest of their lives.

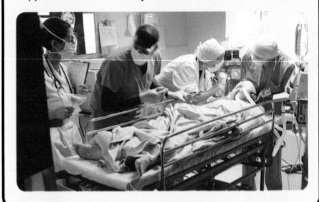

Vaccinations

As long as the memory T-cells for a particular antigen remain in your body, they can provide long-term immunity to the diseases you have already encountered. The reason why people usually do not get chicken pox twice is because they retain memory T-cells for the chicken-pox virus. During a second exposure to an antigen for the chicken-pox virus, memory cells become rapidly activated, divide to form clones of themselves, and quickly produce large amounts of antibodies to act against the antigen. As a result, the invading organism is usually destroyed before it can bloom into a full-blown infection.

Immunity can be artificially developed by a **vaccination**. A vaccination—also called an immunization—involves the injection of an altered or weakened form of a disease-causing pathogen or an inactivated toxin into the body. An exposure to antigens allows the body to produce memory cells and antibodies against the disease. Because the substance used in a vaccination is either a weakened form or a killed form of the disease-causing agent, the risk of becoming sick from the disease is low. Booster shots are subsequent vaccinations of some of the material to ensure that memory cells exist so a quick and intense immune response to any future exposure to the active pathogen can occur.

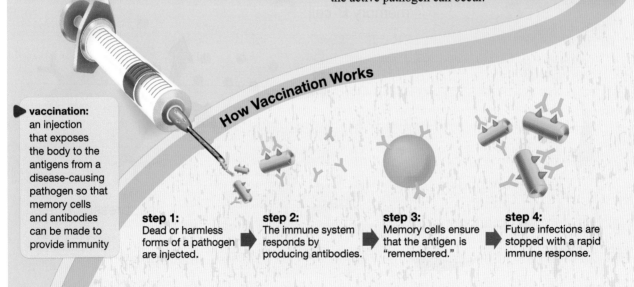

How Vaccination Works

▶ **vaccination:** an injection that exposes the body to the antigens from a disease-causing pathogen so that memory cells and antibodies can be made to provide immunity

step 1:
Dead or harmless forms of a pathogen are injected.

step 2:
The immune system responds by producing antibodies.

step 3:
Memory cells ensure that the antigen is "remembered."

step 4:
Future infections are stopped with a rapid immune response.

In Canada, most people are vaccinated when they are babies against diseases such as measles, mumps, and rubella. People travelling outside of the country may get vaccinated against diseases they would normally not be exposed to in Canada, like yellow fever. Some people choose to be vaccinated each year against strains of the flu virus.

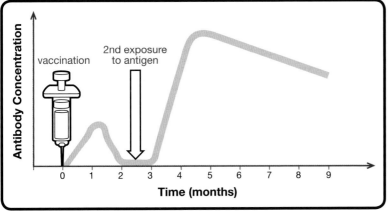

Figure A1.18: This graph shows how the concentration of antibodies is influenced by vaccination and a second exposure.

Practice

50. In your health file, list any vaccinations you have received. Alberta Health keeps a record of your vaccinations. You may need to ask a parent, a guardian, or a caregiver about vaccines you received as a baby.

Note: Some people have not received vaccinations for religious or other reasons.

Investigation

The Value of Mass Vaccinations: Weighing the Evidence

Background Information

There has recently been a debate over the benefit of administering vaccinations to masses of people within a population. Some individuals choose not to vaccinate their children or themselves. Many officials and professionals in the public health field maintain that the benefits of vaccinations still outweigh the risks.

Locate the following articles among the handouts on the Science 30 Textbook CD:

- "A Shot in the Dark"
- "Vaccine Myths and Why They Are Dangerous"

Purpose

You will consider two different opinions on the value of mass vaccinations. Then you will express your own opinion on this topic.

Procedure

step 1: Read through the "Analysis" and "Evaluation" questions to provide a focus for your reading.

step 2: Read each of the articles with the analysis questions in mind. Remember to be an active reader by using a highlighter or by taking notes as you read.

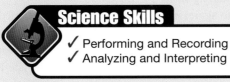

Science Skills

✓ Performing and Recording
✓ Analyzing and Interpreting

Analysis

A Shot in the Dark

1. List the negative effects of vaccination stated by interviewee Barbara Fisher.

2. State the reason Fisher gives to support a greater case for a connection between vaccinations and adverse reactions.

3. What personal experience has she had with vaccination?

Vaccine Myths and Why They Are Dangerous

4. List the negative effects of an unvaccinated population that are stated by author Dr. David Butler-Jones.

5. Describe his opinion on childhood vaccines being linked to seizure disorders, autism, and SIDS (Sudden Infant Death Syndrome).

6. What evidence does he provide to argue for a continued vaccination program?

Evaluation

7. Evaluate the two different sources for these articles. Do they seem like credible information providers?

8. Evaluate the two individuals who provide the information as either an interviewee or an author. Describe any bias or biases that they seem to present. Do you think that one individual is more credible than the other?

9. What is your stance on vaccinations? Against which diseases would you have your child vaccinated? Did your opinion change after reading the articles?

Background Information

Imagine that you have won a dream vacation! You can choose from a cruise down the Amazon River in Brazil, a visit to the famous Taj Mahal in India, an elephant ride in Thailand, or a safari tour in Kenya. Before going, you must find out what health precautions will be necessary for each of your destinations.

In this activity you will gather information from various sources of information, including the Internet, a public health centre, or a public health professional so you can answer each of the following questions.

1. List any vaccinations recommended or required before visiting one of these areas. Also, list the number of injections needed for a complete vaccination, the timeline for injections, the estimated length of immunity, and the cost, if any, for vaccination.

2. List any food or water-borne diseases to be concerned about in the location chosen, and describe precautions that will need to be taken.

3. List any vector-carried diseases—such as malaria—to be concerned about. Describe precautions that will need to be taken.

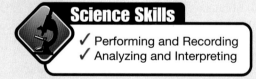

Science Skills

✓ Performing and Recording
✓ Analyzing and Interpreting

Edward Jenner

Smallpox is a potentially deadly virus that can kill as many as one-third of the people that it infects, and it leaves those who survive it disfigured with pockmarks. Smallpox has been a scourge for thousands of years. During European colonization and exploration, the population of many Indigenous peoples was decimated by their first exposure to smallpox in places such as North America, Central America, and Australia.

In the winter of 1781–82, fur traders on the North Saskatchewan River recorded going to First Nation encampments and finding the camps full of dead bodies. An explorer named Samuel Hearne estimated that 90% of First Nations people who traded at the nearby Hudson Bay Company post died of smallpox that winter.

Scientist Edward Jenner carried out a famous smallpox experiment in 1796, which led to the development of the first vaccine. He noticed that people, such as milkmaids, who worked closely with cattle were exposed to the much less deadly cowpox disease. People who had contracted cowpox were resistant to future smallpox infections. Jenner theorized that a human exposed to cowpox may develop some kind of immunity to smallpox—he tested this theory by taking pus from a milkmaid's cowpox sore and putting it into a cut on the arm of an eight-year-old boy named James Phipps, who was the son of Jenner's gardener.

After Phipps recovered from his cowpox infection, Jenner infected him with pus from a smallpox victim; but the boy did not become sick from the disease. This was the first example of an **inoculation**. Although people often use the words *inoculation* and *vaccination* interchangeably, inoculations introduce the antigens through a cut in the skin whereas vaccinations are performed through an injection of the antigens under the skin. The injection is done by a hollow needle.

We now understand that the antigen of the cowpox virus is similar to the antigen of the smallpox virus. By exposing the boy's body to cowpox, Jenner was able to rapidly produce antibodies to the smallpox virus, which prevented Phipps from becoming sick.

Due to aggressive vaccination programs designed by the World Health Organization (WHO), smallpox had been eradicated worldwide by 1979. As a result, most countries stopped vaccinating people for smallpox in the late 1970s.

▶ **inoculation:** a process of producing immunity by introducing antigens of an infectious agent through a cut in the skin's surface

Practice

51. Evaluate Edward Jenner's investigative methods. Was it ethical to use James Phipps as a test subject?

52. Explain why Indigenous populations in North America, Central America, and Australia were particularly susceptible to the smallpox virus.

53. Samples of the smallpox virus are known to exist today in only a couple of laboratories.

   a. Describe some concerns associated with keeping stocks of pathogenic, disease-causing agents.

   b. Describe some benefits for keeping these stocks.

Autoimmune Diseases

Figure A1.19 shows the joints of a woman's hands that are greatly swollen with rheumatoid arthritis. This disabling and painful condition is an example of an **autoimmune disease**. Sometimes a person's immune system forms antibodies against his or her body's own tissues, treating them like the antigens of invading bacteria and viruses. The white blood cells act like a rebel army attacking specific body organs or causing a variety of illnesses. In this case, the person's white blood cells are attacking the bones and cartilage in the joints of her hands. The cause of autoimmune diseases is unknown, but scientists believe that the suppressor T-cells play a role in controlling the rebelling white blood cells. Studies indicate that autoimmune diseases are more common in women than they are in men. These diseases tend to occur later in life.

You have probably heard of multiple sclerosis (MS) and diabetes mellitus (type 1 diabetes). Both are examples of autoimmune diseases. With MS, white blood cells attack parts of the nervous system. In the case of type 1 diabetes, the body mistakenly manufactures antibodies directed against the pancreas. The result is that the pancreas is unable to make insulin, which is a hormone that helps regulate the concentration of glucose in the bloodstream.

> **autoimmune disease:** a disorder in which the immune system produces antibodies against the body's own cells

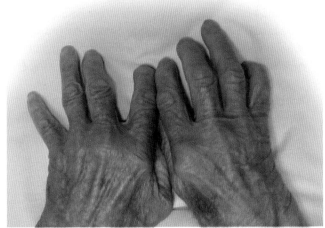

Figure A1.19: Rheumatoid arthritis can be a very debilitating disease.

1.5 Summary

The human body's internal environment is ideal for the growth of many disease-causing organisms, so the body must have defenses to protect itself from disease. The skin, cilia, and secretions—such as stomach acid, tears, and mucus—act as the first line of defence against potential invading organisms. White blood cells act as a defending army to identify and destroy any disease-causing organisms that make it through the skin and secretion barrier.

Disease-causing organisms can be passed on in several ways. These include being spread through droplets in the air, by eating or drinking contaminated food or water, via cuts in the skin, or through vectors such as mosquitoes. Disease-causing organisms, including protozoans, fungi, bacteria, and viruses, all have distinctive antigens on their surfaces that allow the white blood cells to recognize them as foreign invaders.

The white blood cells of the immune system are specialized for specific functions. Macrophages ingest disease-causing organisms displaying antigens from the destroyed invader. Helper T-cells recognize antigens and co-ordinate the attack against the invaders. B-cells produce antibodies that bind to the disease-causing organism's antigens. Killer T-cells destroy virus-infected body cells. Suppressor T-cells end the immune response. Memory T-cells and memory B-cells remain to provide a faster response to subsequent encounters with the antigen.

Vaccinations are a way of artificially exposing someone to an antigen of a disease-causing organism so that the body can produce memory cells and antibodies to create a greater immunity to exposure from the antigen.

Knowledge

1. Explain how each of the following disease-causing organisms overcomes the body's natural defenses to enter the body.

   a. malaria

   b. hepatitis C

   c. tuberculosis

   d. salmonella

2. Explain how an autoimmune disease differs from an infectious disease.

3. Create a table comparing the similarities and differences between bacteria and viruses.

4. Locate the applet "Battles in the Bloodstream" on the Science 30 Textbook CD. Watch the applet to confirm your understanding of how the immune system responds to a microscopic pathogen. Turn the sound off. Then watch the applet again. As you watch it, supply a new audiotrack by providing a description of what is occurring. Be sure to include the following key words in your spoken commentary: macrophage, antigens, helper T-cells, B-cells, antibodies, killer T-cells, suppressor T-cells, memory B-cells, and memory T-cells.

Applying Concepts

5. Explain how the following problems impair the body's ability to fight against disease-causing organisms.

   a. A person with hemophilia has blood that does not clot properly.

   b. The skin is badly damaged so that tissues are exposed.

   c. Someone who has HIV has many helper T-cells destroyed by the virus.

6. Explain how the following methods can be used to assist the body's ability to fight against disease-causing organisms.

   a. vaccinations given at birth

   b. antibiotics prescribed when you have an infection

   c. antiseptics used during operations

7. In a group, act out for the class the body's immune response to an invading bacteria or virus. Each group member will be assigned the role of one immune response component (disease-causing organism, macrophage, helper T-cell, B-cell, killer T-cell, suppressor T-cell, or the memory T-cell). Small groups may need to have members perform the role of more than one component. Before performing for the class, your group may want to spend some time developing a script, finding costumes for different roles, and rehearsing.

Chapter 1 Summary

In this chapter you have examined the structure and function of the circulatory system. You have seen how the heart functions to pump blood through the body, how the vessels of the circulatory system are specialized to carry blood around the body, and how blood functions as a medium to transport substances and to protect against disease-causing pathogens. You have also seen how problems that affect the circulatory system impair its functioning, and you have examined some of the technologies used to treat these problems.

Most diseases that make us feel sick are caused by lifestyle choices or by the invasion of disease-causing organisms. In your health file, you have examined and recorded information about your health and risk factors. In Chapter 2 you will look at the mechanisms of inheritance and learn how certain diseases can arise from inherited traits rather than from the environment. You will also examine the ethics of using genetic technologies.

Summarize Your Learning

In this chapter you have learned a number of new biological terms, processes, and theories. It will be much easier for you to recall and apply the information you have learned if you organize it into patterns.

Since the patterns have to be meaningful to you, there are some options about how you can create this summary. Each of the following options is described in "Summarize Your Learning Activities" in the Reference section. Choose one of these options to create a summary of the key concepts and important terms in Chapter 1.

Option 1: Draw a concept map or a web diagram.	Option 2: Create a point-form summary.	Option 3: Write a story using key terms and concepts.	Option 4: Create a colourful poster.	Option 5: Build a model.	Option 6: Write a script for a skit (a mock news report).

Chapter 1 Review Questions

Knowledge

1. List the four main functions of the human circulatory system.

2. Copy and complete the following table comparing the chambers of the mammalian heart.

Heart Chamber	Location	Type of Blood Found in Chamber	Function
right atrium	top right	deoxygenated	receives blood from body from vena cava
right ventricle			
left atrium			
left ventricle			

3. Describe three ways in which arteries and veins differ.

4. List the four main components of blood. Rank these components by their relative proportion in a blood sample from the largest proportion to the smallest proportion.

5. State which of the four major blood components is responsible for initiating the clotting process.

6. Define *cardiovascular disease.*

7. Distinguish between a heart attack and a stroke.

8. List four ways by which disease-causing pathogens can enter the body.

9. Define *vaccination.*

10. Obtain a printed copy of the handout titled "Overview of Immune Response" from the Science 30 Textbook CD.

    a. Use a pair of scissors to cut out all 13 images.

    b. Without looking at the textbook, place these images in the correct sequence.

    c. Check your answer to question 10.b. with the information presented in this chapter. Make the necessary adjustments or corrections and then use a glue stick or transparent tape to attach the images to a piece of paper in the correct sequence.

Applying Concepts

11. From the following data, carefully examine the relationship between the heart rate and the mass of an organism.

RESTING HEART RATE VERSUS MASS

Organism	Mass (g)	Resting Heart Rate (beats/min)
mouse	25	670
rat	200	420
guinea pig	300	300
rabbit	2000	205
small dog	5000	120
large dog	30 000	85
human	70 000	72
horse	450 000	38
African elephant	6 000 000	30

a. Observe trends from this data. Write a statement that describes how heart rate is affected by the size of an organism.

b. Estimate the heart rate of a 3-kg cat from these data patterns.

c. *Tyrannosaurus rex* was a ferocious carnivore that lived from about 85 to 65 million years ago. Paleontologists estimate that T.rex had a mass of up to 7000 kg. Estimate the resting heart rate of T.rex by extending the trends in this data.

d. The extinct dinosaur *Apatosaurus* (also called *Brontosaurus*) belonged to the long-necked family of sauropods. This family included the largest land animals to ever live. Estimate the heart rate of *Apatosaurus*, which had a mass of 27 metric tons (27 000 kg) by extending the trends in this data.

e. What problem does extending the trends in the data pose for paleontologists who are studying the circulatory systems of large extinct dinosaurs?

Use the following information to answer questions 12 to 14.

In Lesson 1.1 you learned how the parts of the heart work together as a system. A great way to consolidate all that you have learned about the heart is to build a three-dimensional model of this amazing pump.

To build the model, you will need the following:

- modelling materials such as Femo, Plasticine, or playdough
- a piece of stiff cardboard to act as a base for the model
- a copy of the handout titled "The Human Heart—Labelled" from the Science 30 Textbook CD

Note: You can make your own playdough by using one of the recipes on the "Playdough Recipes" handout on the Science 30 Textbook CD.

Design Criteria for the Heart Model

These models are designed to be three-dimensional representations of the handout titled "The Human Heart—Labelled." All the key structures on the heart diagram are to be included in your model. Even though the model will not include labels, if someone points to a heart structure on your model, you should be able to answer the following focusing questions:

- What is the name of this structure?
- Where would blood in this part of the heart go next?
- Does this part contain oxygen-rich blood or oxygen-poor blood?

12. Build your three-dimensional model of the heart according to the design criteria. Make sure all the parts connect so that if the parts were hollow, blood could flow through the heart. Building the model on a piece of stiff cardboard will make it easier to clean up and to move the finished product.

13. When your model is complete, show your work to other students. Ask the other students their opinions about what are the most effective aspects of your model as well as how it could be improved. Provide similar feedback to other students who completed this activity.

14. Use the feedback you received from your classmates as well as what you observed in the other models to answer the following questions.

a. What are the strong points of your model?

b. How could your model be improved?

Use the following information to answer question 15.

You have been asked to volunteer to help children in elementary school learn about the circulatory system. Your task is to create a comic strip to accompany the following description in an elementary school resource.

Robbie the Red Blood Cell is in the vena cavae on his way back from the brain where he just delivered some fresh oxygen to a brain cell and grabbed some waste carbon dioxide. While in the brain, Robbie found out that his friend Tina Toe Cell is in desperate need of oxygen.

15. Create a colourful and attractive comic strip with a series of six to eight sequential panels that explain what happens to Robbie as he moves through the circulatory system from the vena cavae to the toe and back again. You should aim to design a comic strip that could teach about the pathway of blood in the human body to someone who has never studied the circulatory system.

16. The bodies of athletes who compete in endurance events—such as marathon runs, cross-country skiing, or bike races—require a huge amount of oxygen during the competition. Some endurance athletes have tried to improve their performance by removing their own blood, centrifuging it to isolate the red blood cells, storing it while the body replaces the lost blood, and then injecting it back into their own body right before the race. This process of "blood doping" has been banned by the International Cyclist Union (UCI) and also by the International Olympic Committee (IOC).

a. Why would injecting more red blood cells into their bodies create an advantage for athletes?

b. Explain why it is more difficult to prove that athletes are using blood doping rather than taking performance-enhancing drugs.

c. Predict the effects of blood doping on the athlete's blood pressure.

d. List some possible negative health effects of the practice of blood doping.

e. Athletes often train at high altitudes before a competition. The thin air at these altitudes stimulates red blood cell production. Some athletes feel that the practice of blood doping before a competition is no different than training at high altitudes. Evaluate this specific argument.

17. **Design an Experiment**

A new over-the-counter weight-loss drug has just been released onto the market. Most users of the product are reporting fantastic weight-loss results. However, some clients are reporting an increase in their heart rates as a side effect. The drug company claims that there is no connection between these reported heart effects and the proper use of their product. A regular user of the product recently died of a heart attack. There is now public concern about the drug's use.

Your job is to design an experiment that safely tests whether there is a correlation between using the drug and risking an increased or irregular heartbeat that could result in a heart attack. A correlation is an assessment of how strongly two variables are related. If one variable changes and the other variable changes with it, there is said to be a correlation.

Provide a description of an investigation you would carry out, what materials you would use, and how you would ensure that the experiment was done safely. Your experimental design should clearly identify the manipulated and responding variables as well as listing at least three controlled variables. It should also take into account ethical and safety considerations.

18. Whales and seals are mammals well adapted for diving. For example, the Weddell seal is able to remain underwater for over an hour without surfacing to breathe. List some possible adaptations of a diving mammal's circulatory system that would allow it to remain below the water for so long.

19. A doctor looks at three patient files containing information from lab tests and lifestyle data. Note that μL is a microlitre.

Health File Information	Patient 1	Patient 2	Patient 3
Cholesterol Level	200 mg/dL	280 mg/dL	150 mg/dL
Activity Level	moderate regular weekly exercise	little or no weekly exercise	intense physical training
Resting Heart Rate	72 beats per minute	81 beats per minute	50 beats per minute
Smoker?	occasionally	yes	no
Blood Pressure	120/80 mmHg	147/95 mmHg	120/80 mmHg
White Blood Cell Count	14 000 per μL	6500 per μL	5000 per μL

a. Explain which patient the doctor would be most concerned about in terms of circulatory health? What lifestyle changes or future precautions might the doctor recommend to the high-risk patient?

b. Which patient most likely has an infection?

c. State the likely reason why the resting heart rate of Patient 3 is significantly lower than the other two patients.

Use the following information to answer questions 20 to 24.

Investigating Primary Literature: Predicting Sudden Death

Cardiovascular disease is the number one cause of death in Canada, with nearly 80 000 annual victims. For almost half of these people, death occurs within minutes of the first symptoms of a heart attack. In many cases the first heart attack pains were the first indication that this person had poor cardiovascular health—but by then it was too late! Clearly, if there is a way to predict whether an apparently healthy person is at risk of sudden death from a heart attack, preventative measures can be taken and lives can be saved.

Researchers from France and Italy analyzed data over 23 years from men working around Paris in the French civil service. The researchers claim that they have found a practical way to predict which members of a healthy population of men, who have no previous history of cardiovascular disease, may be susceptible to sudden death from heart attack.

This research is described in the article "Heart-Rate Profile During Exercise as a Predictor of Sudden Death." This article is found as a handout on the Science 30 Textbook CD. Since this article was published in the *New England Journal of Medicine*, it can be a challenging piece to read because it was written for physicians and medical science researchers. Nevertheless, there is value in reading primary literature because you can learn about scientific discoveries as they are reported by those people who actually did the research.

20. Obtain a copy of the handout "Heart-Rate Profile During Exercise as a Predictor of Sudden Death" from the Science 30 Textbook CD.

   a. Read questions 21 to 24 to develop a sense of what to focus upon when you read the article.

   b. Carefully read the article with these questions in mind. Remember to be an active reader by using a highlighter pen and/or by taking point-form notes. You can learn more about effective reading strategies by turning to "Reading for Understanding" in the Reference section.

   c. Save this evidence of your active reading strategies to help you answer questions 21 to 24.

21. The researchers used three tests to predict whether one of the men being studied was at risk of sudden death from a heart attack.

   a. Identify and describe each of the tests.

   b. Identify the test that appears to have the best ability to predict sudden death from a heart attack.

22. Describe screening procedures used to choose subjects for the study. Explain why these procedures were necessary.

23. The data was collected from 5713 men in the study.

   a. How many men were in the control group, and how was this group defined?

   b. How many men in the group died sudden deaths from heart attacks?

24. List some limitations of this research.

Chapter 2 Genetics

It's a beautiful fall day, and the young family in the photograph is getting ready to join their extended families for a big barbecue. For the girl, Roxanne, the barbecue will top off a near-perfect day at her grandparent's place where she got to play with her cousins and explore the farm. All day long Roxanne heard from different relatives about how much she is like her mother or how similar she is to her father. In terms of her physical traits, if you look closely at the photograph, you can see that Roxanne inherited some features from her mother and some from her father. The colour of Roxanne's hair and skin seem to be inherited from her father, while the colour and shape of her eyes are attributable to her mother.

How is it determined what traits are inherited from each parent? Is it true that some traits from one parent are "overpowered" by traits from the other parent? Does chance play a role in determining which traits are passed on?

Physical traits and many other characteristics are passed on from parents to offspring as information encoded in long molecules within cells. Genetics is the study of information and instructions inside cells. A greater understanding of how these genetic instructions are written and inherited by offspring has been applied to help solve crimes, understand diseases, make new medicines, and even re-design living organisms.

By the end of Chapter 2 you will have studied some history and major principles behind the science of genetics. You will not only have looked at how some genetic diseases can arise from inherited traits, but you will have examined the effect of genetic mutations. Throughout the chapter you will look at some ethical considerations of genetics by assessing the risks and benefits of using several genetic technologies.

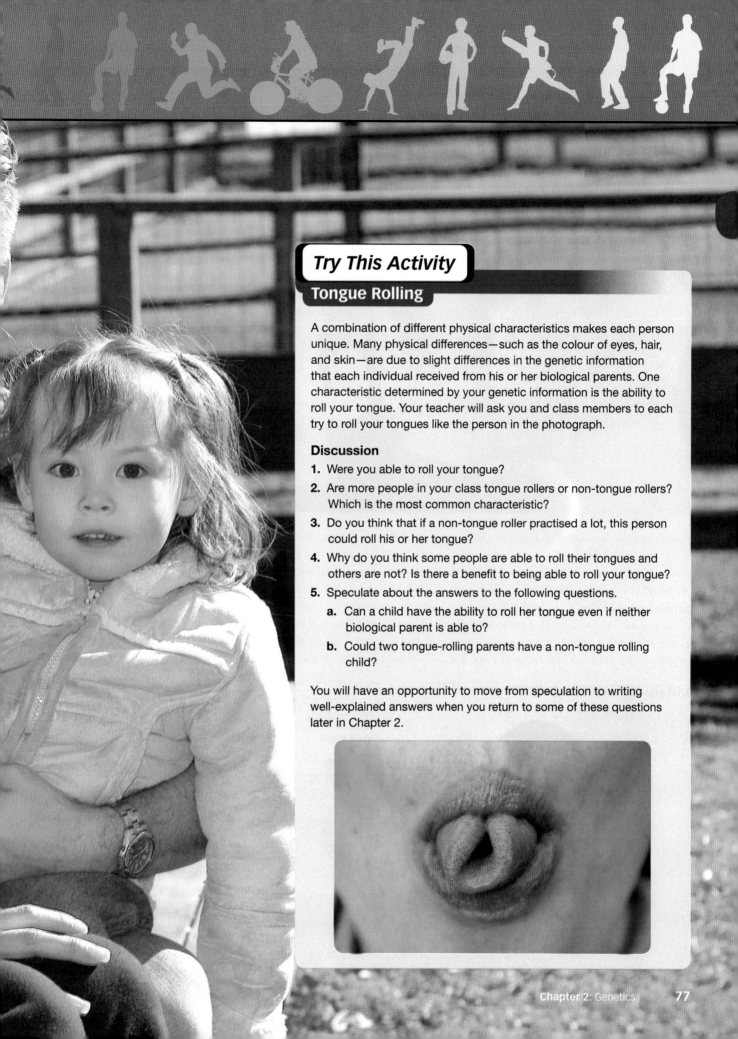

Try This Activity

Tongue Rolling

A combination of different physical characteristics makes each person unique. Many physical differences—such as the colour of eyes, hair, and skin—are due to slight differences in the genetic information that each individual received from his or her biological parents. One characteristic determined by your genetic information is the ability to roll your tongue. Your teacher will ask you and class members to each try to roll your tongues like the person in the photograph.

Discussion

1. Were you able to roll your tongue?

2. Are more people in your class tongue rollers or non-tongue rollers? Which is the most common characteristic?

3. Do you think that if a non-tongue roller practised a lot, this person could roll his or her tongue?

4. Why do you think some people are able to roll their tongues and others are not? Is there a benefit to being able to roll your tongue?

5. Speculate about the answers to the following questions.

   a. Can a child have the ability to roll her tongue even if neither biological parent is able to?

   b. Could two tongue-rolling parents have a non-tongue rolling child?

You will have an opportunity to move from speculation to writing well-explained answers when you return to some of these questions later in Chapter 2.

People come in a wonderful variety of shapes, sizes, and colours. Some aspects of a person's appearance—such as hair style—are changeable and a result of personal grooming choices or current fashion trends. Traits that are not changeable include features such as the natural colour of your skin, your blood type, and whether or not you have dimples in your cheeks. Although it's easy enough to simply say that these traits are inherited, it is considerably more challenging to explain how a person's cells develop in a way that favours one trait over another.

If you were to use a microscope to look closely at any living thing, you would see that the organism is made up of small living units called cells. Some organisms are so tiny that they are made up of just one cell, whereas large and complex organisms are made up of trillions of cells. The cells in your body do all the jobs needed for you to live and remain healthy.

Locating Genetic Information Within the Cell

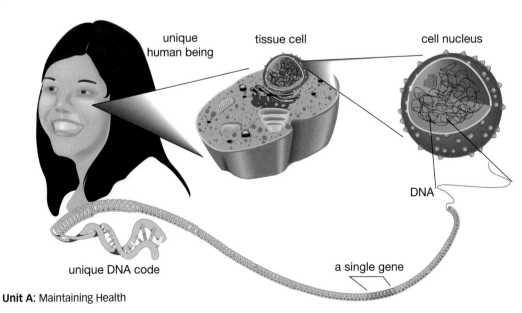

unique human being

tissue cell

cell nucleus

DNA

unique DNA code

a single gene

Chromosomes

In previous science courses you have studied the major parts of a cell. Recall that cells have a region called the nucleus that acts like a command centre to direct cell activity. If you used a very powerful microscope to look deep inside the nucleus of any one of your body's cells, you would find long strands of information called **chromosomes**. Each chromosome can be thought of as a book of instructions: almost like a cookbook full of recipes. A very simple organism, such as a bacterium, has all of its information on a single long strand. More complex organisms, such as people, tend to have several chromosomes. The number of chromosomes in a cell's nucleus depends on the type of species. Humans have 23 pairs of chromosomes or 46 total chromosomes. All the chromosomes in your nuclei are like a library of cookbooks or a complete set of instruction manuals with all the necessary information to run the activities of your cells.

> **chromosome:** a strand of DNA that contains the instructions for making proteins
>
> Chromosomes become X-shaped before cells divide.

Chromosomes are found in pairs. One outcome of this design is that a backup copy of important information is created. However, since one chromosome comes from each parent, there might be slight differences in the instruction subsets. To return to the cookbook analogy, it is like a cookbook with two recipes for chocolate fudge. Despite the fact that the instructions are nearly identical, slight variations in cooking times and temperatures result in food with different textures and consistencies.

Every cell has a complete set of chromosomes even though that particular cell might not need all the information to make a complete organism. The cell only uses the instructions required for its particular needs. This is just like several people who own the same cookbook using different recipes from the same book depending on their individual needs. If you made a cake from a cookbook recipe, you wouldn't have to read through the whole book each time you wanted to make a cake. In the same way, a particular cell from the pancreas only needs to read some of the information. This data could be, for example, a description of how to produce insulin.

Cookbooks and chromosomes differ in an important way. Information in cookbooks is organized by topic with all the recipes for desserts in one chapter or in one specific cookbook in your cookbook library, but the chromosome genes are not organized in a similar way. The instructions for making a hand are not found on one particular chromosome, but the instructions are instead spread among several chromosomes.

Chromosomes are generally long, thin strands that are coiled at regular intervals around protein molecules for protection. Chromosomes are best seen and photographed when the cell is dividing. At this time, each chromosome produces an identical copy of itself. The two copies, which remain attached at one point, shorten by coiling to produce the characteristic X-shape shown in photographs.

Genes

At specific places on each chromosome there are encoded instructions called **genes**. If a chromosome is like a recipe book, then a gene is like a specific recipe that provides the detailed instructions for building certain proteins. In order for instructions to be stored, communicated, and then used to complete a task, a language is necessary. Cookbooks are written in languages—like Korean or German—that people can understand. Genetic instructions are written in a chemical language called **deoxyribonucleic acid** or **DNA** for short. This language is encoded in a molecule. DNA has a distinctive shape, called a double helix, that looks like a twisted ladder or a spiral staircase. The sequence of chemical components in the DNA molecule encodes information. Each rung in the spiral ladder of the DNA molecule can be thought of as an individual letter in the cookbook.

> **gene:** a segment of DNA that carries instructions that result in the production of proteins

> **deoxyribonucleic acid (DNA):** the twisted ladder-shaped molecule that contains the genetic information of cells

> **genetics:** the science of gene function and inheritance

The ability to roll your tongue is controlled by a gene and determined by a certain pattern or sequence along a DNA molecule. People who are unable to roll their tongues do not have the gene instructions that allow the tongue muscles to roll. Even though two people each have the gene instructions for making hair or an eyeball, slightly different recipes create curly hair instead of straight hair or blue eyes rather than brown eyes. The combination of instructions from the genes on your chromosomes determines many of your characteristics. **Genetics** is the scientific study of how genes work to determine characteristics and to resolve how genetic information gets passed from parent to offspring.

Practice

1. **a.** Describe two ways in which chromosomes and cookbooks are similar.
   b. Describe one way that chromosomes and cookbooks are different.
2. How many chromosomes are found in one of the cells in your hand?
3. Why do chromosomes often appear with an X-shape in diagrams and in photos taken through a microscope?
4. Describe what is meant by the term *double helix*.

Human Karyotype

The human body contains 23 pairs of chromosomes, but the chromosomes are not neatly organized in the nucleus. In fact, they are in a jumble that looks like a plate of spaghetti. A **karyotype** is an image of all the chromosomes in one nucleus that have been matched up into their respective pairs and arranged from the largest pair to the smallest pair. A karyotype allows geneticists to better study the chromosomes in a nucleus. Geneticists use three features to identify and match up chromosomes:

> **karyotype:** an image that organizes the chromosomes of a cell in relation to number, shape, and size

> **centromere:** the region on a replicated chromosome that attaches the two identical copies during cell division

- the length of the chromosome (The longest chromosome is numbered as chromosome 1, etc.)
- the pattern of dark bands produced on each chromosome when they are stained
- the position of the chromosome's constricted part, called the **centromere**, which plays a role during cell division

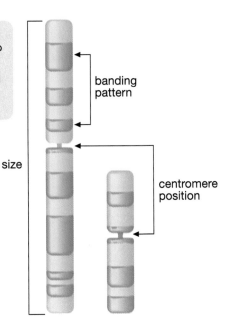

Figure A2.1 illustrates how it is possible for chromosomes to be matched up.

Which chromosome is the best match for Chromosome 1?

A   B   C   Chromosome 1

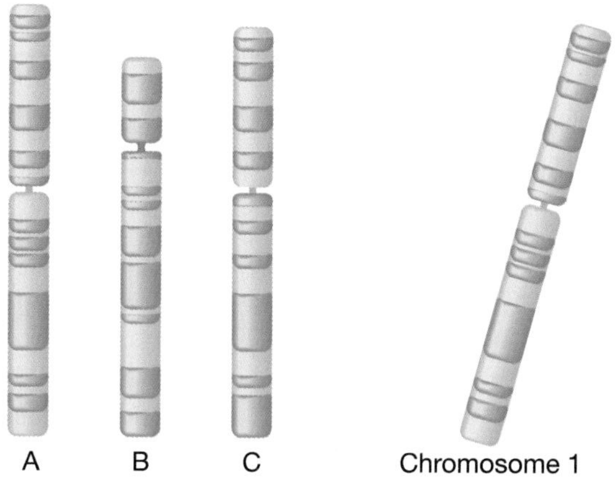

Figure A2.1

An artist's representation of the chromosomes makes the process of chromosome matching look easy—A is clearly the best match for Chromosome 1. However, there are complications when examining photographs of actual chromosomes taken through a microscope—it is challenging to interpret the somewhat grainy photographs of these incredibly tiny objects. Also, the last two chromosomes in the karyotype are called the *sex chromosomes* because they determine the organism's gender.

The pair of chromosomes matched at chromosome 23 determine the sex of the individual.

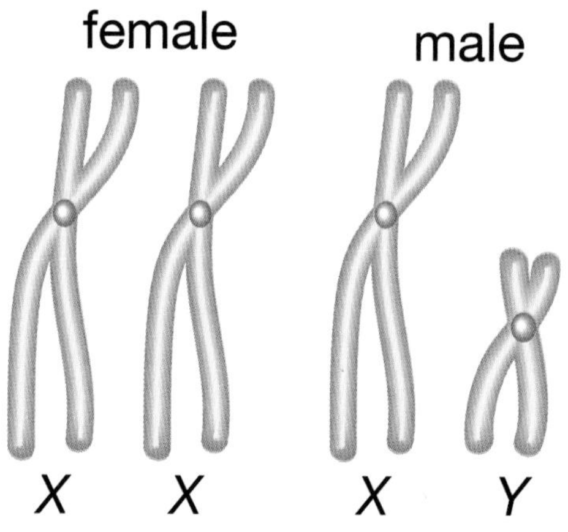

female   **male**

X   X   X   Y

Note that these chromosomes are shown after replication.

If an individual has two X chromosomes, she is a female. If an individual has one X chromosome and one Y chromosome, he is a male. Since the Y chromosome is considerably smaller than the X chromosome, this creates an extra challenge for matching chromosomes for a male.

As you'll discover in the next activity, overcoming these challenges is like sorting out a jigsaw puzzle.

Try This Activity

Make a Human Karyotype

To complete this activity you will need a copy of the handouts "Cut and Paste Karyotype Activity" and "Cut and Paste Karyotype Activity—Matched," which are available on the Science 30 Textbook CD.

Science Skills

✓ Performing and Recording
✓ Analyzing and Interpreting

Purpose

On the handouts you will find the corresponding chromosome that best matches each of the numbered chromosomes to form a human karyotype.

Materials

- "Cut and Paste Karyotype Activity" handout
- "Cut and Paste Karyotype Activity—Matched" handout
- scissors
- glue or transparent adhesive tape

Procedure

step 1: Cut out the 23 unnumbered chromosomes from the handout titled "Cut and Paste Karyotype Activity."

step 2: Place each unnumbered chromosome with a numbered chromosome to produce a matched pair.

step 3: Check your completed karyotype by using the handout named "Cut and Paste Karyotype Activity—Matched."

Analysis

1. Why it is beneficial to have two sets of chromosomes? Where does each set of chromosomes come from?
2. a. Describe what is different in terms of shape and size in the last pair of chromosomes.
   b. Is this individual a male or a female?
3. Explain how a karyotype of an individual might be useful to scientists.

The Role of Proteins

More than 25 000 genes are spread over the 46 chromosomes in the human karyotype. Chromosomes are like cookbooks, and each gene is a recipe for making a specific protein. This means there are more than 25 000 different recipes for proteins. Why is all this vast library of genetic information focused on making proteins? What role do proteins play in the body?

Cell Membrane Proteins

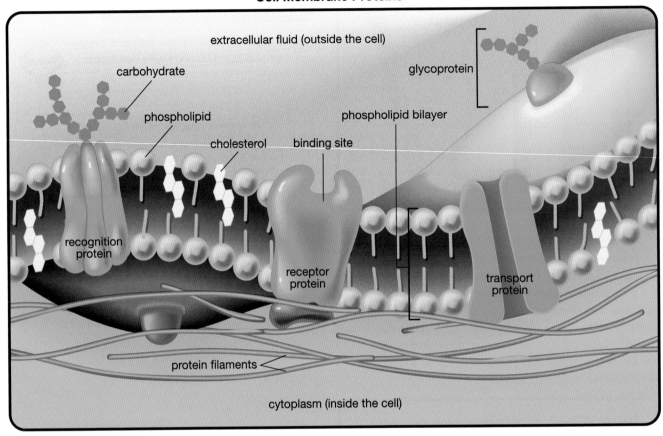

Proteins are molecules that have versatile and important bodily functions. If you took away all the water in the human body, about 50% of the dry mass left behind would be proteins. The human body produces tens of thousands of proteins, each with a unique structure and a specific job. If the body is like an engine, each protein is like a tiny specialized part that completes a specific task to keep the engine running. Hormones are proteins that co-ordinate and regulate the body's activities. This is shown in Figure A2.2.

Figure A2.2

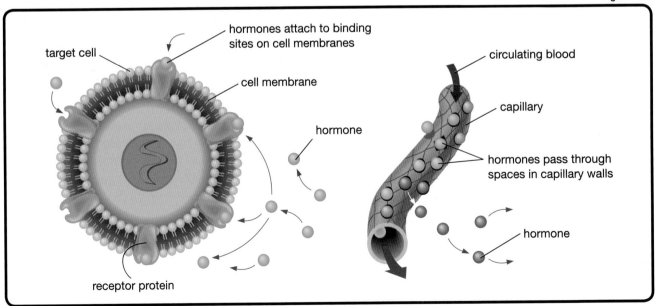

The major types of proteins found in organisms and some of their roles are summarized in the following table.

SUMMARIZING THE ROLES OF PROTEINS

Type of Protein	Role of Protein	Example
enzyme	Enzymes speed up chemical reactions where molecules are broken apart or put together.	Amylase is a digestive enzyme in your saliva that breaks down long starch molecules into shorter, more digestible glucose molecules.
structural	Structural support and frameworks are created to attach to other proteins.	Keratin is a structural protein that makes up your hair and nails. Collagen is a structural protein that provides a framework for skin and internal organs.
transport	Materials are moved within the cell or body.	Cell membrane proteins form channels and pumps in the cell membrane to help needed materials flow into the cell and unwanted materials flow out of the cell.
hormone	Hormones act as signals to co-ordinate and regulate activities in the body.	Insulin is a hormonal protein that regulates blood sugar. Insulin is produced in the pancreas and moves in the bloodstream to other organs to influence their use of glucose.
contractile	Contractile proteins change shape and can create larger movements when they work together.	Actin and myosin are proteins that band together to allow muscles to contract.
defensive	Defensive proteins protect the body against disease.	Antibodies are proteins that act in the body by attaching to disease-causing pathogens and foreign material.
energy	Energy proteins serve as a source of chemical potential energy that can be released by its decomposition.	Casein is an energy protein found in milk.

Practice

5. Identify examples of the kinds of molecules genes are designed to produce.
6. Describe the function of proteins in cell membranes.

Amniocentesis

An **amniocentesis** is a prenatal test done to look at the karyotype of an unborn child. During the test, a small amount of amniotic fluid is drawn out with a large needle from the area around the fetus. An image produced with ultrasound helps to direct the path of the needle. Some of the developing baby's cells are floating in the amniotic fluid and these cells are examined for genetic abnormalities, such as the presence of additional chromosomes, as is the case in Down syndrome. Amniocentesis is not routinely offered to expectant mothers because the procedure can slightly increase the chance of miscarriage, and it is only performed in pregnancies where there is a high risk of genetic diseases or deformities. Factors that can increase the risk of genetic diseases or deformities include the mother's age (above 40) or a history of severe diseases known to have a genetic origin.

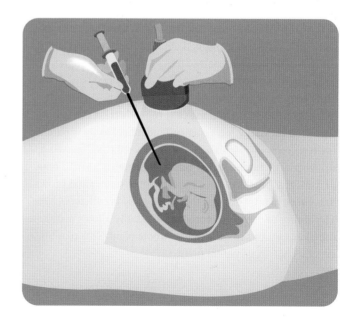

▶ **amniocentesis:** a prenatal test done to look at the karyotype of an unborn child

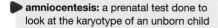

Making More Chromosomes

When a cell divides, it must provide genetic information to each of the new cells that form from the cell division. This means that exact copies must be made of the long strands of DNA within each of the chromosomes. Depending upon the type of cell, there are two basic ways in which this process can occur. These methods are mitosis and meiosis.

Mitosis

In order to grow and to replace cells that are dead or damaged, your body must constantly make new cells. Skin cells, for example, need to be frequently replaced by new cells. A body cell, or an **autosomal cell**, divides by growing large and making extra copies of all its parts and then splitting into two. An autosomal cell is shown at the top of Figure A2.3. Instead of showing 23 pairs of chromosomes, the simplified illustration shows only one pair. Note that one chromosome from the pair is inherited from the father and the other from the mother. Since each chromosome within the pair carries genes for the same characteristics at the same chromosome location, the pair of chromosomes are called **homologous chromosomes**.

To ensure that new cells have the necessary genetic information, autosomal cells must make a copy of their chromosomes before dividing. It is said that the DNA **replicates**. The replicated chromosomes attach at the centromere to form a distinctive X-shape. If each of these chromosomes is thought of as a recipe book, the process of DNA replication increases the number of copies of each book from two to four.

After being replicated, the chromosomes move to line up along the cell's middle or equator. The duplicate strands of the chromosomes are then pulled apart. The cell membrane pinches in to split the cell into two new cells with two sets of chromosomes called **daughter cells**. The process of cell division in autosomal cells is called **mitosis**. Note that with two copies of each chromosome, daughter cells are identical to the original autosomal cell that began the whole process. Biologists refer to the original cell and the daughter cells as **diploid cells** because each of these cells has two copies of each chromosome type.

Some organisms are able to produce a new organism by mitosis. This is called **asexual reproduction**. Offspring produced asexually are genetically identical to their parents. Bacteria reproduce asexually by simply splitting in two. A strawberry plant or a spider plant often makes a small copy of itself that breaks off or shoots off on a runner and grows into a new plant. Growing this small copy is called *budding*. The ability of plants to reproduce asexually allows people to use plant cuttings to grow into a whole plant. This plant is a genetic copy of its parent plant.

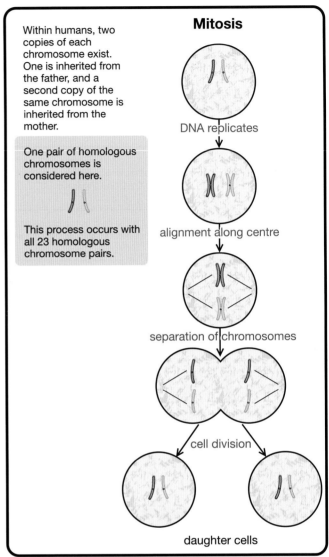

Within humans, two copies of each chromosome exist. One is inherited from the father, and a second copy of the same chromosome is inherited from the mother.

One pair of homologous chromosomes is considered here.

This process occurs with all 23 homologous chromosome pairs.

Mitosis

DNA replicates

alignment along centre

separation of chromosomes

cell division

daughter cells

Figure A2.3

▶ **autosomal cell:** a cell of the body not involved in sexual reproduction

▶ **homologous chromosomes:** a pair of chromosomes that would be matched during karyotyping because they have the same length, centromere position, and staining pattern

▶ **replicate:** to produce an exact copy of a DNA strand

▶ **daughter cells:** the two identical cells produced during mitosis

▶ **mitosis:** the division of an autosomal cell into two identical daughter cells

▶ **diploid cells:** cells with pairs of homologous chromosomes

▶ **asexual reproduction:** the production of genetically identical offspring from one individual

Meiosis

Most organisms do not reproduce asexually. Instead, they produce special reproductive cells called sex cells or **gametes**. These cells combine to make new and unique offspring. In animals the gametes are called sperm and egg, and in plants they are called pollen and egg. The process of producing gametes, called **meiosis**, begins in the same way as mitosis. Cells in the reproductive organs start with chromosomes in homologous pairs. Again, instead of showing 23 pairs, only one pair is noted in Figure A2.4. The DNA replicates and the replicated chromosomes form the characteristic X-shape.

Meiosis begins to differ from mitosis in the steps that follow. The first difference that occurs is that homologous chromosomes pair up and exchange parts. Some DNA segments of the chromosome from one parent are exchanged for corresponding DNA segments on the other parent's chromosome. This process of exchanging genetic material during meiosis is called **crossing over**. Since the pattern of DNA has been altered, crossing over creates slight genetic differences in the chromosomes.

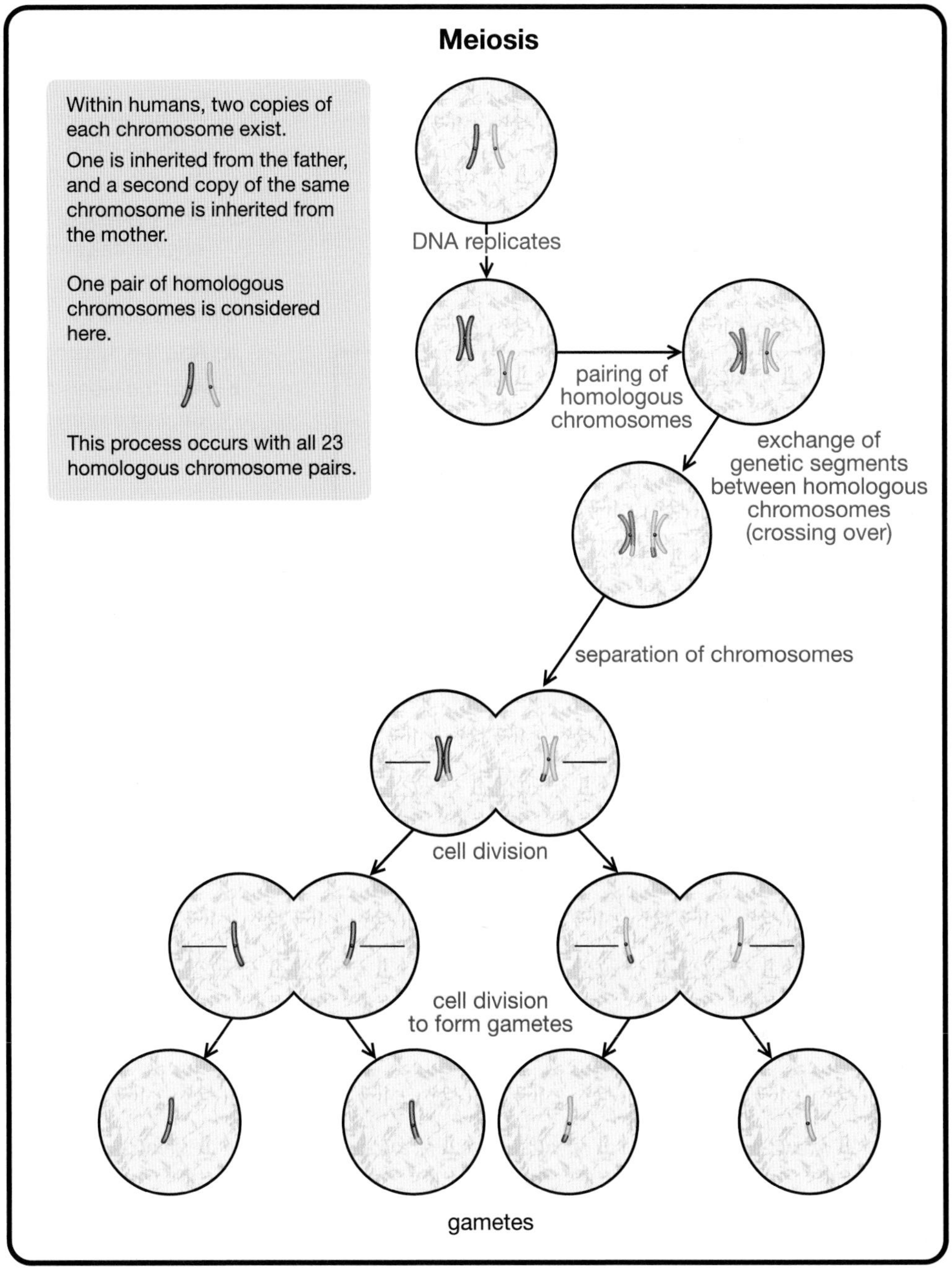

Meiosis

Within humans, two copies of each chromosome exist.

One is inherited from the father, and a second copy of the same chromosome is inherited from the mother.

One pair of homologous chromosomes is considered here.

This process occurs with all 23 homologous chromosome pairs.

DNA replicates

pairing of homologous chromosomes

exchange of genetic segments between homologous chromosomes (crossing over)

separation of chromosomes

cell division

cell division to form gametes

gametes

Figure A2.4

After crossing over, chromosomes align along the centre of the cell so that the homologous chromosomes are side by side. The homologous chromosomes separate and two daughter cells are produced. Next, a second cell division occurs, resulting in four cells that are called gametes.

Compare the number of chromosomes in the gametes with the number in the original cell at the top of Figure A2.4. Since there was no DNA replication prior to this second cell division, the four gametes each carry only one set of chromosomes rather than two sets in autosomal cells. The gametes are referred to as **haploid cells**, as they only have half the number of chromosomes as do autosomal cells.

▶ **gamete:** a sex cell, such as a sperm and an egg, produced during meiosis with only one copy of each chromosome type

▶ **meiosis:** a two-stage form of cell division that produces gametes with only half of the number of chromosomes as the original cell

▶ **crossing over:** the exchange of corresponding segments of DNA between maternal and paternal chromosomes during meiosis

▶ **haploid cell:** a cell that has only one member from each pair of homologous chromosomes

In people there are 23 different types of chromosomes. Biologists use the shorthand *n = 23* to communicate this idea. Each gamete, either a sperm cell or an egg cell, has only one copy of each of these chromosomes. The notation for these cells is 1n, meaning one copy of each type of chromosome.

Each of the other body cells—the autosomal cells—has two copies of each type of chromosome. These cells are described as 2n cells, meaning two copies of each chromosome. The following memory device can help you remember these ideas.

Mitosis is remembered as "mi two sis."	Meiosis is remembered as "mei one sis."
• produces diploid cells (**2n**), with **t**wo copies of each chromosome	• produces haploid cells (**1n**), with **o**ne copy of each chromosome

Practice

7. Obtain a copy of the handout "Mitosis" from the Science 30 Textbook CD.

    a. Add the missing labels to "Mitosis."

    b. Add the labels "1n" and "2n" to describe the original cell and the daughter cells.

8. Obtain a copy of the handout called "Meiosis" from the Science 30 Textbook CD.

    a. Add the missing labels to this diagram.

    b. Add the labels "1n" and "2n" to describe the original cell and the gametes.

Utilizing Technology

Comparing Mitosis and Meiosis

Background Information

Now that you have seen the details of mitosis and meiosis, it's important to be able to keep the big picture in mind and not to lose sight of the main ideas. This activity provides an opportunity to reinforce essential concepts about mitosis and meiosis.

Science Skills

✓ Performing and Recording

Purpose

You will use an applet titled "What Is Mitosis/Meiosis?" to reinforce the essential concepts that are necessary to understand mitosis and meiosis.

Procedure and Observations

step 1: Locate the applet "What Is Mitosis/Meiosis?" from the Science 30 Textbook CD.

step 2: Review the list of analysis questions. Then watch the applet.

step 3: Watch the applet again, only this time use the natural pauses between screens to record your answers.

Analysis

1. A human being begins as one cell and then grows into a body of a hundred trillion cells.

    a. Define the term *diploid cell*.

    b. Describe the arrangement of chromosomes in human body cells.

    c. Explain why it is necessary, before it divides, for a body cell to make a copy of each chromosome.

    d. Identify the process that describes how one cell becomes a body of trillions of cells.

2. Not all cells in the human body are diploid cells.

    a. Define the term *haploid cell*.

    b. Describe in general terms the process that produces haploid cells.

    c. Identify the name of the process that you described in question 2.b.

    d. Explain the purpose of haploid cells.

    e. Explain what happens when two haploid cells combine.

3. Describe the essential difference between mitosis and meiosis.

Fertilization

When chromosomes in a male gamete join up with chromosomes in a female gamete during fertilization, the fused cell contains the two sets of chromosomes found in an autosomal cell. With two sets of chromosomes, the fertilized egg is able to grow and develop through the process of mitosis.

The advantage of sexual reproduction is that diverse offspring are produced. The genetic combination of chromosomes from each parent results in offspring with the possibility of different traits. As shown in Figure A2.5, even with a simplified model using only one pair of chromosomes, there are 16 possible outcomes. If the full complement of 23 pairs of chromosomes are used, there will be more than 70 trillion possible ways for gametes from a mother and a father to join and create a new human being. The number of possibilities would be even greater if crossing over was considered. Given that this number is more than all the people who have ever lived on planet Earth, unless you are an identical twin, there has never been anyone with your exact DNA. In other words, you are a unique creation.

Fertilization

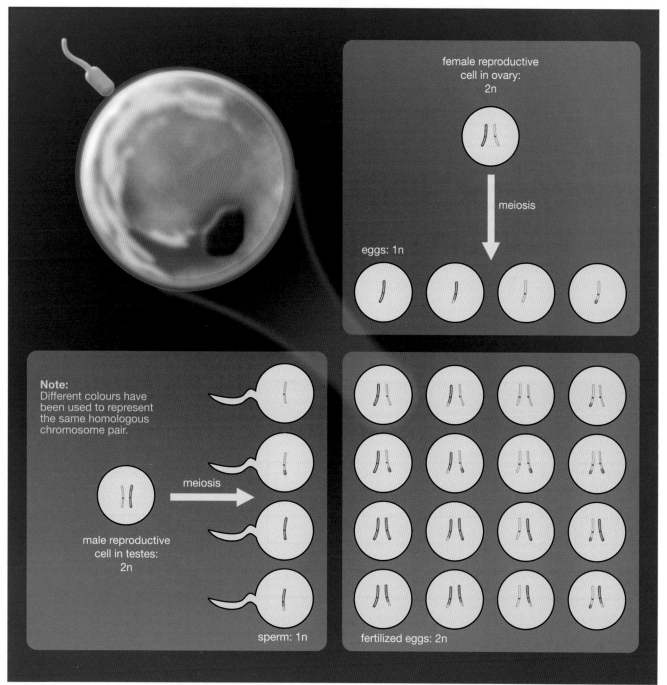

Figure A2.5: This simplified model shows the outcomes from 1 pair of chromosomes instead of 23 pairs.

Sexual reproduction is clearly a valuable mechanism for increasing the variety among organisms in a population. Note the supporting role that crossing over plays to increase variety in the gametes produced by meiosis. The exchange of genetic material during crossing over further increases the genetic diversity of the offspring, and this is part of the reason why two siblings from the same parents can look quite different. Genetic diversity is important because a genetically diverse population is less susceptible to disease.

Utilizing Technology

Determining Numbers of Unique Offspring

Purpose

You will use a spreadsheet to verify the following statement:

" . . . there would be more than 70 trillion possible ways that gametes from a mother and a father can join to create a new human being."

Science Skills

✓ Analyzing and Interpreting

Procedure

You may complete this activity by using a spreadsheet or a graphing calculator. Use the following template as a guide. Continue the patterns shown until the Number of Pairs of Chromosomes column reaches 23 pairs. At this point, the table is complete.

Number of Pairs of Chromosomes	Number of Possible Gametes Produced by One Parent (excluding crossing over)	Number of Possible Unique Combinations of Offspring Produced by Two Parents
n	2^n	$(2^n) \times (2^n)$
1	$2^1 = 2$	$(2^1) \times (2^1) = 2 \times 2 = 4$
2	$2^2 = 4$	$(2^2) \times (2^2) = 4 \times 4 = 16$
3	$2^3 = 8$	$(2^3) \times (2^3) = 8 \times 8 = 64$
4	$2^4 = 16$	
5		

Analysis

If the number of gametes produced by each parent is 2^n, explain why the number of offspring produced by two parents is $(2^n) \times (2^n)$.

Selective Breeding

Long before chromosomes and genes were discovered, people recognized that offspring had a similar appearance to their parents and hypothesized that characteristics could be inherited. However, people were not able to explain how these characteristics were passed on from parents to offspring. They lacked necessary tools—such as microscopes powerful enough to see cells and their parts—to understand mechanisms for the inheritance of traits or the genes responsible for them.

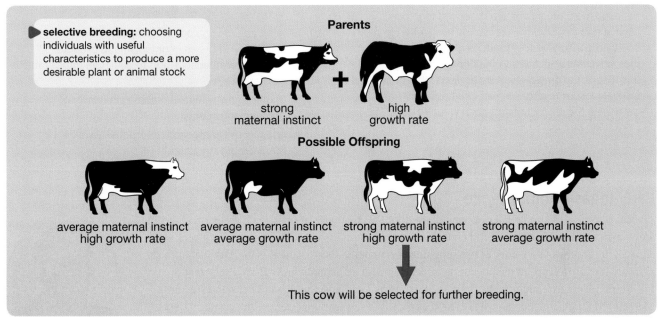

selective breeding: choosing individuals with useful characteristics to produce a more desirable plant or animal stock

Parents

strong maternal instinct + high growth rate

Possible Offspring

average maternal instinct high growth rate | average maternal instinct average growth rate | strong maternal instinct high growth rate | strong maternal instinct average growth rate

This cow will be selected for further breeding.

Figure A2.6: Raising cattle for beef production involves selective breeding. A strong maternal instinct in females means good nurturing and feeding of calves. Orphaned calves often grow poorly or they may die. A high growth rate demonstrates that the animal's metabolism is able to convert ingested food into tissue (meat).

Ancient peoples who lived in aristocratic societies believed that the monarchs passed on their noble or royal blood to their children. These people also realized that they could select individuals with desirable characteristics from their domestic crops and livestock. These crops and livestock could then be bred to produce offspring possessing desirable traits. Farmers could also prevent individuals with undesirable characteristics from breeding. The practice of **selective breeding** allowed farmers to create stocks that met their particular needs.

Figure A2.7: Corn husks were used by Iroquois to make masks or false faces that had special spiritual significance in healing ceremonies.

First Peoples of North America and Central America employed selective breeding to grow domesticated crops—such as maize (corn)—for thousands of years before Europeans arrived in the area. In 1612, French explorers around the Great Lakes recorded that Haudenosaunee (Iroquois) people made popcorn by putting maize kernels in pottery full of heated sand. It is believed that the maize First Nations people grew is a result of centuries of selective breeding of teosinite, a wild grass. The corn and popcorn that you eat today is descended from the breeds developed by First Nations people.

Use the following information to answer question 9.

In previous courses you studied the theory of natural selection. This theory states that evolution takes place because more organisms are produced than can survive and that only the organisms best suited to their environment survive to reproduce and, in turn, pass on their advantageous traits to their offspring. According to this theory, the environment determines what organisms will be successful and will therefore have their traits determine the characteristics seen in future generations.

9. **a.** Describe how selective breeding differs from the process of natural selection.

   b. Describe how selective breeding is similar to the process of natural selection.

10. Genetic engineering can be defined as the manipulation of genes in organisms to produce desirable characteristics and to eliminate undesirable characteristics.

   a. Explain how selective breeding is a form of genetic engineering.

   b. Identify the first people to practise genetic engineering in Canada.

Early Ideas of Inheritance

The development of simple microscopes allowed for the discovery of cells, such as sperm and eggs; but these instruments were not powerful enough to observe chromosomes. During the seventeenth and eighteenth centuries, the theory of preformation was popular. Preformation is the idea that all body parts are already formed at the beginning of development and simply grow from a very tiny full-formed body to a larger body. Prominent scientists including Anton van Leeuwenhoek and Marcello Malpighi, the person who discovered capillaries, were supporters of the preformationist theory. However, there was some debate about whether the pre-formed body was found in the sperm or the egg.

Figure A2.8: Charles Darwin

In the nineteenth century, Charles Darwin used his studies of the natural world to develop and publish his theory of evolution. His theory stated that organisms best suited to their environment survived to pass on their characteristics to their offspring, but Darwin was not able to explain how characteristics are passed on.

Discovering Genes

In the 1860s, Gregor Mendel was the first person to undertake detailed and systematic studies into the inheritance of characteristics. Mendel was a monk who became interested in the breeding of pea plants that grew in the monastery where he lived. Little did he know that he would become known as "the father of genetics."

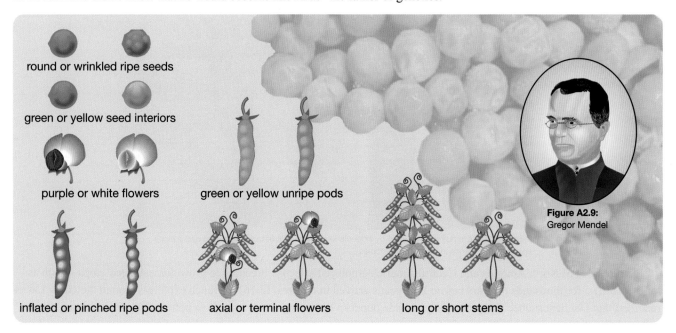

round or wrinkled ripe seeds

green or yellow seed interiors

purple or white flowers

green or yellow unripe pods

inflated or pinched ripe pods

axial or terminal flowers

long or short stems

Figure A2.9: Gregor Mendel

Mendel noticed that certain inherited characteristics were not blended. For example, a pea plant with white flowers when bred with a pea plant with purple flowers did not produce offspring with blended characteristics. Instead, the offspring had either purple flowers or white flowers.

Common garden pea plants were good test subjects for his research because not only are they easy to grow in large numbers, but their reproduction can be manipulated by transferring pollen from one plant to another in a process called **cross-pollinating**. Mendel discovered that several traits in pea plants were easy to recognize and occurred in only one of two distinctive forms—purple flowers or white flowers, round seeds or wrinkled seeds, yellow seeds or green seeds, and other forms.

> ▶ **cross-pollinate:** transferring pollen between genetically different plants
>
> ▶ **self-pollinate:** transferring pollen from one plant to the female part of the same plant or to another plant with the same genetic makeup

Mendel observed that when he cross-pollinated a white flowering plant with a purple flowering plant, the offspring from this cross all had purple flowers. The white-flowered trait had disappeared in the generation of pea plants produced by this cross. When he bred individuals from this first generation, or allowed them to **self-pollinate**, he was surprised to see that the white-flowered trait returned in about a quarter of the second-generation's population. Experiments on other pea traits provided the same results. One trait completely disappeared in the first generation and then re-appeared in about a quarter of the second-generation plants.

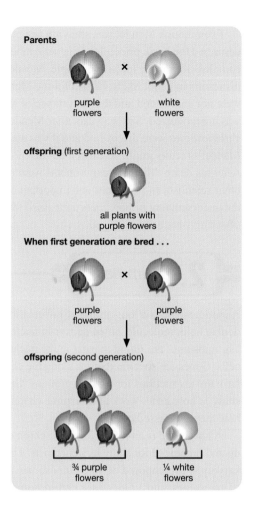

Parents

purple flowers × white flowers

offspring (first generation)

all plants with purple flowers

When first generation are bred ...

purple flowers × purple flowers

offspring (second generation)

¾ purple flowers   ¼ white flowers

Mendel's Conclusions from His Pea Plant Experiments

(1) The inheritance of traits must be determined by factors (now called genes).

(2) Individuals randomly inherit one factor (copy of a gene) from each parent.

(3) Factors or genes are independently passed to the offspring. This means that a pea plant's inheritance of the gene that makes purple flowers does not affect the plant's inheritance of other traits, such as seed colour.

(4) Some genes are more powerful than others; so a trait may not appear in an individual because the more powerful gene masks it (e.g., purple flowers over white flowers), but it can still be passed onto the individual's offspring.

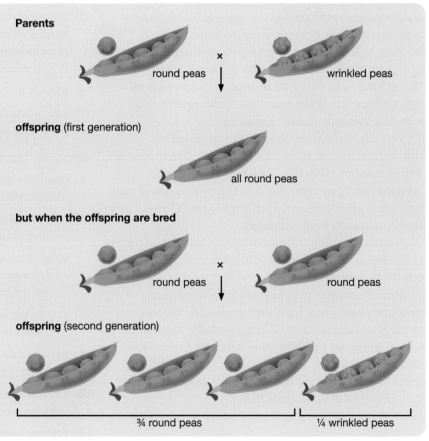

Parents

round peas × wrinkled peas

offspring (first generation)

all round peas

but when the offspring are bred

round peas × round peas

offspring (second generation)

¾ round peas   ¼ wrinkled peas

Even though Mendel was studying pea plants, he actually described the basic principles of genetic inheritance for all complex life forms, including people. Mendel published his results in 1866. Sadly, in his lifetime Mendel's results were not understood and the importance of his work was unrecognized. Sixteen years after Mendel's death, chromosomes were discovered and it was suggested that Mendel's factors might be carried on the chromosomes. After his death, Mendel's experiments were repeated by other scientists and his ideas and important contributions to the understanding of how traits are passed from parents to offspring were acknowledged.

2.1 Summary

A chromosome is a long strand of information made up of a double helix molecule called deoxyribonucleic acid or DNA. Chromosomes are found in pairs in the nuclei of autosomal cells. Genes are specific regions along the chromosomes and have the instructions for making proteins. Genetics is the study of how genes work to determine characteristics and how they get passed on.

A karyotype is an image of all the chromosomes paired up and organized for study by geneticists. The human karyotype is composed of 46 chromosomes, 22 pairs of autosomes, and 1 pair of sex chromosomes. The sex chromosomes determine the gender of an individual. Two X chromosomes produce a female, and one X chromosome combined with one Y chromosome produces a male.

Body cells, or autosomal cells, divide for an organism to grow or replace cells through the process of mitosis. During mitosis, two identical daughter cells are produced with identical sets of chromosomes. Some organisms can reproduce asexually through mitosis alone.

Sex cells, or gametes, are produced for sexual reproduction through the process of meiosis. During meiosis, four gametes are produced—each has half the number of chromosomes of an autosomal cell. The combination of male and female gametes creates a fertilized egg with the required two complete sets of chromosomes.

Selective breeding is a technology that has allowed people to develop more useful breeds of domesticated plants and animals to suit human needs.

Mendel's study of pea plants led to the development of a theory proposed where traits were inherited by factors (later called genes) and in which offspring randomly received a copy of a gene for each trait from its parents. Mendel also stated that possessing a gene for one trait did not affect the genes for other traits and that some genes were able to mask the other forms of an inherited trait.

2.1 Questions

Knowledge

1. Match the following terms with the analogy that best describes each term.

   - DNA
   - gene
   - protein
   - chromosome
   - karyotype

   a. a cookbook with several recipes in it

   b. an entire library of cookbooks neatly arranged in order from the largest book to the smallest book

   c. the cake produced by following recipe instructions

   d. the letters and words in a recipe

   e. the instructions for making a cake

2. How many chromosomes are in a normal human autosomal cell? How many chromosomes are in a normal human gamete?

3. Determine the gender of an individual who has two X chromosomes in each autosomal cell instead of an X and a Y chromosome.

4. Dogs have 78 chromosomes, cats have 34 chromosomes, and goldfish have 94 chromosomes. Explain why the usual number of chromosomes in autosomal cells for any species is always an even number.

5. Describe what would happen if the process of meiosis did not occur and two cells with two sets of chromosomes combined to produce a new child. Why is meiosis necessary?

6. Identify the term Mendel used instead of *gene*.

7. List some reasons why pea plants are so well suited for genetic studies.

Applying Concepts

8. Obtain a copy of the handout "Comparing Mitosis and Meiosis," from the Science 30 Textbook CD.

   a. Without looking at information from this lesson, attempt to add the missing labels to this diagram.

   b. Biologists use the letter n to represent the number of different chromosomes in a cell. Label the cells at the top and bottom of the handout either 1n or 2n.

   c. Use the information in Lesson 2.1 to check and correct your answers to 8.a.

9. Sexual reproduction creates beneficial genetic diversity. List some possible advantages of asexual reproduction.

10. Explain the steps you would take in the process of selective breeding to create a fast-running breed of dog.

11. Propose some reasons why van Leeuwenhoek and other scientists of his time believed in the preformation theory.

> **acquired traits:** traits acquired during a person's lifetime because of experiences, education, and upbringing, such as a scar from a cut or the ability to speak a particular language
>
> **inherited traits:** traits genetically passed on from one generation to the next, such as a particular blood type or eye colour

You have probably been told that you have characteristics similar to another member of your family. Perhaps someone has said that you have your mother's hair, your father's eyes, or that you inherited a trait from one of your grandparents. You might have compared your own characteristics to other family members or wondered which traits you might someday pass on to your children.

Although people have long understood that characteristics are inherited from their parents, they did not understand the mechanisms that enable inheritance to happen. As Mendel's work became more well known and understood, scientists were able to use his observations, terminology, and the results of his experiments to make predictions about how and what characteristics are passed on to offspring.

The discovery of genes and the field of genetic research has helped to answer questions concerning the inheritance of traits and the influence that one's surroundings has on the development of individuals. As more is learned about the role of genes and how they are passed on to offspring, scientists are better able to distinguish between **acquired traits**, which come from the environment and are not passed on to offspring, and **inherited traits**, which are the result of genes.

In Lesson 2.2 you will apply Mendel's work to making predictions about the genetic inheritance of single traits. Using genetic diagrams, you will analyze the probability of offspring inheriting particular traits. Through the study of autosomal and sex-linked patterns of inheritance, you will also learn why some diseases and characteristics are present in a particular gender more than they are in the other gender.

Figure A2.10: Parents who are concerned about passing on a genetic disorder often seek the expertise of a genetics counsellor. A genetics counsellor studies for many years at a university to obtain a master's degree or PhD in medical genetics because it takes considerable expertise to properly interpret human genetic data.

It is important to keep in mind that the study of human genetics is much more complicated than the introductory concepts taught in Science 30. The proper analysis of human genetic traits requires years of study and training. It follows that you must be cautious when it comes to drawing conclusions from an analysis of genetic traits based solely upon the information presented in this course.

11. List five traits you may have inherited from your parents.

12. State some acquired traits that cannot be passed on to offspring.

13. Look at the family in the photograph.

The mother and father have different eye colours, hair colours, hair types, and skin colours. Their little girls inherited some characteristics from each parent. Identify which characteristics the girls may have inherited from each parent.

Alleles

At the beginning of Chapter 2 you looked at the ability to roll your tongue. You observed that there are two distinctive traits—some people can roll their tongues and others cannot. The differences in these traits can be traced to alternate forms of a specific gene. These alternate forms of genes are called **alleles**. In the case of tongue rolling, there are two alleles that can produce the two possible traits. One particular allele provides the genetic instructions that create the tongue-rolling trait; so if you do not possess that allele, you will not have the trait.

Individuals possess two alleles for every trait located at specific sites on homologous chromosomes. Since homologues separate during meiosis, only one of these alleles is passed onto each gamete. The two alleles that you inherit are contained in the particular sperm cell and egg cell

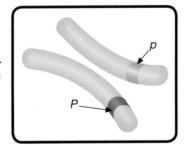

Figure A2.11: Two different alleles are found on a pair of homologous chromosomes.

that joined during fertilization. Therefore, when you think about inheritance, you also have to think about probability. In other words, which one allele of the two possibilities will be in each of the particular gametes that join to form an individual?

Dominant Versus Recessive

Gregor Mendel's studies of pea-plant traits that appear in two distinct forms can also be used to help understand how many traits, like tongue rolling, are expressed and passed on. In Mendel's experiments with pea-flower colour, he found that crossing a white-flowered plant with a purple-flowered plant resulted in all offspring producing purple flowers. This means that if an offspring receives a gene in the form of the purple allele from a parent, the purple colour will be produced even if the allele received from the other parent is the white gene. How can this be explained?

In genetic crosses between two individuals, each gene being studied is assigned a letter. Genes can be assigned any form of symbol, but using letters creates a way to easily represent the related, yet different, alleles.

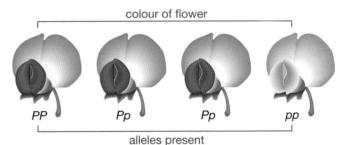

colour of flower

PP   Pp   Pp   pp

alleles present

Figure A2.12: Pea plants with purple flowers have at least one copy of the dominante allele, *P*. Pea plants with white flowers have two copies of the recessive allele, *p*.

Mendel proposed a theory to describe the occurrence of traits that he observed in his pea-plant studies. Since the purple flower colour trait is dominant to the white trait, Mendel stated that the purple flower colour is a **dominant** trait in pea plants. Dominant traits are caused by dominant alleles. If an offspring receives even one dominant allele, the dominant trait will appear in that offspring. He said that the trait that is masked and not expressed when the dominant allele is present is called the **recessive** trait. Recessive traits are only expressed when an offspring receives two copies of the recessive allele. A white-flowered pea plant has two recessive alleles for flower colour.

The ability to roll your tongue is a dominant trait produced by the dominant allele, which you inherited from at least one of your parents. If you cannot roll your tongue, it means that you have two copies of the recessive allele.

▶ **allele:** an alternative form of a gene responsible for a trait

▶ **dominant:** referring to a dominant allele that overpowers a recessive allele—an individual only needs one dominant allele for the dominant trait to be expressed

▶ **recessive:** referring to a recessive allele that is not expressed when the dominant allele is present—two recessive alleles need to be present for the recessive trait to be expressed in an individual

Example Problem 2.1

At a specific location on a particular chromosome within a pea plant is the gene that determines the flower colour. Since the pea plant has two copies of each chromosome, there are two copies of the gene for flower colour. However, the gene for flower colour located on each chromosome copy may not be identical. For example, one allele, *P*, codes for purple flowers, while the other allele, *p*, codes for white flowers. A reproductive cell within a pea plant can produce four gametes so that two of the gametes have the allele *P*, while the other two have the allele *p*.

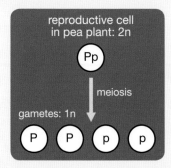

Suppose two pea plants each have the allele *P* that codes for purple flowers and the allele *p* that codes for white flowers. Let these two plants be the parent generation.

a. Determine the colour of the flowers in each of the parent pea plants.

b. Set up a chart to show all the possible outcomes of fertilizing a gamete from one plant with a gamete from the other.

c. Use the chart you developed in b. to determine the percentage probability that a plant in the first generation of offspring will have white flowers.

d. Suppose the two parent plants produced twelve plants in the first generation of offspring. How many of these plants would you expect to have white flowers? Suggest some reasons why the number of plants with white flowers could add up to a different number.

Solution

a. Each of the parent pea plants will produce purple flowers, since the dominant allele, *P*, for purple flowers masks the recessive allele, *p*, for white flowers.

b.

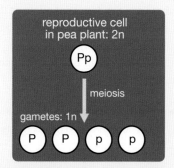

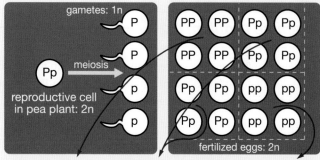

¼ of the fertilized eggs will have two dominant alleles

½ of the fertilized eggs will have one dominant allele and one recessive allele

¼ of the fertilized eggs will have two recessive alleles

The percentage probability that a first-generation plant will be purple is ¾ or 75%.

The percentage probability that a first-generation plant will be white is ¼ or 25%.

c. The two parent plants each produce four gametes, combining for a total of sixteen possible offspring. Of these offspring, four have the two recessive alleles to produce white flowers. Since four of the sixteen possible outcomes produce white flowers, the percentage probability that a plant in the first generation will have white flowers is 1/4 or 25%.

d. Since the percentage probability of an offspring in the first generation having white flowers is 1/4, then it is most likely that three plants (1/4 of the twelve offspring) will have white flowers. This value assumes that all the gametes are produced and fertilized in the exact proportions predicted by the chart. In reality, some of the sperm may not fertilize an egg and some eggs may not be fertilized by any sperm.

Punnett Squares

As shown in Example Problem 2.1, if the alleles for an inherited trait are known, it is possible to predict the probability of the offspring having a particular genetic make-up or **genotype**.

But the method shown is lengthy and quite repetitious. Note that even though four gametes were produced by each parent plant, there were really only two possibilities: a gamete will either have the dominant allele or the recessive allele. A streamlined version of this process uses a more concise chart called a **Punnett square**.

As you'll see in Example Problem 2.2, the Punnett square method is very efficient.

How to Use a Punnett Square

step 1: Draw a square and then label each row and column with the alleles of each gamete.

step 2: Fill in the square with the offspring genotype.

step 3: Determine the fraction of the offspring with each genotype. This fraction is the same as the probability of an individual offspring possessing a particular genotype.

▶ **genotype:** a description of the alleles that an individual possesses
   This is communicated by using letters to represent the different allele versions.
▶ **Punnett square:** a table that uses the alleles of the parents to indicate all possible outcomes resulting from gamete fertilization

---

Example Problem 2.2

Two pea plants in the parent generation each contain the dominant allele P that codes for purple flowers and the recessive allele p that codes for white flowers. Use a Punnett square to predict the percentage probability that a plant in the first generation of offspring will have white flowers.

Solution

step 1:

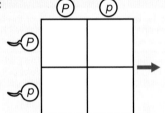

step 2:

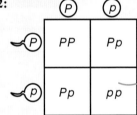

The percentage probability of plants in the first generation having white flowers is 25%.

Practice

Use the following information to answer questions 14 and 15.

In human beings, the ability to roll one's tongue is dominant over non-tongue rolling. As you solve the following questions, use R to represent the dominant allele for tongue rolling and r to represent the recessive allele for non-tongue rolling.

14. Two parents each possess the dominant allele R and the recessive allele r.

   Use a Punnett square to determine the percentage probability that their offspring will be able to roll their tongues.

15. One parent possesses the dominant allele R and the recessive allele r. The other parent possesses two copies of the recessive allele r.

   a. Are both of these parents able to roll their tongues?

   b. Use a Punnett square to determine the percentage probability that their offspring will be able to roll their tongues.

Homozygous and Heterozygous

Punnett squares are a powerful tool to show the outcomes of several types of crosses. When an organism has two copies of the same alleles that are either both dominant or both recessive, the organism is called **homozygous**. In the case of pea plants, the purple flowers are homozygous for the dominant condition and the white flowers are homozygous for the recessive condition. When an organism possesses one dominant allele and one recessive allele for a trait, it is said to be **heterozygous** for that trait.

> ▶ **homozygous:** referring to an organism that has two copies of the same allele for a given trait—*pp* or *PP*
>
> ▶ **heterozygous:** referring to an organism that has a dominant allele and a recessive allele for a given trait—*Pp*

The following table shows some of these possibilities.

USING PUNNETT SQUARES TO PREDICT THE OUTCOMES OF GENETIC CROSSES

Heterozygous Parents	Homozygous Dominant Parents	Homozygous Recessive Parents
Two pea plants, each with one dominant allele, *P*, and one recessive allele, *p*, are crossed.	Two pea plants, each with two copies of the same dominant allele, *P*, are crossed.	Two pea plants, each with two copies of the same recessive allele, *p*, are crossed.
Possible outcomes of first generation offspring: • 1/2 of the offspring are **heterozygous** • 1/4 of the offspring are **homozygous** for the dominant allele *P* • 1/4 of the offspring are **homozygous** for the recessive allele *p*	Possible outcomes of first generation offspring: • all the offspring are **homozygous** for the dominant allele *P* • all the offspring are true breeding for purple flowers	Possible outcomes of first generation offspring: • all the offspring are **homozygous** for the recessive allele *p* • all the offspring are true breeding for white flowers

The left column summarizes the work in Example Problems 2.1 and 2.2. Each time Mendel set up a heterozygous cross, he noted that close to 1/4 of the offspring demonstrated the recessive trait and about 3/4 of the offspring demonstrated the dominant trait. Remember, the fractions that result from Punnett squares only indicate the probability of that characteristic appearing with each cross.

Practice

In people, the ability to roll a tongue is dominant over non-tongue rolling. As you solve the following problems, use *R* to represent the dominant allele for tongue rolling and *r* to represent the recessive allele for non-tongue rolling.

16. Use letters to describe the genotype of each following individual.
    a. a homozygous tongue roller
    b. a heterozygous tongue roller
    c. a homozygous non-tongue roller

17. a. Draw a Punnett square for the cross of a homozygous tongue roller with a homozygous non-tongue roller.
    b. State the likely percentage probability that the offspring will be able to roll their tongues.
    c. State the likely percentage probability that the offspring will not be able to roll their tongues.
    d. State the likely percentage probability that the offspring will be able to roll their tongues but will also carry the recessive non-tongue rolling gene.

Genotype Versus Phenotype

Since dominant traits are expressed and recessive traits are masked, if a dominant allele is present it is easy to determine whether someone possesses at least one dominant allele. If you can roll your tongue, it means that you have a dominant allele for tongue rolling. The physical expression of the alleles that you possess is called the **phenotype**. The phenotype for the tongue-rolling trait would either be *tongue roller* or *non-tongue roller*. An organism's genotype is a description of the alleles that it possesses. The genotype for tongue rolling could be homozygous dominant (*RR*) heterozygous (*Rr*) or homozygous recessive (*rr*). It should be noted that a person with the genotype *RR* and the genotype *Rr* both have the same phenotype since they can both roll their tongues, even though their genotypes are different.

> **phenotype:** the physical and physiological traits of an organism

Practice

Use the following information to answer questions 18 to 20.

Nectarines and peaches are genetic variations of the same fruit. The fuzzy skin of a peach is produced by a dominant allele, *N*, and the smooth skin of a nectarine is produced by a recessive allele, *n*.

18. State whether the skin phenotype of the following individuals is fuzzy or smooth.
    a. *NN*
    b. *Nn*
    c. *nn*
19. State the likely genotype of each example.
    a. a smooth-skinned nectarine
    b. a fuzzy-skinned peach bred from a cross between a peach-producing tree and a nectarine-producing tree
    c. a fuzzy-skinned peach produced from a long line of peach-producing trees

20. a. Draw a Punnett square for a cross between a heterozygous peach and a homozygous nectarine.
    b. Use your answer from question 20.a. to determine the probability of this cross producing the genotypes *NN*, *Nn*, and *nn*.
    c. Use your answer from question 20.a. to determine from this cross the probability of offspring produced with the smooth-skinned nectarine phenotype and the probability of offspring produced with the fuzzy-skinned peach phenotype.
    d. Determine what percentage of the offspring will carry the allele for smooth skin.
    e. Is it possible for a nectarine to be heterozygous for the skin-type trait? Explain.
21. The ability to taste the chemical phenylthiocarbamide (PTC) is dominant over the inability to taste the chemical. Observe the following Punnett square from a cross between a male PTC taster and a female PTC non-taster (*TT* × *tt*).

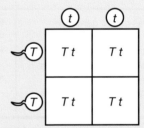

	t	*t*
T	*T t*	*T t*
T	*T t*	*T t*

    a. Describe the PTC tasting genotype of the offspring.
    b. Describe the PTC tasting phenotype of the offspring.
22. In people, curly hair is dominant over straight hair. A homozygous, curly haired man (*CC*) is about to have a child with a homozygous, straight-haired woman (*cc*).

    a. Draw the Punnett square for this cross.
    b. Determine the probability that their child will have curly hair.
    c. Re-examine the photo of the family on pages 76 and 77. Use a Punnett square to suggest an explanation for the child's straight hair.

Other Mechanisms of Inheritance

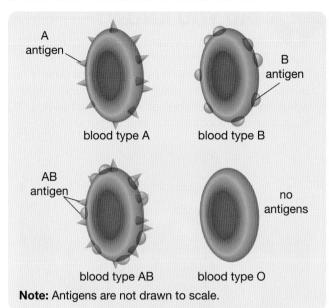

A antigen — blood type A

B antigen — blood type B

AB antigen — blood type AB

no antigens — blood type O

Note: Antigens are not drawn to scale.

Not all traits are controlled by one gene or have only two alleles for a gene. Hair and eye colour do not appear in only two forms because they are controlled by more than one pair of genes. Blood type is an example of a trait with more than two possible alleles. There are three forms or alleles of the blood-type gene represented by the letters *A*, *B*, and *O*. These three alleles can produce four phenotypes. The different forms of *A* and *B* produce a modified surface protein on red blood cells that give the cell its unique phenotype. In this case, the phenotype is observed in terms of the type and presence of antigens on the surface of the blood cell. The *O* allele is a recessive form of the gene that does not produce a modified surface protein and can be masked by the *A* and *B* alleles. To express the *O* blood type, an individual must be homozygous for the *O* allele. Although the *A* and *B* alleles are both dominant over the *O* allele, *A* and *B* are different modifications of the surface and do not mask one another. Since neither state *A* nor *B* is dominant over the other, they are said to exhibit codominance, which is a condition where both allele products are expressed at the same time. This results in the *AB* phenotype.

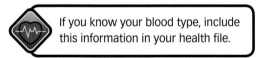

If you know your blood type, include this information in your health file.

Table of Blood Types

Genotype	Phenotype
OO	blood type O
AA or AO	blood type A
BB or BO	blood type B
AB	blood type AB

Boy or Girl? Determining Gender

In Lesson 2.1 you looked at the different chromosomes present in a cell nucleus. If you compare the chromosome pairs of human males and females, you will find that 22 of the 23 pairs look the same. The one major difference between the chromosomes of a male and a female is that females possess two *X* chromosomes, whereas males possess one *X* chromosome and one *Y* chromosome. *X* and *Y* chromosome inheritance determines the gender of an offspring. You can use a Punnett square to illustrate how gender is determined by an offspring's inheritance of the *X* and *Y* sex chromosomes.

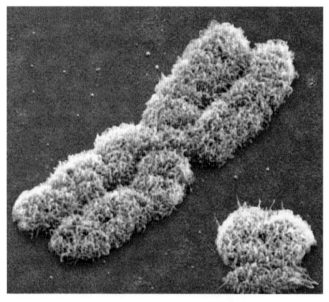

Since the female, or mother, only has *X* chromosomes to give, all her eggs produced during meiosis normally contain a single *X* chromosome. The male, or father, has either an *X* chromosome or a *Y* chromosome to give, so his sperm will normally have either an *X* or a *Y*. When you make a Punnett square, you can see that there is always a 50% percentage probability of the gametes uniting to become a boy and a 50% chance of the gametes combining to become a girl. These percentages are probabilities, like the 50% chance of getting heads when flipping a coin. It does not mean that children will be born boy, girl, boy, girl . . . .

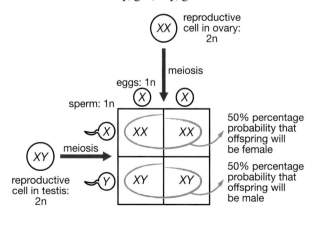

reproductive cell in ovary: 2n

meiosis

eggs: 1n

sperm: 1n

meiosis

XY

reproductive cell in testis: 2n

	X	X
X	XX	XX
Y	XY	XY

50% percentage probability that offspring will be female

50% percentage probability that offspring will be male

Traits Associated with the *X* Chromosome

The *X* and *Y* chromosomes that determine gender also carry other genes that do not determine the sexual characteristics of the individual. Genes like these are said to be responsible for **sex-linked inheritance**. Genes carried on the other 22 pairs of chromosomes are said to be responsible for **autosomal inheritance**.

> **sex-linked inheritance:** traits not directly related to primary or secondary sexual characteristics that are coded by the genes located on the sex chromosomes

> **autosomal inheritance:** traits controlled by genes found on the 22 pairs of autosomal chromosomes

Colour-Blindness

The term *colour-blindness* is used to refer to the inability to perceive differences between some or all colours readily recognized by people with full-colour vision. There are many types of colour-blindness. Some are caused by damage to the eyes or the optic nerves, but most are hereditary. In this chapter, colour-blindness will refer to red-green colour-blindness. People with red-green colour-blindness would be unable to identify the 8 or 5 within the following circles. This is one of the most common types of colour-blindness, and it is caused by sex-linked inheritance.

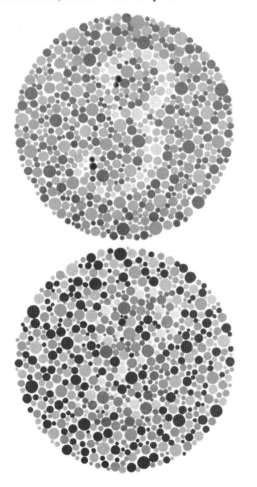

DID YOU KNOW?

Colour-blindness is often assumed to be a disability because persons with colour-blindness are unable to detect colours to the same degree as persons without colour-blindness. However, whether a condition is a disability, an inconvenience, or an ability depends very much upon the specific environment the person is in.

In a hunting or a military environment, people with colour-blindness have an advantage when it comes to seeing objects against confusing backgrounds. In this case, colour-blindness should be referred to as *special counter-camouflage ability*.

Clearly, the context provided by the environment plays a key role in determining whether a condition is also a disability.

A Punnett square can be used to make predictions about sex-linked traits. The traits are represented as uppercase and lowercase letters for dominant and recessive alleles, like they are with autosomal traits. The only difference between autosomal and sex-linked Punnett squares is that the letters used to represent the sex-linked traits for alleles are written as superscripts above the chromosome on which they are carried. Let *N* represent the allele for full-colour vision and let *n* represent a recessive allele that produces the condition of colour-blindness.

Because colour-blindness is an *X* chromosome, sex-linked trait, the allele is not carried on the *Y* chromosome, and the possible genotypes are X^N and X^n. A complete male genotype for a colour-blind man would be represented as X^nY and a man with full-colour vision would be represented as X^NY. A female with full-colour vision who carries the recessive allele for colour-blindness would be written as X^NX^n and a colour-blind female would be written as X^nX^n.

A homozygous woman who has two alleles for full-colour vision has children with a colour-blind man.

a. Describe the genotype of each parent.

b. Build a Punnett square to predict the possible genotypes of their children.

c. Use the Punnett square to explain why the sons have full-colour vision even though their father is colour-blind.

d. Use the Punnett square to explain why the daughters are carriers for the colour-blind allele, even though they have full-colour vision.

Solution

a. The mother's genotype would be $X^N X^N$, and the father's genotype would be $X^n Y$.

b.

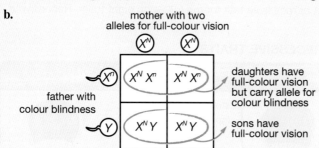

c. The sons are male because they inherited a Y chromosome from their father and an X chromosome from their mother. Since the X chromosome is the location of the allele for colour-blindness, and since the sons inherited this allele from their homozygous dominant mother, the sons have full-colour vision.

d. The daughters are female because they have inherited an X chromosome from their mother and an X chromosome from their father. Since the X chromosome is the location of the allele for colour-blindness, and since the X chromosome from their father contains this allele, each daughter is a carrier of the allele for colour-blindness. However, the daughters are not colour-blind themselves because they inherited an X chromosome for full-colour vision from their mother.

23. **a.** Draw a sex-linked Punnett square for the cross between a man with full colour vision and a woman with full-colour vision who is a female carrier of the recessive colour-blind allele.
    b. Determine the percentage probability of their sons being colour-blind.
    c. Determine the percentage probability that their daughters will be carriers of the recessive colour-blind allele even though the daughters have full-colour vision.

24. **a.** Draw a sex-linked Punnett square for the cross between a colour-blind man and a woman with full-colour vision who is a female carrier of the recessive colour-blind allele.
    b. Determine the percentage probability of their sons being colour-blind.
    c. Determine the percentage probability of their daughters being colour-blind.
    d. Determine the percentage probability that their daughters have full-colour vision but will be carriers of the recessive colour-blind allele.

25. An expectant father who is colour-blind is afraid that his soon-to-be born son will also be colour-blind. Explain to this expectant father why it is best to look at the mother's side of the family for an indication about whether their son will become colour-blind.

26. Determine which gender would be most affected if a trait were found only on a gene from the Y chromosome.

Investigation

Investigating Dominant and Recessive Human Traits

Background Information

Several human physical traits are both distinctive and easily observed. Like tongue rolling, they are caused by the presence of either dominant or recessive alleles inherited from parents.

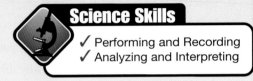

Science Skills

✓ Performing and Recording
✓ Analyzing and Interpreting

Purpose

You will survey the members of your class to obtain data on the presence of dominant and recessive alleles.

Procedure

Survey each person to discover if he or she has a dominant or recessive trait for the following eight traits. Record your findings in a table.

DOMINANT OR RECESSIVE TRAITS

Trait	Dominant Phenotype	Recessive Phenotype
(1) hair type	curly hair (genotype *CC* or *Cc*)	straight hair (genotype *cc*)
(2) hairline	widow's peak (genotype *WW* or *Ww*)	straight hairline (genotype *ww*)
(3) ear lobes	free floating (genotype *EE* or *Ee*)	attached (genotype *ee*)
(4) left-handed or right-handed	right-handed (genotype *RR* or *Rr*)	left-handed (genotype *rr*)
(5) thumb position with hand folding	left thumb over right thumb (genotype *TT* or *Tt*)	right thumb over left thumb (genotype *tt*)
(6) finger length	ring finger longer than index finger (genotype *FF* or *Ff*)	index finger longer than ring finger (genotype *ff*)

| (7) thumb curvature | "hitchhiker's thumb" (genotype *DD* or *Dd*) | | straight thumb (genotype *dd*) | |
| (8) second toe | second toe longer than big toe (genotype *GG* or *Gg*) | | second toe shorter than big toe (genotype *gg*) | |

Analysis

1. Use your recorded class data to draw a bar graph with a dominant bar and a recessive bar for each trait.
2. Observe the number of traits where the dominant phenotype is greater than the recessive phenotype. Identify a reason for the higher frequency of certain traits in the population by using a Punnett square.
3. List your own phenotype for all eight traits.
4. Explain why it is difficult to accurately list your genotype for all eight traits.
5. Describe the phenotype of the individual who has the following genotype based on the letter used for the traits in the "Dominant or Recessive Traits" table: *CC, Ww, EE, rr, Tt, Ff, DD, gg*.
6. Perform the following crosses for the traits studied in the table by preparing a Punnett square for each noted cross. State the predicted genotype ratios and phenotype ratios of the offspring for each cross noted.
   a. An individual homozygous for attached ear lobes has a child with a heterozygous free-floating, ear-lobed person.
   b. *GG* × *gg*
   c. A straight-haired individual has a child with another straight-haired individual.

2.2 Summary

Traits such as hair colour and eye colour passed on from your parents are called inherited traits. Traits learned or gained from the results of experiences, such as languages and injuries, are called acquired traits.

The forms of a gene are called alleles and can be either dominant or recessive. Dominant alleles are expressed or they mask the presence of recessive alleles. The effect of recessive alleles is observed only when an individual possesses two recessive copies of the allele for that particular trait.

Punnett squares are one way to predict the probability of inheriting genetic traits. Letters are used to represent genes in a Punnett square cross—upper-case letters are used to represent dominant alleles and lower-case letters are used to represent recessive alleles. When the two copies of an allele are either both dominant or both recessive, it is called a homozygous condition (e.g., *PP* or *pp*); and when the two genes are a different allele form, it is called heterozygous (e.g., *Pp*).

The expression of genes as observable characteristics is called a phenotype and is determined by the alleles present in an individual's genotype.

Punnett squares can also be used to predict the gender of offspring. Some genes that do not directly relate to sexual characteristics are found on sex chromosomes. These genes are said to be sex-linked rather than autosomal. Colour-blindness is an example of a trait that affects men more often than women.

Knowledge

1. Jim has dark curly hair, brown eyes, and a large scar on his cheek. As a child, he regularly practised the piano and became a gifted pianist. He is a skilled downhill skier and loves all winter sports. From this description, list Jim's genetically inherited traits and the traits that he has acquired.

2. A genotype for the fur-colour trait in mice is abbreviated as *Mm*.

   a. State the dominant allele in the genotype.

   b. State the recessive allele in the genotype.

   c. Is this individual described as homozygous or heterozygous?

   d. If black fur is dominant over white fur in mice, state the phenotype of the mouse with the genotype *Mm*.

3. In cats, the gene that causes the ginger- or orange-fur colour is a sex-linked trait carried on the *X* chromosome. The ginger colour (*G*) is dominant to the black colour (*g*).

   a. Write the genotype for a ginger male cat.

   b. Describe the phenotype of a cat with the genotype X^gY.

   c. Describe the phenotype of a cat with the genotype X^GX^G.

Applying Concepts

4. A family has three girls and is expecting a fourth child. What is the probability that the fourth child will be a boy?

5. Explain the difference between autosomal inheritance and sex-linked inheritance.

6. In garden peas, the yellow-seed colour is an autosomal dominant trait over the green-seed colour.

   a. Choose letters to represent the dominant and recessive alleles for this trait. Write the genotypes for a pea plant that is homozygous for yellow, homozygous for green, and heterozygous for yellow.

   b. Draw a Punnett square for a cross between a homozygous yellow-seeded pea plant and a homozygous green-seeded pea plant. State the predicted genotypes and phenotypes of the offspring.

   c. Draw a Punnett square for a cross between two of the offspring produced in question 6.b. State the predicted genotypes and phenotypes of the offspring.

7. The gene for eye colour in fruit flies is located on the *X* chromosome. The allele for the dominant red-eye colour could be represented by the allele X^R, while the allele for the recessive white-eye colour could be represented by the allele X^r.

   a. Draw a sex-linked Punnett square for a male with red eyes who breeds with a female with white eyes.

   b. Determine the percentage probability that the male offspring will have white eyes.

   c. Determine the percentage probability that the daughters will have white eyes.

   d. Determine the percentage probability that the female offspring are carriers of the recessive white-eyed allele.

Have you ever listened to music at an outdoor concert on a warm summer's evening? If you have, can you remember the particular songs or pieces that were played? Depending upon the type of music and the performers, the musicians sometimes memorize the music. In other cases they use sheet music. On one level, a performer who is reading the sheet music is translating the information from the page into a tune or a song. But lovers of music would argue that there is much more to performing than playing the notes in the right order—a good musician is an artist.

To someone who doesn't read music, the symbols used for notes look like simple shapes on a page in random order. The information on a deoxyribonucleic acid (DNA) molecule might also seem like a random arrangement of chemical units, but to the cells in your body this arrangement is a meaningful set of instructions for making essential products. Just like a huge variety of songs can be written on sheet music from a limited number of musical notes, a huge variety of instructions can be encoded on a DNA molecule from a limited number of chemical units. While music is the product that can be produced by playing the notes on sheet music, proteins are the product that can be produced by translating the code on a DNA molecule. These proteins make life possible by forming structural and regulatory molecules within cells.

Understanding how DNA works is a bit like understanding sheet music. First, you need to understand how the symbols are used to represent the sound that each note makes and the rules used in writing music. Once you understand the language of music, then you can look at how the notes are put together for a particular song and can use an instrument to translate written notes into played notes. Recognizing the symbols used to represent the chemical units of DNA and understanding how the DNA molecule is put together are important skills that allow scientists to read and translate this genetic information into the protein products that make up an organism.

In this lesson you will identify the structure and components of DNA. You will learn how to read and translate elementary sections of DNA code and explain the process of DNA replication. Just as there is more to music than playing notes in the correct order, there is more to a full understanding of DNA than learning how to assemble simple structures. Nevertheless, just as some musical training leads to a greater appreciation of a performing artist's skill, your work with DNA will provide you with a new appreciation of the instructions that made you.

Extracting DNA from Wheat Germ

Purpose

In this investigation you will extract DNA from raw wheat germ.

Materials

- 1 g of raw wheat germ (not toasted)
- liquid detergent
- 95% ethanol (ethyl alcohol) or 70% isopropyl alcohol
- 2 50-mL test tubes with stoppers
- hot tap water (approximately 50–60°C)
- graduated cylinder
- 2 glass stirring rods
- paper towel
- paper clip

Science Skills

✓ Performing and Recording
✓ Analyzing and Interpreting

Procedure

step 1: Add 20 mL of warm tap water to both test tubes.

step 2: Add 1 g of raw wheat germ to only one of the test tubes. Mix continuously for at least 3 min.

step 3: Add 1 mL of liquid detergent to each test tube, and use a glass stirring rod to stir each gently for 5 min, creating as little foam as possible. Vigorous stirring will break up any DNA into smaller pieces, which are more difficult to see.

step 4: Use a sheet of paper towel to remove any foam produced.

step 5: Tilt the test tubes and slowly pour 14 mL of alcohol down the side of each test tube. The alcohol should form a separate layer on top of the test-tube mixture. Do not stir or mix the two layers.

step 6: Let the test tube sit for a few minutes. Extracted DNA will appear as a white filmy substance and should precipitate and clump together at the boundary of the two layers. If you continue to let it sit, the DNA should float to the top of the alcohol or you can use your glass stirring rod or the loop of a partially straightened paper clip to pull the DNA out of the solution.

Analysis

1. Explain why you prepared a test tube with wheat germ and then—following the identical procedure—another test tube without any wheat germ.
2. Compare the amount of DNA in the test tube with the wheat germ to the test tube without the wheat germ.
3. Do you think it would be possible to use a similar procedure to extract DNA from other materials such as split-green peas, strawberries, or chicken livers? Explain why.

Figure A2.13

The Structure of DNA

The overall shape of a DNA molecule has been compared to a twisted ladder or a spiral staircase. Just as the spiral staircase in Figure A2.13 was assembled from individual wedge-shaped steps, the DNA molecule is composed of chemical units called **nucleotides**. Each nucleotide contains a phosphate molecule, a sugar called deoxyribose, and one of four nitrogen-base molecules.

> **nucleotide:** a chemical unit consisting of a phosphate molecule, a deoxyribose sugar molecule, and one of the four nitrogen-base molecules—adenine, cytosine, thymine, or guanine
>
> Two complementary nucleotide chains combine to form DNA.

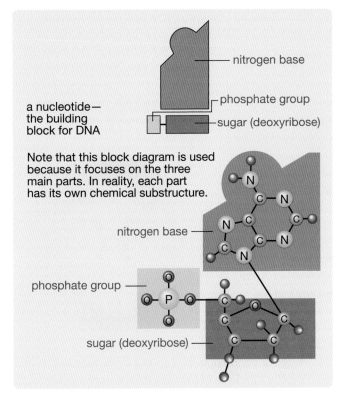

a nucleotide— the building block for DNA

— nitrogen base
— phosphate group
— sugar (deoxyribose)

Note that this block diagram is used because it focuses on the three main parts. In reality, each part has its own chemical substructure.

nitrogen base

phosphate group

sugar (deoxyribose)

The phosphate and sugar parts of the nucleotide attach to each other to form a repeating chain that makes up the "backbone" of a DNA molecule. The nitrogen base part of the nucleotide sticks out from the sides of this chain. The four nitrogen bases are adenine, cytosine, thymine, and guanine.

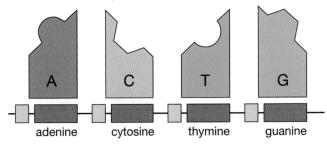

The four types of nitrogen bases in nucleotides join to form a single chain—half of a DNA molecule.

adenine   cytosine   thymine   guanine

These bases are usually abbreviated using the first letter of their name. The long chain of nucleotides can be very long—in this arrangement it makes up half of the DNA molecule. The other half of a DNA molecule is formed from another long chain of nucleotides that attaches to the first strand of nucleotides by hydrogen bonds between the nitrogen bases on opposite strands.

DNA consists of two long chains of nucleotides connected by complementary nitrogen base pairs.

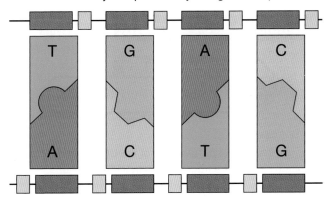

▶ **base pair:** the two nucleotides connected on opposite sides of complementary strands of the DNA molecule

Complementary base pairings for DNA are adenine with thymine and cytosine with guanine.

The four possible bases have a unique chemical structure that allows them to bond only with one other base. When the two bases are bonded together, they are called a **base pair**. Adenine can only bond to thymine and vice versa (A-T or T-A) and cytosine can only bond to guanine and vice versa (C-G or G-C). As a result of the specific bonding between bases, the DNA molecule is comprised of two long chains of nucleotides with bases of one chain paired up with another chain containing complementary bases. For example, if the base pairs on one side of the molecule are ACTGTTA, then the other side of that section of DNA has the complementary base pairs of TGACAAT. The two paired strands form a structure that looks like a twisted ladder, with the base pairs acting like the rungs of the ladder and the sugar and phosphate molecules acting as the ladder's side. The distinctive coiled shape of DNA, which is similar to the appearance of a spiral staircase or a twisted phone cord, is called a double helix.

The double-helix shape of DNA is made as the two interlocking chains of nucleotides are twisted.

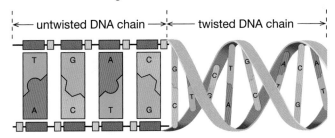

← untwisted DNA chain → ← twisted DNA chain →

Utilizing Technology

Building a DNA Segment

Science Skills

✓ Analyzing and Interpreting

Purpose

You will build a short segment of the DNA strand by matching up the nitrogen bases in the nucleotides.

Procedure

Locate the applet "Building a DNA Molecule" on the Science 30 Textbook CD. Follow the instructions.

Discovering the Structure of the DNA Molecule

The discovery of the three-dimensional structure of the DNA molecule is credited to James Watson and Francis Crick. Their description of DNA's structure was only possible by incorporating the findings of other scientists whose experiments produced unexplained results.

For example, Erwin Chargaff discovered a one-to-one ratio between the bases of adenine and thymine and between the bases of cytosine and guanine. Chargaff could not explain this ratio found in all DNA samples analyzed.

When Rosalind Franklin fired a beam of X-rays at a hair-like thread of DNA, the X-rays changed direction as they encountered the delicate DNA structures. After passing through the DNA, the redirected X-rays created a distinct pattern—coincidentally, the letter X—on photographic film on the other side. Franklin interpreted this photo to mean that the X-rays had encountered a molecule shaped like a helix. She had also discovered that the phosphate part of the molecule was on its outside. Franklin's supervisor Maurice Wilkins, who began the X-ray research, showed her X-ray picture and the results of her work to Watson and Crick without her knowledge or permission. Watson and Crick were able to use Franklin's findings to help assemble a working structure. Franklin died of ovarian cancer in 1958, four years before Watson, Crick, and Wilkins jointly received the Nobel Prize in medicine or physiology for their work on the structure of DNA. The Nobel Prize is awarded only to living scientists.

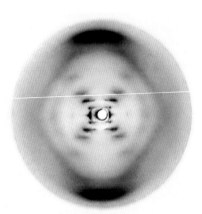

Science Links

In Franklin's work, the X-rays passed through the DNA but changed direction in the process. This left an interesting pattern on photographic film. When you go to a dentist for teeth X-rays, high energy X-rays are used to create a shadow image of your teeth. Denser areas—corresponding to fillings and jewellery—create shadows on the photographic film placed in your mouth. These shadow areas appear white. You'll learn more about X-rays and how they are used in Unit C.

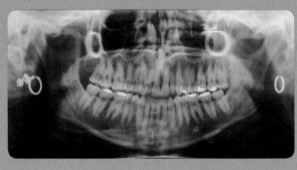

27. The nucleotides are the building blocks of the DNA molecule.
    a. Sketch the nucleotide that has thymine as its nitrogen base, and label the three distinct parts of the nucleotide.
    b. The DNA molecule has been described as a twisted ladder. Add labels to your sketch from question 27.a. to indicate which part(s) of the nucleotide will form the rungs of the twisted ladder and which part(s) will form the long sides.

28. Four types of nucleotides can be identified by the individual nitrogen bases or their abbreviations—adenine (A), cytosine (C), thymine (T), and guanine (G).
    a. Identify the complementary base pairs that form in a DNA molecule.
    b. State the reason why the nucleotides can pair up only in these combinations.

29. Write the base sequence that makes up the complementary strand for the nucleotide sequence of each provided strand.
    a. AAATGTCGCCT   b. TAGTCTA   c. GATTGATTCCGGGCTAA

30. A student correctly copied down a nucleotide sequence but made a mistake when writing the complementary strand below it. Identify the mistake in the complementary strand.

There is an error in the complementary strand.

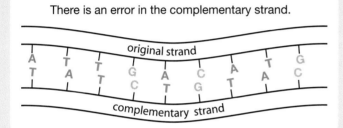

original strand

complementary strand

31. Using what you know about DNA structure, account for the findings of Erwin Chargaff.
32. Describe Rosalind Franklin's contribution to the discovery of the DNA molecule's structure.

Histones—Spools for DNA

A DNA molecule is extremely long. If DNA from the chromosomes in just one human cell was stretched out and placed end to end, it would be more than two metres long. All of that genetic material has to fit into cells that are smaller than the period at the end of this sentence. Since space is very limited when you are a cell, getting long DNA molecules into your tiny nucleus means that the DNA needs to be very thin and compact. The twisted double-helix shape makes DNA more compact than if it were uncoiled and flat. To further compact the molecule, the coiled DNA wraps around protein spools called **histones**.

histones

histone: a protein that acts like a spool for DNA to wind around—it helps to compact and package the DNA in the nucleus

In the next investigation you will have an opportunity to explore the advantages of spooling when it comes to packaging long strings of material.

Investigation

Packaging DNA

Purpose

You will perform a simulation that relates how DNA is packed to fit into the nucleus of a cell, and you will also perform calculations involving DNA length.

Science Skills

✓ Performing and Recording
✓ Analyzing and Interpreting

Materials (for each group of students)

• one spool of sewing thread
• scissors
• tape measure or metre-stick
• one size '000' or '00' empty gelatin capsule per group—available at health food and supplement stores

Procedure

step 1: Imagine that the small gelatin capsule that your group has been given represents an enlarged nucleus.

step 2: Measure and cut a piece of thread 10-m long from your group's spool. This piece of thread will represent the DNA from one set of chromosomes that has been unraveled, attached end to end, and enlarged five times.

step 3: Your objective is to coil and wrap the thread so that it is compact enough to be inserted into the gelatin capsule and the capsule can be closed.

Analysis

1. Was this activity difficult to perform? Were you able to get the thread into the capsule? Could you have put the thread into the capsule without coiling and wrapping it?

2. **a.** Describe how the method you used to get thread into the capsule is similar to the way DNA is compacted and packaged into the nucleus.

   b. Describe how it is different.

3. Explain some methods or tools that would have made an easier job of getting the thread into the capsule.

Calculations

4. The nucleus of an average cell has a radius of about 5 micrometres or 5.0×10^{-3} mm.

   a. Calculate the volume of a spherical nucleus using the formula for the volume of a sphere: $V = \frac{4}{3}\pi r^3$. Express your answer in mm^3.

   b. Measure both the length and radius of your gelatin capsule in millimetres. Use your measurements to calculate the approximate capsule volume by using the formula for the volume of a cylinder: $V = \pi r^2 L$. Your teacher may provide the dimensions of the capsule from the bottle.

   c. Calculate the ratio of how many times larger the capsule you used for the activity is than an actual human cell nucleus. Do this by dividing capsule volume by nucleus volume.

5. It is often stated that within the nucleus of a typical human cell, the total length of all the DNA would be about 2 m if it were stretched out end to end. Use the following information to confirm this statistic:

   • There are two sets of chromosomes in each nucleus.
   • One set of chromosomes has approximately three billion base pairs (3.0×10^9).
   • One base pair is approximately 0.34 nanometres in length (3.4×10^{-10} m).

6. An adult human body has at least 50 trillion cells (50×10^{12}). Use this information and your answer to question 5 to determine the total length of all DNA in a human body if it were stretched out end to end.

7. The distance from the Sun to Earth is 1.5×10^{11} m. This is called one astronomical unit or A.U. Calculate the ratio of approximately how many times longer the total length of DNA in a human body is relative to the distance between Earth and the Sun.

8. Consider your answers to questions 4.a., 6, and 7. Comment on these values in light of your struggles to pack 10 m of thread into a gelatin capsule.

One of the best ways to understand the process of copying a strand of DNA is to try a simple pencil-and-paper version yourself. This is what you will be doing in the next activity.

Try This Activity

Simulating DNA Replication

Purpose
You will use simple materials to simulate the process of DNA replication.

Materials
- blank piece of paper
- pencil

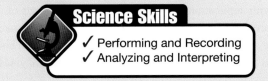

Science Skills

✓ Performing and Recording
✓ Analyzing and Interpreting

Procedure
step 1: Fold the piece of paper as shown on the following illustration.

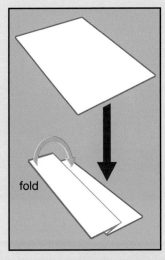

fold

step 2: On the left side of the fold, record a random list of 15 nitrogen bases. Use the initials A, C, T, and G to represent each base.

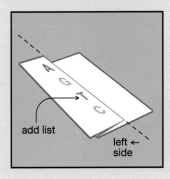

add list

left ← side

step 3: On the right side of the fold, record the complementary strand of base pairs to complete the DNA molecule.

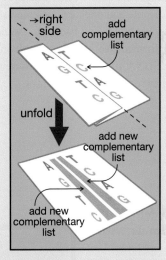

→right side

add complementary list

unfold

add new complementary list

add new complementary list

step 4: Unfold the piece of paper and lay it out flat in front of you so that the two strands of bases are now separated. Add the complementary strand of base pairs to each of the separated strands.

step 5: Save the piece of paper to help you answer the "Analysis" questions.

Analysis
1. You now have three complete sets of DNA to compare. These are the original strand that can be viewed by re-folding the paper, and the two duplicate strands that can be seen by unfolding the paper and pressing it flat. Compare all three strands of DNA.

2. How do you account for the trends you identified in your answer to question 1?

DNA Replication

When a cell needs to multiply to aid in the growth or repair of an organism, its DNA must first be copied. It is important that each of the two daughter cells produced during mitosis receives an exact copy of the parent cell's DNA. The process of making an extra copy of DNA for a new cell is called DNA **replication**. This is illustrated in Figure A2.14.

During replication, the two complementary strands of DNA are untwisted, the bonds between the bases are broken, and the strands separate like a zipper being unzipped. This process is controlled and aided by several protein enzymes.

> **replication:** the process of making two DNA molecules from one original molecule prior to cell division

The bases of free-floating nucleotides in the nucleus attach to the complementary bases of nucleotides exposed along the halves of the unzipped DNA. This process creates two new DNA molecules, each with one strand of the original DNA molecule and one newly created strand.

The newly paired strands coil back into the double-helix shape as they are formed. Working from each one of the separated original DNA strands to make two new molecules makes DNA replication less prone to errors.

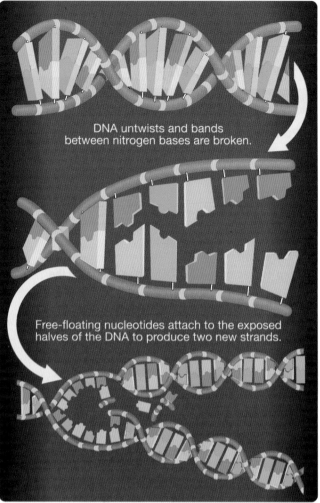

DNA untwists and bands between nitrogen bases are broken.

Free-floating nucleotides attach to the exposed halves of the DNA to produce two new strands.

Figure A2.14

The Genetic Code

You may have been surprised to discover that only four different nucleotides make up DNA. How can such complex instructions—like the gene to make a protein that helps to clot blood—be written by so few letters?

Think of how the many English words you read every day are all made up of different combinations of just 26 letters. The order in which these letters are put together, combined with the spaces and punctuation

between them, can form words, sentences, and instructions meaningful to the reader. Some forms of communication, such as musical notes, Morse code, or the binary language of computers, can be accomplished by using far fewer than 26 letters. Morse code, which is a series of dots and dashes, was used to pass messages along telegraph lines and until recently was used for visual communication between ships.

Binary language is made up of just two digits: 0 and 1. By using these two digits, a computer can be told how to carry out complicated operations. DNA code works on the same principle as other code systems. The arrangement of nucleotides on the DNA molecule creates a meaningful information sequence able to direct complicated processes in your cells.

Using the Genetic Code—Protein Synthesis

DNA, sheet music, and cookbooks are all sets of instructions. The DNA molecule does not actually make proteins, any more than a sheet of music plays a song or a cookbook makes a cake. Products can be made by following the step-by-step instructions of a recipe, a sheet of music, or a gene.

In Lesson 2.1 you learned that genes are regions along a DNA molecule. A gene is like a recipe for making a protein. A person doesn't have to read through each recipe in a cookbook to make a desired recipe. Similarly, the entire DNA doesn't have to be read to make one protein, but only the part where the gene occurs.

Proteins are chain-like molecules composed of smaller units called **amino acids**. Amino acids are like the individual links in the protein chain or the ingredients that get put together to make a recipe. The instructions contained on the gene are written in three-letter groups, with each group acting like a word. Any combination of three of the four DNA nitrogen bases (adenine, cytosine, thymine, or guanine) forms a **DNA triplet code**. Each group of triplet bases stands for an amino acid. For example, the DNA triplet code AAA corresponds to the production of the lysine amino acid. The amino acid produced for each triplet is summarized in "DNA Triplet Codes and Their Corresponding Amino Acids."

Even though there are 64 possible combinations of three DNA bases that can be composed from the four bases found in DNA, only 20 amino acids are used to construct amino acid chains in humans. This allows for some code redundancy. For example, the DNA triplet code AAG and the DNA triplet code AAA both correspond to lysine amino acid. These two DNA triplet codes are like synonyms. One of the DNA triplet codes, ATG, acts like the capital letter at the beginning of a sentence. The ATG triplet code marks the place where a gene is to start being read. There are also three DNA triplet codes, known as TAA, TAG, and TGA, which act like periods at the end of a sentence. They mark the place where the gene finishes being read.

> **amino acid:** one of the 20 possible building blocks of proteins determined by the genetic code of DNA
>
> **DNA triplet code:** three adjacent nitrogen bases found on a gene that codes for the amino acid to be produced, begin, or end the reading of a gene

```
CCAGAAAGGC CGAGGCTCTG CAGCGGGAGG AAGTCCTGCG ATGTCCTGGG
GCAGGGCACA GGGACAGCCC CCCTCCACAG CTCTTCCTGG CCAGCCCTCC
CCAGGAGGTT GCTTCTTCCA GGAGGCTTTT CCCGACCAGC CCAGGGGTCC
GCTCCCAGCT GCTGTGAGTG CTGCACATTC TCTTGAGGAC AGCCCCCTCC
CACTTCTGGT GCCCACTGTG GCCACAGCAA GCACTGGGGC CTGCACTCAG
GCCTCCTGGG GAGCTGCTGA CCCTAGGCAG AGAGATTGCA CATCCCTAAG
CACCCCAGTG TTTGCCAGTG TTTGCCCGTG TTCACCAGTG TTTGCCAGTG
TTTGCTCGCC AGTGTTCGCC ACTTGTCCCT CTGGCTGCAA GAGTGACTGG
GAAGTTGCAG GTCCCTCCAG GACAGTTGGC CGATGACGTG GAGACAGACC
TCCTGGCTCC CTGCAGGACG CGGGGCCCCC CGAGATCCTG GCGGTGCTCA
CACCTCCGTG TTCACCAGTC CAATGGGCAC GGAGCGTGGC TTTATTTGCA
CCTAACGACT TCAGCCTCTG CACCTCCTGG GTTTTCCCTG CTGCAAATTG
TCGTCCCCAA TTTCCGGCCA AGGCCGCGTC GTCGTGCTGC TGTGTAATTT
GTTCTAGATA CCAAGTGTCT GTCGGTTTTA GACATCGCAA ACGTCCTTCA
CGTCCATTCG CTTCTGTGCA GCAAAATCTT TAATTATTTG ATGGCATCAA
CAGTTTTACC TTCTAGTTTA TACTTTCGAA CATTTGTTTG AGAAATCTTT
TGGCTGATAG TGACGTCTTC TAACTTCCCA TTTACTATGT TACATTCAGA
TCAGGAAGAC GCTTGTGTGC GAGACGGGTA TGAGGCCCCC ACACCCCGCC
TGTCCATGGT TCCACCCCTG ACCCCGGACT CCGCTCCCCA GACCTCCTAA
```

DNA Nitrogen Bases

Nitrogen Base	Abbreviation
Adenine	A
Cytosine	C
Guanine	G
Thymine	T

DNA Triplet Codes and Their Corresponding Amino Acids

FIRST BASE		SECOND BASE								THIRD BASE
		T		**C**		**A**		**G**		
T	TTT	Phenylanine	TCT	Serine	TAT	Tyrosine	TGT	Cysteine	**T**	
	TTC	Phenylanine	TCC	Serine	TAC	Tyrosine	TGC	Cysteine	**C**	
	TTA	Leucine	TCA	Serine	TAA	STOP**	TGA	STOP**	**A**	
	TTG	Leucine	TCG	Serine	TAG	STOP**	TGG	Tryptophan	**G**	
C	CTT	Leucine	CCT	Proline	CAT	Histidine	CGT	Arginine	**T**	
	CTC	Leucine	CCC	Proline	CAC	Histidine	CGC	Arginine	**C**	
	CTA	Leucine	CCA	Proline	CAA	Glutamine	CGA	Arginine	**A**	
	CTG	Leucine	CCG	Proline	CAG	Glutamine	CGG	Arginine	**G**	
A	ATT	Isoleucine	ACT	Threonine	AAT	Asparagine	AGT	Serine	**T**	
	ATC	Isoleucine	ACC	Threonine	AAC	Asparagine	AGC	Serine	**C**	
	ATA	Isoleucine	ACA	Threonine	AAA	Lysine	AGA	Arginine	**A**	
	ATG	MET or START*	ACG	Threonine	AAG	Lysine	AGG	Arginine	**G**	
G	GTT	Valine	GCT	Alanine	GAT	Asparate	GGT	Glycine	**T**	
	GTC	Valine	GCC	Alanine	GAC	Asparate	GGC	Glycine	**C**	
	GTA	Valine	GCA	Alanine	GAA	Glutamate	GGA	Glycine	**A**	
	GTG	Valine	GCG	Alanine	GAG	Glutamate	GGG	Glycine	**G**	

* ATG is an initiator triplet code and also codes for the amino acid methionine.
** TAA, TAG, and TGA are terminator triplet codes.

The Versatility of Proteins

Earlier in this unit you learned that proteins are molecules that serve a variety of useful and important bodily functions. Hemoglobin is the oxygen-carrying protein in red blood cells. Like every other protein, hemoglobin is a molecule composed of one or more chains of amino acids. The unique sequence of amino acids within this protein, combined with its particular coiled shape, accounts for the protein's distinct properties.

Proteins have one or more amino acid chains and are coiled into a variety of shapes. The versatility of an amino acid chain means that protein structure can take on a variety of forms to suit different body needs. The way that the chains of amino acids are folded and combined together determines the protein function. In the case of hemoglobin, the amino acids on the outside of the hemoglobin molecule maintain solubility, while special amino acids on the inside of the molecule act to hold the iron compounds that bind to oxygen. Some proteins can even change their shape to perform a task and return to their original shape when the task is finished.

Hemoglobin—A Protein Molecule

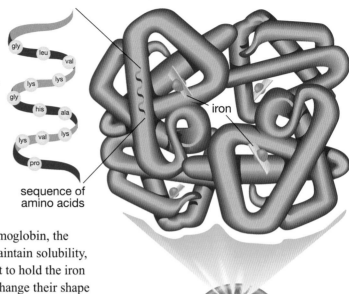

sequence of amino acids

iron

red blood cell

Practice

33. List the amino acid sequence that would be produced from the following base sequence found on a gene segment.
    a. ATAAAGCGACTTCCC
    b. AGAGGGGGTCTAGCC
    c. GTATTAGATTACGTTACA
34. Write a DNA sequence of bases that coded for the production of the following amino acid chains.
    a. Tryptophan-Phenylanine-Tyrosine
    b. Methionine-Glutamate-Aspartate
    c. Glutamate-Methionine-Cysteine

Utilizing Technology

Interpreting the Genetic Code

Science Skills

✓ Performing and Recording

Purpose

To construct a sequence of amino acids, you will decipher the coding along a segment of DNA.

Procedure

Locate the applet called "DNA—The Genetic Material," on the Science 30 Textbook CD. Follow the instructions.

2.3 Summary

Deoxyribonucleic acid, or DNA, is the molecule that contains the coded instructions for creating proteins. Genes are regions along the DNA that code for a specific protein. A nucleotide is a chemical unit made up of a phosphate, a deoxyribose sugar, and a nitrogen base.

There are four nitrogen bases: adenine, thymine, cytosine, and guanine. Adenine only bonds to thymine and cytosine only bonds to guanine (A-T or T-A and C-G or G-C). When one base is bonded with its complementary base, the two bases are called a base pair.

DNA structure is two strands of nucleotides attached by their complementary bases and twisted into a double-helix shape. DNA has to be wound very tightly to fit into the nucleus. The molecule must become very twisted and it gets wound around proteins—called histones—that act like spools. To replicate, DNA pulls apart and complementary free-floating nucleotides attach to the appropriate exposed bases of the strands to create two new molecules, each with half of the original DNA molecule.

Within a gene, the nitrogen bases are read as triplets. Each triplet provides information about the formation of a polypeptide chain of amino acids used to make proteins.

Knowledge

1. Indicate whether each of the following statements is true or false. If a statement is false, explain why.

   a. A DNA triplet code is made up of three amino acids.

   b. A DNA triplet code may code for the same amino acid as another DNA triplet code.

   c. Adenine bases can only bond to cytosine bases.

   d. A double helix is similar in shape to a spiral staircase.

   e. Genes provide the instructions to make proteins.

   f. There are ten different amino acids.

   g. Histone is one of the four base pairs found along the DNA molecule.

   h. Alternating phosphate and deoxyribose sugar make up the backbone of a DNA strand with the base pairs attached in the middle.

   i. During replication, the DNA breaks into small pieces and re-forms as two smaller halves.

   j. A DNA molecule has three strands of nucleotides braided together.

Applying Concepts

2. Use the "DNA Triplet Codes and Their Corresponding Amino Acids" table to determine which of the following DNA sequences would code for the production of valine-alanine-asparagine.

   I. AAAAGAATA

   II. CATCGCACA

   III. GTGGCTAAT

3. Draw a series of diagrams to show how DNA is replicated. Use two colours to distinguish between the original DNA strands and the newly produced DNA strands.

4. Like every other protein, hemoglobin consists of chains of amino acids. The sequence of amino acids in one section of a hemoglobin molecule is Glycine-Leucine-Valine . . . . Determine the corresponding DNA triplet codes that would provide the instructions for building the first three amino acids in this sequence.

5. Complete the following table that compares protein synthesis to making a cake from a recipe.

Making a Cake	Protein Synthesis
• a library of cookbooks	• a karyotype of all the chromosomes for one individual
• a cookbook of recipes	
• a recipe for a particular cake	
• the words of the recipe	
• ingredients that go into the cake	
• the finished cake product	

Rain or shine, people will show their support for a fundraising walkathon. The Great Strides Walk is held annually to support the efforts of the Cystic Fibrosis Foundation. In 2006 this event raised more than $775 000, as thousands of Canadians participated in more than 40 locations.

The Effects of Cystic Fibrosis

mucus blocks air sacs
(alveoli) in the lungs

mucus blocks
pancreatic ducts

stomach

pancreas

pancreatic
duct

Cystic fibrosis is an inherited condition. It affects the cells that produce the juices of mucus, sweat, saliva, and digestion. One of the functions of these secretions is to act as lubricants, so they normally have thin and slippery consistencies. In cystic fibrosis, a defective gene causes these secretions to become thick and sticky. The result is that they can plug up lung and pancreas passageways.

Earlier in Chapter 2 you learned that genes are like recipes or sets of instructions. You also learned that the sequence of bases in the DNA molecule is comparable to the letters in the words of a written recipe. Imagine that you are copying down a set of instructions in a recipe and you don't notice that you made a mistake. How could the mistake affect your finished product? What if a mistake is made during DNA replication and the base sequence of DNA is copied incorrectly? What effect might such a change have in the DNA sequence, its structure, or how it affects the protein product derived from this DNA molecule?

A change in the sequence of bases along DNA is called a **mutation**. When you hear the word *mutation*, you might think of a science fiction story or a horror movie where a dramatic event causes a character to become described as a mutant with a changed appearance or abilities. Most mutations are actually small changes to the DNA sequence that occur naturally, or are due to exposure to high energy radiation or chemicals. An important characteristic of mutations is that the changes to DNA are carried forward in subsequent DNA replications and are inherited by future generations.

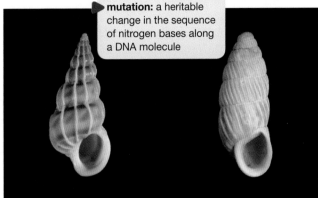

mutation: a heritable change in the sequence of nitrogen bases along a DNA molecule

As you learned in previous science courses, mutations are the source of variation within wildlife populations. This variation leads to adaptations, which are acted upon by natural

Figure A2.15: Mutations are responsible for variations within a species.

selection to drive evolutionary change. Mutations clearly play an enormous role in the study of biological systems.

In this lesson you will learn how mutations in DNA affect the proteins produced. This occasionally results in human diseases that can be inherited by offspring. Using Mendel's theories and Punnett squares, you will predict the probability of offspring inheriting a genetic disease. You will also learn how to read a pedigree chart that traces genetic diseases through families. Mutations that benefit an organism and mutations that result in resistance to bacteria will also be examined in this lesson.

Mechanisms of Mutation

Mutations are like "typos" in a word-processing document. For both recipes and genes, the effect that a copying mistake has on the product depends on where it happened and on what kind of mistake was made. For example, if you made a slight spelling mistake to the word *salt* and instead wrote *saltt* when copying a recipe, it wouldn't change how you carry out the recipe. And it would have little effect on the finished product. The recipe would still work. But if you wrote *25 mL of salt* instead of the original *2.5 mL of salt*, your recipe would most likely be ruined. In most cases, the mutation of DNA has little effect on the products produced from a gene—the mutations occur in chromosome regions that do not include genetic instructions, or the affected gene sequence is still able to function despite the mistake. Cells can usually repair minor DNA mutations that frequently occur in the human body. Mutations to DNA can occasionally cause the gene to stop working or to work differently, as is the case with cystic fibrosis.

How Mutations Affect Genetic Information

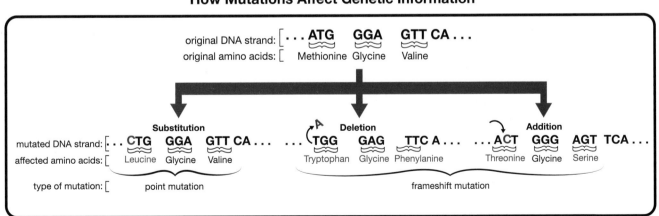

Mutations in DNA can happen when one nucleotide—during replication—accidentally gets substituted for another nucleotide. The chart "How Mutations Affect Genetic Information" illustrates what happens when there is a substitution of one nucleotide—ATGGGAGTT changes to become CTGGGAGTT. The amino acid chain produced from this sequence is now altered, possibly affecting the protein functioning. A nucleotide base substitution is called a **point mutation**, which is similar to a typo where one letter of a word gets changed and often alters the word's meaning. If the phrase "the fox can run" was mistyped as "the box can run," the single letter substitution not only changes the meaning of the phrase but it makes the phrase confusing.

The deletion or addition of a nucleotide can also affect the DNA base sequence resulting in an altered or incomplete amino acid chain. The results tend to be more serious in this case because all of the nucleotides "downstream" of the mutation are affected. In other words, the grouping into sets of three or the framing of all the nucleotides that follow is changed. That is why this is called a **frameshift mutation**. If the phrase "the fox can run" had an extra letter added at the beginning of the phrase but the phrase was still separated into three-letter words, it would read "ath efo xca nru n." The frameshift mutation turns the original phrase into nonsense.

> ▶ **point mutation:** the substitution of one nucleotide base for another during DNA replication
> ▶ **frameshift mutation:** the deletion or addition of a nucleotide during DNA replication
> This change causes the three-letter groupings or frames in DNA to be read in an alternate pattern.

Practice

35. Figure A2.16 shows two DNA strands—the lower strand is a product of replication. A mutation occurs in the middle of a gene sequence. The sequence of bases gets changed from TAT to TAA.

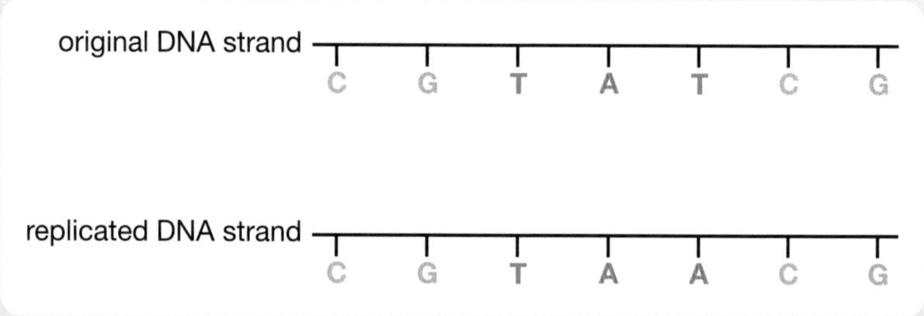

    original DNA strand
    C G T A T C G

    replicated DNA strand
    C G T A A C G

    Figure A2.16

    a. Is this a point mutation or a frameshift mutation?

    b. Use your table "DNA Triplet Codes and Their Corresponding Amino Acids" to identify what amino acid corresponds with the DNA sequence of TAT.

    c. What corresponds with the DNA sequence of TAA?

    d. Explain what effect the change to the DNA sequence has on the production of the amino acid chain.

36. A gene sequence reads GGATTAGAG. A mutation occurs and the sequence now appears as GGGATTAGAG.

    a. Identify the sequence change as either a point mutation or a frameshift mutation.

    b. Use your table of DNA triplet codes to list the amino acid sequence produced by the original DNA strand.

    c. Use your table of DNA triplet codes to list the amino acid sequence produced by the new, mutated strand.

    d. Explain the effect of this sequence change on the production of the amino acid chain.

Passing On Mutations

When you think of a disease you probably think of an illness spread by a disease-causing pathogen, but some illnesses result from the presence of one or several mutated genes. Initially, a mutation can be caused in one individual by an exposure to something in the environment, such as X-rays, ultraviolet radiation, toxic chemicals, or some other factor that causes a change to the nitrogen bases in DNA. The mutations that result often have little effect on the functioning of our bodies. However, in other instances the mutation impairs the function of a gene or the amino acid chain produced, which results in negative consequences for the individual.

If a mutated gene is present in one body cell and that cell is no longer able to fulfill its role, the cell usually dies and other body cells of the same type compensate for the loss of one faulty cell. Recall that there are not only body (somatic) cells but sex cells, such as eggs and sperm. What effect could a mutation have in the genes of a sex cell?

If a mutation is capable of being passed between generations and if that mutation results in illness, then the resulting condition is called a **genetic disease**. Cystic fibrosis is a genetic disease passed on from parents to their children. In this case, chromosome 7 carries the mutated gene that results in the disease.

When the gamete with the mutation combines with the gamete of the other parent to produce offspring, the mutated gene is present in every cell of the newly developing offspring. The presence of this mutated gene in each cell can cause the offspring to develop abnormally, die at an early age, or develop a genetic disease. Recent advances in medications and therapies can allow an individual to live longer with an improved quality of life. In spite of this, genetic diseases like cystic fibrosis are difficult to treat and cure because the illness is caused by a mistake in the genes of every body cell, rather than a foreign invading pathogen.

Having one set of genes from each parent can result in a decreased incidence of genetic disease. In many genetic diseases, symptoms are associated with a mutation. The inheritance of a non-mutated copy of a gene from one parent can often compensate for the mutations present in the gene inherited from the other parent. This is why some individuals carry a mutated gene but do not develop the symptoms of a genetic disease. The non-mutated copy of the gene that they received from their other parent is working properly to produce the necessary protein to keep them healthy. An individual who possesses a disease-causing, mutated copy of a gene but who does not develop the symptoms of that genetic disease is called a **carrier**. When a carrier of a genetic disease has a child, there is an increased chance of the child developing the genetic disease. When doctors and other medical practitioners ask about your family history of certain diseases, they are trying to determine the probability of you developing genetically inherited diseases or conditions.

> **genetic disease:** a disease caused by a mutation of one or more genes that can be inherited by future generations

> **carrier:** an individual who possesses a form of a gene (allele) that results in a disease but does not demonstrate, exhibit, show, or have the symptoms of that disease
>
> However, this individual can pass the disease-causing allele to his or her offspring.

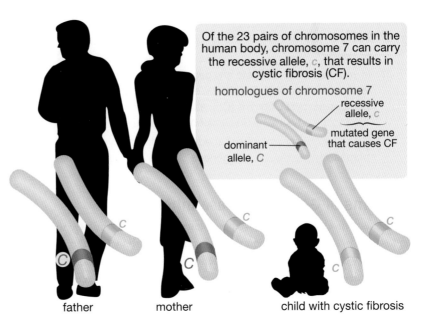

Of the 23 pairs of chromosomes in the human body, chromosome 7 can carry the recessive allele, c, that results in cystic fibrosis (CF).

homologues of chromosome 7

recessive allele, c

mutated gene that causes CF

dominant allele, C

father   mother   child with cystic fibrosis

Each parent carries the dominant allele, C, and the recessive allele, c. A Punnett square can be used to show that the probability of their offspring inheriting two recessive alleles is ¼ or 25%.

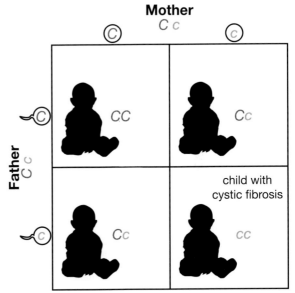

Mother
C c

	C	c
Father C	CC	Cc
c	Cc	cc child with cystic fibrosis

Note that both parents and probably half of the children will be carriers of cystic fibrosis because they have the genotype Cc.

Practice

37. In your health file, indicate any genetic diseases that run in your family. Some examples of genetic diseases include the following: Tay-Sachs disease, sickle cell anemia, phenylketonuria (PKU), Huntington disease, hemophilia, cystic fibrosis (CF), albinism, Marfan syndrome, polycystic kidney disease, Zellweger syndrome, Adrenoleukodystrophy (ALD), achondroplasia, and maple syrup urine disease.

   If you are not sure whether a medical condition in your family is a genetic disease, you can try entering the phrase, "Is _____ a genetic disease?" in your Internet search engine.

Patterns of Genetic Disease Inheritance

Genetic diseases can be caused by alleles that behave similarly to other recessive or dominant alleles, and they can be autosomal or sex-linked in their mechanisms of inheritance. If the genetic disease is caused by a recessive allele, what genotype would a person with the genetic disease possess? A dominant allele?

If the disease is caused by a recessive allele, an individual requires two copies of a mutated recessive allele (homozygous recessive) to develop the disease. If caused by a dominant allele, only one copy of the mutated allele (heterozygous dominant or homozygous dominant) is needed to cause the disease to develop. Check the following table.

TABLE OF GENETIC DISEASES

Genetic Disease	Symptoms	Location of Gene	Mechanism of Inheritance	Prevalence
cystic fibrosis (CF)	People with CF produce thick sticky mucus that builds up in their lungs and digestive tract. This makes it difficult to properly breathe and digest food. People with CF are also prone to lung infections because they cannot easily clear bacteria from their lungs.	chromosome 7	autosomal recessive	Approximately 1 in 2500 children born in Canada has CF and 1 in 25 Canadians is a carrier of the defective allele that causes cystic fibrosis.
Huntington disease (once called Huntington's chorea)	Huntington disease causes brain cells to die in particular regions. This results in a continual reduction in the ability to control movements, remember events, make decisions, and control emotions. Symptoms usually appear between the ages of 30 and 45.	chromosome 4	autosomal dominant	Approximately 1 in 10 000 Canadians has Huntington disease.
hemophilia	There are two forms of this disease: hemophilia A and hemophilia B. Both forms are caused by a mutation of one of the genes that produces blood-clotting proteins. Both of the genes involved with producing the proteins for blood clotting are found on the X chromosome. A defective allele for either of these two X-chromosome genes can result in impaired blood-clotting ability. People with hemophilia bleed for a longer time period than people without this condition. Internal bleeding, or hemorrhaging, is a common risk associated with this dangerous condition.	X chromosome	sex-linked recessive	Hemophilia A affects about 1 in 10 000 people in Canada and hemophilia B affects as few as 1 in 50 000 people. Because of the sex-linked nature of the disease, males develop the disease more than females do.

Use the following information to answer questions 38 to 40. When genetic diseases are controlled by a single pair of alleles, the patterns of inheritance described by Mendel's studies and depicted using Punnett squares can help determine the probability of offspring developing a genetic disease. For each of the following crosses involving the inheritance of genetic diseases, choose letters to represent alleles, draw a Punnett square for each cross, and answer the questions about the cross.

38. A couple discover that they both have a family history of cystic fibrosis. They are thinking of having a child, and they ask for a genetic test to be done. Both the man and the woman discover that they are carriers of the recessive cystic fibrosis allele.

   a. Build a Punnett square to describe this cross.

   b. What is the percentage probability that their child will develop cystic fibrosis?

   c. What is the percentage probability that their child will be a carrier of the cystic fibrosis allele?

   d. What is the percentage probability that their child will not inherit the cystic fibrosis allele?

39. A man is heterozygous for the dominant Huntington allele, and he has a child with a woman who does not have a Huntington allele.

   a. Build a Punnett square to describe this cross.

   b. Write the possible offspring genotypes from this cross.

   c. What is the percentage probability that their child will not develop Huntington disease?

   d. What is the percentage probability that their child will develop Huntington disease?

40. A woman carries one of the defective recessive alleles on her *X* chromosome that causes hemophilia. She has a child with a man who does not possess the hemophilia allele.

   a. Build a Punnett square to describe this cross.

   b. What is the percentage probability that she will have a child with hemophilia?

   c. What percentage of females born from this cross are likely to have hemophilia?

   d. What percentage of males born from this cross are likely to have hemophilia?

41. Use the Internet to gather information about the specific organizations in Canada that raise funds and provide support for persons with the following genetic diseases.

   a. cystic fibrosis

   b. Huntington disease

   c. hemophilia

In each case, find the organization's website. Use the site to determine the organization's mission statement and opportunities for people to volunteer or make donations.

Factors That Increase Mutations

Environmental influences can affect the frequency with which mutations occur naturally. People are exposed to some chemicals and electromagnetic radiation that have been shown to increase the frequency of mutations that occur in the human body. An environmental influence that increases the chance of mutation is called a **mutagen**. A mutation in body cells may cause a mistake in the genes that control cell division, resulting in the uncontrolled division of body cells. The abnormal and uncontrolled division of body cells is called *cancer*, and a mutagen known to cause cancer is called a **carcinogen**. Common carcinogens include many chemical agents found in ionizing electromagnetic radiation—such as ultraviolet rays and X-rays —as well as agents in cigarette smoke and pesticides.

▶ **mutagen:** any agent that causes the likelihood of mutations to increase

▶ **carcinogen:** any agent that causes the likelihood of cancer to increase
   Many carcinogens are also mutagens.

Science Links

What's the definition of a cigarette? One official in the health-care field described a cigarette as ". . . a delivery system for toxic chemicals and carcinogens."

There are more than 4000 chemicals found in cigarette smoke. And 40 or more of them are known carcinogens, including benzene—a petroleum solvent—and formaldehyde, which is used to preserve dead bodies. In Unit B you'll learn more about the chemistry of some of these toxic organic compounds.

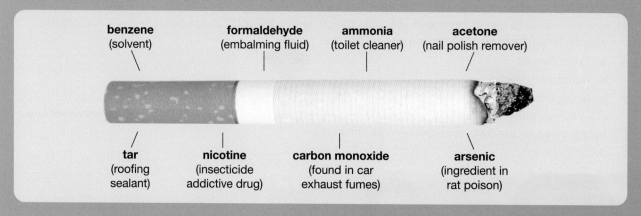

benzene (solvent)

formaldehyde (embalming fluid)

ammonia (toilet cleaner)

acetone (nail polish remover)

tar (roofing sealant)

nicotine (insecticide addictive drug)

carbon monoxide (found in car exhaust fumes)

arsenic (ingredient in rat poison)

Tracing Genetic Disease: Pedigree Charts

If you observe an individual with a dominant trait, such as the ability to roll her tongue, can you tell if that individual is homozygous or heterozygous for the dominant allele? Is it possible to tell if this person carries a recessive allele? Is there a simple way to detect whether his or her genotype is *Rr* or *RR*? Unfortunately, there is no way to do so by only looking at this specific person, but if you can look at the individual's family, sometimes the answer is staring directly at you. For example, if two tongue-rolling individuals have a child without tongue-rolling ability, it indicates that they both carry the recessive gene for tongue rolling. They would both have to be heterozygous (*Rr* × *Rr*) to produce a child who is homozygous recessive (*rr*).

Geneticists use a tool called a **pedigree** to predict the genotype of an individual. A pedigree is like a genetic family tree. You may have previously heard the term in relation to dog breeding or horse breeding. This is because many animal breeders keep detailed lineage records of the animals they breed, and then they use the pedigrees to trace specific traits. A pedigree is a useful technology for tracing genetic diseases.

Genetic pedigrees use a specific set of symbols to identify known genotypes of family members so that unknown genotypes can be predicted. Circles are used to represent females, and squares are used to represent males. On some pedigree charts, a shaded individual indicates a person with the condition being studied. Individuals who are known carriers are sometimes identified by being drawn as half-shaded. A line drawn between two individuals indicates that they have had offspring. Roman numerals and a new row are used to indicate each generation, and individuals are numbered within each generation.

The "Cystic Fibrosis Pedigree" is for a family with members who have the autosomal recessive genetic disease known as cystic fibrosis.

The "Cystic Fibrosis Pedigree" reveals that a first-generation couple had four children—three girls and one boy. The shading indicates that the first generation female (I-1), or the grandmother, had cystic fibrosis. This means that she had to possess two recessive alleles for the condition. The pedigree also shows that none of her four children developed the disease, since the symbols to represent them are not shaded. Because the mother only has the recessive allele to donate, her children all received the allele for cystic fibrosis. Each of her children is a carrier for the disease. Her eldest daughter (II-2) had four children, and the youngest son (III-4) of this daughter developed the disease. In order for this grandson to have the disease, his father (II-1) also has to be a carrier of the recessive allele.

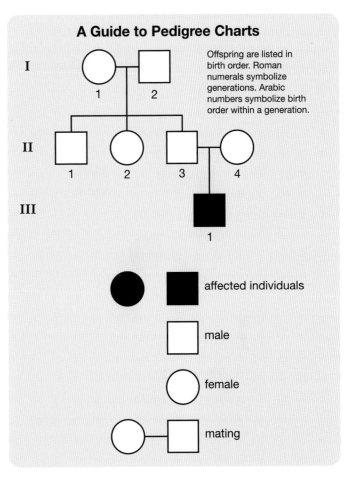

A Guide to Pedigree Charts

Offspring are listed in birth order. Roman numerals symbolize generations. Arabic numbers symbolize birth order within a generation.

affected individuals

male

female

mating

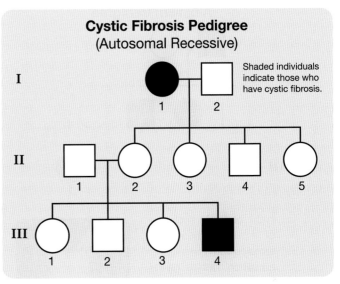

Cystic Fibrosis Pedigree
(Autosomal Recessive)

Shaded individuals indicate those who have cystic fibrosis.

> **pedigree:** a set of standard symbols used as a tool for geneticists to trace a particular trait
>
> It is like a genetic family tree.

The pedigree in Figure A2.17 is for a family with members having the autosomal dominant genetic disease called Huntington disease. A trait that re-appears in each successive generation, as with Huntington disease, is usually caused by a dominant allele.

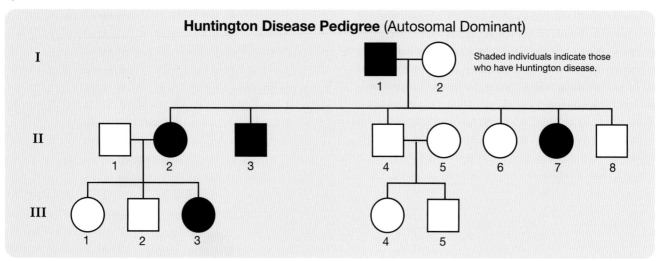

Huntington Disease Pedigree (Autosomal Dominant)

Shaded individuals indicate those who have Huntington disease.

Figure A2.17

Practice

42. Albinism is a genetic condition that causes an absense of pigmentation in skin, hair, and eyes. In humans, the most severe form of albinism—called *oculocutaneous albinism*—is an autosomal recessive genetic disease. Examine the "Albinism Pedigree" and answer questions 42.a. to 42.c.

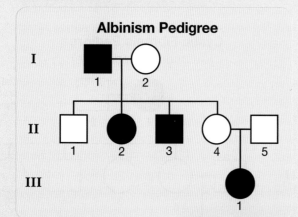

Albinism Pedigree

a. In the pedigree shown, determine the number of females with the albino condition. Determine the number of males with the albino condition.

b. Describe the phenotype of the individual (III-1) and her parents. Account for the differences between phenotypes in these two generations.

Figure A2.18: albino wallaby

c. List the most likely genotypes with respect to the albino trait for the eight people shown in this pedigree.

43. Sonja is not able to roll her tongue but her brother, Mikail, can roll his tongue. When Sonja surveys her family members, she finds that her mother is a tongue roller, and her father is not. Her father's only sister and brother cannot roll their tongues either. The two grandparents on Sonja's father's side are also non-tongue rollers. For the grandparents on the mother's side, the grandfather is a tongue roller, but the grandmother is not. Develop a pedigree for the family described.

44. Phenylketonuria (PKU) is a genetic disease caused by an inability to produce an enzyme. This missing enzyme causes a buildup of an amino acid in the body to toxic levels—this can result in organ damage and impaired intellectual development. Draw a pedigree for the following description of a family's genetic history for the autosomal recessive disease of phenylketonuria.

A male who does not exhibit PKU and a female who does not exhibit PKU have four boys. The two oldest sons are carriers of the recessive allele, and the youngest son develops the genetic disease. The third son neither has the disease nor is he a carrier. The oldest son has two daughters with another PKU carrier—both of these daughters develop the PKU genetic disease.

Beneficial Mutations Affect Populations—Evolution

You have learned that most mutations have little effect on an organism's functioning. In rare cases a mutation can impair a gene's ability to produce a protein, and this results in the disease symptoms. A mutation occasionally creates an advantage for the individual.

A gene produces an enzyme that makes black pigment to colour an insect's exterior.

A mutation to the gene causes the enzyme to produce green pigments instead of black pigments.

The individual insect coloured green blends better with its surroundings, so it is more difficult for predators to locate it. The green-coloured insects have a better chance of survival and, therefore, improved reproductive success.

Over time, more individuals with the mutated gene survive. The gene that codes for green colour is selected by environmental pressures and becomes widespread in the population.

Perhaps the mutation causes a brighter colour of flower to be produced, which makes the flower with the mutation more successful at attracting pollinators.

Or perhaps a mutation in genes controlling its colour provides the individual with improved camouflage to help protect it from predators.

In cases where mutations result in an advantage to the organism's survival, organisms possessing the mutation have a better chance to survive and breed. This means that this new variety is able to generate a greater number of offspring.

Perhaps you may recall from previous science courses that Charles Darwin used the term "survival of the fittest." This refers to the idea that the organisms best able to survive have the opportunity to reproduce and pass along their traits to their offspring. Mutations play a key role in this process of natural selection because they introduce the new alleles selected by the environment as being more favourable. In this way, advantageous traits become more widespread in a population and change a population's overall characteristics.

Resistance in Bacteria

Antibiotics are chemicals that have saved countless lives by killling bacteria that cause infections and illnesses. When antibiotics are used, most of the bacteria die. Recently, the number of infectious bacteria resistant to antibiotics has increased. You have seen how mutations can result in the change or evolution in a species. Can mutations in bacteria be the cause of an increase in resistance to antibiotics?

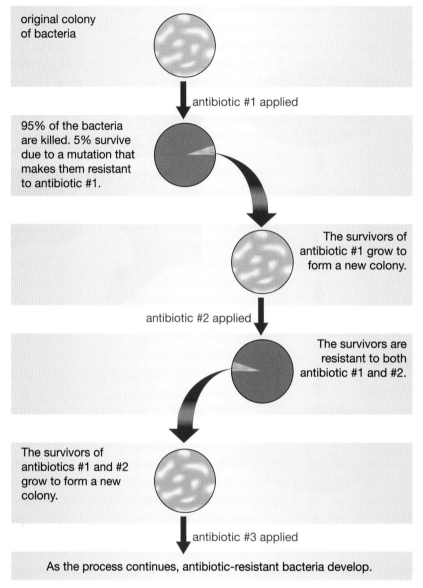

original colony of bacteria

antibiotic #1 applied

95% of the bacteria are killed. 5% survive due to a mutation that makes them resistant to antibiotic #1.

The survivors of antibiotic #1 grow to form a new colony.

antibiotic #2 applied

The survivors are resistant to both antibiotic #1 and #2.

The survivors of antibiotics #1 and #2 grow to form a new colony.

antibiotic #3 applied

As the process continues, antibiotic-resistant bacteria develop.

If some bacteria possess a mutant gene that makes them resistant to antibiotics, they will not be killed. The resistant bacteria not killed by the antibiotic are the only individuals remaining to reproduce. Over time the new population—or strain—of bacteria consists almost entirely of members that possess genes resistant to that antibiotic. Each time a bacterial population is exposed to a new antibiotic, this process of natural selection repeats and only the resistant survive. Many scientists and doctors are becoming worried about the development of bacterial strains that are resistant to antibiotics. For this reason, antibiotics are prescribed less frequently than before, and patients who are prescribed antibiotics are advised to take all their medication even after they have begun to feel better to make certain a large percentage of the bacterial population is killed.

The process of antibiotic products "selecting" resistant bacteria is based not only upon the same principles of selective breeding that you studied earlier in this chapter, but upon the same principles of natural selection that you examined in earlier science courses. The main idea here is that individuals most suitable to a particular environment live to breed and pass on their genes.

Transformation of DNA Fragments

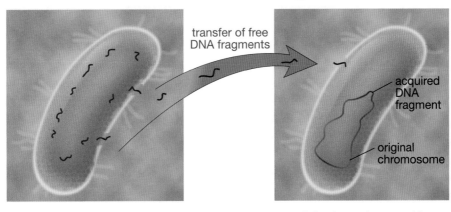

transfer of free DNA fragments

acquired DNA fragment

original chromosome

a dead bacterium

a living bacterium acquiring DNA from environment

As you learned earlier, evolution takes place over long periods of time and involves many generations. Because bacteria reproduce very quickly—as fast as once every 20 minutes—the speed of their evolution can appear to be rapid. The appearance of bacterial superbugs resistant to several kinds of antibiotics has made the scientific community question the exact mechanism for the evolution of this trait. Even though bacteria reproduce asexually, they have methods of exchanging DNA that create more genetic diversity and can result in the development of new traits, such as antibiotic resistance. Some bacteria can acquire foreign DNA from their surrounding environment and incorporate it into their own DNA in a process known as **transformation**.

Transformation of Plasmids

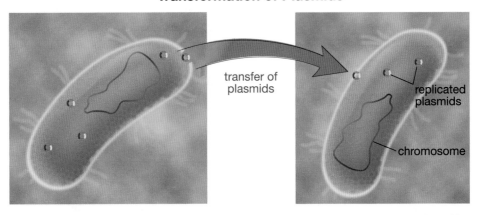

transfer of plasmids

replicated plasmids

chromosome

a living bacterium with plasmids

a bacterium acquiring plasmids

Many bacteria can also possess a small circular piece of DNA molecule, called a **plasmid**, which is separate from the DNA in the bacteria's chromosome. Plasmids are self-replicating and some have the ability to temporarily join to the bacterial DNA. The plasmids may only have a few genes not necessary for the regular functioning or survival of the bacteria, but these genes may influence other traits or lead to advantageous properties for the organism—this may include antibiotic resistance. Bacteria with a plasmid containing genes that provide antibiotic resistance make the bacteria exposed to antibiotics resistant to the drugs. Because plasmids can be transferred quite easily between bacterial cells when they contact one another, a plasmid can be transferred between individuals. This results in the sharing of antibiotic-resistant genes.

▶ **transformation:** the process by which free DNA is incorporated into a bacterial cell

▶ **plasmid:** a self-replicating circular piece of DNA that can be transferred between bacteria

Plasmid transfer allows for the sharing of genes on the plasmids between bacteria.

Mutations are changes in the sequence of DNA that can be inherited by future generations. These changes spontaneously occur and do not usually affect an individual. Mutations occasionally impair gene functioning or result in beneficial advantages. They can occur when nucleotides are substituted by point mutation, while deletions or additions of nucleotides result in frameshift mutation. Mutations that improve an organism's success within a population lead to adaptations selected by the environment. Natural selection is what drives the process of evolution. Resistance to antibiotic drugs has occurred in bacteria as a result of mutation, transformation, plasmid transfer, and natural selection.

A genetic disease is an illness resulting from faulty or impaired genes that can be inherited by future generations. The presence of two alleles for each gene in the human genetic make-up helps prevent the development of many genetic diseases. Individuals can be carriers of alleles that cause genetic diseases.

The pattern of inheritance for genetic diseases is the same studied previously for autosomal, sex-linked, dominant, or recessive alleles. Punnett squares can be used to predict the probability of offspring inheriting a genetic disease when the disease is caused by a single gene. Pedigrees can be used to trace the inheritance of a genetic disease in a family.

2.4 Questions

Knowledge

1. Define *mutation*.

2. Explain why a doctor may ask questions about the history of certain traits or illnesses in your family.

3. Explain how people who are carriers of the allele for cystic fibrosis do not have disease symptoms.

4. Red-green colour-blindness is a sex-linked trait. The pedigree in "Inheritance of Red-Green Colour-Blindness" shows the occurrence of the colour-blindness disorder for one family. Study the diagram and answer the following questions.

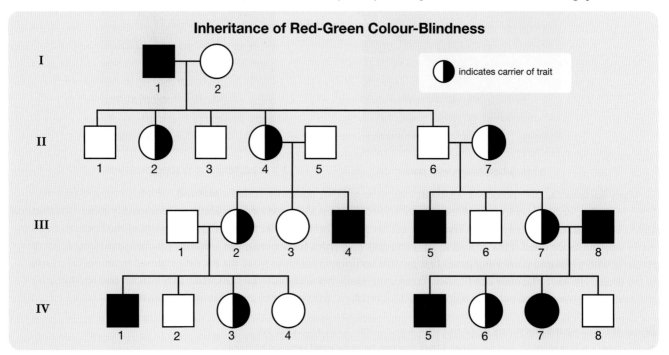

Inheritance of Red-Green Colour-Blindness

indicates carrier of trait

a. In the first generation, is the father or the mother colour-blind?

b. Determine the number of males and the number of females produced by the father and mother of the first generation.

c. State the number of individuals in this pedigree who are carriers for colour-blindness.

d. How many males and how many females have colour-blindness in this pedigree?

5. List several mutagens that can increase the frequency of mutations.

Applying Concepts

6. List two similarities and two differences between Punnett squares and pedigree charts.

7. Despite new therapies and other medical breakthroughs, cystic fibrosis and other genetic diseases can still cause death before adulthood. Identify the significance of the symptoms of Huntington disease not usually appearing until later in a person's life.

8. Explain why your reproductive organs are usually shielded with lead sheets during an X-ray.

Use the following information to answer question 9.

Sickle cell anemia is an autosomal recessive genetic disease. The impaired gene causes red blood cells to be produced that are shrunken sickle shapes rather than the normal round disc shapes. These deformed red blood cells can block narrow blood vessels. People with two recessive sickle cell alleles become very ill and often die while they are very young. Most people who suffer from sickle cell anemia or carry the recessive gene tend to be from areas affected by malaria, which is a deadly disease carried by mosquitoes. The malaria parasite reproduces inside a person's red blood cells. People who are carriers of one of the mutated sickle cell anemia alleles actually have an advantage over non-carriers—they are resistant to malaria. This accounts for the fact that this allele is more common in people from areas affected by malaria.

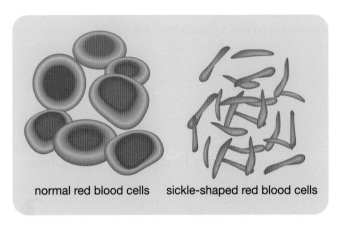

normal red blood cells   sickle-shaped red blood cells

Figure A2.19: The distribution of malaria prior to mosquito control programs is highlighted on this map by green shading.

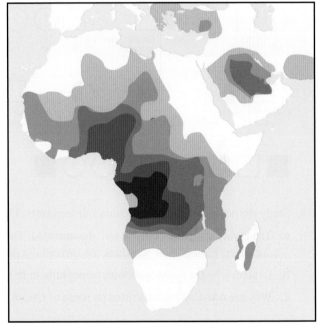

Figure A2.20: This map shows the distribution of sickle cell disease. The darker the shade of purple, the greater the percentage of people who have the disease.

9. a. Use a Punnett square to show the probable results of the cross between two people who are heterozygous for the sickle cell trait (*Ss* × *Ss*) and are malaria resistant.

   b. List the possible genotypes of the children from this couple.

   c. State the probability of a child of this couple being resistant to malaria.

   d. State the probability of a child of this couple developing sickle cell anemia.

   e. Explain why the sickle cell anemia allele is more common in areas infected with malaria.

Use the following information to answer question 10.

Queen Victoria of England was a carrier of the sex-linked genetic disease called hemophilia. Victoria had many children, but only one of them developed hemophilia. Several of her children married into other European royal families and passed on Victoria's hemophilia allele. The most famous case of hemophilia was Victoria's great-grandson Alexei, the heir to the Russian throne. The controversial historical figure Rasputin gained influence with the Russian royal family by claiming to be able to heal Alexis' hemophilia.

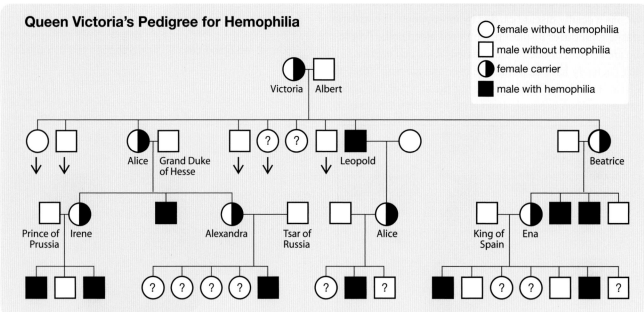

10. Study the pedigree of Queen Victoria's descendants. Then answer questions 10.a. to 10.c.

   a. The royal family's ancestry is well documented. There is no history of hemophilia in any of Queen Victoria's ancestors. Explain how you think the hemophilia defect appeared in her genes.

   b. Explain why the individuals with hemophilia in this pedigree are all males.

   c. Why are question marks written on some of Queen Victoria's female descendants?

In 2000, the remains of an unidentified Canadian soldier who died during the First World War (1914–1918) were moved from their burial place near Vimy Ridge in France to a special tomb in front of Ottawa's National War Museum. This symbolic "Tomb of The Unknown Soldier" was created to honour the thousands of Canadians who have died in battle and, in particular, those who died without being identified or found.

Methods used by militaries to identify their dead have changed with advances in technology. You may be familiar with the term *dog tag*, which refers to an identification number engraved on a small metal plate that soldiers wear around their necks. Metal dog tags were first used in World War I because, unlike human bodies, they could withstand the force from some bomb blasts and gunfire. Identification tags can be collected after a battle and used to trace which soldiers were killed in an attack. However, as you can imagine, there are many variables in using identification tags as a way to identify troops—tags may fall off, become buried in debris, and be taken by other people at a battle site.

Until recently, an external examination of the body was the most efficient identification method available. The Canadian military has started using DNA obtained by taking a blood or saliva sample from new recruits as a way to store soldiers' biological information for use in identification. Every cell of a person's body contains DNA. When the DNA is extracted and processed it forms a pattern unique to each individual, so examining a person's DNA can be an accurate way of identification. Using libraries of DNA patterns can be a reliable way of keeping track of military personnel, making the possibility of another "Unknown Soldier" a thing of the past.

Advances in the understanding of genetics and the use of genetic technologies have created a scientific revolution. Genetic technologies are being used to identify, treat, and prevent hereditary diseases; to develop new medicines; to solve crimes; to identify individuals such as unknown soldiers; and even to re-design organisms. Although the science of molecular genetics is just over 50 years old, these uses have already made significant impacts on society. Some people worry about the safety and ethics of using these technologies. In this lesson you will learn about and research some genetic technologies. From several perspectives you will be asked to look at issues created with the use of genetic technology. You will also explore the potential ethical implications of using these technologies by performing a risk-benefit analysis of a genetic technology and making a decision about the extent of its use.

DNA Fingerprinting

Analyzing DNA has become a useful and popular tool in forensic investigations. Using DNA testing to solve a crime or to prove a person's innocence has been the subject of many books, popular television shows, and movies. This technology works because of the uniqueness of each person's DNA. In order to identify a person, strands of DNA are isolated from that person's cells and cut into smaller fragments. Then these DNA fragments are separated as they move through a special gel placed within an electric field. As DNA fragments are pulled through the gel by the charged ends of the field, a pattern of bands form. The DNA pattern that appears on the gel for a tested individual is as unique as the swirling patterns of an individual's fingerprints. That's why this process has been called DNA profiling or **DNA fingerprinting**. Identical twins or triplets have the same DNA fingerprints. A DNA fingerprint can be analyzed and compared to DNA collected on a battlefield or at a crime scene, matching evidence to soldiers' remains or to suspects. Similar processes are also used to determine whether people are genetic relatives or to carry out wildlife forensics.

The uniqueness of a DNA fingerprint and the information gained from a person's DNA can be stored in a computerized database. In most countries, only criminals have their DNA profiles stored in computerized DNA databanks. Some people would like to see everyone's DNA stored in a DNA bank. A more complete databank of DNA could be very useful, since a computer can quickly search the stored information. As a result, police would have a better chance of matching evidence from a crime scene that contains DNA—cells, tissue, hair, and saliva—to individuals in the database.

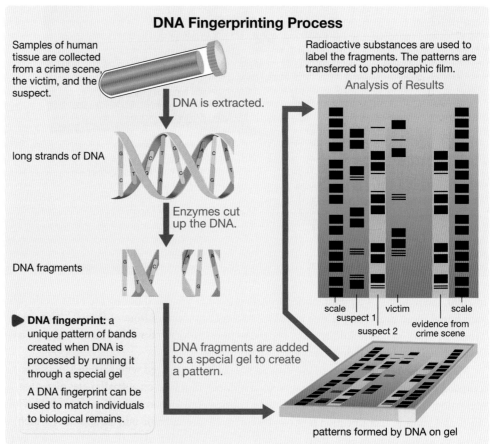

DNA Fingerprinting Process

Samples of human tissue are collected from a crime scene, the victim, and the suspect.

DNA is extracted.

long strands of DNA

Enzymes cut up the DNA.

DNA fragments

▶ **DNA fingerprint:** a unique pattern of bands created when DNA is processed by running it through a special gel

A DNA fingerprint can be used to match individuals to biological remains.

DNA fragments are added to a special gel to create a pattern.

Radioactive substances are used to label the fragments. The patterns are transferred to photographic film.

Analysis of Results

scale   suspect 1   victim   scale
suspect 2   evidence from crime scene

patterns formed by DNA on gel

Practice

45. Health benefits provided by employers and health-insurance companies help pay an employee's wages when the employee becomes ill. Explain how a genetic test could be used against a prospective employee or someone applying for health insurance.

46. Genetic information—including the identification of genes that make it more likely to develop certain diseases—can be revealed about an unborn baby by performing an amniocentesis. Describe one risk and one benefit related to the use of genetic test results from an unborn baby.

47. DNA for testing can be collected from a small amount of blood, hair, saliva, and other body fluids. Do you think authorities have the right to collect samples and perform DNA profiling on an individual without this person's permission? Do you think that an individual has the right to refuse to provide a DNA sample for authorities? Once a DNA profile or a genetic screen has been performed, is it possible to keep the results private? Explain your answers.

Transgenics

The mice in Figure A2.21 are glowing because some of the genes they possess have been altered to produce a unique protein with the ability to glow when exposed to ultraviolet light. Jellyfish produce a protein that enables them to glow in certain light, and scientists have isolated this jellyfish gene and then used a modified virus to insert it into the DNA of a mouse embryo. When the mouse embryo develops, each cell has the instructions to make the luminescent jellyfish protein to create a mouse with the ability to glow.

The process of intentionally altering the genetic traits of an organism is called genetic modification. As you learned earlier, genetic modification can be done through traditional selective breeding within a species by cross-breeding between closely related species. However, it is much faster to transfer the isolated genes from one species into another species in a process called **transgenics**. People often use the terms **genetic engineering** and transgenics interchangeably, but genetic engineering is a more general term, which includes technology that is hundreds of years old. The result of transgenics is called a **genetically modified organism** or **GMO**.

Imagine having the ability to combine the traits from one organism with the traits of another organism. This technology is used to create new foods, medicines, or materials with the potential to increase crop yields, improve health, cure diseases, and produce new products. Many modifications to organisms are being made by genetic engineering, including crop plants containing genes from other organisms that naturally produce their own pesticides. Another modification is bacteria containing a human gene capable of producing insulin required by diabetics.

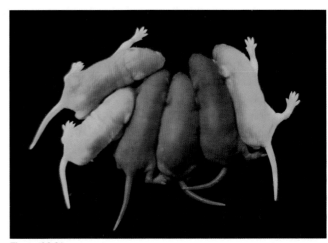

Figure A2.21

> **transgenics:** a type of genetic modification in which the gene or genes from one species are transferred and spliced into the DNA of another species

> **genetic engineering:** the modification of genetic material through the actions of people, including selective breeding and modern techniques outside the normal reproductive process of organisms

> **genetically modified organism (GMO):** an organism whose genetic material has been deliberately altered through transgenics

Scientists are also using this technology to develop pigs with human genes that produce the necessary antigens to make pig organs more compatible with humans and, therefore, more useful for organ transplants. Some researchers are developing goats with genes associated with the silk a spider produces so that goat milk has strands of very strong spider silk for making rope.

The ability to alter organisms with transgenics has an almost limitless number of possible applications. Many industries and companies are interested in this technology, and there is a huge potential to produce both useful and novel inventions that can be sold to make a profit. For example, if the glowing jellyfish gene is combined with an evergreen tree, the inventors could sell glowing Christmas trees that don't need strings of lights.

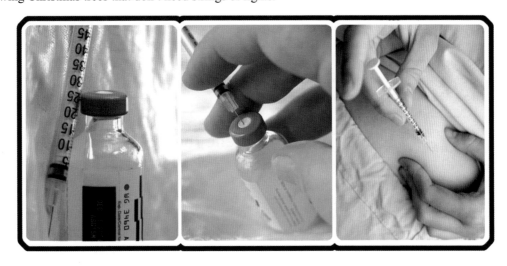

Opinions on genetic technologies come from many perspectives. From an ethical perspective, some people may question creating genetically modified organisms because they have concerns about harming living organisms. Other people are in favour of transgenics from an economic perspective because the products of this technology have proven to be valuable.

Opposition to the use of this technology has also come from a scientific perspective because some people fear that genetically modified organisms can produce unexpected effects on ecosystems if they are released accidentally. For example, there is a concern that herbicide-tolerant canola may cross-pollinate with related weeds to produce weeds that are herbicide-tolerant. One type of corn has been genetically modified to produce a pesticide. A scientific study has indicated that this corn unfortunately caused the death of monarch butterfly caterpillars.

Many people are opposed to transgenics because they are afraid that some scientists may use genetic engineering to create monstrous creatures like the chimera. The chimera is a mythical beast made from the parts of several different animals. These genetically modified organisms could endure lives of suffering because of genetic experiments. Even more fearful is the possibility that these transgenic organisms could become dangerous either by accident or on purpose. For example, disease-causing organisms could be engineered to become more infectious and deadly by combining the traits of two or more pathogens and then used as a weapon. Genetically modified disease-causing organisms designed to infect people and make them sick or kill them are called **bioweapons**.

People who have concerns or fears about transgenics often refer to works of science fiction where the use of technology goes horribly wrong. Examples include *Frankenstein* and *Jurassic Park*. Foods that have been genetically modified are sometimes even called "Frankenfoods" by people fearful of this technology.

▶ **bioweapons:** genetically modified disease-causing organisms designed to infect people and either make them sick or kill them

Practice

48. At the time this textbook was written, Canada did not require manufacturers to indicate ingredients on their food labels that originate from genetically modified organisms. European Union countries do require such labels. Genetically modified (GM) foods are almost impossible to distinguish from non-genetically modified foods because they usually look the same. Herbicide-resistant GM versions of corn, canola, flax, soybeans, sugarbeets, and wheat are grown in Canada. You have most likely eaten some of these genetically modified foods. Do you think food manufacturers in Canada should be required to indicate genetically modified foods in their products? Explain your answer.

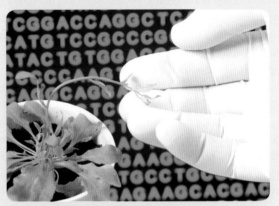

49. A research facility has produced a mouse that does not produce hair and does not initiate an immune response that would reject the ear grafted on its back. The ear grown on a mouse could be used to replace an ear that a person has lost due to an accident. Transgenics could be used to insert human genes into mice, pigs, or other animals to make them even more suited to growing organs that would not be rejected when transplanted into humans. From an ethical perspective, do you think transgenics should be used to create animals with organs compatible for transplanting into humans? Explain your answer.

Applying Transgenics—Medicines and Gene Therapy

Scientists have begun using transgenics to produce medicines instead of having to chemically manufacture medicines or have them collected and extracted from plant or animal parts. Extraction from animal parts is a lengthy process that requires a large input of animal tissue to yield relatively little product. The extraction process requires the use of many noxious chemicals, and the insulin extracted from animals can trigger allergic reactions in some patients.

Producing Insulin Through Transgenics

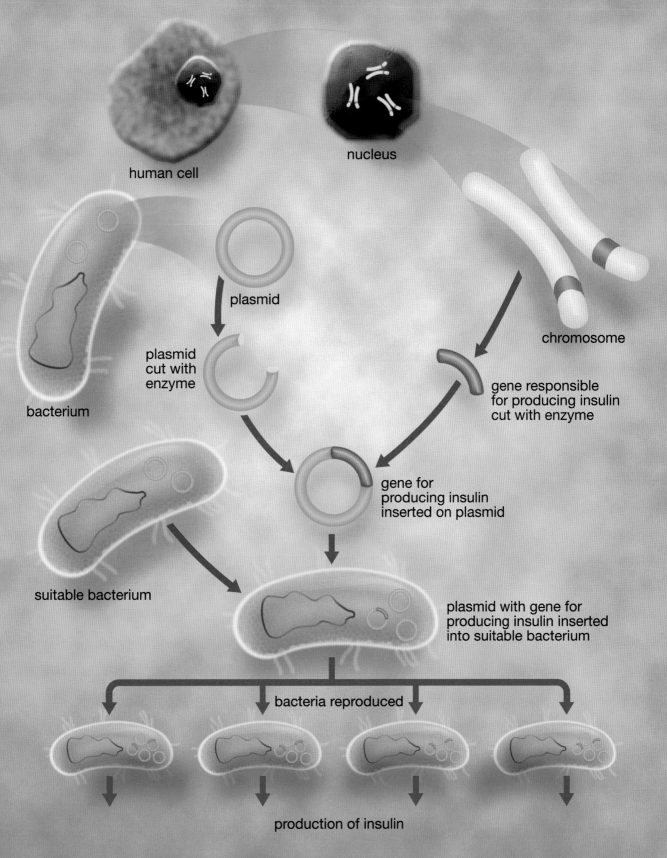

human cell

nucleus

chromosome

bacterium

plasmid

plasmid cut with enzyme

gene responsible for producing insulin cut with enzyme

gene for producing insulin inserted on plasmid

suitable bacterium

plasmid with gene for producing insulin inserted into suitable bacterium

bacteria reproduced

production of insulin

Gene Therapy for Cystic Fibrosis

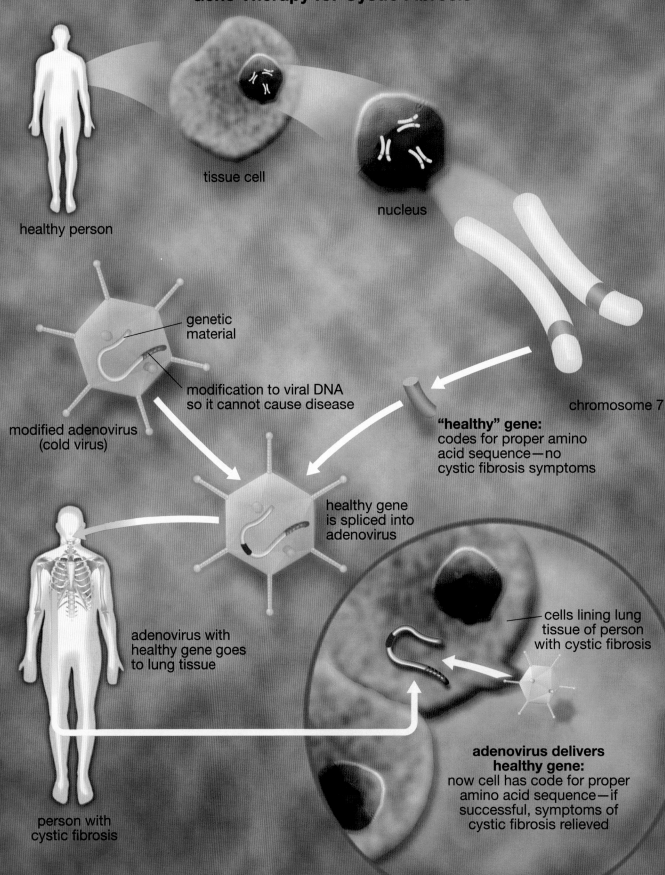

tissue cell

nucleus

healthy person

genetic material

modification to viral DNA so it cannot cause disease

modified adenovirus (cold virus)

chromosome 7

"healthy" gene: codes for proper amino acid sequence—no cystic fibrosis symptoms

healthy gene is spliced into adenovirus

adenovirus with healthy gene goes to lung tissue

cells lining lung tissue of person with cystic fibrosis

person with cystic fibrosis

adenovirus delivers healthy gene: now cell has code for proper amino acid sequence—if successful, symptoms of cystic fibrosis relieved

Scientists can now isolate the gene in a healthy human that produces a substance lacking in other people, such as the gene that produces insulin. Enzymes are used to cut a sample of the healthy individual's DNA into pieces. The segment of DNA with the needed gene is isolated, and the gene is inserted or spliced into a plasmid removed from bacteria. DNA containing the genes from two or more organisms—such as combined plasmid with inserted human DNA—is called **recombinant DNA**. The recombinant plasmid is put into a bacterium and huge amounts of this new bacterium are grown. This creates a strain of bacteria that produce insulin. The insulin can be collected and given to people who have diabetes.

> **recombinant DNA:** DNA containing the genes spliced from two or more organisms
>
> **gene therapy:** the technique of using a vector, such as a virus, to repair or replace defective genes in the treatment and possible cure of genetic diseases

Genetic diseases are difficult to cure because they are caused by a defective copy or copies of an allele present in every cell of a person's body. Some people with genetic diseases can be treated by being given a product that their bodies cannot produce on its own. For example, people with hemophilia cannot produce a type of blood-clotting protein, so they have to receive several injections of clotting proteins per week. Scientists are working on ways to repair or replace non-functioning genes so that genetic diseases can be treated more effectively or even cured. Using genes instead of drugs to treat or cure a disease is called **gene therapy**.

Gene therapy works by identifying and isolating a desired gene from one individual and using it to replace a non-functional gene in another individual. In order for the isolated therapeutic gene to be effective, it must get spliced into the DNA of the person with the non-functional gene. A gene cannot be directly inserted into a person's cells, so one way to insert the therapeutic gene into cells that need to produce the missing protein is to use a vector, such as a virus. Scientists have taken advantage of the way that viruses deliver their genes when they infect cells. The disease-causing genes of the virus are removed and the therapeutic gene is spliced into viral DNA. Patients are infected with many of the altered viruses. Each virus injects the recombinant DNA—containing the therapeutic gene—into a patient's cell to allow the cell to produce the missing or defective protein.

"Bubble Baby" Cured Using Gene Therapy

Figure A2.22 shows a small girl named Salsabil, who had a mutation to the one gene that is responsible for producing an essential enzyme called adenosine deaminase, or ADA. Salsabil did not have a trace of the ADA enzyme in her body because the mutated gene was defective. Since ADA is responsible for producing T-cells and B-cells, Salsabil had virtually no immune system and had to live the first seven months of her life in a plastic bubble to protect her from pathogens. This is why this illness—severe combined immunodeficiency or SCID—is often called "bubble baby syndrome" in the media.

Children with SCID used to be treated with injections of the ADA enzyme every two days or they received a transplant of healthy bone marrow from a compatible donor. If neither treatment was possible, the only alternative was for the children to live their lives in artificial, germ-free environments.

Figure A2.22: Dr. Shimon Slavin holds a healthy Salsabil prior to her second birthday.

In Salsabil's case a team of doctors and medical researchers, led by Dr. Shimon Slavin, were able to use gene therapy. A sample of Salsabil's bone marrow cells were extracted and mixed with a genetically engineered virus containing a healthy copy of the defective gene. The virus injected the human gene directly into the nucleus of the bone marrow cells. Before the healthy bone marrow cells were transfused back into Salsabil, the medical team subjected her to a mild form of chemotherapy to suppress her defective bone marrow cells. When the healthy cells were introduced to Salsabil's body, they had not been subjected to the chemotherapy and had an advantage—they began to take over and grow rapidly. Within months, Salsabil had T-cells and B-cells working together to produce antibodies. A year later, Salsabil returned to her family. She was effectively cured of SCID.

50. Describe some concerns that arise from using viruses to carry and insert therapeutic genes into patients.

51. The use of gene therapy is currently focused on treating and curing genetic diseases. As more genes become identified and studied and this technology becomes more advanced and accessible, some people who can afford this technology might seek to use it to alter genes that control traits—such as height, intelligence, or athletic ability—other than those causing disease. People might use this genetic technique to insert desirable genes either into themselves or into embryos before they begin to develop. Describe some risks associated with using gene therapy techniques for goals other than treating and curing diseases.

52. Insulin can now be produced by genetically engineered bacteria. Before these bacteria were approved, insulin could only be obtained through extractions from the pancreases of pigs or other livestock. List some benefits of using genetically engineered bacteria instead of animal glands.

53. Choose one of the following problems to design an experimental procedure to investigate a characteristic of a genetically modified organism. In your experimental design, list the steps you would take to carry out your experiment. State the manipulated variable, responding variable, and at least three controlled variables.

    a. A genetic engineering company has produced a genetically modified variety of onions. The company isolated the protein that makes our eyes water when onions are cut, and people who work for the company believe that they can make the gene that produces the protein non-functional. This genetically modified (GM) onion will not make people's eyes tear when they cut the onion. Some researchers are worried that removing this gene will affect the taste of the new GM variety. Design an experiment to determine whether the onion's flavour has been affected by removing the eye-watering gene.

    b. Genetic engineers have isolated a gene from a cold-water fish called a flounder. This gene produces a protein that acts like antifreeze—it prevents the fish from freezing in the icy waters where it lives. Researchers have inserted the gene responsible for producing the antifreeze protein into a tomato plant's genetic instructions to make a new variety of tomatoes more resistant to frost.

    If the new variety of tomatoes proves to be effective and popular, then fewer tomatoes will spoil during shipping. Design an experiment to determine whether the new tomato variety is more resistant to frost than non-modified varieties.

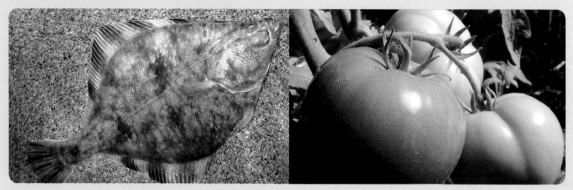

    c. Agricultural scientists have used the genetic modification technology of gene splicing to insert a gene into a canola plant that makes the canola more resistant to strong chemical herbicides. A crop of GM canola can then be sprayed with a strong chemical herbicide to kill competing weeds and leave the canola crop unaffected. With no competition from weeds, the GM canola should grow more easily and produce a greater yield of canola oil than a non-engineered crop. Design an experiment to determine whether the herbicide-resistant canola crop produces a greater yield than a non-modified crop.

Genetic Techniques Used in Molecular Biology

The transfer of DNA fragments between bacteria species is at the heart of much current work in molecular biology. As shown in Figure A2.23, the data collection for this research involves specialized equipment and carefully developed techniques. In the next activity you can learn more about how this research is conducted.

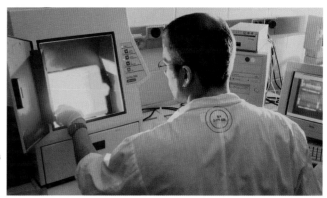

Figure A2.23: A researcher collects data using a fluorescent dye to determine the quantity of specific proteins from a DNA sample.

Investigation

Risk-Benefit Analysis—Genetically Modified Foods

Science Skills

✓ Initiating and Planning
✓ Performing and Recording
✓ Analyzing and Interpreting
✓ Communication and Teamwork

Purpose

You will use information presented in this chapter and from the Internet to gather data regarding the risks and benefits of genetically modified foods. You will develop a position on this issue and then defend this position in light of information presented by other students.

Identify Alternatives/Perspectives

1. To what extent should genetically modified (GM) foods be developed and used? Begin to brainstorm alternative solutions to this question. One approach is to consider the question from as many points of view as possible. Think of several different groups or individuals who have a particular view or interest on the use of genetically modified foods. Create a table with "Stakeholder" at the top of one column and "Point of View/Perspective" at the top of the other column. Complete the table by listing at least three stakeholders and their viewpoints.

Research the Issue

2. Conduct research to collect and assess information for all the perspectives of stakeholders you have identified. Assemble the relevant information as points on a page. People use a variety of terms when referring to genetically modified foods. For a more effective Internet search, you should perform several searches using the many variations on terms in your search engine: *genetically modified foods*; *GM foods*; *genetically engineered foods*; *GE foods*; *biotech foods*; *biotechnology*; *genetically modified organisms*; *GMO*; and other examples.

Analyze the Issue

3. **a.** Analyze the results of your research by concisely organizing your findings in a second table, with "Risks" at the top of one column and "Benefits" at the top of the other.

   b. Review the risks and benefits. How would each stakeholder react to the entries? Record the reactions of three of your stakeholders to the data on your Risk/Benefit table.

Take a Stand and Defend Your Position

4. To what extent should genetically modified (GM) foods be used? What is your position? Take a clear position on this issue by writing a few concise paragraphs. Your position should be supported by the body of research and should indicate that you have considered the question from more than one viewpoint.

Evaluation

5. It is very helpful at this stage to share your findings with other students. How do their points of view differ from yours? Are the arguments made to support these views consistent with the information that you researched? Did other students find additional information that was unknown to you? How has your position changed since you started? If you had to make this decision again, what would you have done differently?

   Write a few concise paragraphs to evaluate your position and the process you used to develop this point of view. Your response should indicate that you have considered the positions of other students and that these alternative viewpoints have been addressed.

Each person's DNA is unique, and the technology of DNA fingerprinting can be used for identification purposes.

People can genetically alter the genetic traits of an organism. This genetic modification can be done using selective breeding within a species or a closely related species. When genetic modification is done by inserting a gene or genes from one species into another species, it is called transgenics. Transgenics can be used to produce genetically modified organisms, or GMOs, used for new kinds of foods, medicines, or materials.

Some people oppose the production of genetically modified organisms. Concern about the development of genetically engineered organisms tends to focus on issues regarding possible dangerous or as yet unknown effects on people or the ecology. Some people feel that it is cruel to make experimental organisms, or they disagree with changing organisms at all. Others fear that genetic engineering technology will be used to make bioweapons. Opposition can also be based on moral or religious reasons.

Transgenics is accomplished by making recombinant DNA, which is a combination of genes from two or more species spliced together.

Recombinant plasmids are used in bacteria to produce large amounts of needed medical enzymes such as insulin.

Repairing defective genes by inserting a non-defective copy into a person's DNA is called gene therapy. Therapeutic genes are inserted with the help of virus vectors that have had their disease-causing genes removed. The viruses deliver the therapeutic gene to cells in patients.

2.5 Questions

Knowledge

1. Match the following terms with the example that best describes each term.

   - transgenics
   - genetic modification
   - DNA fingerprinting
   - recombinant DNA
   - gene therapy

   a. A farmer uses a plastic bag to collect pollen from his fastest-growing corn plants and then sprinkles some pollen on the corn silk of his most disease-resistant corn plants. He collects the seeds produced from this cross-pollination and grows his next crop from these seeds.

   b. Enzymes are used to cut up DNA left at a crime scene, and then the DNA is run through a gel. The distinctive pattern of bands produced is used to compare with the patterns of suspects in the crime.

   c. A modified virus is used to deliver a non-defective version of the gene that causes cystic fibrosis in body cells.

   d. A researcher uses enzymes to cut some human DNA into smaller pieces and then uses different enzymes to splice the DNA into a bacterial plasmid. The new DNA is a combination of bacterial DNA and human DNA.

   e. A gene from the bacterium *Bacillus thuringiensis* (Bt) produces a protein with insecticidal properties. The bacterial gene is isolated and spliced into the DNA of a cotton plant. When the cotton plant is grown, it produces the bacterial insecticide.

2. List some potential advantages of genetically modified plant crops.

3. Describe one possible risk of applying transgenics to produce a new type of organism.

4. Explain why virus vectors need to be used in gene therapy.

Applying Concepts

5. A sample of biological material was left at a crime scene. The DNA from this sample was isolated and a DNA fingerprint was created. The three crime suspects all volunteered to let their DNA be taken, and a DNA fingerprint was created for each person. Compare the unique banding pattern produced for each suspect to identify the suspect who was at the crime scene. This information can be seen in "DNA Fingerprint Patterns."

6. Explain why a person who receives gene therapy will not pass on to her offspring the repaired gene that has been inserted into her cells by a virus.

7. The gene that produces a blood-clotting factor that some people who have hemophilia lack has been isolated. Explain the steps used to develop a strain of genetically engineered bacteria that produce large amounts of this factor to treat people with hemophilia.

8. Most of the citizens of Iceland have volunteered to have their genetic information collected and compiled in an electronic database. The genetic make-up of Iceland's population has changed little since the Vikings colonized the island in the ninth century. This history makes it easier for researchers to identify gene mutations that may be associated with diseases. Describe one risk and one benefit of a nation possessing a gene bank for its citizens.

DNA Fingerprint Patterns

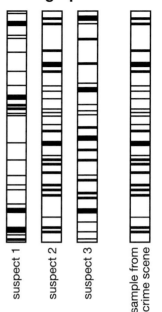

suspect 1 suspect 2 suspect 3 sample from crime scene

Chapter 2 Summary

In this chapter you have examined the structure and function of DNA and have applied your understanding of the mechanisms of DNA inheritance to predict the probability of offspring inheriting traits caused by a single gene. You have also seen how mutations can affect the functioning of DNA and how certain diseases can arise from inherited mutations rather than from environmental factors. You used tools, such as a Punnett square and a pedigree chart, to predict and trace the inheritance of traits in individuals within a family. In Lesson 2.5 you examined the use of genetic technologies and looked at the ethical implications related to their use. Throughout the chapter you learned about the contribution of Mendel and other scientists to the field of genetics.

In future units of Science 30, you will learn more about factors that increase the likelihood of mutation. These factors include chemical substances used in the production of commonly used materials—or substances considered to be pollutants—and some forms of radiation within the electromagnetic spectrum.

Summarize Your Learning

In this chapter you learned a number of new biological terms, processes, and theories. It will be much easier for you to recall and apply the information you have learned if you organize it into patterns.

Since the patterns have to be meaningful to you, there are some options about how you can create this summary. Each of the following options is described in "Summarize Your Learning Activities" in the Reference section. Choose one of these options to create a summary of the key concepts and important terms in Chapter 2.

Option 1: Draw a concept map or a web diagram.	Option 2: Create a point-form summary.	Option 3: Write a story using key terms and concepts.	Option 4: Create a colourful poster.	Option 5: Build a model.	Option 6: Write a script for a skit (a mock news report).

Knowledge

1. Describe the differences among the terms *chromosome*, *DNA*, and *gene*.

2. How many chromosomes are found in a human autosomal cell?

3. Compare the processes of mitosis and meiosis.

4. What are the differences between acquired and inherited characteristics?

5. A pea plant with green pea pods is crossed with a pea plant with yellow pea pods. Both plants come from lines of pea plants that have only produced one colour of pod. All offspring from this cross develop green pea pods.

    a. Determine whether the green colour for pea pods is dominant or recessive.

    b. Using letters to represent alleles, write the most likely genotypes for the two parent plants and the genotype of the offspring.

6. Distinguish between the terms *genotype* and *phenotype*.

7. For each of the following DNA nucleotide sequences, write the sequence for the complementary strand and for the chain of amino acids that code for this strand.

    a. ATATACCAGCCGATA

    b. GCATGGTTCATAAGG

    c. CGTATGCCAGTTTAT

    d. GGTTTATGCATTTCT

8. For each of the following amino acid chains, write all the corresponding DNA sequences that could code for that chain.

    a. Methionine-Threonine-Glutamine

    b. Arginine-Lysine-Tryptophan

    c. Serine-Proline-Aspartate

    d. Leucine-Cysteine-Valine

9. Describe the importance of proteins.

10. Compare and contrast a point mutation and a frameshift mutation.

11. List the steps used to create recombinant DNA.

Applying Concepts

12. Draw a series of diagrams to compare and contrast mitosis and meiosis. For each step, use one pair of chromosomes and include labels to describe the process.

13. A rare recessive allele causes a lack of fur pigment in tigers to produce the distinctive "white tiger" phenotype. These animals have sometimes been incorporated into the extravagant stage shows of Las Vegas magicians.

    a. Explain why entertainers who use the white tigers in their shows only want their white tigers to breed with other white tigers or the offspring of white tigers.

    b. State possible problems with the selective inbreeding of closely related white tigers.

14. A dog breeder owns a dog that has just given birth to a litter of puppies. Both the father and the mother were selected from long lines of well-known and recorded pedigrees. One of the puppies has a red fur colouring that the breeder has never seen in any of the puppy's ancestors.

    a. Explain the likely cause of this new trait.

    b. Describe how you can determine if the new colour trait is dominant or recessive. Use Punnett squares to illustrate your answer.

    c. Explain the steps you would take to develop a breed of dogs with this particular trait.

15. The use of antibacterial soaps has become popular. Describe how bacteria can develop a resistance to antibacterial soaps. Include the role of bacterial plasmids in your answer.

16. Draw a series of images that illustrate the process of gene therapy on a patient who has the autosomal recessive disease of cystic fibrosis.

17. A breeder of Labrador retrievers is told that black fur is dominant over yellow fur. The breeder crosses a black Lab with a yellow Lab. When the puppies are born, some are black, some are yellow, and some are chocolate in colour. Evaluate the following statements regarding this Labrador cross. State whether you agree or disagree with each one. For those statements you disagree with, explain why.

   a. The gene for coat colour in Labrador retrievers must be controlled by more than one gene or have more than two possible alleles.

   b. All the puppies have homozygous genotypes for their coat colour.

   c. The female must have bred with both a black Labrador male and a chocolate Labrador male to produce three kinds of coats in her puppies.

   d. A pedigree of coat colours is helpful to determine the genotype of the parents and offspring.

18. The allele that produces hairy ears in humans is found on the *Y* chromosome.

   a. State which gender is affected by the presence of a gene on the *Y* chromosome.

   b. Explain why a Y-linked gene cannot be recessive or dominant.

   c. State the probability of a male with hairy ears passing this trait onto his son.

   d. State the probability of a male with hairy ears passing this trait onto his daughter.

   e. Can a person be a carrier for this trait? Explain your answer.

19. Elliptocytosis is a genetic disorder affecting a protein that influences the cell membrane structure in red blood cells. Red blood cells with the altered protein have an elliptical, or oval, shape when compared to red blood cells containing the unaltered protein.

   The pedigree in Figure A2.24 shows how elliptocytosis is inherited within one family.

   a. Based on the evidence shown in this pedigree, determine which pattern of inheritance—sex-linked, autosomal recessive, or autosomal dominant—is exhibited by elliptocytosis. Explain how evidence in the pedigree supports your answer.

   b. Predict the possible genotypes and phenotypes of offspring in generation V.

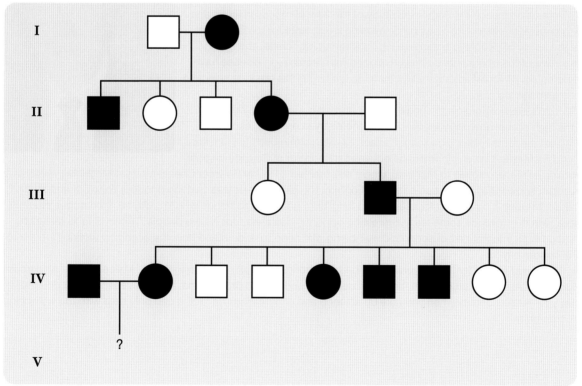

Figure A2.24

Unit A Conclusion

A key theme in Unit A has been the idea of keeping healthy. This unit has examined how your health can be affected by both lifestyle choices and the genes that you inherit. In the first part of the unit you examined how the circulatory and immune systems work together to keep you healthy. You studied the major components of these two systems and considered factors that can affect how they function. A better understanding of these two body systems will help you make healthy choices. In the second chapter of Unit A you looked at the major principles of genetics, and you used these concepts to explain how some traits and diseases can appear more often in some families.

Throughout the unit you investigated and evaluated technologies used to explore, maintain, repair, and assist our bodies. Genetic discoveries and—in particular—the use of genetic technologies can be controversial, and you evaluated their use and made decisions about the extent they should or could be used.

The theme of maintaining health will still be relevant in upcoming units as you study the health effects of radiation and of chemicals released into the environment.

Career Profile

Research Scientist—Pulmonary Medicine

Malcolm King's father was the first person on his reserve to graduate from university. His example made Malcolm seriously consider following in his dad's footsteps to become a high school teacher. Malcolm took that dream down a different path; and today, he teaches pulmonary medicine at the University of Alberta in Edmonton.

Malcolm is not only a professor, but a prominent research scientist. His main area of interest is mucus rheology—the study of the flow of mucus in lungs and other organs. His research focuses on developing treatments for diseases that affect the ability of people to breathe, such as asthma, bronchitis, and cystic fibrosis. Two of the treatments he has developed for chronic lung disease have been patented. Malcolm admits that the patents are two of his greatest scientific accomplishments so far.

Malcolm's passion for science began as a young man. He recalls, "Mr. E.R.S. Hall, my high school chemistry teacher, made chemistry interesting, especially [the] lab experiments." After high school, at age 17, Malcolm moved to Hamilton to attend McMaster University, where he obtained a Bachelor of Science degree in chemistry. He then moved to Montreal, where he obtained a PhD in Polymer Chemistry from McGill University in 1973.

Malcolm knows that school can be tough. For him, the hardest part was "setting priorities for work and study." But he got through it by staying focused on his long-term goals. As someone who knows, he encourages students to "stick with it—there are some really interesting opportunities ahead for Native people." According to Malcolm, "education is an integral part of economic well-being. We need to understand how the economy works if we are to control our destiny."

As the project leader for the University of Alberta's Aboriginal Health Training Initiative, Malcolm aims at increasing the number of Aboriginal students in medicine, dentistry, and related professions. He believes that "you don't have to give up your Native identity when you take up science and engineering. "In fact, it can only help with the well-being of your community."

Unit A Review Questions

1. Match each of the following definitions relating to heart structures to its correct term.

   - pulmonary artery
   - vena cava
   - pulmonary vein
   - ventricle
   - septum
   - atrium
   - heart valve
   - aorta

   a. one of the heart's upper chambers that receives blood returning to the heart

   b. one of the heart's lower chambers that pumps blood from the heart

   c. a thick wall of muscle that divides the left and right sides of the heart

   d. a thin flap of tissue inside the heart that regulates the direction of blood flow within the heart by preventing the backflow of blood

   e. the large vein that collects oxygen-poor and carbon dioxide-rich blood from the upper (superior) body and lower (inferior) body

   f. the vessel that carries blood away from the heart and toward the lungs

   g. the vessel through which oxygen-rich blood flows toward the heart

   h. the body's largest artery

2. Record the following table in your notebook. Leave enough room for your responses. Sketch a cross section of the three main types of blood vessels to indicate the relative differences in size and structure between these three types of vessels. Below each sketch, indicate the role of that vessel in the circulatory system.

Artery	Vein	Capillary
Sketch	Sketch	Sketch
Role	Role	Role

3. Match each blood component listed on the left with its correct function.

   - red blood cell
   - white blood cell
   - platelet
   - sample of plasma

   a. a cell that defends the body against disease

   b. a yellowish liquid like the broth of a soup made up mostly of water with substances dissolved or floating in it

   c. a blood cell that contains hemoglobin and transports oxygen from the lungs to the body's cells

   d. a very tiny cell fragment that helps seal skin cuts by initiating clot formation

4. State similarities and differences between the following three disorders of the circulatory system—angina, a heart attack, and a stroke.

5. The different types of white blood cells each have a specific role that can be compared to the role of people and objects associated with a hockey game. Complete the following table by matching each type of white blood cell to a person or object from a hockey game.

a. macrophage
b. memory B- and T-cells
c. B-cells
d. helper T-cells
e. suppressor T-cells
f. antigen

Person or Object and Role	Type of White Blood Cell
Coach—co-ordinates and directs team's moves and analyzes other team's plays	
Offensive players—try to keep opposing team's players and puck on opposition side	
Coach's playbook—keeps records of strategies used to win games	
Referee—calls an end to game	
Jersey—makes a distinction between players	
Defensive players—respond to opposing players who have broken through their defensive line	

6. Match each term relating to the structure of genetic material with its corresponding definition.

- DNA base triplet
- chromosome
- gene
- karyotype
- amino acid
- protein
- gamete
- DNA

a. all chromosomes from one nucleus matched into their respective pairs and arranged from the largest pair to the smallest pair

b. a sex cell, such as a sperm or an egg, produced during meiosis

c. a molecule that forms a twisted-ladder shape

d. a segment of a DNA molecule that carries information resulting in the production of a specific protein

e. one of 20 possible building blocks used to form proteins as determined by the sequence of bases along a DNA molecule

f. the condensed form of all DNA visible when cells are viewed with a microscope

g. a molecule made from a chain of amino acids that serves a variety of functions in the body including transport, communication, and regulation

h. three adjacent nitrogen bases found along a DNA molecule that code for an amino acid to be produced or begin or end the reading of a gene

7. *Drosophila melanogaster* is a commonly studied species of fruit fly having normal-sized wings. *Drosophila* is dominant over a fruit fly having much smaller wings, called vestigial wings. Use the symbol W to represent the allele for normal-sized wings and the symbol w to represent the allele for vestigial wings.

a. Write the possible genotypes for a fruit fly with wings of a normal size.

b. Write the genotype for a fruit fly with vestigial wings.

c. Write the possible genotype of the gametes for a fruit fly that is heterozygous for the wing-size trait.

d. State the phenotype of a fruit fly with the *ww* genotype.

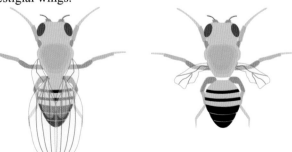

8. Describe how the listed components of DNA combine to form a DNA molecule.

> deoxyribose sugars
> phosphate groups
> four nitrogen bases

9. Identify the key characteristics in the following genetic diseases.

   a. an autosomal dominant disease

   b. an autosomal recessive disease

   c. a sex-linked disease

10. List the basic steps involved in producing and using a DNA fingerprint to positively identify biological evidence left at a crime scene.

Use the following information to answer question 11.

A baby will occasionally be born with a hole in the septum between the right and left ventricles. This causes the flow of blood through the heart to be disrupted. Septal defects result in a large amount of blood bypassing the lungs as it leaks through the septum. This impairs the efficient delivery of oxygenated blood to the body. A small hole in a baby's septum usually closes up on its own, but larger holes require surgery to be sealed. Babies born with this defect are often referred to as *blue babies* because they have a bluish tinge to their skin.

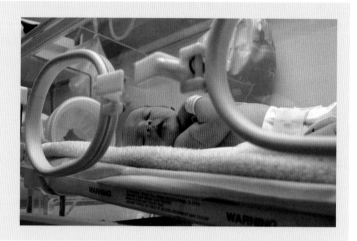

11. Explain why the skin of a baby with a septal defect might seem bluer than the usual pinkish-red coloured skin of a newborn baby.

Use the following information to help you answer question 12.

Blood types are determined by the presence of antigens on the surface of a red blood cell. One type of antigen is called the Rhesus factor or Rh factor. The production of the Rh antigen is determined by a single gene with two different alleles. The Rh positive (or Rh^+) allele produces the antigen and the Rh negative (or Rh^-) allele does not produce the antigen. The Rh^+ allele is dominant over the Rh^- allele.

12. a. Draw a Punnett square for a cross between a male with the genotype Rh^+/Rh^- and a female with the genotype Rh^-/Rh^-.

   b. State the percentage probability—as a percentage or a ratio—that the offspring will have the *Rh* positive blood type.

   c. State the percentage probability that the offspring will have the *Rh* negative blood type.

   d. State the percentage probability that the offspring will have the *Rh* positive blood type but carry the *Rh* negative blood type allele.

   e. Individuals with the *Rh* negative phenotype produce an immune response to the presence of blood cells possessing the *Rh* antigen. Describe the action of the immune system if someone with the *Rh* negative phenotype is given a transfusion of blood containing cells that are *Rh* positive.

13. A patient has a blood sample taken. Describe the possible symptoms a patient will likely experience given each of the following blood test results.

Blood Test Results	Possible Symptoms
a low red blood cell count	
a high white blood cell count	
a very low T-cell count	
a low platelet count	

14. Scientists are using genetic engineering to develop pigs that incorporate human genes. The pigs can then produce human antigens. The purpose of this technology is to make organs from the genetically engineered pigs usable for transplantation into humans.

   a. Explain, in general terms, how the process of genetic engineering can be used to place human genes into pigs.

   b. List one risk and one benefit of using genetic engineering to produce these modified pigs.

15. Cyclosporin is a drug that suppresses the immune system. It is given to recipients of organ transplants. Cyclosporin acts to reduce the number of white blood cells—particularly the killer T-cells—thereby reducing the number of white blood cells able to attack the transplanted organ. In many cases, recipients have to take immune-suppressant drugs for the rest of their lives to avoid rejecting the new organ.

   a. Identify a negative effect that might result from taking an immune-suppressant drug like cyclosporin.

   b. Explain why a person who receives an organ transplant from an identical twin would have much less of a chance of having the organ rejected.

16. A karyotype of an individual is completed by using samples of the individual's blood. State what a karyotype distinguishes, and explain its uses.

17. A gardener crossed a white-flowered tulip with a red-flowered tulip. He then collected the seeds from the offspring of this cross and later planted them. The offspring from this cross all grew red flowers.

   a. Identify which of the two colours is dominant.

   b. State the genotype for offspring of the cross of two parents.

   c. When Carter, a gardener allowed the second-generation tulips to self-fertilize, he found that the seeds produced both red tulip and white tulip plants. When Carter counted and compared the differently coloured plants, he found that there were about three red tulips for every single white tulip. Explain the proportion of each colour observed in the most recent generation of plants.

18. Examine the three different point mutations that have occurred in copies of the same DNA sequence. Identify the mutation with the greatest effect on the amino acid chain produced relative to the original strand.

   Original DNA sequence: AGGGCGCCGTTATAT

   Mutated DNA sequence # 1:   CGGGCGCCGTTATAT

   Mutated DNA sequence # 2:   AGGGCGCCGTAATAT

   Mutated DNA sequence # 3:   AGGGCGCCGTTATAC

Use the following information to answer question 19.

Tsarina Alexandra of Russia carried the recessive form of the gene causing hemophilia, which is found on the *X* chromosome. Tsar Nicholas II did not have hemophilia.

19. **a.** Construct a Punnett square to demonstrate the cross of alleles possessed by the Russian Monarch Tsar Nicholas II and his wife, Tsarina Alexandra.

    b. State the probability of a male offspring from this cross developing hemophilia.

    c. Nicholas and Alexandra's only son, Alexei, developed hemophilia, but his four older sisters did not have hemophilia. Explain how it is possible that none of his sisters developed hemophilia.

    d. The famous historical figure named Rasputin gained influence with the Russian royal family because he claimed that he could heal Alexei's hemophilia. Use your knowledge of the circulatory system and genetics to explain why it could not have been possible for Rasputin to cure Alexei of hemophilia.

    e. The Tsar and his family were assassinated as part of the Russian Revolution of 1917. Years later, a woman appeared and claimed to be Anastasia, one of the daughters of Nicholas and Alexandra. Throughout her life, this woman maintained that she was Anastasia. A DNA sample from a piece of her intestine was removed during an operation and preserved. This sample was compared to DNA from the royal family members, whose bodies were uncovered in 1998. This DNA comparison was used to prove that she was not Anastasia. How can DNA be used to identify members of the same family?

20. Use the following information to answer questions 20.a. to 20.f.

During the process used to create the clone of a sheep, scientists took an egg cell from one sheep and removed its chromosomes. An autosomal cell from a second adult sheep was isolated and placed next to the egg cell. Electricity was used to fuse the two cells together, and they began to divide into a zygote, which was genetically identical to the adult sheep's autosomal cell. The clone zygote was implanted into a third sheep's uterus, where it developed into a baby sheep.

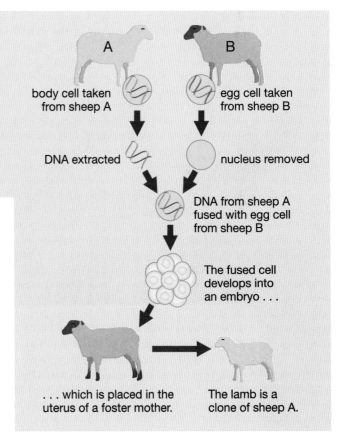

    a. Would the egg cell be described as haploid (1n) or diploid (2n) before its chromosomes were removed?

    b. Would the autosomal cell from the adult sheep be described as haploid (1n) or diploid (2n)?

    c. Would the clone zygote produced from the two fused cells be described as haploid (1n) or diploid (2n)?

    d. Explain why the chromosomes needed to be removed from the egg cell to create the clone zygote.

    e. Compare and contrast the process of cloning with the process of fertilization.

    f. Even though the cloned sheep and the sheep from which the autosomal cell was taken share all the same genes, they may differ slightly. Explain how slight differences such as adult size and behaviour are possible.

Unit B Chemistry and the Environment

The prairies during harvest are an impressive sight. After careful seeding and management of crops, farmers look forward to harvest time as the final step. As you have seen in Unit A, agriculture—although steeped in tradition—has benefited from new technologies: improved machinery for seeding and harvesting; herbicides to remove unwanted plants; and new varieties of hardier plants.

Advancements in technology provide a way to fulfill society's needs. Discoveries and developments in science and technology have changed the practices in modern-day agriculture. Recent innovations have improved the processes for refining raw materials and manufacturing consumer products.

The use of processes to manipulate raw materials is a common practice in chemistry. New combinations of atoms or the isolation of one substance from a mixture can have intended or unintended effects. The manipulation of matter, and other technologies, affects people and the environment.

In this unit you will find out about some chemical processes that are important to society. You will also learn about the environmental consequences of these processes and the actions being taken to counteract the unintended effects.

What You Will Cover

Chapter 1: Acid Deposition

Chapter 2: The Chemical Legacy of Human Activity

Chapter 1 Acid Deposition

Camping is an activity enjoyed by many people worldwide. After a full day of activities such as hiking or canoeing, there is nothing like sitting around and enjoying the light and warmth of a campfire with friends or family.

To enjoy a camping trip, you need activities and manufactured items that require the combustion of fuel. At the campsite, fuels are burned for heating, cooking, and light. To drive to the campsite, you need fuel for automobiles and camping trailers. Even the manufacturing processes for making the tent, trailer, and camping equipment requires an abundance of fuel.

Since the 1960s, scientists have been collecting evidence that some of the products of fuel combustion are negatively affecting the environment. What evidence is there? What are some of the effects on the environment? Are there ways to reverse or control these effects? These are some of the questions you will explore throughout this chapter.

Try This Activity

Detection Limits

Advances in technology have led to sophisticated and sensitive apparatus that are able to detect substances at very low concentrations. The detection of a substance is the first step toward understanding the impact of its presence within the environment.

Purpose

You and a partner will perform an analysis that simulates the relationship between detection limits and the amount of information available.

Procedure

Obtain the "Detection Limits" handout from the Science 30 Textbook CD. You will need one copy for each person.

step 1: You and your partner must create a sentence that contains 8 to 15 words. Do not share your sentences.

step 2: Write the words of your sentence into the top part of the bars—one word per bar—on the "Detection Limits" handout.

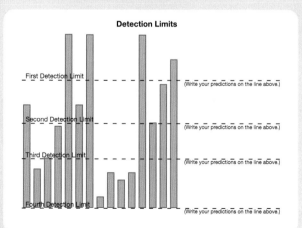

✓ Analyzing and Interpreting

step 3: Cover the handout you prepared in step 2 with cardboard or a sheet of heavy paper.

step 4: Have your partner pull the piece of cardboard down to the dotted line labelled "First Detection Limit" and read the words that are visible.

step 5: Have your partner use the visible words to predict what the sentence is. His or her prediction should be written in the space provided on the handout.

step 6: Repeat steps 4 and 5 for the remaining detection limits.

Analysis

1. Compare the predictions you made at each detection limit. At what point was your prediction reasonably close to the actual sentence? At what point was your prediction identical (or nearly identical)?

2. Assume that each bar on the page represents a different chemical substance associated with a chemical process. These may be reactants, products, or by-products of the process. Assume that the height of each bar represents the concentration of a substance. If you were studying the chemical process, at which detection limit would you want to collect information? Explain your reasoning.

3. If each bar represents a different chemical substance that could be released into the environment, identify which bars would be of greatest concern. Support your answer.

Working as a team in a local dogsled race, Kayla and her dogs challenge the cold and their physical limits. They are all working and breathing hard. With each breath Kayla and her dogs take, they must exhale the products of **cellular respiration**—a process that converts the chemical potential energy within food into a form the body's muscles can use. Energy-converting processes, like cellular respiration and the **combustion** of fuels, are important; however, they produce emissions.

In the next investigation you will look at the chemical properties of the gases produced from cellular respiration and from the combustion of a hydrocarbon.

▶ **cellular respiration:** the process by which cells convert the chemical energy stored in organic molecules (sugars) into energy that cells can use

▶ **combustion:** a chemical reaction that occurs in the presence of oxygen and results in the release of energy

Investigation

Comparing the Effects of the Products of Cellular Respiration and Combustion

Cells use molecules within food as an energy source. Cellular respiration is a process similar to the combustion of hydrocarbons in that oxygen is required, carbon dioxide and water are produced, and energy is released.

Science Skills

✓ Performing and Recording
✓ Analyzing and Interpreting

Purpose
You will compare the effects of the products of cellular respiration with the products of the combustion of a hydrocarbon (coal).

Part 1: Cellular Respiration

Materials

- 125-mL Erlenmeyer flask
- 75 mL of distilled water
- bromothymol blue indicator
- 100-mL graduated cylinder
- drinking straw
- eyedropper
- stopwatch

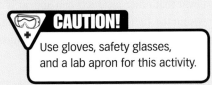
CAUTION!
Use gloves, safety glasses, and a lab apron for this activity.

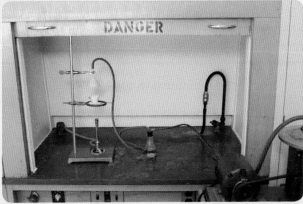

Figure B1.1

Procedure

step 1: Use the graduated cylinder to measure 75 mL of distilled water; then transfer the water to the Erlenmeyer flask.

step 2: Add four drops of bromothymol blue to the distilled water. Note the colour of the mixture.

step 3: Insert the drinking straw into the mixture in the flask, and exhale through the straw until the colour of the indicator changes to yellow. Record the time taken for the indicator to change colour.

Observations

1. Complete the following table.

Colour of Indicator Before Exhaling	Time Taken for Indicator to Turn Yellow

Analysis

2. Explain the significance of the colour change.

3. Identify the reason for the mixture to change colour. **Note:** Refer to the "Acid-Base Indicators" table on page 184.

4. Write the balanced chemical equation for the cellular respiration of glucose, $C_6H_{12}O_6(aq)$.

5. Hypothesize the effect that carbon dioxide released by many processes could have on water within the biosphere.

Part 2: Teacher Demonstration—Combustion of Coal

Materials

Your teacher will set up the materials as shown in Figure B1.1.

CAUTION!
Be careful near an exposed flame and hot objects.

Procedure for Teacher

step 1: Measure 75 mL of distilled water, and transfer it to the flask.

step 2: Add four drops of bromothymol blue to the distilled water. Note the colour of the mixture.

step 3: Place the coal in a crucible, and ignite the coal using a Bunsen burner or torch.

step 4: Once the coal is glowing and producing smoke, position the crucible below the inverted funnel.

step 5: Turn on the vacuum to draw the smoke into the flask. Record the time it takes for the indicator inside the flask to change colour.

step 6: Turn off the vacuum, and let the system sit untouched for a few minutes to allow the air pressure in the flask to return to normal. Remove the crucible, and extinguish the coal with water.

Observations

6. Complete the following table.

Colour of Indicator Before	Time Taken for Indicator to Turn Yellow

Analysis

7. Explain the significance of the colour change.

8. Suggest a reason why the water containing the bromothymol blue indicator in Parts 1 and 2 took different lengths of time to change colour.

9. Write the balanced chemical equation for the combustion of coal, $C(s)$.

10. Identify a process or technology where coal is used.

Combustion Reactions and Their Products

Natural gas used to heat most homes contains mostly methane, $CH_4(g)$, and is an example of a **hydrocarbon** and a **fuel**. During combustion, collisions between the molecules of methane and oxygen result in the formation of new molecules.

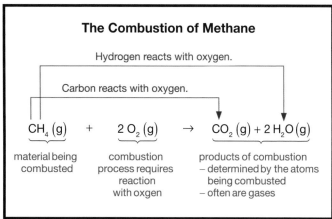

The Combustion of Methane

Hydrogen reacts with oxygen.

Carbon reacts with oxygen.

$$CH_4 (g) \quad + \quad 2\,O_2 (g) \quad \rightarrow \quad CO_2 (g) + 2\,H_2O (g)$$

material being combusted

combustion process requires reaction with oxgen

products of combustion
– determined by the atoms being combusted
– often are gases

Figure B1.2

The equation in Figure B1.2 shows that the products of combustion are carbon dioxide, $CO_2(g)$, and water vapour, $H_2O(g)$—oxides of carbon and hydrogen.

The products formed during a combustion reaction are directly related to the atoms present in the substance being combusted. When a hydrocarbon combusts, the products are usually carbon dioxide and water. Later, you will discover that other products can appear if other atoms appear within the fuel. During most combustion reactions, the oxides produced are released into the atmosphere. These are referred to as **emissions**.

▶ **hydrocarbon:** an organic compound containing only carbon and hydrogen atoms

▶ **fuel:** a substance that releases energy when involved in a chemical reaction (often combustion) or a nuclear reaction

▶ **emission:** a substance discharged into the atmosphere or into surface water

Balancing Chemical Equations

Substances do not always react with each other on a one-to-one basis. To indicate the relative proportions of each substance involved in a reaction, you need to balance the chemical equation. Matter is conserved in all chemical processes. Therefore, a balanced chemical equation has an equal number of each type of atom appearing on the reactants side and on the products side of the equation. Balance the equation using coefficients. Carefully work through Example Problem 1.1.

Example Problem 1.1

Ethane is one of the components in natural gas. Balance the following combustion equation for ethane.

$$C_2H_6(g) + O_2(g) \rightarrow CO_2(g) + H_2O(g)$$

Solution

$$\underline{\quad}\ C_2H_6(g) + \underline{\quad}\ O_2(g) \rightarrow \underline{\quad}\ CO_2(g) + \underline{\quad}\ H_2O(g)$$

↓ Add a coefficient to balance the carbon atoms.

$$\underline{\ 1\ }\ C_2H_6(g) + \underline{\quad}\ O_2(g) \rightarrow \underline{\ 2\ }\ CO_2(g) + \underline{\quad}\ H_2O(g)$$

↓ Add a coefficient to balance the hydrogen atoms.

$$\underline{\ 1\ }\ C_2H_6(g) + \underline{\quad}\ O_2(g) \rightarrow \underline{\ 2\ }\ CO_2(g) + \underline{\ 3\ }\ H_2O(g)$$

↓ Add a coefficient to balance the oxygen atoms.

$$\underline{\ 1\ }\ C_2H_6(g) + \underline{\ 3.5\ }\ O_2(g) \rightarrow \underline{\ 2\ }\ CO_2(g) + \underline{\ 3\ }\ H_2O(g)$$

Recall that coefficients of 1 are not normally shown. Therefore, the balanced chemical equation is

$$C_2H_6(g) + 3.5\,O_2(g) \rightarrow 3\,CO_2(g) + 4\,H_2O(g)$$

Note: If you wish to have whole-number coefficients, multiply all coefficients in the equation by 2.

$$\underline{\ 2\ }\ C_2H_6(g) + \underline{\ 7\ }\ O_2(g) \rightarrow \underline{\ 4\ }\ CO_2(g) + \underline{\ 6\ }\ H_2O(g)$$

Practice

1. Balance the following combustion reactions.
   a. _____ $C_5H_{12}(l)$ + _____ $O_2(g)$ → _____ $CO_2(g)$ + _____ $H_2O(g)$
   b. _____ $C_4H_8(g)$ + _____ $O_2(g)$ → _____ $CO_2(g)$ + _____ $H_2O(g)$
   c. _____ $C_4H_{10}(g)$ + _____ $O_2(g)$ → _____ $CO_2(g)$ + _____ $H_2O(g)$
   d. combustion of octane, $C_8H_{18}(g)$

Oxides of Carbon

Burning carbon compounds, like wood and other forms of **biomass**, or burning hydrocarbon molecules, such as those present in natural gas and gasoline, results in the production of carbon dioxide. Within the biosphere, natural processes that produce carbon dioxide include the cellular respiration of organisms, forest fires, volcanic eruptions, and the weathering of some forms of rock. As a result of these natural processes, carbon dioxide is present within the collection of gases that make up Earth's atmosphere.

▶ **biomass:** plant matter or agricultural waste from recently living sources used as a fuel or as an energy source

The Carbon Cycle

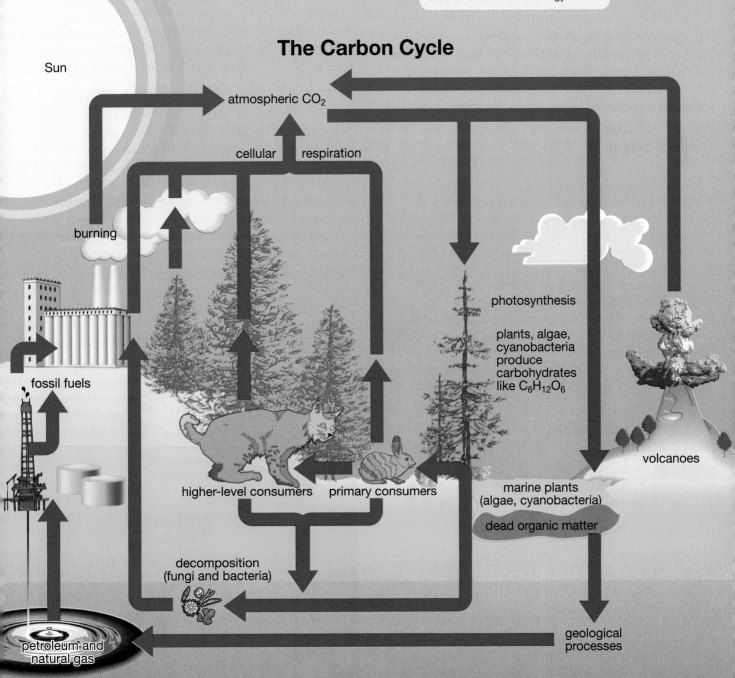

Sun

atmospheric CO_2

cellular respiration

burning

fossil fuels

photosynthesis

plants, algae, cyanobacteria produce carbohydrates like $C_6H_{12}O_6$

volcanoes

higher-level consumers   primary consumers

marine plants (algae, cyanobacteria)

dead organic matter

decomposition (fungi and bacteria)

petroleum and natural gas

geological processes

Recall from previous courses that carbon dioxide is an important gas with respect to life on Earth. Carbon dioxide is a component of the carbon cycle—the series of reactions of carbon-containing compounds in the biosphere. Within the carbon cycle, processes are interrelated. Cellular respiration, which produces carbon dioxide, and photosynthesis, which uses carbon dioxide, act to maintain a relatively steady amount of carbon dioxide in the atmosphere. Also, recall that carbon dioxide is a greenhouse gas, meaning that it has the ability to absorb thermal energy (heat). By absorbing thermal energy, greenhouse gases prevent the loss of thermal energy into space and, thus, have a direct impact on Earth's climate. Since the industrial revolution in the late 1800s, society has increased its reliance on combustion technologies involving fossil fuels. Higher levels of carbon dioxide emissions are believed to be a major contributor to current changes to global climate. Scientific evidence shows that as the amount of carbon dioxide in the atmosphere increases, the quantity of thermal energy retained also increases. The retention of thermal energy results in an increase in the atmospheric temperature, which, in turn, affects climate and ecosystems.

Practice

2. Refer to the diagram of the carbon cycle on page 157. Explain how the increased use of combustion processes by society and deforestation could result in a higher level of atmospheric carbon dioxide, a level that cannot be removed by natural mechanisms.

3. Use the Internet to research the terms *carbon sink* and *carbon sequestering*. Explain how carbon sinks or carbon sequestering are possible mechanisms for reducing the concentration of carbon dioxide in the atmosphere. Identify how carbon sinks or carbon sequestering would impact the carbon cycle.

Carbon Monoxide

Another oxide of carbon—carbon monoxide, $CO(g)$—is a common product of combustion. Carbon monoxide is produced when the quantity of oxygen is limited during the reaction process.

$$2\ CH_4(g) + 3\ O_2(g) \rightarrow 2\ CO(g) + 4\ H_2O(g)$$

↑

Carbon monoxide is a product of an incomplete combustion of a carbon compound.

Concern exists over the presence of carbon monoxide in emissions. As a result, its concentration is often measured during environmental monitoring.

Figure B1.3: Mechanics often have to work on an engine while it is operating. To prevent exposure to carbon monoxide, an exhaust vacuum is used.

Carbon monoxide is associated with inefficient combustion processes, which include automobile emissions. Carbon monoxide can pose a threat to your health. In Unit A you discovered that the circulatory system transports oxygen to cells within the body and that this is only possible by the interaction of oxygen with hemoglobin. Because of the similarities between oxygen and carbon monoxide molecules, carbon monoxide is able to compete with oxygen for binding sites on a hemoglobin molecule. When carbon monoxide is present in inhaled air, it binds to hemoglobin, preventing hemoglobin from binding to oxygen. This decreases the amount of oxygen available to the cells in your body, and can result in death. Emissions-testing programs measure the carbon monoxide concentration in vehicle exhaust. These programs can indicate whether maintenance is required to improve the efficiency of an automobile's engine.

A carbon monoxide detector, present in many homes today, provides one means of monitoring combustion processes. A furnace that has poor combustion efficiency not only produces carbon monoxide, a health threat, but also converts less of the potential energy from the fuel it uses into thermal energy. Regular inspection and maintenance ensures the proper operation of a furnace. There is a great deal of concern about maximizing the efficiency of combustion and other energy-conversion processes.

Figure B1.4: Proper maintenance is essential to maintaining efficient combustion. Efficient combustion of natural gas within a furnace reduces the production of carbon monoxide, a lethal gas.

? DID YOU KNOW?

On average, the concentration of CO(g) in a room may be 0 to 2 parts per million (ppm). Carbon monoxide detectors emit a warning when levels reach 75 ppm to 100 ppm. Expressed as a percent, the detector is set to recognize a CO(g) concentration between 0.0075% and 0.0100%.

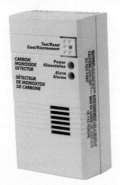

Practice

4. Balance the equations representing the complete and incomplete combustions of methane.

   complete combustion:
   $$CH_4(g) + O_2(g) \rightarrow CO_2(g) + H_2O(g)$$
   incomplete combustion:
   $$CH_4(g) + O_2(g) \rightarrow CO(g) + H_2O(g)$$

5. Use the coefficients from the balanced equations in question 4 to determine the ratio of methane to oxygen in each process. Which reaction uses more oxygen per molecule of methane? Explain how you used the ratios to determine your answer.

Oxides of Sulfur

Sulfur is an element found in small quantities within many of the natural resources burned as fuels. Coal—a fuel commonly used in the production of electricity throughout Alberta and the world—often contains sulfur in varying amounts. Other energy resources, like crude oil and tar sands, also contain sulfur.

Natural gas is another energy source that commonly contains sulfur; but it is in the form of hydrogen sulfide, $H_2S(g)$. The hydrogen sulfide present in **sour gas** is toxic to humans and forms an acidic solution if combined with water. Some sources of sour gas contain more than 30% hydrogen sulfide. Processing natural gas often involves removing the hydrogen sulfide. This is called sweetening. The sweetening process not only reduces the risk to humans in the case of an accidental gas leak, but also reduces the corrosive effects sour gas has on pipelines.

> **sour gas:** natural gas that contains greater than 1% hydrogen sulfide

It is estimated that about 40% of the natural gas reserves in Alberta are sour. Therefore, the removal of hydrogen sulfide is a vital industrial process.

Figure B1.5: Sour gas flare

During the lifespan of a gas well, low-quality natural gas is sometimes released. This low-quality gas—often containing hydrogen sulfide—is flared. Flaring converts hydrogen sulfide into sulfur dioxide and sulfur trioxide emissions.

**Flaring Process—
Unbalanced Chemical Equations**

$H_2S(g) + O_2(g) \rightarrow SO_2(g) + H_2O(g)$

$SO_2(g) + O_2(g) \rightarrow SO_3(g)$

The combustion of coal also results in the production of sulfur dioxide, although the amount can vary depending on the quantity of sulfur in the coal. The coal mined in Alberta contains less sulfur than the coal mined in eastern Canada. What do you think the effect would have been if sulfur-rich coal were used in the investigation on page 155?

Figure B1.6: Stockpile of sulfur from desulfurization

The yellow stockpiles seen near facilities that process natural resources (e.g., petroleum, oil sand, and very sour gas) consist of elemental sulfur—the product of desulfurization. Sulfur is commonly combined with metal atoms within metal ores. Refining metal ores involves removing sulfur by heating the ore in the presence of oxygen. In eastern Canada, particularly southern Ontario, the refining of nickel and other metals produces sulfur dioxide emissions.

Practice

6. Balance the chemical equations that occur during the flaring process.

Oxides of Nitrogen

You probably already know that Earth's atmosphere is a mixture of many gases. Nitrogen, $N_2(g)$, makes up 78.1% of Earth's atmosphere. Whenever you inhale or whenever air is drawn into an engine to combust a fuel, nitrogen is present. If the temperature of the combustion process is high enough (above 650°C), the normally unreactive nitrogen molecule is activated and will react, often producing nitrogen oxides. The oxides of nitrogen produced by combustion reactions are nitrogen monoxide, $NO(g)$, and nitrogen dioxide, $NO_2(g)$. These are commonly referred to as NO_x compounds.

Production of NO_x Compounds

$N_2(g) + O_2(g) \rightarrow 2\ NO(g)$

$2\ NO(g) + O_2(g) \rightarrow 2\ NO_2(g)$

The most common sources of NO_x compounds are high-temperature combustion processes. These include the combustion of hydrocarbon fuels by automobiles and by furnaces used in homes and industry. Studies have shown that higher NO_x emissions occur in urban areas and that NO_x levels can fluctuate daily or monthly depending on the season.

Practice

7. Explain why NO_x emissions are higher in urban areas than in rural areas.
8. For each situation given, predict whether levels of NO_x emission will increase or decrease.
   a. morning and evening rush hour
   b. a cold snap in the winter
   c. a heat wave in the summer months

Chemical Reactions in the Atmosphere

Sulfur Dioxide (SO₂) Emissions in Canada (2000)

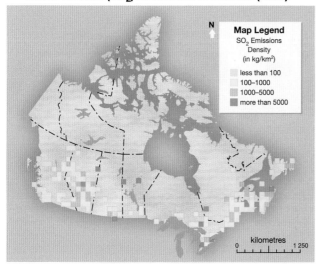

Nitrogen Oxide (NOₓ) Emissions in Canada (2000)

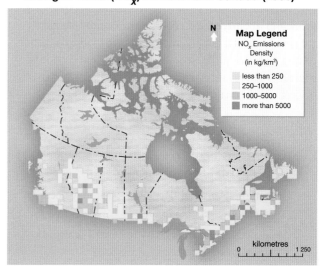

Figure B1.7: Greater emissions of SO_2 and NO_x occur near major Canadian centres.

A list of natural and human activities that produce SO_2 and NO_x is shown in the "Sources of SO_2 and NO_x" table.

SOURCES OF SO₂ AND NOₓ

Sources of SO_2	Sources of NO_x
Natural	**Natural**
• hot springs • volcanic outgassing	• forest fires
Human-made	**Human-made**

emissions from
    • coal-fired power plants
    • pulp and paper mills
    • refining crude oil
    • refining oil sands
    • refining metals and smelting
    • automobiles
	emissions from
	    • fossil fuel power plants
	    • industrial and domestic furnaces
	    • production of fertilizers
	    • burning of crops
	    • automobiles

Notice that many of these emissions are the result of human activity, with the result that larger emissions occur close to major cities. As you will see in later lessons, Earth's atmosphere can provide suitable conditions for emissions—such as the oxides of carbon, sulfur, and nitrogen—to undergo additional chemical reactions. You will examine the impact that NO_x and SO_2 emissions have on the biosphere. But first, you will see how emissions are monitored in Alberta and who is involved.

Monitoring Emissions in Alberta

Alberta Environment is involved in programs that monitor and maintain the quality of Alberta's environment to protect the health of citizens and ecosystems. Desired standards for environmental quality are determined by the collection of data from scientific, societal, technical, and economic sources. Factors considered when establishing standards for environmental quality include the

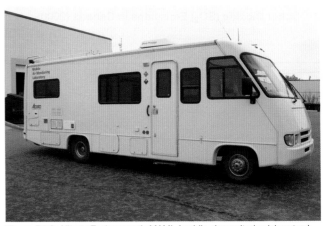

Figure B1.8: Alberta Environment's MAML (mobile air monitoring laboratory) is specially equipped to sample and monitor the air in any location throughout Alberta.

- sensitivity of organisms to the presence of substances of concern
- behaviour of substances when in the atmosphere or other parts of the environment
- natural levels and fluctuations that may occur in concentration of substances
- availability of technology to control or avoid emissions
- ability to detect and monitor the presence of substances of concern

In Alberta, air quality is monitored using data collected by monitoring stations operated by industry and the provincial and federal government. Currently, you are able to use the Internet to access information about air quality throughout the province. Depending on the location of the monitoring stations in your immediate area, you may be able to view the concentrations for a variety of substances that are used to determine air quality in the area immediately near your school or home.

Alberta Environment also uses a mobile monitoring system to perform measurements of air quality. View the segment "Mobile Air Monitoring Labs (MAML)" on the Science 30 Textbook CD for additional information about the mobile monitoring system.

Metals and Metal Oxides

Metal atoms, either in their elemental form or as a compound, can also be present in emissions from processes that rely on combustion reactions. For example, coal may contain small amounts of metals, like lead or mercury. When coal is combusted, these metals may be carried great distances before depositing on the ground. Monitoring processes pay close attention to the detection and measurement of the concentrations of heavy metals, like lead and mercury, in emissions and elsewhere in the environment, especially since these metals have been known to adversely affect human health.

Particulate Matter

A higher incidence of asthma and other respiratory diseases occurs in populations of individuals exposed to higher levels of particulate matter. Particulate matter consists of solids suspended in the atmosphere that come from natural and human-made sources. Soot, smoke, and ash produced by either industrial processes or forest fires; soil particles; and pollen are examples of particulate matter that may irritate parts of the respiratory system. Cigarette smoke is an especially dangerous source of particulate matter because it contains organic compounds (e.g., benzene) that are **carcinogens**. You will learn more about organic compounds in Chapter 2 of this unit.

carcinogen: any agent that causes the likelihood of cancer to increase. Many carcinogens are also mutagens.

Utilizing Technology

Taking a Stand—Emissions Testing

Albertans have a high dependence on the cars and trucks they drive for pleasure or for work. In addition, Albertans enjoy their recreation vehicles (e.g., motorcycles, quads, boats, and snowmobiles). Albertans also place a high priority on their health and the health of the diverse habitats that exist throughout the province.

Science Skills

✓ Performing and Recording
✓ Communication and Teamwork

As you know, pollution from vehicles affects both society and the environment. Is it time to place standards on the emissions from vehicles? Currently, three Canadian provinces—British Columbia, Ontario, and New Brunswick—have emissions-testing programs for vehicles. Should Alberta be next?

Purpose

You will debate the following question:

Should Alberta have an emissions-testing program for vehicles similar to those used in British Columbia, Ontario, and New Brunswick?

Background Information

Before you begin, use the Internet to answer the following questions.

1. Why is emissions testing required in some provinces and not in others? In provinces that have emissions-testing programs, are all vehicles tested in all regions of the province?
2. Identify the reason for initiating emissions-testing programs in these provinces.
3. List the items being tested for during an emissions test.
4. What do emissions tests cost consumers in the provinces with testing programs?

Procedure

5. Prepare a position statement that clearly defines whether you support or do not support mandatory emissions testing of all vehicles in Alberta. When developing your position statement, review the list of perspectives listed on page 590. Use this list to help justify your position.
6. Prepare a rebuttal—a second statement that responds to a criticism of your position. When preparing your rebuttal, imagine you are the opponent in the debate. What part of your position statement would your opponent most likely challenge? Would it be the credibility of the information you present or the conclusions you make? Your rebuttal is your opportunity to develop a plan to further defend your position.

1.1 Summary

Combustion processes, both complete and incomplete, involve a reaction with oxygen that results in the formation of oxide compounds. Some of the oxides produced include carbon dioxide, carbon monoxide, sulfur dioxide, and NO_x compounds (e.g., nitrogen monoxide and nitrogen dioxide). Other emissions that can result from combustion processes include heavy metals and particulate matter.

Because emissions react with elements in the atmosphere that may affect humans and other organisms, monitoring programs have been implemented to measure emissions from combustion processes. These programs provide information that can be used to address issues regarding the quality of the environment.

Knowledge

1. Define each term, and describe its significance to this lesson.

   a. combustion   b. oxide

   c. pollution   d. greenhouse gas

   e. hemoglobin   f. sour gas

   g. NO_x h. particulate matter

   i. carcinogen

2. Describe, at the atomic level, what happens to the molecules in a fuel during combustion.

3. "The products of a combustion reaction are dependent on the substance being combusted." Explain the meaning of this statement, and include an example.

4. Explain why nitrogen oxides are often referred to as NO_x.

5. Natural gas is a collection of hydrocarbons. Balance the combustion reactions for three hydrocarbons often found in natural gas.

   a. ___ $CH_4(g)$ + ___ $O_2(g) \rightarrow$ ___ $CO_2(g)$ + ___ $H_2O(g)$

   b. ___ $C_2H_6(g)$ + ___ $O_2(g) \rightarrow$ ___ $CO_2(g)$ + ___ $H_2O(g)$

   c. ___ $C_3H_8(g)$ + ___ $O_2(g) \rightarrow$ ___ $CO_2(g)$ + ___ $H_2O(g)$

Applying Concepts

6. Gasoline is a mixture of hydrocarbons, none of which contain nitrogen. Explain how the combustion of gasoline in automobiles can be considered to be a major source of the production of NO_x compounds.

7. The Claus process can be used to remove hydrogen sulfide from sour natural gas. The Claus process occurs in two steps:

   1) **Thermal Step**

   $H_2S(g) + O_2(g) \rightarrow S(s) + H_2O(g)$

   $H_2S(g) + O_2(g) \rightarrow SO_2(g) + H_2O(g)$

   This step occurs in a furnace at high temperatures.

   2) **Catalytic Step**

   $H_2S(g) + SO_2(g) \rightarrow S(s) + H_2O(g)$

   a. Balance the three reactions in the Claus process.

   b. Identify one emission, other than those listed in the equations, that is produced by the Claus process.

   c. Improvements to the Claus process focus on reducing emissions. One improvement requires the use of pure oxygen rather than atmospheric air in the furnace. Explain how the use of pure oxygen could result in a reduction to emissions from the Claus process.

8. Prepare a table that summarizes the similarities and differences between the properties and processes that result in the formation of the carbon, nitrogen, and sulfur oxides described in this lesson.

9. Obtain the handout "NO_x and SO_2 Emissions in Canada (2000)" from the Science 30 Textbook CD.

   a. Use the information from each map to prepare a table that identifies the locations in Alberta where emissions of SO_2 and NO_x are moderate and high. Provide a reason as to why emissions are moderate to high.

   b. Identify a location in Alberta with high levels of NO_x emissions and low levels of SO_2 emissions. Explain how this situation could exist.

   c. Use the Internet to obtain information on other locations in Canada where SO_2 and NO_x emissions are relatively high. Add this information to your table in question 9.a.

10. In 2000, emissions of SO_2 in Canada were estimated to be 2.4×10^6 t (tonnes). Prepare a table that shows the mass of sulfur dioxide emissions from each of the sources shown in Figure B1.9.

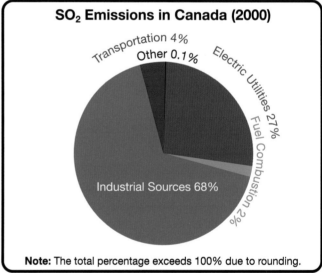

SO₂ Emissions in Canada (2000)

Transportation 4%
Other 0.1%
Electric Utilities 27%
Fuel Combustion 2%
Industrial Sources 68%

Note: The total percentage exceeds 100% due to rounding.

Figure B1.9

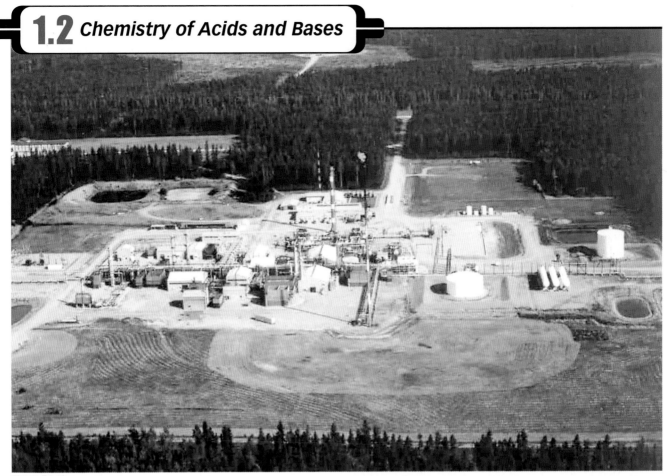

Figure B1.10

Most of the natural gas collected and processed from gas wells in Alberta contains hydrogen sulfide, $H_2S(g)$. At sour gas processing facilities (like the one shown in Figure B1.10), the hydrogen sulfide is removed and is converted into sulfur. Metal pipes, like the one shown in Figure B1.11, can be damaged by exposure to sour gas. Recall from previous science courses that the corrosion of metal objects occurs when certain substances come into contact with one another.

Workers in the oil and gas industry continually monitor the corrosion of pipes, especially where sour gas is extracted and processed. Strict safety standards are maintained to protect people and the environment from the effects of sour gas.

In this lesson you will closely study the chemical components within sour gas that enable it to affect metals and other substances. You will also see how the products of combustion reactions can further react to produce acidic solutions. You will examine how acidic solutions can affect other substances, including bases, within chemical systems. You will then discover methods to measure and describe the acidity of solutions.

Figure B1.11: A metal pipe damaged by corrosion

What Makes Sour Gas Sour?

Figure B1.12: The sour taste of many foods is distinctive and is produced by the acids naturally present within the food or by acids added during its production.

Words like *sour* are used to provide a description. Oranges, lemon juice, or perhaps your favourite candy can be described as having a sour taste. Likewise, scientists use descriptive terms to communicate the behaviour of substances they investigate. Often, these descriptions are based on observations of the matter during experimentation. Descriptions of the response of substances to tests performed during an experiment can be used to make **empirical** definitions.

As described earlier, sour gas contains hydrogen sulfide, $H_2S(g)$. Since water is often present within pipes containing sour gas, hydrogen sulfide can dissolve into water to form an **aqueous solution**, represented as $H_2S(aq)$.

▶ **empirical:** a result of an observation
▶ **aqueous solution:** a solution in which water is the solvent

Practice

9. In previous science courses you were introduced to the terms *ionic compound*, *molecular compound*, *acid*, and *base*. Match each term with one of the following definitions.

   a. a compound composed of oppositely charged particles, often metal and non-metal atoms; usually forms conductive solutions, called electrolytes, when dissolved in water

   b. a corrosive solution containing hydrogen in the chemical formula of the solute

   c. a compound composed of two or more non-metal atoms; may dissolve in water; only some form electrolytes, but most often form non-electrolytes

   d. a caustic, corrosive solution; often contains a hydroxide ion and a group 1 or 2 metal in the periodic table

10. a. In previous science courses you worked with conductivity meters and litmus paper (red and blue litmus). Familiarize yourself with how and why each of these pieces of equipment is used. Summarize your review by copying and completing the following table.

Apparatus	Used to Identify	Expected Result for a Positive Test	Expected Result for a Negative Test
conductivity meter			
red litmus paper			
blue litmus paper			

   b. Describe the experimental control used with each apparatus. Include the solution tested and the expected result for the test.

Empirical Properties of Acids, Bases, and Neutral Solutions

Careful planning and attention to detail is essential when you design an experiment or investigation. Your attention to detail, such as performing the same test on experimental controls, improves the quality of the data you collect. The quality of data is determined by considering validity and reliability when designing and performing the investigation. The "Reliability and Validity" table on page 167 demonstrates some questions and actions you might take to make your experimental design and procedure reliable and valid. By paying attention to these aspects, you will become more confident in your data.

RELIABILITY AND VALIDITY

Reliability	Validity
Questions the Way Experiment Is Performed Is it possible to obtain the same result if I repeat the experiment using the same method?	**Questions the Process Used to Obtain Measurements** Does this process measure what it is supposed to?
How to Improve Reliability • Repeat tests with both positive and negative experimental controls. • Perform frequent calibration checks. • Practise techniques and use of equipment.	**How to Improve Validity** • Select equipment that is appropriate for the experiment. • Select methods that others have used successfully to perform similar tasks. • Use the equipment appropriately.

In the next investigation you will test some aqueous solutions and describe the response of each solution to the tests. Once you are finished, you should be able to identify trends within your observations and develop a set of empirical definitions for the solutions tested.

Investigation

Testing Aqueous Solutions

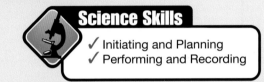

Science Skills

✓ Initiating and Planning
✓ Performing and Recording

Purpose

You will design and perform an experiment to identify acidic, basic, neutral molecular, and neutral ionic solutions.

Materials

- 0.100-mol/L solutions of
  - $HCl(aq)$ – $Na_2CO_3(aq)$
  - $HNO_3(aq)$ – $Na_2SO_4(aq)$
  - $H_2SO_4(aq)$ – $NaCl(aq)$
  - $H_2S(aq)$ – $CH_3OH(aq)$
  - $NaOH(aq)$
- distilled or de-ionized water
- multiwell dish (or 13 watch glasses or Petri dishes)
- blue and red litmus paper
- magnesium turnings (or iron filings)
- stirring rod
- forceps or tweezers
- MSDS (Material Safety Data Sheet) for each solution
- conductivity meter (or tester)

Procedure

step 1: Develop an experimental design that includes the following considerations:

- **Safety:** Identify solutions that contain compounds that are irritants or that may cause some other safety concern. Consult the MSDS information for each solution.
- **Manipulation of apparatus:** If necessary, seek further instruction from your teacher regarding the use of the apparatus (e.g., the conductivity meter).
- **Cleanup:** Learn the proper procedure for the disposal of the chemicals. Determine how the apparatus should be cleaned.

step 2: Have your teacher approve your procedure before you begin.

step 3: Follow your procedure, and record your results.

CAUTION!

Use gloves, safety glasses, and a lab apron for this activity.

Analysis

1. Identify the positive and negative controls in the investigation.
2. Identify actions taken during the investigation that improved the quality of the data collected.
3. Describe how the data collected during the investigation demonstrates reliability.
4. Describe how the tests completed during the investigation address validity.

Trends and Patterns in Data

Trends and patterns within experimental data are important. When you look at the data from the "Testing Aqueous Solutions" investigation, do you notice that some of the solutions behaved in a similar manner? Is it possible to sort the solutions using the similarities in their behaviour to certain tests?

Did you notice how many of the solutions had a similar reaction to each type of litmus paper used in the tests? The sorting of substances based on their similar behaviours to certain tests was used to create the empirical definitions you explored earlier. Refer to the "Properties of Acids, Bases, and Neutral Solutions" table.

PROPERTIES OF ACIDS, BASES, AND NEUTRAL SOLUTIONS

Solution	Properties
acid	• electrolytic (conducts a current) • corrosive • turns blue litmus red • reacts with active metals (e.g., Mg, Zn, and Fe) to produce hydrogen gas • neutralized by bases and basic solutions • tastes sour
base	• electrolytic (conducts a current) • corrosive • turns red litmus blue • feels slippery (when diluted) • neutralized by acids and acidic solutions • tastes bitter
neutral	• can be electrolytic (if solute is an ionic compound) • does not change red or blue litmus

Types of Deposition

Emissions from industrial activities can carry sulfur dioxide and other substances great distances. A major factor in determining how long emissions will stay in the atmosphere is how quickly they come into contact with other materials in the environment. Emissions that contact liquid or solid forms of water in the atmosphere can dissolve and return as **wet deposition**. Gases and particles within emissions that are absorbed by Earth's surface are called **dry deposition**. Alberta has a dry climate. It is estimated that most of the pollution from emissions in Alberta occurs in the form of dry deposition. The terms *wet* and *dry* refer to the state of the material being deposited; therefore, it is possible for dry deposition to be deposited onto any surface, including bodies of water (e.g., lakes and rivers).

▶ **wet deposition:** gases or particles that are removed from the atmosphere by water (liquid or solid) and deposited as precipitation

▶ **dry deposition:** gases or particles that are transported by winds and absorbed by Earth's surface

11. Copy and complete the following table to summarize the results from the "Testing Aqueous Solutions" investigation. For now, do not complete the Definition column.

Solution	Definition	Empirical Properties	Examples
acidic			
basic			
neutral			

What Makes a Solution Acidic?

Earlier, you were able to use similarities within your observations to classify a solution as being acidic, basic, or neutral. You also saw that the groupings you made coincided with the known empirical properties for acids, bases, and neutral solutions. Apart from these similarities, did you note any other similarities among the acidic solutions?

Acids are a special group of chemical compounds. Did you notice that all of the substances categorized as acids contain hydrogen and were dissolved in water? You may have also noted that all the acidic solutions tested were **electrolytic solutions**, even if their chemical formula suggests that the **solute** is a **molecular compound**. Although many acids are molecular compounds, all acids appear to behave like **ionic compounds** when dissolved in water. Acids tend to form electrolytic solutions, whereas molecular compounds form non-electrolytic solutions. As you will soon see, the microscopic changes that occur within a solution containing a dissolved acid are important when explaining the properties of acids.

solute: a substance in a solution whose bonds are broken by a solvent; a substance that dissolves

electrolytic solution: an aqueous solution that conducts an electric current

ionic compound: a chemical substance formed from the mutual attraction of positive and negative ions

molecular compound: a chemical substance formed by elements sharing valence electrons

Acids and Bases in Solutions

Conductive solutions contain freely moving ions. In previous science courses you discovered that water molecules break the bonds between ions in an ionic solute, causing the ions to dissociate. **Dissociation** occurs due to **electrostatic attraction** between the charged ions of the solute and the charges on water molecules. Although dissociation cannot be seen, a positive conductivity test—implying that charged particles are present and are able to move within the solution being tested—is indirect evidence of this microscopic change. In 1834, an English physicist by the name of Michael Faraday was the first scientist to demonstrate that acids, bases, and salts (later determined to be composed of ionic compounds) all dissolve in water to form electrolytes.

dissociation: the separation of a chemical substance into its individual ions in a solution

electrostatic attraction: a force that acts to pull oppositely charged objects toward each other

Science Links

Many phenomena, including lightning, result from electrostatic attraction between oppositely charged particles. In Unit C you will study the fields that surround objects and how forces like electrostatics are the product of fields.

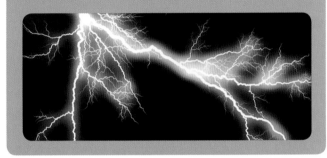

Water Molecules Dissolving an Ionic Crystal

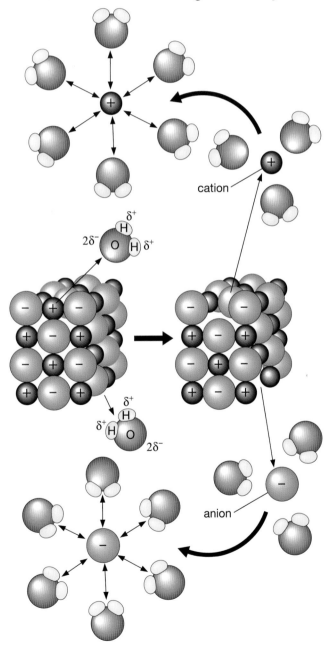

Conductivity tests have demonstrated that all acidic solutions also conduct an electric current, indicating that the acid molecule has formed ions. Is this observation connected to the fact that all acids contain hydrogen? Some scientific theories attempting to explain the properties and behaviours of acids have focused on the ability of acids to form hydrogen ions in water.

In 1887, a Swedish chemist named Svante Arrhenius published a theory that suggested that acids form aqueous solutions that contain hydrogen ions, $H^+(aq)$, and a negatively charged ion. His theory also proposed that bases form solutions that contain hydroxide ions, $OH^-(aq)$, and a positively charged ion. Although not defined by this theory, solutions that produced neither a hydrogen ion nor a hydroxide ion can be considered neutral electrolytic solutions.

Figure B1.13: Svante Arrhenius (1859–1927)

Changes to Solutes in Aqueous Solutions

Acids: e.g., hydrochloric acid
$HCl(aq) \rightarrow H^+(aq) + Cl^-(aq)$

Bases: e.g., potassium hydroxide
$KOH(aq) \rightarrow K^+(aq) + OH^-(aq)$

Neutral Substances: e.g., calcium chloride
$CaCl_2(aq) \rightarrow Ca^{2+}(aq) + 2\ Cl^-(aq)$

Balancing Chemical Equations

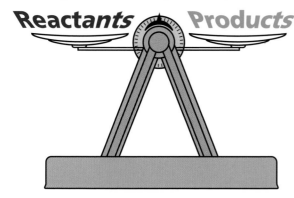

Balancing a chemical equation using coefficients demonstrates that all the atoms on the reactants side of the equation have been accounted for on the products side. Recall that matter cannot be created nor destroyed. Coefficients represent the number of each particle involved. When properly balanced, the net charge on each side of the equation will be the same.

Balancing Equations

$$HCl(aq) \rightarrow H^+(aq) + Cl^-(aq)$$

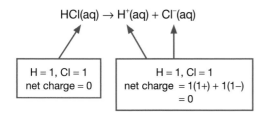

| H = 1, Cl = 1 net charge = 0 | H = 1, Cl = 1 net charge = 1(1+) + 1(1−) = 0 |

coefficient needed to balance chloride ions

↓

$$CaCl_2(aq) \rightarrow Ca^{2+}(aq) + 2\ Cl^-(aq)$$

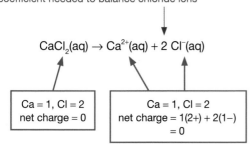

| Ca = 1, Cl = 2 net charge = 0 | Ca = 1, Cl = 2 net charge = 1(2+) + 2(1−) = 0 |

Chemical equations are balanced when

- an equal number of each type of atom appears on each side of the equation
- the net charge on each side of the equation is equal

Practice

12. Write a balanced equation for the change that occurred with each substance when it was dissolved in water.
   a. $HNO_3(aq)$
   b. $H_2SO_4(aq)$
   c. $H_2S(aq)$
   d. $NaOH(aq)$
   e. $Na_2CO_3(aq)$
   f. $Na_2SO_4(aq)$
   g. $NaCl(aq)$

13. Use the equations written in question 12 to predict whether each solution listed is acidic, basic, or neutral. List any inconsistencies.

Limitations to Arrhenius's Theory

As previously stated, when chemical substances separate into their individual ions in a solution, this is called dissociation. Dissociation equations like that for $Na_2CO_3(aq)$, may be written to explain how ionic solutions can conduct an electric current.

$$Na_2CO_3(aq) \rightarrow 2Na^+(aq) + CO_3^{2-}(aq)$$

Arrhenius's theory states that the presence of hydroxide ions in the chemical formula of a solute explain its basic properties. $Na_2CO_3(aq)$, in solution, has definite basic properties. However, you can see that the above equation does not show the presence of $OH^-(aq)$ ions. How can these ions be responsible for basic properties? A similar problem exists for substances like $AlCl_3(aq)$, which is acidic in solution.

A second problem with Arrhenius's theory focuses on the possible existence of a free hydrogen ion moving among water molecules in a solution. Scientists questioned the possibility of free hydrogen ions existing within an aqueous solution. The simplest element is hydrogen, composed of one proton and one electron. Hydrogen atoms become positively charged when the single electron is removed. The absence of any electron, combined with the small size of hydrogen's atomic nucleus, results in the hydrogen ion having a very strong positive charge.

Hydrogen Atom, H   **Hydrogen Ion, H⁺**

Figure B1.14: *Hydrogen ion, proton* . . . there are times when scientific terms can seem confusing. Can you explain why scientists sometimes refer to a hydrogen ion as a proton?

Many of the unique properties of a water molecule, including its ability to dissociate a solute, are explained by the **polarity** of the water molecule. Part of the polarity of the water molecule is due to exposed pairs of electrons located on the molecule's surface. Since electrons have a negative charge, the areas on the surface of a water molecule where these pairs of electrons are located will also have a partial negative charge. An electrostatic attraction between the positively charged hydrogen atom and the negatively charged areas of the water molecule provides an opportunity for these two objects to combine. The hydrogen ion becomes bound to the water molecule. The product of this reaction is the **hydronium ion**, $H_3O^+(aq)$.

> ▶ **polarity:** the presence of different regions of charge on a molecule
>
> ▶ **hydronium ion:** an ion created when a water molecule combines with a hydrogen ion; $H_3O^+(aq)$

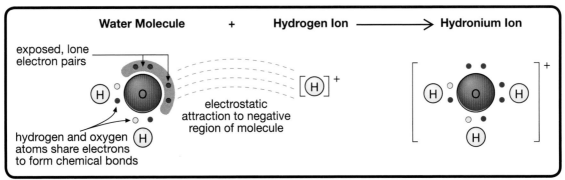

Figure B1.15: The creation of hydronium

Since the development of Arrhenius's theory, evidence has supported the existence of the hydronium ion, $H_3O^+(aq)$, within aqueous solutions. Currently, the hydronium ion is recognized as the acidic particle.

Apart from clarifying that the hydronium ion is the particle responsible for the acidity of solutions, later theories emphasized the importance of collisions between substances, including water, within a chemical system. In previous science courses, water was referred to as an excellent medium for chemical change that enables other particles to collide. Now, when you think of reactions within a solution, you may find that water is one of the reactants.

Exchange of Hydrogen Ions

You may have wondered if a collision between a hydronium ion and a water molecule could result in the transfer of the hydrogen ion to other water molecules or to other substances. The possibility of transferring hydrogen ions between substances within a solution stimulated the development of other theories to explain the behaviour of acids and bases.

In 1923, a Danish chemist—Johannes Brønsted—and an English chemist—Thomas Lowry—independently published similar theories that described an alternate way of explaining the behaviour of acids and bases. The coincidence of two scientists working in the same area of research and publishing similar theories was rare at the time. If you think this coincidence is strange, at the time Brønsted and Lowry did their work, there was no e-mail, Internet, or jet-airplane travel. Back then, the opportunities for scientists to meet and exchange ideas were greatly limited. The significance of these two researchers independently developing the same theory was great.

Scientific ideas and discoveries undergo a process of peer review that is designed to ensure the reliability of the experimentation, the validity of the data, and its interpretation. Peer review is one way scientists can check the work of others. During peer review, scientists analyze the details of how the data was collected, the data itself, the methods used to interpret data, and the ideas and theories developed from the interpretation of the data. Often, during the peer-review process, the reviewers may suggest that further experimentation is needed to provide better support for the conclusions.

Figure B1.16: Johannes Brønsted (1879–1947)

Figure B1.17: Thomas Lowry (1874–1936)

For scientists, the peer-review process is a means by which scientific knowledge is scrutinized and determined to be meaningful and valid. Before publishing their theories, Brønsted and Lowry would have had their work examined by groups of scientists. By following the peer-review process, the Brønsted-Lowry theory was quickly accepted into the scientific body of knowledge.

Writing Brønsted-Lowry Acid-Base Reactions

Unlike the theories you have seen to this point, the Brønsted-Lowry theory attempts to describe the action of acids and bases during a chemical reaction. According to this theory, a hydrogen ion is transferred from an **acid** (the donor) to a **base** (the acceptor) during acid-base reactions. The Brønsted-Lowry theory often refers to the hydrogen ion as a proton. The products of an acid-base reaction are a **conjugate acid** and a **conjugate base**.

According to the Brønsted-Lowry Acid-Base Reactions, an acid-base reaction involves the transfer of a hydrogen ion from an acid to a base. The loss or donation of a hydrogen ion by an acid converts it into a conjugate base—another form of the substance. The conjugate base form of the substance can be recognized by the loss of a hydrogen ion in its chemical formula. The gain or acceptance of a hydrogen ion by a base converts it into a conjugate acid—its alternate form that contains the transferred hydrogen ion. The chemical formulas for many acids and bases, including their conjugate forms, are shown on the "Table of Acids and Bases." This table also appears in the Science Data Booklet, called "Relative Strengths of Selected Acids and Bases for 0.10 mol/L Solution at 25°C."

TABLE OF ACIDS AND BASES

Acid Name	Acid Formula	Conjugate Base Formula
hydrochloric acid	$HCl(aq)$	$Cl^-(aq)$
sulfuric acid	$H_2SO_4(aq)$	$HSO_4^-(aq)$
nitric acid	$HNO_3(aq)$	$NO_3^-(aq)$
hydronium ion	$H_3O^+(aq)$	$H_2O(l)$
oxalic acid	$HOOCCOOH(aq)$	$HOOCCOO^-(aq)$
sulfurous acid	$H_2SO_3(aq)$	$HSO_3^-(aq)$
hydrogen sulfate ion	$HSO_4^-(aq)$	$SO_4^{2-}(aq)$
phosphoric acid	$H_3PO_4(aq)$	$H_2PO_4^-(aq)$
orange IV	$HOr(aq)$	$Or^-(aq)$
nitrous acid	$HNO_2(aq)$	$NO_2^-(aq)$
hydrofluoric acid	$HF(aq)$	$F^-(aq)$
methanoic acid	$HCOOH(aq)$	$HCOO^-(aq)$
methyl orange	$HMo(aq)$	$Mo^-(aq)$
benzoic acid	$C_6H_5COOH(aq)$	$C_6H_5COO^-(aq)$
ethanoic (acetic) acid	$CH_3COOH(aq)$	$CH_3COO^-(aq)$
carbonic acid, $CO_2(g) + H_2O(l)$	$H_2CO_3(aq)$	$HCO_3^-(aq)$
bromothymol blue	$HBb(aq)$	$Bb^-(aq)$
hydrosulfuric acid	$H_2S(aq)$	$HS^-(aq)$
phenolphthalein	$HPh(aq)$	$Ph^-(aq)$
boric acid	$H_3BO_3(aq)$	$H_2BO_3^-(aq)$
ammonium ion	$NH_4^+(aq)$	$NH_3(aq)$
hydrogen carbonate ion	$HCO_3^-(aq)$	$CO_3^{2-}(aq)$
indigo carmine	$HIc(aq)$	$Ic^-(aq)$
water (55.5 mol/L)	$H_2O(l)$	$OH^-(aq)$

acid: the substance that donates or loses a hydrogen ion to another substance during a chemical reaction

base: the substance that accepts or gains a hydrogen ion from another substance during a chemical reaction

conjugate acid: an acid formed in an acid-base reaction when a base accepts a hydrogen ion (or proton)

conjugate base: a base formed in an acid-base reaction when an acid donates a hydrogen ion (or proton)

The information in the "Table of Acids and Bases" can be used to identify the reactants and predict the products of an acid-base reaction between certain substances.

Example Problem 1.2

Sour gas contains hydrogen sulfide, $H_2S(g)$. Hydrogen sulfide can dissolve and react with water in the atmosphere. Write the chemical equation of the reaction between aqueous hydrogen sulfide and water.

Solution

step 1: Locate $H_2S(aq)$ and $H_2O(l)$ on the "Table of Acids and Bases."

TABLE OF ACIDS AND BASES

Acid Name	Acid Formula	Conjugate Base Formula
hydrochloric acid	$HCl(aq)$	$Cl^-(aq)$
sulfuric acid	$H_2SO_4(aq)$	$HSO_4^-(aq)$
nitric acid	$HNO_3(aq)$	$NO_3^-(aq)$
hydronium ion	$H_3O^+(aq)$	$H_2O(l)$
⋮	⋮	⋮
bromothymol blue	$HBb(aq)$	$Bb^-(aq)$
hydrosulfuric acid	$H_2S(aq)$	$HS^-(aq)$
phenolphthalein	$HPh(aq)$	$Ph^-(aq)$
⋮	⋮	⋮
hydrogen carbonate ion	$HCO_3^-(aq)$	$CO_3^{2-}(aq)$
indigo carmine	$HIc(aq)$	$Ic^-(aq)$
water (55.5 mol/L)	$H_2O(l)$	$OH^-(aq)$

step 2: Identify the acid and the base in the reaction. Recall that the stronger acids appear higher in the Acid Formula column and the stronger bases appear lower in the Conjugate Base Formula column.

The acid is $H_2S(aq)$ because it appears higher in the column than $H_2O(l)$. The base is $H_2O(l)$.

step 3: Write the reactants side of the chemical equation.

$$H_2S(aq) + H_2O(l) \rightarrow$$

step 4: Identify the conjugate forms of the acid and the base.

TABLE OF ACIDS AND BASES

Acid Name	Acid Formula	Conjugate Base Formula
⋮	⋮	⋮
nitric acid	$HNO_3(aq)$	$NO_3^-(aq)$
hydronium ion	$H_3O^+(aq)$	$H_2O(l)$
⋮	⋮	⋮
bromothymol blue	$HBb(aq)$	$Bb^-(aq)$
hydrosulfuric acid	$H_2S(aq)$	$HS^-(aq)$
⋮	⋮	⋮

step 5: Write the conjugate forms on the products side of the chemical equation.

acid loses a hydrogen ion to form the conjugate base

$$H_2S(aq) + H_2O(l) \rightarrow HS^-(aq) + H_3O^+(aq)$$

base gains a hydrogen ion to form the conjugate acid

Therefore, the chemical equation for the reaction of aqueous hydrogen sulfide and water is

$$H_2S(aq) + H_2O(l) \rightarrow HS^-(aq) + H_3O^+(aq)$$

The Brønsted-Lowry theory gained acceptance within the scientific community because it was able to describe a mechanism for the reaction between acids and bases in aqueous solutions. The theory also explained the production of a hydronium ion by acids when dissolved in water.

Practice

14. Write the chemical equation for the following reactions. Label the acid, the base, the conjugate acid, and the conjugate base in each reaction.
    a. Dissolved nitric acid, $HNO_3(aq)$, reacts with water, $H_2O(l)$.
    b. Carbonic acid in rainwater reacts with water.

Example Problem 1.3

Hydrofluoric acid, HF(aq), used to remove oxide coatings from metals prior to electroplating, can be neutralized by a reaction with the hydroxide ion, $OH^-(aq)$, of aqueous sodium hydroxide. Write the chemical equation for this neutralization reaction.

Solution

step 1: Locate HF(aq) and $OH^-(aq)$ on the "Table of Acids and Bases."

TABLE OF ACIDS AND BASES

Acid Name	Acid Formula	Conjugate Base Formula
hydrochloric acid	HCl(aq)	$Cl^-(aq)$
sulfuric acid	$H_2SO_4(aq)$	$HSO_4^-(aq)$
⋮	⋮	⋮
nitrous acid	$HNO_2(aq)$	$NO_2^-(aq)$
hydrofluoric acid	HF(aq)	$F^-(aq)$
methanoic acid	HCOOH(aq)	$HCOO^-(aq)$
⋮	⋮	⋮
hydrogen carbonate ion	$HCO_3^-(aq)$	$CO_3^{2-}(aq)$
indigo carmine	HIc(aq)	$Ic^-(aq)$
water (55.5 mol/L)	$H_2O(l)$	$OH^-(aq)$

step 2: Identify the acid and the base in the reaction.

The acid is HF(aq), and the base is $OH^-(aq)$.

step 3: Write the reactants side of the chemical equation.

$$HF(aq) + OH^-(aq) \rightarrow$$

step 4: Identify the conjugate forms of the acid and the base.

acid: $HF(aq) \rightarrow F^-(aq)$

base: $OH^-(aq) \rightarrow H_2O(l)$

step 5: Write the conjugate forms on the products side of the chemical equation.

acid loses a hydrogen ion to form the conjugate base

$$HF(aq) + OH^-(aq) \rightarrow F^-(aq) + H_2O(l)$$

base gains a hydrogen ion to form the conjugate acid

Therefore, the chemical equation for this neutralization reaction is

$$HF(aq) + OH^-(aq) \rightarrow F^-(aq) + H_2O(l)$$

15. Oxalic acid, HOOCCOOH(aq), is often used in industry to clean and sterilize containers. Write the chemical equation for the reaction of oxalic acid, HOOCCOOH(aq), and the hydroxide ion, OH⁻(aq). Label the acid, the base, the conjugate acid, and the conjugate base.

Arrhenius's theory was not able to explain the basic properties of solutions like sodium carbonate, Na_2CO_3(aq). Solutions like these are not composed of hydroxide ions; however, they can produce hydroxide ions due to a reaction with water.

Example Problem 1.4

In the "Testing Aqueous Solutions" investigation, aqueous sodium carbonate, Na_2CO_3(aq), turned red litmus paper blue, indicating a basic solution. Write the chemical equation for the reaction between dissociated carbonate ions, CO_3^{2-}(aq), and water.

Solution

Locate CO_3^{2-}(aq) and H_2O(l) on the "Table of Acids and Bases," and identify the acid and the base in the reaction.

The acid is H_2O(l), and the base is CO_3^{2-}(aq).

Next, write the reactants side of the chemical equation.

$$H_2O(l) + CO_3^{2-}(aq) \rightarrow$$

Now, identify the conjugate forms of the acid and the base. Write these on the products side of the chemical equation.

acid loses a hydrogen ion to form the conjugate base

$$H_2O(l) + CO_3^{2-}(aq) \rightarrow OH^-(aq) + HCO_3^-(l)$$

base gains a hydrogen ion to form the conjugate acid

Therefore, the chemical equation for the reaction is

$$H_2O(l) + CO_3^{2-}(aq) \rightarrow OH^-(aq) + HCO_3^-(aq)$$

Note: The product OH⁻(aq) is responsible for the basic properties of the solution.

Example Problem 1.4 shows that another aspect of the Brønsted-Lowry theory is its ability to describe the behaviour of water—either donating or accepting a hydrogen ion—and to explain its important role in acid-base reactions.

Practice

16. Write the chemical equation for each reaction given. Label the acid, the base, the conjugate acid, and the conjugate base in each reaction.
    a. Sulfuric acid, H_2SO_4(aq), spilled during a lab procedure, reacts with the hydrogen carbonate ion, HCO_3^-(aq), present within an acid spill kit.
    b. During the production of fertilizer, aqueous ammonia, NH_3(aq), reacts with phosphoric acid, H_3PO_4(aq).
17. Earlier, you determined that one of the empirical properties of acids and bases is that they act to neutralize each other. Using the Brønsted-Lowry theory, concisely explain how the neutralization of an acid or base occurs during an acid-base reaction.

Proton Hopping

Recent experiments to investigate the mechanism of hydrogen-ion transfer between acids and bases in aqueous solutions appear to have confirmed the description of the behaviour of acids and bases provided by the Brønsted-Lowry theory. Using lasers, a group of scientists were able to capture a series of images, like snapshots, of the motion of a chemical reaction between an acid and a base. The scientists expected to see the transfer of the hydrogen ion between the acid and the base present in the system, as would be described by a chemical equation similar to those you have written thus far. What the snapshots showed was unexpected: the acid and the base did not appear to come in contact with each other. The snapshots showed water molecules being converted into hydronium ions when they collided with the acid, followed by a collision between the hydronium and the base. This reaction resulted in the loss of a hydrogen ion to the base. The experiment demonstrated that water molecules in the system underwent many acid-base reactions, acting like a shuttle to transfer hydrogen ions between the acid and the base.

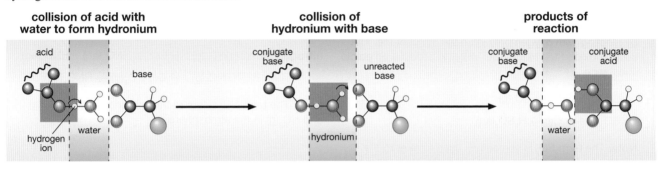

Although this research won't affect the way you write a reaction between an acid and a base, it provides a great deal of insight into the mechanism involved during a reaction. The research further supports the use of the Brønsted-Lowry theory when you write, explain, or predict reactions between acids and bases within an aqueous chemical system.

Emissions Can React

In Lesson 1.1 you saw how products from combustion reactions had an effect on bromothymol blue (an acid-base indicator). When the gases within exhaled air or gases from the combustion of coal were bubbled through the water containing bromothymol blue, a colour change occurred that indicated a change to an acidic system. How can bubbling gases through water result in a change to the acidity of the water?

PRODUCTS OF COMBUSTION REACTIONS AND THEIR SOURCES

Product of Combustion	Source
$CO(g)$, $CO_2(g)$	• carbon present in hydrocarbon fuels
$SO_2(g)$, $SO_3(g)$	• sulfur present in fuels • combustion of $H_2S(g)$, a component of sour gas
$NO(g)$, $NO_2(g)$	• air from the atmosphere that contains nitrogen

To summarize, products of combustion reactions (the substances shown in the table) are released into the atmosphere as emissions. Also, water is present in the atmosphere and on Earth's surface, and emissions are removed from the atmosphere in the form of wet or dry deposition. Even as dry deposition, these substances eventually come into contact with water. As you have seen, water can react with many substances.

Figure B1.18: Condensation that forms on the outside of a drinking glass was once water vapour present in the atmosphere. The presence of water and other substances makes the atmosphere a chemical system—a site for many chemical changes.

Most of the oxides of carbon, sulfur, and nitrogen shown in the "Products of Combustion Reactions and Their Sources" table can react with water. Refer to Figure B1.19.

Reactions of Certain Oxides with Water

Oxides of Carbon

carbon dioxide: $CO_2(g) + H_2O(l) \rightarrow H_2CO_3(aq)$

Oxides of Sulfur

sulfur dioxide: $SO_2(g) + H_2O(l) \rightarrow H_2SO_3(aq)$

sulfur trioxide: Sulfur dioxide, produced during combustion reactions, can convert into sulfur trioxide by reacting with oxygen present in the atmosphere. The sulfur trioxide then reacts with water to produce an acidic substance.

$$SO_2(g) + O_2(g) \rightarrow SO_3(g)$$
$$SO_3(g) + H_2O(l) \rightarrow H_2SO_4(aq)$$

Note: The term SO_x is sometimes used to refer to the presence of both $SO_2(g)$ and $SO_3(g)$ in the atmosphere.

Oxides of Nitrogen

nitrogen monoxide: Nitrogen monoxide, produced by combustion reactions, can convert into nitrogen dioxide by reacting with oxygen present in the atmosphere.

$$NO(g) + O_2(g) \rightarrow NO_2(g)$$

It is the $NO_2(g)$ that reacts with water to produce acidic substances.

nitrogen dioxide: $NO_2(g) + H_2O(l) \rightarrow HNO_2(aq) + HNO_3(aq)$
$$NO_2(g) + H_2O(l) + O_2(g) \rightarrow HNO_3(aq)$$

Note: The term NO_x refers to the presence of both $NO(g)$ and $NO_2(g)$ in the atmosphere.

Figure B1.19

Practice

18. Copy each reaction equation listed in Figure B1.19. Balance each equation.

19. Use the "Table of Acids and Bases" on page 173 to identify the names of the hydrogen-containing products in the reaction equations. Write the name for each of the products beside its chemical formula shown in the equation.

20. The products of the reactions in Figure B1.19 often remain dissolved in water that falls toward Earth as precipitation or exists in lakes and other bodies of water. Predict the effect that the products of the reactions shown in Figure B1.19 will have on the water it dissolves in. If possible, use chemical equations to support your prediction.

anthropogenic: coming from human activity

acid deposition: airborne particles containing acids or acid-forming substances contained within precipitation (wet deposition) or that absorb directly into parts of Earth's surface (dry deposition)

Acid Deposition

The chemical reactions you have studied thus far describe the origin and consequences of substances released as emissions from human activity. **Anthropogenic** emissions of carbon dioxide, $CO_2(g)$, sulfur oxides, $SO_2(g)$ and $SO_3(g)$, NO_x or nitrous oxides, $NO(g)$ and $NO_2(g)$, originate from human-made processes that involve combustion, such as energy production and transportation. The chemical equations you have written describe how these emissions are able to react with water and form **acid deposition**. Areas exposed to wet or dry acid deposition can experience a number of effects, some of which you may be able to predict based on what you have already learned about acids from previous investigations.

Figure B1.20: Water from melting snow can contain acids that were originally deposited in either wet or dry form.

The term **acid rain** describes the excessive amount of acidity within precipitation. It surprises many people to learn that rainfall is naturally acidic. Natural processes, like cellular respiration, produce substances that can form acids. Carbon dioxide, $CO_2(g)$, for example, can react with water to form carbonic acid, $H_2CO_3(aq)$, which results in the production of hydronium ions, $H_3O^+(aq)$. The oxides of carbon, nitrogen, and sulfur are present in Earth's atmosphere as a result of natural processes and anthropogenic sources. Other natural processes that release emissions include burning biomass (forest fires), lightning, the erosion of carbonate-based rock formations, the release of volcanic gases, and the action of bacteria in marine or terrestrial habitats.

▶ **acid rain:** any form of precipitation (wet deposition) containing an excess of dissolved acids; wet deposition with a pH of 5.6 or less

The amount of acid present within a solution can be measured. The method used can determine whether precipitation contains higher amounts of acids than would be expected. In many areas of the world, acid deposition is largely due to the emissions from human activities. The amount of acid deposition in a region can vary over time, even over seasons. Can you predict the effect that melting snow has on the amount of acid present in streams and bodies of water in Alberta?

Practice

21. Analyze the graph "Global Sulfur Emissions (1998)."
    a. Prepare a table that lists the following values by latitude:
       • percentage of emissions from anthropogenic sources
       • percentage of emissions from natural sources
    b. Calculate a ratio of anthropogenic sources to natural sources for each latitude zone shown and for the world.
    c. Identify areas where you suspect higher levels of acid deposition may occur.

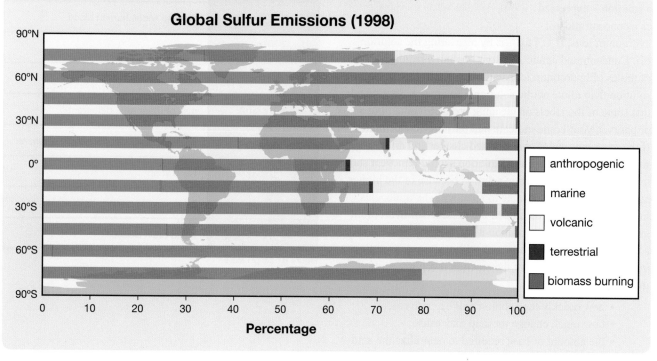

Measuring Acids

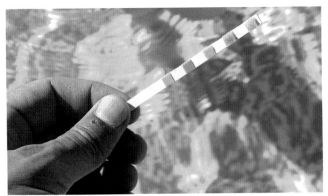

Figure B1.21: The level of acidity in a swimming pool is checked by measuring the water's pH.

During the hot summer days, the place to be is at the local swimming pool. But before anyone can go in the water, lifeguards must take measurements of the water's acidity to ensure that it will not cause any harm. Acids are corrosive. Acidic solutions react with metals and often have warning labels to remind you of their ability to react with your skin.

Figure B1.22: Labelling products using WHMIS symbols or HHPS (Household Hazardous Products Symbols) alert users of the possible risks and appropriate safety precautions.

pH

One way to measure the amount of acid in a solution—expressed as a concentration of

> **pH:** a value that represents the concentration of dissolved hydronium ions, $H_3O^+(aq)$, within a solution

hydronium ions, $H_3O^+(aq)$—is by measuring the solution's pH. Concentrated acidic solutions contain a larger number of moles of hydronium ions within each millilitre or litre of solution than dilute acidic solutions. You may have noticed that some of the labels on cleaning products containing acids or bases in your home indicate that they are "concentrated." If the same amount of concentrated cleaner and dilute cleaner were tested, the concentrated solution should remove a stain more quickly than the dilute solution because of the higher number of particles available to react with the molecules in the affected area. Recall that the presence of hydronium ions, $H_3O^+(aq)$, gives a solution its acidic properties. The concentration of hydronium ions within an acidic solution influences other aspects of the reaction involving acids, including

- how quickly the solution will begin to react
- how much change the acid may cause
- the amount of base required to neutralize the acid
- the amount of base or metal it will react with

In Alberta, the pH of rainfall is routinely measured at a number of locations throughout the province to provide information about acid deposition.

Calculating pH and the pH Scale

The pH scale was developed in 1909 by a Danish scientist named Soren Sörenson. He developed the scale as a means to better communicate the acidity of a solution. Scientists at that time observed that the level of acidity of a solution did not always correspond to the concentration of the acid dissolved in the solution. Not all acids react completely with water, thus producing solutions with lower concentrations of hydronium ions. Sörenson's system was designed to measure the concentration of hydronium ions present in dilute solutions, thereby providing a better description of a solution's level of acidity. A solution with a pH of 7 is considered to be neutral; a solution with a pH less than 7 is considered to be acidic; and a solution with a pH greater than 7 is considered to be basic. Figure B1.23 shows the pH scale along with examples of common substances.

pH = 0	battery acid
pH = 1	stomach acid
pH = 2	lemon juice
pH = 3	vinegar, orange juice, cola
pH = 4	tomato juice, acid rain
pH = 5	coffee (black), rain
pH = 6	urine, saliva (healthy), cow's milk
pH = 7	distilled water, human blood
pH = 8	sea water
pH = 9	baking soda
pH = 10	milk of magnesia, detergent
pH = 11	ammonia solution, household cleaners
pH = 12	hand soap
pH = 13	bleach, oven cleaner, household lye
pH = 14	liquid drain cleaner

Figure B1.23: pH scale

The exponent of the hydronium-ion concentration, when expressed in scientific notation, can be used to approximate a solution's pH. For example, a pH of 6.0 corresponds with a hydronium-ion concentration of 1×10^{-6} mol/L, which can also be expressed as 0.000 001 mol/L. A solution with a pH of 6.0 has a larger concentration of hydronium ions than a solution with a pH of 7.0, which corresponds to a hydronium-ion concentration of 1×10^{-7} mol/L or 0.000 000 1 mol/L. By dividing the hydronium-ion concentration of a solution with a pH of 6.0 by the hydronium-ion concentration of a solution with a pH of 7.0, you will see that the solution with the pH of 6.0 has ten times more hydronium ions than the solution with the pH of 7.0.

$$\frac{\text{solution with pH 6.0}}{\text{solution with pH 7.0}} = \frac{H_3O^+ \text{concentration}}{H_3O^+ \text{concentration}}$$

$$= \frac{1 \times 10^{-6} \text{ mol/L}}{1 \times 10^{-7} \text{ mol/L}}$$

$$= 10$$

Each whole-number division on the pH scale represents a ten-fold difference in the concentration of hydronium ions from the value above or below it. As you move down the scale toward higher pH values, the hydronium-ion concentration decreases, and vice versa as you move up the scale toward lower pH values. A change of two pH steps on the scale represents two ten-fold changes, or a 100-fold change, to the hydronium-ion concentration. If you compare the hydronium-ion concentration of a solution with a pH of 4 with that of a solution with a pH of 9, there is a 100 000-fold $\left(10^5\right)$ difference in hydronium-ion concentration.

The pH scale was developed using dilute solutions of acids and bases. The concentration of hydronium ions within a dilute solution is small and is often expressed in scientific notation as an exponent to the base 10. Because logarithms calculate exponents, you can use the logarithm function on your calculator. Use the following equation to calculate pH.

$$pH = -\log_{10}\left[H_3O^+(aq)\right]$$

The pH of concentrated acid solutions can be below the range of the pH scale. A pH of 0 corresponds to a solution containing a hydrogen-ion concentration of 1.00 mol/L $(1 \times 10^0$ mol/L). Concentrated stock acid solutions used in laboratories can have negative pH values.

Example Problem 1.5

Determine the pH of a sample of rainwater that has a hydronium-ion concentration, $\left[H_3O^+(aq)\right]$, of 1.00×10^{-4} mol/L.

Solution

$pH = -\log_{10}\left[H_3O^+(aq)\right]$

$= -\log_{10}\left(1.00 \times 10^{-4} \text{ mol/L}\right)$ ← Substitute the hydronium-ion concentration.

$= 4$

Keystrokes for Graphing Calculator

The pH of the rainwater is 4.000, expressed to the appropriate number of significant digits.

Example Problem 1.6

A sample of lake water has a hydronium-ion concentration of 2.27×10^{-7} mol/L. Determine the pH of the lake water.

Solution

$$pH = -\log_{10}[H_3O^+(aq)]$$
$$= -\log_{10}(2.27 \times 10^{-7} \text{ mol/L})$$
$$= 6.644 \leftarrow \text{3 significant digits}$$

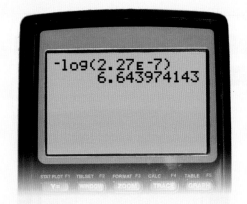

The lake water has a pH of 6.644.

Significant Digits and pH Calculations

Using logarithms to represent calculations is convenient, but care must be taken to show the appropriate number of significant digits. The number to the left of the decimal point in a pH value represents the order of magnitude of the hydronium-ion concentration, reflected by the exponent of the base 10 when that concentration is written in scientific notation. The exponent provides information only about how large or small the number is, not how accurately it was measured. Accuracy of measurement is determined by examining the other numbers before and after the decimal point. Significant digits in a pH value are written using the appropriate number of digits after the decimal point.

Significant Digits and pH Values

$[H_3O^+(aq)]$ concentration = 0.000 010 mol/L

$$= 1.0 \times 10^{-5} \text{ mol/L}$$

— 2 significant digits —

$$pH = -\log_{10}[H_3O^+(aq)]$$

$$= -\log_{10}(1.0 \times 10^{-5} \text{ mol/L})$$

$$= 5.00$$

└ 2 significant digits ┘

Calculating Hydronium Ions

An algebraic relationship in mathematics, such as a formula, can be rearranged to solve for any variable in the formula. Therefore, the formula to calculate pH can be rearranged to solve for the hydronium-ion concentration when a solution's pH value is known.

$$pH = -\log_{10}[H_3O^+(aq)]$$
$$[H_3O^+(aq)] = 10^{-pH}$$

Example Problem 1.7

Calculate the hydronium-ion concentration, $[H_3O^+(aq)]$ in a shampoo with a pH of 5.72.

Solution

$$[H_3O^+(aq)] = 10^{-pH}$$
$$= 10^{-5.72} \leftarrow \text{2 significant digits in pH values}$$
$$= 1.905\ 460\ 718 \times 10^{-6} \text{ mol/L}$$
$$= 1.9 \times 10^{-6} \text{ mol/L} \leftarrow \text{2 signficant digits}$$

Keystrokes for Graphing Calculator

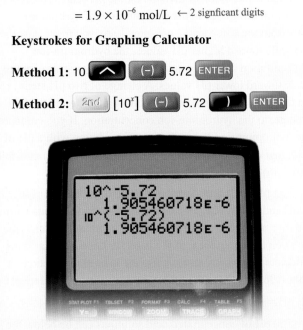

The shampoo has a hydronium-ion concentration of 1.9×10^{-6} mol/L.

The formula for pH and the formula for hydronium-ion concentration appear in the Science Data Booklet.

22. For each hydronium-ion concentration, calculate the pH. Classify each solution as being acidic, basic, or neutral.

    a. 0.001 00 mol/L

    b. 2.00×10^{-4} mol/L

    c. 1.5×10^{-6} mol/L

    d. 1.35×10^{-8} mol/L

    e. 1.54×10^{-12} mol/L

23. For each pH value, calculate the hydronium-ion concentration.

    a. 7.00   **b.** 2.98   **c.** 8.912   **d.** 13.1

24. Obtain the handout "pH and Hydronium-Ion Concentration" from the Science 30 Textbook CD. Complete the table by calculating values for the $[H_3O^+(aq)]$ column and the Relative Change in Hydronium-Ion Concentration with pH Value Below column. State a general trend in the last column regarding the change to hydronium-ion concentration along the pH scale.

Investigation

Measuring pH Using Indicators

Purpose

You will demonstrate the use of indicators as a means to determine the pH of a solution.

Science Skills

✓ Performing and Recording
✓ Analyzing and Interpreting

Materials

- 2 copies of the handout "Determining pH Using Indicators" from the Science 30 Textbook CD

- 1 letter-size overhead transparency sheet
- masking tape
- dropper bottles (or eyedroppers)
- solutions with pHs of 1, 3, 5, 7, 9, 11, and 13
- pH indicators
  - alizarin yellow R
  - thymol blue
  - bromothymol blue
  - bromocresol green
  - methyl orange
- water containing juice extracted from red cabbage when boiled
- unknown solutions A, B, and C

⚠ CAUTION!
Use gloves, safety glasses, and a lab apron for this activity.

Procedure

step 1: Place one of the handouts on the surface of your work area. Cover the handout with the transparency sheet. Use masking tape to ensure the sheet lays flat and remains attached to the surface of your work area throughout the experiment.

step 2: Place one drop of the solution labelled "pH 1" into each circle in its designated column on the transparency, which is overtop the handout.

step 3: Repeat step 2 with the other pH solutions and the unknown solutions.

step 4: Carefully add a drop of alizarin yellow R indicator to the circles in the first row of the handout. When adding the indicator, ensure that the end of the bottle does not touch the drop of solution already in the circle.

step 5: Repeat step 4 using the other indicators listed in the handout.

step 6: Record the colour of the resulting mixture within each circle in a data table.

step 7: Use paper towel to absorb most of the solutions on the transparency; then rinse the transparency in the sink.

step 8: Return all apparatus to their proper location in the lab.

Observations

1. Show your results of this investigation.

Analysis

2. Use the data to estimate the pH of solutions A, B, and C. Explain how you arrived at your estimation. State a reason why using indicators results in only an estimation of the pH of the three solutions.

Use of Natural Indicators by First Nations

The name for the Blackfoot First Nation is reported to have originated from the black moccasins worn by their members when first encountered by European settlers. Research has shown that the Blackfoot used over 150 different plant species to support their traditional lifestyle. The skunkbush, as well as other prairie plants, were sources of coloured molecules that could be used to dye leather, cloth, and even the porcupine quills for ceremonial dress. The Blackfoot, as well as other First Nations, used naturally occurring acids to adjust the colour of the dyes made from the extracts of berries, leaves, or bark. They used ash from fire pits because ash combined with water forms a basic solution. Changing colour as a response to differing pH is a property of many natural substances, making them useful **indicators** of changes in the pH of a system that are often the result of an acid-base reaction.

Figure B1.24: A black dye can be prepared from the leaves of the skunkbush plant.

▶ **indicator:** a substance that changes colour in response to the change in pH of a system

Using Indicators to Estimate pH

The colours shown by many indicators at various pH values are summarized in the "Acid-Base Indicators" table. The information in this table can be used to interpret and estimate the pH of a solution. This table also appears in the Science Data Booklet.

ACID-BASE INDICATORS

Indicator	Abbreviation (acid / conjugate base)	pH Range	Colour Change as pH Increases
methyl violet	$HMv(aq)/Mv^-(aq)$	0.0 – 1.6	yellow to blue
thymol blue	$H_2Tb(aq)/HTb^-(aq)$	1.2 – 2.8	red to yellow
thymol blue	$HTb^-(aq)/Tb^-(aq)$	8.0 – 9.6	yellow to blue
orange IV	$HOr(aq)/Or^-(aq)$	1.4 – 2.8	red to yellow
methyl orange	$HMo(aq)/Mo^-(aq)$	3.2 – 4.4	red to yellow
bromocresol green	$HBg(aq)/Bg^-(aq)$	3.8 – 5.4	yellow to blue
litmus	$HLt(aq)/Lt^-(aq)$	4.5 – 8.3	red to blue
methyl red	$HMr(aq)/Mr^-(aq)$	4.8 – 6.0	red to yellow
chlorophenol red	$HCh(aq)/Ch^-(aq)$	5.2 – 6.8	yellow to red
bromothymol blue	$HBb(aq)/Bb^-(aq)$	6.0 – 7.6	yellow to blue
phenol red	$HPr(aq)/Pr^-(aq)$	6.6 – 8.0	yellow to red
phenolphthalein	$HPh(aq)/Ph^-(aq)$	8.2 – 10.0	colourless to pink
thymolphthalein	$HTh(aq)/Th^-(aq)$	9.4 – 10.6	colourless to blue
alizarin yellow R	$HAy(aq)/Ay^-(aq)$	10.1 – 12.0	yellow to red
indigo carmine	$HIc(aq)/Ic^-(aq)$	11.4 – 13.0	blue to yellow
1,3,5–trinitrobenzene	$HNb(aq)/Nb(aq)$	12.0 – 14.0	colourless to orange

At the beginning of this unit, you observed a colour change for bromothymol blue, one of the pH indicators listed in the "Acid-Base Indicators" table. As you may recall, the colour of the indicator in the water solution within the flask was either blue or green. As gases from exhaled air and from the products of the combustion of coal were added to the respective flasks, the colour of the indicator within the water turned yellow. As can be interpreted from the "Acid-Base Indicators" table, the yellow colour observed for the flask that contained bromothymol blue indicates that the pH of the solution must have been below 6.0. Earlier in the demonstration, the blue colour indicated that the pH of the water in the flask was above 7.6. (A green colour would have indicated that the pH of the water in the flask was between 6.0 and 7.6.)

In the "Measuring pH Using Indicators" investigation, observations from more than one indicator were needed to estimate the pH of a solution to a reasonable degree of accuracy. When an observation can only estimate that a solution's pH is below 6, additional indicator data must be used to narrow the range for a more accurate estimate. Example Problem 1.8 demonstrates how data from several indicators can be used to determine the pH of a solution.

Example Problem 1.8

A solution is tested with three indicators. Here are the results.

Indicator	Colour
bromothymol blue	blue
phenolphthalein	colourless
phenol red	red

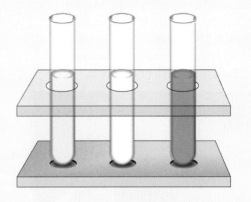

Estimate the pH of this solution.

Solution

step 1: Use the "Acid-Base Indicators" table to determine the pH range.

ACID-BASE INDICATORS

Indicator	Abbreviation (acid/conjugate base)	pH Range	Colour Change as pH Increases
methyl violet	$HMv(aq)/Mv^-(aq)$	0.0 – 1.6	yellow to blue
thymol blue	$H_2Tb(aq)/HTb^-(aq)$	1.2 – 2.8	red to yellow
⋮	⋮	⋮	⋮
bromothymol blue	$HBb(aq)/Bb^-(aq)$	6.0 – 7.6	yellow to blue
phenol red	$HPr(aq)/Pr^-(aq)$	6.6 – 8.0	yellow to red
phenolphthalein	$HPh(aq)/Ph^-(aq)$	8.2 – 10.0	colourless to pink
⋮	⋮	⋮	⋮

According to the table, the three indicators show the following:

- **bromothymol blue:** blue = above pH 7.6
- **phenolphthalein:** colourless = below pH 8.2
- **phenol red:** red = above pH 8.0

step 2: Use a number line to narrow the range of pH values.

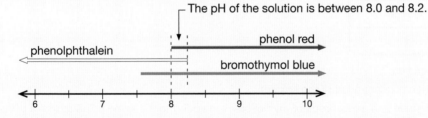

The pH of the solution is between 8.0 and 8.2.

The estimated pH of the solution is between 8.0 and 8.2.

A pH meter is used when more accurate measurements of the pH of solutions are required. A pH meter contains a probe that detects the concentration of hydronium ions in a solution. The sensitivity of the probe enables pH meters to measure values to the hundredth or thousandth of a pH unit.

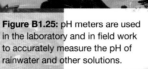

Figure B1.25: pH meters are used in the laboratory and in field work to accurately measure the pH of rainwater and other solutions.

Practice

25. Describe what an indicator is and how it can determine the pH of a solution.
26. "Methyl orange is always red in an acidic solution and yellow in a basic solution." Explain whether this statement is correct or incorrect.
27. A solution is tested with three indicators. Here are the results.

Indicator	Colour
litmus	red
thymol blue	orange
orange IV	red

   a. Estimate the pH of the solution.
   b. Estimate the hydronium-ion concentration of the solution.
28. A few drops of bromocresol green and a few drops of thymol blue are added to the same solution with a pH of 5.6. What colour do you expect the solution to be? Concisely explain your answer.

Sources of Acid Deposition

Earlier, equations demonstrated how carbon dioxide, sulfur oxides, and nitrous oxides reacted with water to produce hydronium ions and form acidic solutions. Carbon dioxide—although produced by many combustion processes—is not considered a major source of acid deposition. Carbon dioxide is only slightly soluble in water, which limits the extent to which it can react with water. On the other hand, the oxides of nitrogen and sulfur are considerably more soluble in water and, thus, make a greater contribution to the acidification of wet and dry deposition.

In this lesson you examined the chemistry of acids and bases. You wrote chemical equations to describe the changes that occur when acids and bases react and discovered how substances released into the atmosphere can convert into acids. You discovered that chemical reactions that occur between acids and water produce hydronium ions. You also determined that the substances released as emissions can return to Earth's surface as either wet or dry deposition and that the deposition can be acidic. You then measured the pH of a solution and studied how pH relates to the concentration of hydronium ions within a solution. In the next lesson you will cover the effects of acidic deposition on the environment.

1.2 Questions

Knowledge

1. Define the following terms.

   a. acid
   b. base
   c. dissociation
   d. hydrogen ion
   e. hydronium ion
   f. pH scale
   g. wet deposition
   h. acid deposition
   i. acid rain

2. Write balanced chemical equations for the reactions between the following substances. For each equation, label the acid, the base, the conjugate acid, and the conjugate base.

   a. hydronium ion, $H_3O^+(aq)$, and hydroxide ion, $OH^-(aq)$
   b. ethanoic acid and ammonia

3. List similarities and differences between Arrhenius's theory and the Brønsted-Lowry theory.

4. Calculate the pH values for each hydronium-ion concentration given. Identify whether the solution is acidic, basic, or neutral.

   a. 0.001 25 mol/L
   b. 2.3×10^{-9} mol/L
   c. 4.42×10^{-13} mol/L
   d. 5.6×10^{-2} mol/L
   e. 8.10×10^{-8} mol/L

5. Calculate hydronium-ion concentration for each pH value given.

   a. 2.14
   b. 7.1
   c. 9.437
   d. 11.00

Applying Concepts

6. Compare and contrast the terms *proton*, *hydrogen ion*, and *hydronium ion*.

7. Antacids are usually taken to relieve heartburn. State the type of compound an antacid needs to be in order to be effective. Calcium carbonate, $CaCO_3(s)$, and aluminium hydroxide, $Al(OH)_3(s)$, are substances used in commercially available antacids. List the empirical properties common to these two antacids. Write a balanced chemical equation that represents the reaction between each of these antacids and aqueous hydronium ions that would occur in the stomach.

8. A chemical spill releases concentrated ammonia, $NH_3(aq)$, along a dangerous-goods route. The spill has been contained. Identify the general properties of the concentrated ammonia spill. If a decision is made to treat the spill to reduce the risk to people or the environment, indicate a substance that can be used. Support your answer with a balanced chemical equation.

9. A solution is yellow with thymol blue and blue with bromocresol green. Determine the colour of the solution with the following indicators.

   a. methyl violet
   b. indigo carmine
   c. methyl orange
   d. alizarin yellow R

10. "The total amount of acid being deposited in an area is equal to the amount of wet acidic deposition deposited in the area plus the amount of dry acidic deposition deposited in the area." Use the concepts you applied in this lesson to explain whether you think this statement is correct or incorrect.

11. Identify whether each example affects the validity or reliability of scientific work.

    a. repeating an experiment
    b. comparing your data with the data collected by other students completing the same experiment
    c. two groups of scientists arriving at the same result using different methods

12. Refer to the table you prepared in Practice Problem 11 on page 169. Complete the Definition column.

Figure B1.26: Data collection is an important process toward developing an understanding of the interactions of substances within ecosystems.

The study of environmental chemistry involves more than just the detection of substances. Scientists who study the environment conduct investigations to determine whether there is evidence of change in the environment. The area of the forest shown in Figure B1.26 has very little vegetation on the ground. Is there a connection between the dropped needles covering the forest floor and the amount of plant growth beneath these trees? Is the lack of plant growth related to the soil pH? Studies performed by environmental scientists in the field are a critical link toward understanding the changes that occur in ecosystems versus those that might be predicted.

Figure B1.27: Some mushroom species and some plant species can grow in the soil directly underneath pine trees.

Predictions currently being made by scientists rely upon the knowledge that comes from careful study of interactions within the environment. As many scientists will tell you, the complexity of interactions within an ecosystem makes the current level of understanding limited. Since the environment is the one thing that all organisms share, research is necessary to understand its ability to cope with stress from pollution.

In this lesson you will expand your knowledge of the complexity of ecosystems and the chemical interactions that can occur. Before you continue, however, do you have a hypothesis that describes the relationship between the presence of emissions in the environment and their effects? What kinds of experiments would you need to conduct to test and support your hypothesis? Do you have an idea of what you might expect to observe?

Given all that you have learned about the ability of some substances within emissions to react with water, does a relationship exist between the presence of these substances in water and the water's acidity? In a previous investigation, the emissions from burning coal acidified water. Do similar reactions occur in nature? In the next investigation you will have the opportunity to analyze data and gain further insight into this question.

Purpose

You will investigate the relationship between the presence of substances in rainwater and the pH of rainwater.

Science Skills

✓ Analyzing and Interpreting
✓ Communication and Teamwork

Background Information

In previous courses you described the relationship between two variables as a **direct variation**, an **inverse variation**, or having **no relationship**. In this investigation you will analyze the data collected from rainwater and determine which type of relationship is demonstrated. The data provided are from rainfall monitoring sites throughout Alberta. Included in the data are information about the quantity of rainfall, pH, total acidity of rainfall, and the nitrate and sulfate concentrations. Each of these headings is considered to be a variable—information that was measured and recorded during this study.

Pre-Lab Questions

1. Identify a relationship between two of the variables (sets of information) listed in the background information.

2. Describe the relationship—direct variation, inverse variation, or no relationship—you feel exists between the two variables defined in question 1. Explain why you chose this relationship.

3. Predict what you think the trends within the data for these two variables will show.

4. Repeat questions 1 to 3 for other combinations of variables you feel will demonstrate a direct variation, an inverse variation, or no relationship.

> **direct variation:** a relationship between two related variables where an increase in the magnitude of one variable results in an increase in the magnitude of the related variable

> **inverse variation:** a relationship between two related variables where an increase in the magnitude of one variable results in a decrease in the magnitude of the related variable

> **no relationship:** a situation where no recognizable pattern is demonstrated between two variables

Materials

- computer with a spreadsheet program (e.g., Excel)
- printer

Procedure

Open the "Rainfall Data" spreadsheet on the Science 30 Textbook CD. Check with your teacher for directions about how many areas within this spreadsheet you will be analyzing. Complete the following steps for each set of data you analyze.

step 1: Identify the headings listed in the background information as they appear on the spreadsheet.

step 2: Graph two or more variables shown in the data. Use appropriate titles and axes labels. Then save your graph.

step 3: Repeat step 2 for other data you may want to investigate or for other areas your teacher instructs you to analyze. Save any additional graphs.

step 4: On each graph, use a text box to insert the hypothesis between the variables graphed.

step 5: Describe any trends on each graph. Add labels and descriptive text to your graphs that indicate these regions.

step 6: On each graph, write an explanation of how the trends or patterns demonstrated by the data support or do not support the hypothesis.

step 7: Create a new document that includes each of the graphs analyzed. At the front of this document, create a summary table that lists the variables that were compared and the relationships identified. Ensure that the order in which the graphs appear is logical and easy to reference from the summary table.

step 8: Below the summary table described in step 7, write a brief commentary indicating whether the relationships between variables you investigated were consistent with the relationships you predicted earlier. Indicate how these relationships are consistent with or differ from what you know about acid deposition.

step 9: Print a copy of the document containing the summary table, commentary on trends and relationships between variables, and the annotated graphs you prepared during your analysis.

Wind Patterns

The "Testing a Hypothesis" investigation provided an opportunity for you to use data to test a hypothesis you developed. As you may have expected, higher levels of sulfates and nitrates in rainwater result in a higher concentration of hydronium ions in the water (direct variation) and, thus, results in a lower pH (inverse variation). These types of relationships are consistent with what is known about the effect of natural and human-made sources of emissions and their respective roles in the production of acid rain.

As mentioned earlier, many other factors can have an influence within an environmental system. One of these factors is wind. Weather in Alberta can be quite variable. There is a saying, "If you don't like the weather in Alberta, wait five minutes." One day it is excessively hot; the next day you are sure it is going to snow. In the next activity you will look at a major feature of the weather patterns across North America. As you complete this activity, remember to consider what influences weather patterns might have on acid deposition.

Utilizing Technology

Prevailing Wind Patterns

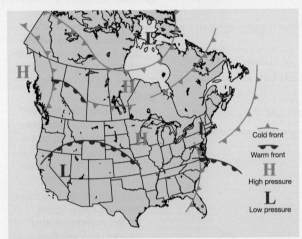

Cold front
Warm front
H High pressure
L Low pressure

Figure B1.28: Precipitation and wind are weather patterns that influence acid deposition.

Purpose
You will examine the prevailing wind patterns in Alberta and in Canada.

Background Information
Have you completed a field study where you measured wind speed and direction? Wind is an abiotic factor of an ecosystem. Wind enables the movement of matter, whether it is water vapour in clouds, solid matter eroded by winds, or gases within atmospheric currents. The jet stream is the most influential wind current in North America. In this activity you will be asked to locate, download, and assemble information about wind patterns. The maps you create in this activity will be used in other activities within this lesson to further investigate issues related to acid deposition.

Materials
- computer with Internet connection
- handouts from the Science 30 Textbook CD
  - "Map of Canada and the US"
  - "Map of Alberta" (2 copies)

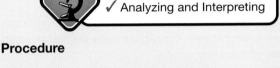

Science Skills

✓ Analyzing and Interpreting

Procedure

Part A: Map of Canada and the US
step 1: Search the Internet for images of daily, monthly, and seasonal patterns of the jet stream.

step 2: Draw a line representing an approximate average location for the jet stream across North America.

step 3: Determine the direction of the winds in areas north and south of the jet stream. Use vector arrows to indicate the direction of the winds on your map.

Part B: Map of Alberta
step 1: Search the Internet for images of daily, monthly, and seasonal wind patterns in Alberta.

step 2: Use vector arrows to indicate the direction of the winds in Alberta. **Note:** If you notice there is a change in the direction of wind patterns in the province during different seasons, use additional maps to identify these patterns. Ensure that all maps are properly labelled.

Analysis
1. Define the term *jet stream*. State the general direction of the jet stream.
2. Explain the effect the jet stream has on weather and climate in western Canada.
3. Comment on the statement, "Wind patterns in Canada and Alberta are always the same."
4. From your analysis of wind patterns, does Canada's position in the northern hemisphere ensure that air transported by currents, such as the jet stream, are relatively clean and unpolluted?

The Jet Stream and Acid Deposition

Wind patterns like the jet stream provide a way for acid deposition to be transported. As you will see later, acid deposition can be transported short and long distances. The predictability of wind patterns provides a way to trace the path of acid deposition back to its source. What happens to an ecosystem when acid deposition settles? How would it affect the plants, soil, and water it touches? Maybe the next activity will help you answer these questions.

Investigation

Acid Deposition and Its Effect on Simulated Lake Water—Demonstration

 CAUTION!

This demonstration should be performed only by your teacher. Avoid exposure to sulfur dioxide. Do not handle any of the solutions used in this demonstration.

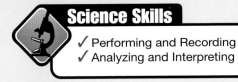 **Science Skills**

✓ Performing and Recording
✓ Analyzing and Interpreting

Purpose

You will see a demonstration of the effect of acid deposition on simulated lake water.

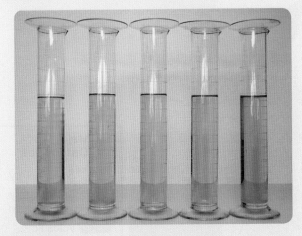

Materials

- 5 large graduated cylinders
- simulated lake water
- bromocresol green indicator
- calcium carbonate, $CaCO_3$(s)
- spray bottle containing water
- sulfur dioxide (prepared prior to demonstration)
- stopwatch

Experimental Design

Samples of simulated lake water will be placed into each cylinder. A small piece of calcium carbonate will be added to two of the cylinders. To test the cylinders, sulfur dioxide gas will be added. A spray bottle of water will be used with some of the cylinders to simulate precipitation. All cylinders will be monitored for changes that occur and the length of time over which the changes occur.

Data Collection

step 1: Construct a data table with the headings Cylinder, Initial Colour of Contents, SO_2(g) Added, Water Spray Added, $CaCO_3$(s) Added, and Relative Time for Colour Change.

step 2: Observe the colours of the contents of each cylinder before adding the SO_2(g). Record each colour in your table.

step 3: Record which cylinders had SO_2(g) added, which had $CaCO_3$(s) added, and which received water spray.

step 4: To simulate the mixing effect made by waves and by water currents, swirl the contents of each flask once during each 10-min interval. Observe changes to colour and other aspects over the next 50 min. Record any changes that occur over each 10-min interval.

Analysis

1. Earlier, you discovered the importance of experimental controls. Identify the cylinders that were experimental controls. Briefly describe their purpose. In some experiments, only one control is used. Why are two control cylinders used in this experiment?

2. Identify the samples of simulated lake water that were exposed to wet acid deposition, that were exposed to dry acid deposition, and that were not exposed to acid deposition.

3. Describe the effect that $CaCO_3$(s) had on the simulated lake-water samples. Support your answer using the evidence collected during the experiments and, if possible, a balanced chemical equation.

4. This demonstration was designed to simulate conditions that could occur in nature. List natural sources of $CaCO_3$(s). Explain how $CaCO_3$(s) could come into contact with lake water to form a chemical system.

Effects of Acid Deposition on the Environment and Ecosystems

Acid deposition can affect the pH of water. The hydronium ions formed during the chemical reaction between acids and water not only act to lower the pH of a body of water, but can react with other substances in the system. Carbonate ions, CO_3^{2-}(aq), are a naturally occurring base present in many bodies of water and in the soil. In Alberta, the pH of most lakes is above 7 and can be as high as 8.3. The slightly **alkaline** pH of the lake water is due to the presence of dissociated carbonate ions that enter the water from dissolving **minerals**, such as calcium carbonate and magnesium carbonate present in limestone.

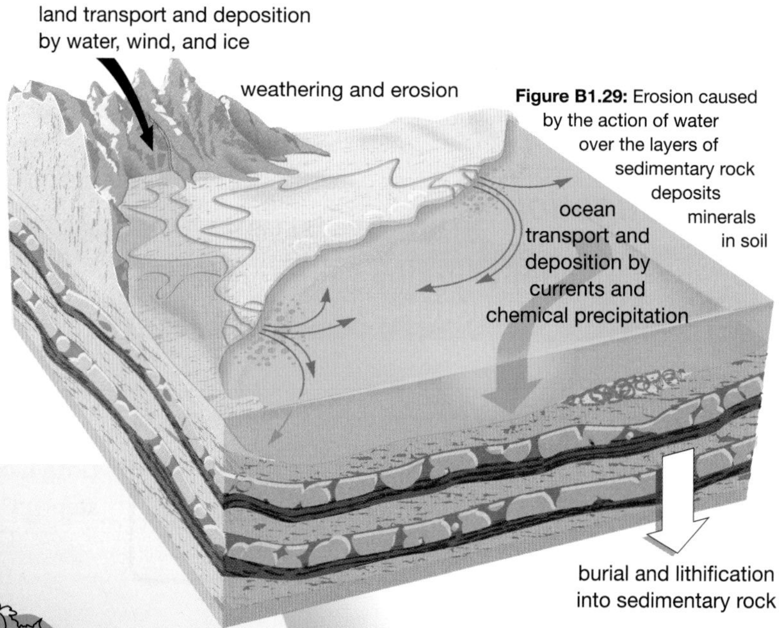

land transport and deposition by water, wind, and ice

weathering and erosion

ocean transport and deposition by currents and chemical precipitation

minerals in soil

burial and lithification into sedimentary rock

Figure B1.29: Erosion caused by the action of water over the layers of sedimentary rock deposits

▶ **alkaline:** having the properties of a base

▶ **mineral:** a solid, inorganic chemical compound produced by natural chemical processes

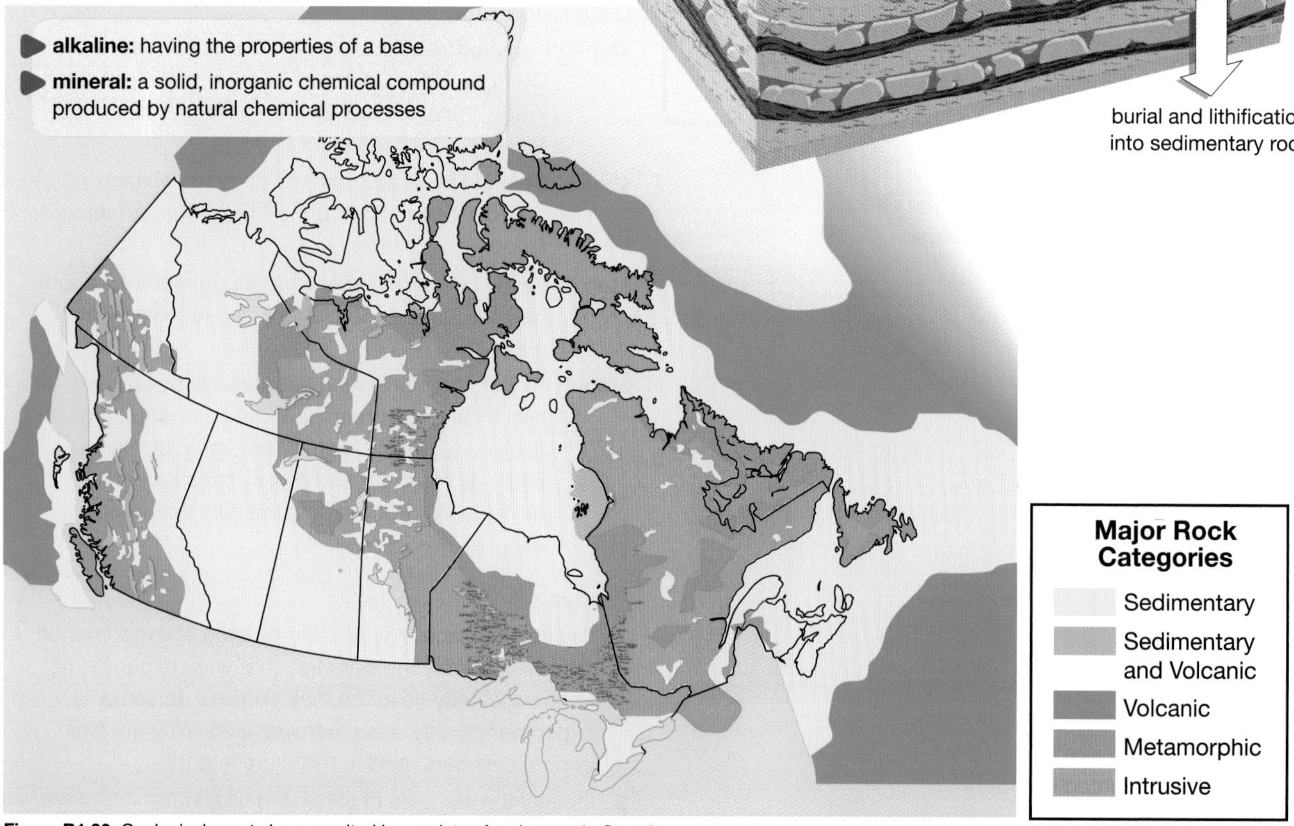

Major Rock Categories

	Sedimentary
	Sedimentary and Volcanic
	Volcanic
	Metamorphic
	Intrusive

Figure B1.30: Geological events have resulted in a variety of rock types in Canada.

Figure B1.31: Soil contains small particles (a component of which is shown in this magnified sample) of eroded rocks from layers of exposed sedimentary rock. The chemical composition of the rock within a region influences the sensitivity of soil and lakes to acid deposition.

The area now called Alberta has undergone many geological changes. Many times throughout its history, Alberta has been covered by water. The coral reefs that developed at the bottom of these oceans were made up of calcium carbonate, $CaCO_3(s)$. Over time, the layers of calcium carbonate formed into limestone—a type of sedimentary rock. As limestone undergoes erosion, small crystals of calcium carbonate present in the limestone form particles in the soil.

The chemical components of soil have a great impact on its sensitivity to acid deposition. In the acid deposition demonstration earlier, the acid deposited into some of the cylinders containing simulated lake water was neutralized. Recall that the reaction between hydronium ions and carbonate ions involves the transfer of a hydrogen ion. The carbonate ions, acting as acceptors for hydrogen ions, convert hydronium ions into water molecules, thereby neutralizing the acid.

Reaction of Hydronium Ion and Carbonate Ion

loses a hydrogen ion

$$H_3O^+ (aq) + CO_3^{2-} (aq) \rightarrow H_2O (l) + HCO_3^- (aq)$$

acid   base   conjugate base   conjugate acid

gains a hydrogen ion

Only a small percentage of soils in Canada have a high potential for neutralizing acid deposition. Much of the soil within the province of Alberta has a high potential, mainly due to the presence of carbonate.

Practice

Obtain a copy of the handouts "Potential of Soils and Bedrock to Reduce Acidity" and "Major Rock Categories" from the Science 30 Textbook CD. Use these maps to answer questions 29 to 36. In developing your answers, consult both maps and look for similarities, differences, and correlations.

29. Do all areas of Canada have similarities in their ability to neutralize acid deposition?

30. Indicate regions in Canada that have the highest potential to reduce acid deposition.

31. Do all of the areas with the highest potential to reduce acid deposition have a similar rock type? If so, identify it.

32. Indicate regions in Canada with the least ability to reduce acid deposition.

33. Do all of the areas with the lowest potential to reduce acid deposition have similar rock types? If so, identify the types of rock found in these regions.

34. Do all regions of Alberta have equal potential to reduce acid deposition? Support your answer.

35. Predict the effect of acid deposition on the pH of soil and the pH of lake water in Canada. Do you expect the pH values to increase, decrease, or remain constant? Explain why there may be more than one answer.

36. Within the map depicting the potential of soils to reduce the acidity from the atmosphere, there is a table describing aquatic sensitivity by province. Use this information to answer questions 36.a. to 36.d. **Note:** Zooming in on this table on your computer monitor will provide a clear view of the information.

   a. Identify the province with the largest percentage of lakes with a high sensitivity to acid deposition.

   b. Identify the province with the lowest percentage of lakes with a high sensitivity to acid deposition.

   c. Is there a correlation between the sensitivity of lakes to acid deposition and the sensitivity to soil within a province? Explain whether there is a direct variation, indirect variation, or no relationship between the sensitivity of lakes and soils to acid deposition.

   d. Hypothesize a reason for the relationship you identified in question 36.c.

Buffering and Buffering Capacity

The neutralization of acid deposition by bases, such as calcium carbonate—whether present in the soil, bedrock, or lake water—prevents the accumulation of hydronium ions. An increase in the concentration of hydronium ions makes a solution more acidic and lowers the solution's pH. As you will soon see, pH is an important factor that contributes to the viability of ecosystems; and changes in pH can have drastic effects on the survival of many organisms. The neutralization of acids by bases that prevents any change to the pH of soil or lake water is called **buffering**.

As you may expect, some areas exposed to acid rain for longer periods of time eventually develop soil or surface water with lower pH values. In these situations, the accumulation of hydronium ions is due to an absence of basic substances within the soil or water. **Buffering capacity** is a measure of the amount of acid that can be neutralized by soil or surface water. In the acid deposition demonstration you observed earlier, which samples of lake water had the highest buffering capacity? If you look back at "The Potential of Soils and Bedrock to Reduce the Acidity of Atmospheric Deposition" map, can you predict which regions have higher, moderate, and lower buffering capacities?

> ▶ **buffering:** a chemical reaction to minimize a change to the hydronium-ion concentration in soil or water
>
> ▶ **buffering capacity:** the relative ability of a substance to resist change to its pH despite the addition of an acid or base

Response of Plants to pH

Plants respond to the level of acidity in a variety of ways. The area directly underneath conifers is often lacking any other plant growth. As needles fall from pine and spruce trees to the ground, acids from the needles are transferred to the soil. This results in acidification of the soil. Few species of plants can tolerate the low pH of the soil immediately underneath these trees. Similarly, crop plants used in agriculture have limited tolerance for variation in pH. Therefore, it is important for farmers to select crops best suited to the pH of the soil. Soil exposed to acid deposition or to certain crops can become acidified and, as you will learn later, must be properly managed to remain fertile.

AGRICULTURAL PLANTS AND SOIL pH FOR OPTIMAL GROWTH

Plant	Soil pH for Optimal Growth
alfalfa	6.5 to 7.0
barley	6.3 to 6.5
blueberries	4.5
canola	5.5 to 8.3
clover	5.8 to 6.2
corn	5.8 to 6.2
oats	5.8 to 6.2
pasture grass	5.5 to 6.2
sugar beets	6.5 to 8.0
potatoes	5.2 to 8.0
wheat	5.5 to 6.5

?▶ DID YOU KNOW?

The dark patches on this potato are potato scabs, the result of an infection by bacteria that live in the soil. Although the infection does not affect the taste of the potato, farmers often choose to plant potatoes in soils with a pH below 5.3 to prevent the development of potato scabs. The bacteria cannot tolerate a pH this low.

?▶ DID YOU KNOW?

Canola is a variety of the rapeseed plant. Canola was developed by selective plant breeding technologies to produce an oil with specific properties.

Plant Nutrients, Metal Leaching, and pH

Reactions between acids and minerals in the soil are important to the cycling of matter as described in **biogeochemical cycles**. In previous science courses you examined cycles that describe the conversions of carbon, oxygen, nitrogen, and water in the environment. Reactions involving other elements are of equal importance to environmental scientists. Calcium ions, $Ca^{2+}(aq)$, are one of the required nutrients for plant growth. The reaction of $CaCO_3(s)$ that neutralizes acids present in rainfall is one manner in which calcium ions—normally bound to carbonate and other ions—become available to plants.

Other nutrients are listed in Figure B1.32, along with their function. One of these functions is the production of chlorophyl—the molecule essential for photosynthesis and for influencing a plant's growth or reproduction.

▶ **biogeochemical cycle:** a diagram representing the movement of elements and compounds between living and non-living components of an ecosystem

REQUIRED PLANT NUTRIENTS

Type	Element	Forms Used by Plants	Function
macronutrients (essential nutrients needed in large quantities)	calcium	Ca^{2+}	• important for root growth • component of cell walls
	magnesium	Mg^{2+}	• essential for chlorophyl formation
	nitrogen	NH_4^+, NO_3^-	• essential for proper leaf and stem growth • protein synthesis
	phosphorus	PO_4^{3-}, HPO_4^{2-}, $H_2PO_4^-$	• important for germination and growth of seeds, root growth, flower, and fruit production
	potassium	K^+	• promotes quick growth and disease resistance
micronutrients (essential elements needed in small quantities)	boron	BO_3^{3-}, $B_4O_7^{2-}$	• required for transporting matter within plant and for reproduction
	chlorine	Cl^-	• may affect use and production of sugars by plant
	copper	Cu^+, Cu^{2+}	• important in plant reproduction
	iron	Fe^{2+}	• required for the production of chlorophyl and oxygen
	manganese	Mn^{2+}	• required in reactions to make sugars and chlorophyl
	molybdenum	MoO_4^{2-}	• required for reactions that convert nitrogen in the atmosphere into forms that plants can use
	zinc	Zn^{2+}	• required for protein synthesis and reactions involving sugars

Figure B1.32: Some plant nutrients may take a variety of forms; but each nutrient is involved in an important role in plant growth, function, or reproduction.

Plants absorb nutrients from the soil through their roots. Prior to planting, farmers may conduct a soil analysis to determine the mineral and nutrient content of the soil. Plants have an optimal pH for growth. In addition to pH, many plants also have specific nutrient requirements.

Figure B1.33: The yellow leaves of the soybean plant in this photo are the result of chlorosis—nutrient deficiencies in the soil.

Acid deposition can present another problem that complicates the ability to grow plants or crops. Nutrients must be in a form that allows them to be absorbed through the roots of plants.

A change in soil pH can result in the formation of insoluble forms of these nutrients, making them unattainable by roots. Chlorosis—the yellowing of plant leaves due to a lack of chlorophyl—is caused by nutrient deficiencies in soil. The yellow appearance of plant leaves is one indicator that a plant may have been exposed to acid deposition. As shown in Figure B1.34, the availability of nutrients is affected by pH. Can you identify a general trend regarding the availability of the nutrients over the pH range shown?

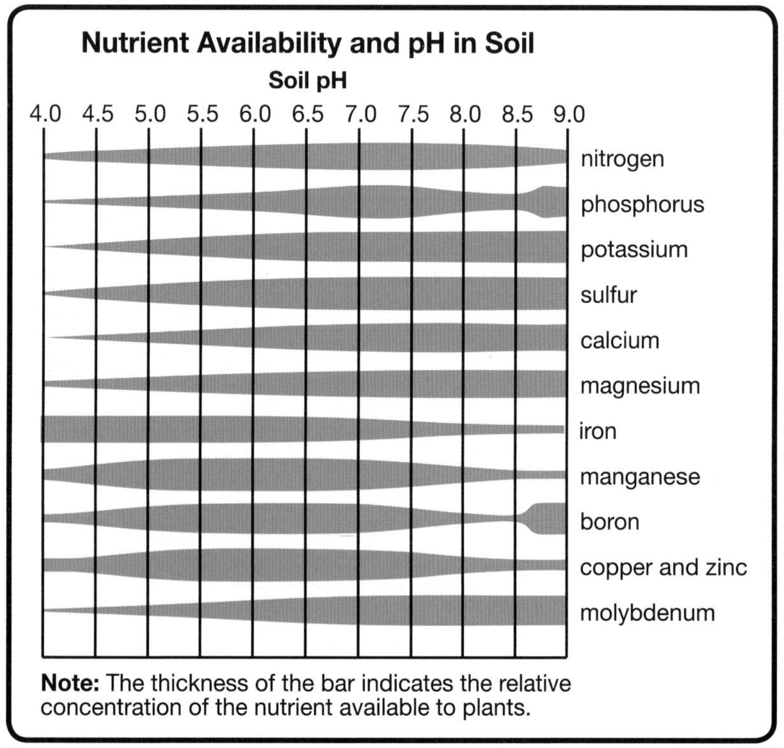

The addition of acids to the soil can make metal ions, like Ca^{2+} and Mg^{2+}, available to plants. Hydronium ions present in soil, as a result of prolonged acid deposition, can react with other compounds in the soil. One effect of prolonged acid deposition is the **leaching** of aluminium ions, $Al^{3+}(aq)$, and mercury(II) ions, $Hg^{2+}(aq)$.

> **leaching:** extracting a substance from a solid by dissolving it in a liquid; the removal of metal ions from topsoil that allows for their movement into lower levels of soil or into surface water

Within soil, aluminium ions are normally bound to hydroxide ions as aluminium hydroxide, $Al(OH)_3(s)$. Since aluminium hydroxide does not dissolve in water easily, very little dissociation occurs. This keeps the concentration of aluminium ions in the soil very low. When exposed to acids, the chemical reaction between aluminium hydroxide and hydronium ions allows aluminium ions to exist as dissociated ions in the soil. Unless precipitated by a reaction with another substance in the soil, the concentration of aluminium ions will accumulate over time. Higher concentrations of aluminium ions can affect plants and soil in many ways, including

- decreasing the growth of roots
- preventing the absorption of calcium
- reducing the population of soil bacteria involved in the decomposition of dead plant matter

Higher concentrations of aluminium ions in lakes and streams are toxic to fish. Exposure to aluminium ions has been known to damage the gills of older fish and increase the number of deaths of young fish.

Mercury is another metal found in soil, but in very small amounts. In acidic soils, a reaction between hydronium ions and compounds containing mercury can occur, resulting in the leaching of mercury(II) ions, $Hg^{2+}(aq)$. Once in the water or in the soil, micro-organisms convert mercury(II) ions into methyl mercury—a substance that is rapidly absorbed by other organisms. Mercury has no real function in living things and cannot be excreted. Since it is not removed, mercury tends to accumulate within cells and tissues of exposed organisms over their lifetime, often to levels that can be toxic to the organism itself and to any other organism that consumes it.

Nutrient Availability and pH in Soil

Soil pH

4.0 4.5 5.0 5.5 6.0 6.5 7.0 7.5 8.0 8.5 9.0

nitrogen
phosphorus
potassium
sulfur
calcium
magnesium
iron
manganese
boron
copper and zinc
molybdenum

Note: The thickness of the bar indicates the relative concentration of the nutrient available to plants.

Figure B1.34: Soil pH influences the availability of nutrients. The thickness of the bars indicates where soil concentrations of each nutrient (in forms that plants can absorb) are highest and lowest.

Concentration of Mercury in Body Tissue

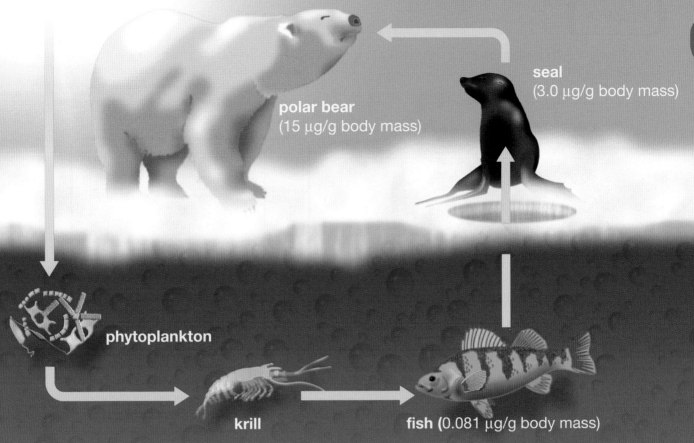

Figure B1.35: The transfer of energy within a food chain can also be used to demonstrate biomagnification of mercury.

Biomagnification can occur with a variety of substances. Regardless of the substance, bioaccumulation occurs because of the inability of an organism to use or eliminate the substance. In a situation where biomagnification occurs, the concentration of mercury within the body of each organism is higher than the concentration of mercury in its environment. Also, as you compare the concentration of mercury at each successive level of the food chain, you will see that there is a significantly higher concentration in the tissues of a predator than in its prey. Can you estimate the magnitude of the change?

Mercury poisoning occurs when the concentration of mercury within an organism reaches a toxic level. In many ecosystems, an organism suffering from mercury poisoning tends to be high up in the food chain. Where do humans fit in a food chain? Do you think information about the bioaccumulation of mercury in food chains would be useful to Aboriginal communities, many of whom have retained their traditional diets?

Acid deposition can cause other metals to have toxic effects on an ecosystem through leaching. These metals include lead, zinc, copper, cadmium, chromium, manganese, and vanadium.

▶ **biomagnification:** the tendency of a pollutant to appear at higher concentrations at higher levels in a food chain

Expressing Concentration

In environmental science, the concentration of a substance is expressed in many ways. You have seen that hydrogen-ion concentration can be expressed as mol/L or as pH. Because the concentrations of substances that bioaccumulate are very low, units like μg/g of body mass, parts per million, parts per billion, and even parts per trillion are used. The formula to calculate parts per million is in the Science Data Booklet. You can adapt this formula to parts per billion by replacing 10^6 with 10^9 or to parts per trillion by replacing 10^6 with 10^{12}.

Practice

37. The plant in this photograph was grown in soil with a pH of 5.5.

   a. State the name that describes the yellowing of the plant leaves.
   b. Explain why the plant leaves are yellowing.
   c. Indicate a possible cause for the condition of the plant.
   d. Explain the relationship between soil pH and the yellowing of the plant leaves.

38. The term *biomagnification* refers to the progressive buildup of heavy metals (or other substances) in successive levels of a food chain. Use the concentrations of mercury in Figure B1.35 (on page 197) to calculate ratios of the concentration of mercury in a seal and a polar bear relative to their prey. Explain how the ratios you calculated demonstrate that bioaccumulation is occurring.

39. Use the information in Figure B1.35 to calculate concentration levels of mercury in other organisms in the arctic food chain.

   a. Fish concentrate mercury to a level 500 times greater than the concentration of mercury in the krill they consume. Calculate the approximate concentration of mercury in krill.
   b. The concentration of mercury in krill is 1000 times greater than that of phytoplankton. Calculate the concentration of mercury in phytoplankton.

40. Scientists sampled fish from one lake over a ten-year period and collected data on the concentration of mercury within the bodies of the same species of fish of various sizes. The graph given summarizes the data they collected.

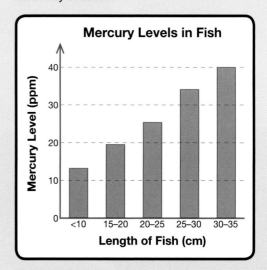

The scientists who conducted the study concluded that mercury levels are higher in older fish.

   a. How does the data support this conclusion?
   b. Concisely explain why the older fish most likely have a higher concentration of mercury in their bodies than the younger fish.
   c. Identify one experimental control used in the study. Explain the importance of this control.

Effect on Biotic Factors

In your study of ecosystems—and maybe even during a field study—you may have measured temperature, moisture content of soil, amount of sunlight, soil pH, and other **abiotic factors**. The pH of soil within an ecosystem can determine the type of plants that will grow. In turn, the types of plants present can determine the types of animals that exist within the community. Changes to the abiotic factors, especially those brought about by acid deposition, have an impact on the **biotic factors** within an ecosystem.

Recall that soil bacteria can be directly affected by acid deposition or indirectly affected by changes to the concentration of metal ions due to leaching. Besides affecting a plant's ability to produce chlorophyl, causing chlorosis, acids that directly contact plants damage the protective waxy coating on leaves. The loss of this coating permits further damage to the leaf, either by additional acid or by disease.

Aquatic organisms also demonstrate sensitivity to changes in pH. These changes are summarized in the "Sensitivity of Aquatic Organisms to pH" handout on the Science 30 Textbook CD. Because ecosystems involve complex interactions between many organisms, any change that impacts the health and survival of one organism affects the **biodiversity** of the whole ecosystem. How would you use the information in this table if you were asked to investigate whether acid deposition was affecting the area where you live? In the next investigation you will look at some locations where acid deposition has occurred and read about the effects.

▶ **abiotic factor:** a physical, non-living part of the environment

▶ **biotic factor:** a living organism in the environment

▶ **biodiversity:** the variety of life in all its forms, including the genetic diversity and numbers and types of organisms within an ecosystem

---

Utilizing Technology

Effects of Acid Deposition on Ecosystems

Purpose

You will examine information describing the effects of acid deposition on ecosystems in eastern Canada.

Science Skills

✓ Analyzing and Interpreting

Procedure

The information for this activity is located on the Science 30 Textbook CD. Obtain the document "Case Study: Eastern Canada." Read the case study; and use the information, along with what you have learned in this lesson, to answer questions 1 to 3.

Analysis

1. Are the changes to the environment in eastern Canada the result of acid deposition only? Identify any other sources that may have contributed to these effects.

2. Describe the type of data used in the material you read. Was adequate information provided regarding the effects acid deposition had on these ecosystems?

3. Evaluate the descriptions provided about the changes to the environment in eastern Canada. Are the descriptions and claims consistent with what you learned about the effects of acid deposition? Identify any similarities.

Try This Activity

Assessing Factors Involved in Acid Deposition in Alberta

Background Information

Throughout this chapter you examined activities that produce emissions related to acid deposition. The major processes that produce emissions of $SO_2(g)$ and $NO_x(g)$ in Alberta include

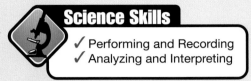

Science Skills

✓ Performing and Recording
✓ Analyzing and Interpreting

- the production of electricity by the combustion of coal, natural gas, or biomass
- upstream petroleum and gas production, including the processes of exploration, extracting, and processing (refining) petroleum and natural gas such as
  - sour gas flaring
  - sweetening or removal of sulfur from sour natural gas
  - removal of sulfur from crude oil
- oil sands (tar sands) production
- transportation
- use of fossil fuels as a heat source in homes or in industry (considered as stationary sources)

You also discovered that wind and quantity of precipitation can be major factors in determining where deposition of acidic particles or solutions will occur. In addition, you studied how the role that soil components, including calcium carbonate from limestone, can have in neutralizing acids. You also saw how acid deposition affects abiotic and biotic components of the environment and how this may impact the balance that exists within ecosystems.

With what you know about acid deposition, it is logical to wonder about Alberta's situation.

Purpose

You will research emissions related to acid deposition to obtain a clearer picture of the impact of acid deposition.

Procedure

Obtain the following handouts from the Science 30 Textbook CD.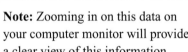

- "Map of Alberta"
- "Canadian and US Crude Oil Pipelines and Refineries"
- "Gas Flaring and Venting in Alberta"
- "All Generating Stations by Fuel Used (1997)"
- "Sour Gas Facilities in Alberta"

Note: Zooming in on this data on your computer monitor will provide a clear view of this information.

step 1: Consult with your teacher regarding the magnitude of the area for which you are required to collect information. Is it only for your local area? province? country?

step 2: Gather information (from this textbook, the Internet, or other materials) about the following topics:

- potential of soils to reduce effects of or neutralize acid deposition
- direction of prevailing winds
- locations of electrical power generation facilities
- locations of gas wells, flares, and sour gas processing facilities
- locations of oil wells, flaring, and oil refining
- locations of tar sands (oil sands) processing
- amount of precipitation, both as rain and as snow
- pH of rainfall
- locations of major bodies of water (including rivers and lakes)

step 3: On a map of Alberta, record in an organized manner the information you collected. If codes, colours, or symbols are used, be sure to include a legend.

Analysis

Use the information on your map to identify locations in Alberta where you either

(1) consider acid deposition to currently be a problem

(2) predict acid deposition will be a problem in the future

Justify your answer.

1.3 Summary

In this lesson you learned about the complexity of the environment by studying the effect acid deposition has on soil and on the living components of ecosystems. You were introduced to the effects weather patterns (e.g., prevailing winds and precipitation) have on the transfer and deposition of acidic substances. You examined the chemical interactions between substances in the soil and hydronium ions and how these interactions can result in buffering or in leaching of metal ions. Leaching metals can be a problem associated with acid deposition. Leaching may result in the loss of nutrients from soil or an increase in the concentration in either the soil or water of certain metals that can be toxic. Mercury is an example of one metal that may biomagnify within a food chain when leached from soil. You then looked at examples from eastern Canada where acid deposition has occurred. Finally, you were asked to analyze a number of factors and apply your understanding to the situation in Alberta. In the next lesson you will examine the processes used to monitor and study acid deposition.

1.3 Questions

Knowledge

1. Define the following terms.

   a. jet stream
   b. alkaline
   c. minerals
   d. buffering
   e. buffering capacity
   f. biogeochemical cycles
   g. leaching
   h. biomagnification
   i. biodiversity

2. State the type of relationship that exists between the concentration of sulfur dioxide, $SO_2(g)$, in the atmosphere and the pH of rain.

3. a. Name the type of rock that has a high buffering capacity.

   b. Identify the chemical compound present in the rock type identified in question 3.a.

   c. Write the chemical equation between the hydronium ions and the chemical substance identified in question 3.b.

4. List factors that contributed to the occurrence of acid deposition in eastern Canada.

5. Is acid deposition entirely the result of human activity? Support your answer.

Applying Concepts

6. At the start of this lesson you were asked to develop a hypothesis describing a relationship between the presence of emissions in the environment and their effects.

   a. State a hypothesis that describes a relationship between the presence of emissions in the environment and their effects.

   b. List experiments you need to conduct to test and support your hypothesis.

   c. The people within a community who are closely connected to the local surroundings are often the first to notice environmental change. Identify a societal group you can consult with to determine whether they have noticed environmental changes.

   d. Which type of information will you collect from the sources identified in question 6.c.? Explain how this information would help you understand the relationship between emissions and their effects on the environment.

7. Use your knowledge of soil pH to explain how it is possible for soil to be rich in nutrients but unable to support good plant growth.

8. In a study of soil exposed to acid rain, measurements of calcium ions and aluminium ions were taken at regular intervals. Ratios of the concentrations of calcium ions to aluminium ions are shown in the following table.

Soil Sample	Ratio $[Ca^{2+}] : [Al^{3+}]$	Comments
1 (pre-acidification)	1 : 1	concentrations of calcium ions and aluminium ions similar to control soil samples
2 (early stages of acidification)	2 : 1	signs of stress observed in some plant species
3 (late stages of acidification)	0.2 : 1	extreme stress observed in many plant species

   a. Explain why the level of calcium ions present in soil changed.

   b. It was hypothesized that the concentration of aluminium ions in soil would increase as the soil became acidified. Explain whether the ratios listed in the table support this statement.

9. Aluminium is often present in the soil as aluminium hydroxide, $Al(OH)_3(s)$.

   a. Write the balanced chemical equation that occurs between hydroxide ions in the soil and hydronium ions in acid rain.

   b. Explain how the reaction of hydroxide ions with hydronium ions could bring about the leaching of aluminium ions into stream and lake water.

10. A study investigating biomagnification sampled the different tissues of fish, seals, and polar bears in an arctic food chain.

Tissue Sample	Concentration of Mercury ($\mu g/g$ body mass)		
	Fish	Seal	Polar Bear
muscle	0.079	0.25	0.07
liver	0.080	3.0	15
kidney	0.080	1.2	15

   a. Explain how the data demonstrates that mercury biomagnifies within a food chain.

   b. Hypothesize why differences may exist in the concentration of mercury in different tissues in some organisms.

   c. Explain how the results of this study may impact the work of other scientists.

11. The accumulation of acid deposition in soil and water can result in a lowering of pH, which causes a decrease in the number of bacteria that decompose plant and animal matter in an ecosystem. Explain how a decrease in the number of bacteria that decompose plant and animal matter would negatively affect an ecosystem.

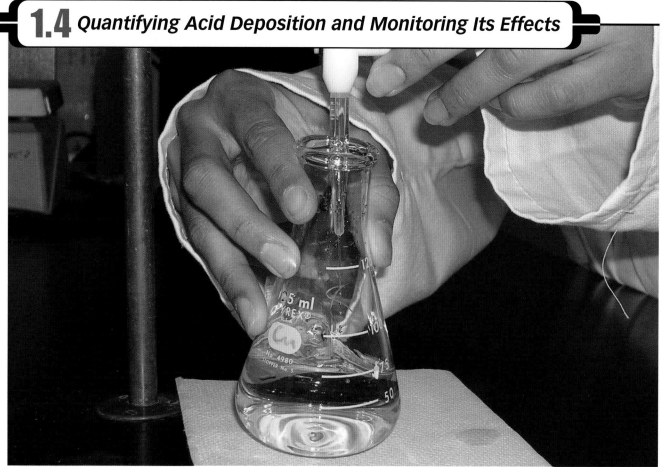

Figure B1.36: Titration is one method used to determine the amount of acid in a sample.

In Lesson 1.2 you made observations that led to developing empirical definitions of acids and bases and used indicators to estimate the pH of a solution. In Lesson 1.3 you discovered the value of using information from chemical tests as well as information about the organisms within the environment to investigate the effects of acid deposition. Earlier, you made observations that led to developing empirical definitions of acids and bases and used indicators to estimate the pH of a solution. Information about acids and acid deposition can be categorized in two ways: as **qualitative data** or **quantitative data**.

You have seen how important the ability to resist the effects of acid deposition can be. In this lesson you will examine a process that is used to determine the concentration of an acid or base in a sample. You have seen how important the ability to resist the effects of acid deposition can be. Now, you will develop a plan to measure buffering capacity.

▶ **qualitative data:** a description of a substance by identifying its properties, characteristics, or attributes

▶ **quantitative data:** a description of a substance that involves a measurement and a numerical magnitude

Practice

41. A group of environmental scientists collected the following data to assess the effects of acid deposition in a specific area:

- spots present on surfaces of leaves
- population sizes of organisms within the ecosystem
- information from hunters and inhabitants within the area
- number of plants demonstrating chlorosis
- soil pH

- concentration of Al^{3+}(aq) in soil and water
- population of young fish
- observations of fish health
- list of insect populations within the area
- list of plant species within the area

Using a table, classify the information collected as being either qualitative data or quantitative data.

Traditional Ecological Knowledge

In Lesson 1.3 you analyzed changes to the environment that scientists and others who depend on the land might observe. You also noted that these observations might be interpreted as being related to the effects of acid deposition, but they are often best considered within a larger context. When studying acid deposition, scientists recognize the intricate connections within ecosystems and have come to recognize the value of **traditional ecological knowledge** possessed by some members of Canada's First Nations, Métis, and Inuit. Traditional ecological knowledge provides a holistic or "big-picture" view. This is not only about an intimate knowledge of plants, animals, and natural phenomena, it also involves an understanding of how technologies used by First Nations, Métis, and Inuit groups have impacted the environment.

▶ **traditional ecological knowledge:** the accumulated observations and understanding of the people living within an area, acquired over many hundreds of years through direct contact with the environment

When investigating environmental issues, the holistic data provided through traditional ecological knowledge often complements the methods used by scientists. This combination of perspectives provides for a fuller understanding of the complex web of interactions and relationships within an ecosystem.

Try This Activity

Identifying the More Acidic Solution

Purpose

You will perform an experiment and use the data to determine which of two solutions contains the most acid.

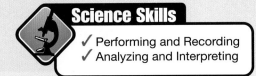

Science Skills

✓ Performing and Recording
✓ Analyzing and Interpreting

Background Information

pH is one way to measure the acidity of a solution. One of the empirical properties of an acid is its ability to be neutralized by a base. In this activity you will use a basic solution to test the two acidic solutions you are comparing.

Materials

- commercial lemon juice
- vinegar
- 0.100-mol/L NaOH(aq)
- 3, 50-mL beakers
- 3 plastic (berol) pipettes (or medicine droppers)
- multiwell dish (or 2 watch glasses)
- phenolphthalein
- grease pencil (or waterproof marker)
- "Identifying the More Acidic Solution" handout from the Science 30 Textbook CD

Procedure

Note: When performing this procedure, make sure all the drops are as similar in size as possible. To deliver similar-sized drops, hold the pipette vertically and maintain the same pressure on the bulb.

step 1: Pour approximately 10 mL of the commercial lemon juice and vinegar into separate 50-mL beakers. Label each beaker appropriately.

step 2: Pour approximately 20 mL of the NaOH(aq) solution into the third 50-mL beaker. Label this beaker appropriately.

step 3: Depress the bulb of the first pipette, and draw some of the lemon juice solution into the pipette.

step 4: Gently squeeze the bulb of the pipette and carefully deliver 3 drops of the lemon juice into the first well of the multiwell dish (or to the first watch glass).

step 5: Add 1 drop of phenolphthalein to the commercial lemon juice in the multiwell dish (or watch glass). Record the colour of the indicator as the initial colour in "Identifying the More Acidic Solution" handout.

step 6: Depress the bulb of the second pipette, and draw some of the NaOH(aq) solution into the pipette.

step 7: Hold the pipette containing the NaOH(aq) over the well (or watch glass) containing the lemon juice.

step 8: Gently squeeze the bulb and carefully deliver drops of NaOH(aq) solution into the well until the indicator changes colour. Record the number of drops required and the final indicator colour in your table.

step 9: Repeat steps 3 to 8 using the third pipette to deliver the vinegar solution to the second well (or watch glass).

Analysis

Use the data collected to identify which of the two solutions tested—the commercial lemon juice or the vinegar—contains more acid.

Titration—Quantifying Acid in a Solution

Previously, you examined rainfall data to further examine the factors related to acid deposition. While analyzing the graphs, you may have noted that higher values for total acidity for the rainfall occurred at times when higher concentrations of sulfate ions were present. This pattern contrasts with the inverse variation that occurs when comparing the total acidity and pH. Although pH is a measure of the concentration of hydronium ions in a solution, other methods often have to be used to determine the amount of acid present.

Titration is a method of determining the quantity of acid or base present in a sample. As you know, acids can be neutralized by a reaction with a base. Also, the colour change for some indicators can be used to signify when the pH of a solution changes from acidic to basic.

> **titration:** a technique used to determine the concentration of a substance in a solution by adding measured quantities of another substance that it is known to react with until an endpoint is reached

How is it possible to determine which solution contains more acid using such simple equipment? What is the significance of using NaOH(aq) and an indicator? Perhaps measuring the volume and proportions of each reactant involved is a key to using your observations from a titration.

From your observations, were you able to identify which solution was more concentrated in the previous activity, "Identifying the More Acidic Solution"? In fact, you counted and compared the number of drops required to bring about a colour change to the indicator. There is always a need for quantitative data (in this case, number of drops) along with qualitative data (the colour change signifying the completion of the reaction) to find an answer. Now that you have completed your first titration, it is time for you to see how this method can be used to provide precise numerical data.

Improving Precision

Figure B1.37: Carefully reading a burette improves the precision of the results of a titration.

How would you modify your procedure if you were asked to perform a titration to determine the concentration of acid in a sample of rainwater? A titration can be adapted to produce an answer with greater precision. If you choose to use equipment—such as a burette, a graduated cylinder, or a pipette—to more accurately measure the volumes of the solutions you use, you will collect data that has greater precision than the titration you just performed.

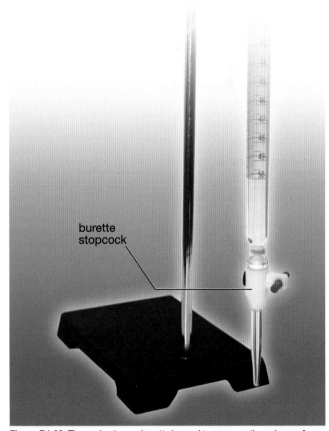

burette
stopcock

Figure B1.38: The scale along a burette is used to measure the volume of solution that flows through the stopcock during the reaction between an acid and a base.

Titration of an Acid with a Base—Demonstration

Background Information

Your teacher will demonstrate the procedure for performing a titration. As you watch the demonstration, refer to the instructions given. You will be asked to perform titrations later in this lesson, so paying careful attention to the values you need to measure and record is essential to your ability to adapt this process.

Titrations can be performed in microscale or macroscale. This activity uses the macroscale method; however, if you wish to view the instructions describing the microscale method, they are located on the Science 30 Textbook CD.

CAUTION!

Use gloves, safety glasses, and a lab apron for this activity.

Materials

- bromothymol blue (or phenolphthalein)
- acid solution, containing an unknown concentration of $H_3O^+(aq)$
- 0.100-mol/L NaOH(aq)
- de-ionized or distilled water in a wash bottle
- 250-mL beaker
- 2, 50-mL beakers
- 125-mL Erlenmeyer flask
- 10-mL graduated cylinder (or 10-mL pipette and pipette bulb)
- small liquid funnel
- 50-mL burette
- burette clamp
- ring stand
- grease pencil (or waterproof marker)

Macroscale Method

step 1: Use the grease pencil to label a 50-mL beaker "Acid." Transfer approximately 40 mL of the acid solution (of unknown concentration) to this beaker.

step 2: Use the grease pencil to label another 50-mL beaker "Base Sodium Hydroxide." Transfer approximately 45 mL of the NaOH(aq) to this beaker.

step 3: Attach and secure the burette clamp half-way along the ring stand.

Science Skills

✓ Analyzing and Interpreting

step 4: Carefully wash the burette. Close the stopcock; then fill it one-third full with water from the wash bottle. Tilt the burette sideways to wash the inside walls with the water; then tilt the burette vertically and hold it over the 250 mL beaker, which will serve as the waste beaker. Open the stopcock and transfer the wash water from the burette into the waste beaker. Repeat this step one more time.

step 5: Place the burette into the burette clamp attached to the ring stand.

step 6: Close the stopcock; place the funnel into the upper end of the burette; and add approximately 15–20 mL of NaOH(aq) to the burette. Remove the funnel from the top of the burette.

step 7: Carefully remove the burette from the clamp; then tilt and wash the inside walls with the sodium hydroxide solution. Return the burette to the clamp. Position the waste beaker under the burette. Open the stopcock to drain the burette.

step 8: Close the stopcock and replace the funnel in the upper end of the burette. Add NaOH(aq) to fill the burette so that the liquid level is within the range of 0 and 5 mL.

step 9: Position the burette so that the level of the NaOH(aq) is at eye level, and measure the position of the lower surface of the meniscus. (You should be able to measure this to at least one decimal place; however, two decimal places is preferred. You might find that using a card with a dark line on it improves the visibility of the bottom of the meniscus.) Record this level in your table.

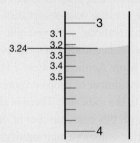

step 10: Using either a graduated cylinder or a pipette, transfer 10.0 mL of the acid solution to the 125-mL Erlenmeyer flask. Record the volume of acid sample transferred in your table.

step 11: Add 3 to 4 drops of bromothymol blue (or phenolphthalein). Record the colour of the indicator in the acid sample in your table.

step 12: Position the Erlenmeyer flask containing the acid and indicator under the burette and then open the stopcock. Add a small amount of the solution from the burette to the contents of the flask. As you add solution from the burette, swirl the contents of the flask to ensure mixing. Repeat adding small amounts of solution from the burette to the flask until the indicator changes colour. Record this colour in your table.

step 13: Once a permanent colour change has been reached, position the burette so that the level of the NaOH(aq) is at eye level. Measure the position of the lower surface of the meniscus. Record this level in your table.

step 14: Transfer the contents of the Erlenmeyer flask to the waste beaker. Rinse the flask with some water from the wash bottle. Repeat steps 8 to 13 to obtain data from two more trials.

step 15: Disassemble, wash, and return equipment to its proper location. Repeat step 4 to wash the burette.

Note: Save your data from this investigation. You will analyze it later in this lesson.

Using Titration Data

When a base is added to an acid, a neutralization reaction occurs.

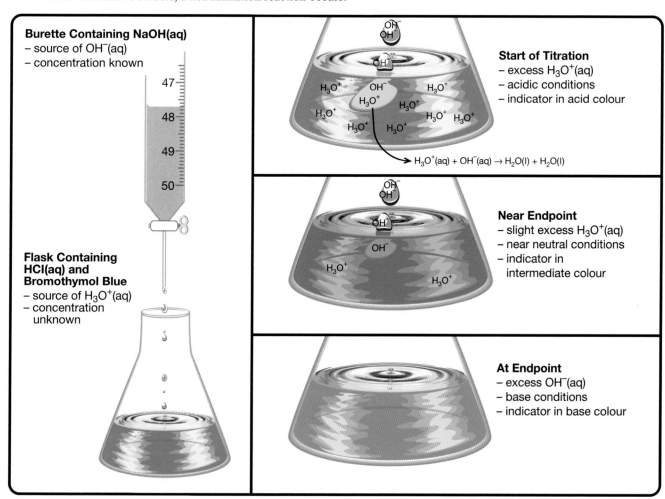

Figure B1.39: Events of titration

In Figure B1.39 on page 207, hydroxide ions within the sodium hydroxide solution were added to neutralize the hydronium ions present in the acid solution being tested. As sodium hydroxide from the burette is added, hydroxide ions enter the acid solution in the flask. A reaction between hydronium ions and hydroxide ions occurs until an excess of hydronium ions no longer exists. The decrease in the quantity of hydronium ions causes the pH of the solution in the flask to increase. The increase in pH is noticeable because of the colour change of the indicator. Once the indicator changes colour to indicate a basic condition, the endpoint of the titration has been reached and the addition of more hydroxide ions causes no further chemical change.

As demonstrated in Figure B1.39, it is critical to note the proportion of hydroxide ions required to neutralize the hydronium ions in the solution. Previously, you studied reactions between an acid and a base that did not require coefficients larger than 1 in order to be balanced. You might like the simplicity of not having to use larger coefficients, but the ratio of one particle of acid reacting with one particle of base has even greater significance.

A balanced chemical equation is like a recipe describing how to carry out a reaction. The chemical formulas you write tell you what to use, and the coefficients that appear in front of the chemical formulas describe how much of each component to use. If you read the reaction between hydronium and hydroxide aloud, it would sound like, "One hydronium ion reacts with one hydroxide ion to produce two molecules of water." The pattern can then be expanded to any number of particles, including the number of moles. You may recall from previous science courses that the amount of particles within a chemical system is measured as moles. A mole refers to a set number of molecules or particles. *One mole* refers to the same number of particles for any substance. Using moles, you can read the statement as, "One mole of hydronium reacts with one mole of hydroxide to produce two moles of water molecules." If you were to focus on the relationship between the relative amounts of hydronium and hydroxide involved in the reaction, the same equation could be stated as, "For each mole of hydronium that reacts, one mole of hydroxide is required."

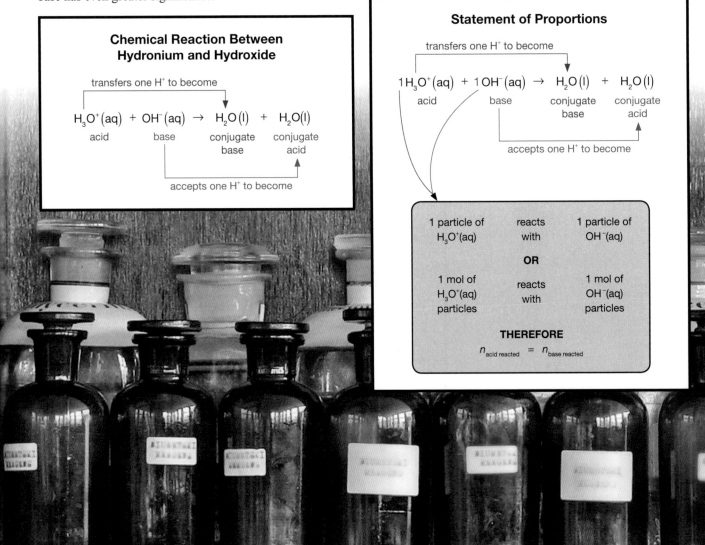

The statement of proportions demonstrated by the balanced chemical equation is what makes it possible to determine the concentration of the unknown solution titrated in the "Titration of an Acid with a Base" demonstration. During the demonstration, moles of hydroxide were added until the acid was neutralized. If you can determine the number of moles of hydroxide that were added, the statement of proportions for this equation indicates that an equal number of moles of hydronium had to be neutralized by the reaction.

The molar concentration of a solution is the number of moles of dissolved solute per litre of solution.

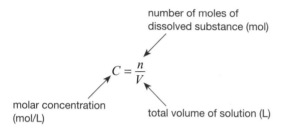

number of moles of dissolved substance (mol)

$$C = \frac{n}{V}$$

molar concentration (mol/L)

total volume of solution (L)

The concentration formula can be rearranged to determine the number of moles.

$$C = \frac{n}{V}$$

$$C \times V = \frac{n}{\cancel{V}} \times \cancel{V}$$

$$n = CV$$

When working with solutions, it is common to know the concentration and volume of the solution you used during the process. In the case of a titration, you tend to use a **standard solution** in the burette and the graduations along the burette to determine the volume delivered during the titration. The values for the concentration of the standard solution (in the burette) and the volume of solution used to reach the endpoint are substituted into the formula to calculate the number of moles of reactant in the standard solution used to complete the reaction.

> **standard solution:** a solution that has a known concentration

standard solution ⟶ $C = \frac{n}{V}$ ⟵ reactant in standard solution
⟵ standard solution used in each titration

If the acid and the base react in a 1:1 proportion, then

$$n_{\text{acid reacted}} = n_{\text{base reacted}}$$

This statement of proportions for an acid-base reaction, where there is a transfer of a single hydrogen ion, can be interpreted as the number of moles of reactant in the standard solution is equal to the number of moles of reactant in the test solution.

Recall that the problem identified at the start of the titration demonstration was to determine the molar concentration of the hydronium ions in the acidic solution. Up to this point, you have been able to determine the number of moles of reactant in the standard solution—hydroxide—and, thus, the number of moles of reactant in the test solution—the acid. Now, using the concentration formula, you can determine the molar concentration of the test solution. This time, use the number of moles of reactant and the volume of the test solution.

test solution ⟶ $C = \frac{n}{V}$ ⟵ reactant in test solution
⟵ test solution used in each titration

The data recorded in the titration demonstration can be used to calculate the concentration of the acid in the solution tested. Work through the calculations performed in Example Problem 1.9 on pages 210 and 211. Use the data you recorded from the demonstration to determine the concentration of hydronium ions in the hydrochloric acid tested.

The table given shows data from the titration of four 10.0-mL samples of a solution containing hydronium ions and phenolphthalein using 0.130-mol/L sodium hydroxide solution (the standard solution).

	Volume of Standard Solution (mL)			Endpoint Colour
Trial	Final	Initial	Added	
1	13.44	1.22		dark pink
2	25.35	13.44		light pink
3	37.33	25.35		light pink
4	49.22	37.33		light pink

Calculate the concentration of the hydronium ions in the acid solution.

Solution

step 1: Complete the table.

	Volume of Standard Solution (mL)			Endpoint Colour
Trial	Final	Initial	Added	
1	13.44	1.22	12.22	dark pink
2	25.35	13.44	11.91	light pink
3	37.33	25.35	11.98	light pink
4	49.22	37.33	11.89	light pink

step 2: Select the most consistent trials, and calculate the average volume of standard solution added.

Trials 2 to 4 are the most consistent. This is shown by the similar endpoint colour and the similar volume of standard solution required (within 0.09 mL of each other). Therefore,

$$V_{\text{standard solution}} = \frac{(11.91+11.98+11.89) \text{ mL}}{3}$$
$$= 11.926\,666\,67 \text{ mL}$$
$$= 11.93 \text{ mL}$$

step 3: Confirm proportions by writing the balanced chemical equation for the titration process.

$$H_3O^+(aq) + OH^-(aq) \rightarrow H_2O(l) + H_2O(l)$$

Therefore, for every mole of base, $OH^-(aq)$, that reacts, one mole of acid, $H_3O^+(aq)$, reacts. This means $n_{\text{base reacted}} = n_{\text{acid reacted}}$.

continued

step 4: Calculate the number of moles of acid that reacted.

$$C = 0.130 \text{ mol/L}$$

$$V = 11.926\,666\,67 \text{ mL} \times \frac{1 \text{ L}}{1000 \text{ mL}}$$

$$= 0.011\,926\,666\,7 \text{ L}$$

$$n_{\text{base reacted}} = n_{\text{acid reacted}} = ?$$

$$C = \frac{n_{\text{base reacted}}}{V}$$

$$n_{\text{base reacted}} = CV$$

$$n_{\text{acid reacted}} = (0.130 \text{ mol/L})(0.011\,926\,666\,7 \text{ L})$$

$$= 0.001\,550\,466\,7 \text{ mol}$$

$$= 0.001\,55 \text{ mol}$$

step 5: Calculate the concentration of the acid solution.

$$V = 10.0 \text{ mL} \times \frac{1 \text{ L}}{1000 \text{ mL}}$$

$$= 0.0100 \text{ L}$$

$$n_{\text{acid reacted}} = 0.001\,550\,466\,7 \text{ mol}$$

$$C = ?$$

$$C = \frac{n_{\text{acid reacted}}}{V}$$

$$= \frac{0.001\,550\,466\,7 \text{ mol}}{0.0100 \text{ L}}$$

$$= 0.155 \text{ mol/L}$$

The concentration of the hydronium ions in the acid solution is 0.155 mol/L.

Practice

42. Use the following information to answer questions 42.a. to 42.c.

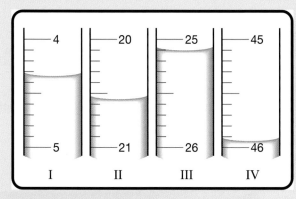

4	20	25	45
5	21	26	46
I	II	III	IV

a. Read and record the volume in each of the four burettes.

b. If burettes I and II represent the initial and final reading for a titration respectively, calculate the volume of solution used.

c. If burettes III and IV represent the initial and final readings respectively for a second trial, comment on whether the two trials had similar results.

43. Use the following information to calculate the hydronium-ion concentration in a sample of lake water titrated using a standardized solution of sodium hydroxide.

> **Concentration of hydroxide ions:**
> 0.000 125 mol/L
> **Initial burette reading:** 2.25 mL
> **Final burette reading:** 12.13 mL
> **Volume of lake water in titration:** 10.00 mL

44. Waste water from a mining operation was tested using a titration with a sodium hydroxide solution containing a hydroxide-ion concentration of 0.125 mol/L. It required 44.5 mL of the sodium hydroxide solution to react with the hydronium ions in a 75.0-mL sample of the waste water.

a. Calculate the molar concentration of the hydronium ions in the waste-water sample.

b. Use the molar concentration of the hydronium ions to determine the pH of the waste-water sample.

Why Use a Titration?

For situations where the amount of substance in a solution is required, titration is the preferred method. Titrations can be performed quickly and with relatively inexpensive equipment. Because many trials are done on samples of the test solution, the results can be used to demonstrate consistent results. Consistent results improve confidence in the data and emphasize the reliability of the titration process.

Investigation

Performing a Titration

Science Skills

✓ Performing and Recording
✓ Analyzing and Interpreting
✓ Communication and Teamwork

Purpose

You will determine the concentration of acid or base in a test sample.

Background Information

The process of titration can be adapted to a variety of situations. Consult with your teacher for further instructions as to which solutions or substances you will be using in this investigation. You may wish to refer to the detailed procedure shown in the titration demonstration earlier in this lesson (pages 206 and 207) and, if necessary, adapt the procedure.

Performing and Recording

Prepare a data table to record qualitative and quantitative observations from each of the trials performed. Ensure that your data is recorded in a logical and understandable manner.

Analysis

1. Use the data you collected to complete the calculations as instructed by your teacher.

Communication and Teamwork

Obtain a copy of a data table from another group of students. Use the data to perform the calculations as instructed by your teacher. Then meet with other students to review the results of the calculations performed on your data and the data of other students.

2. Identify similarities and differences between the sets of data.

3. Comment on whether consistency is observed within the data analyzed. Identify how consistency is evident or not evident within a set of data and between the sets of data.

4. How does the consistency (or lack thereof) in the data affect your confidence in being able to state the concentration of the solution tested? Identify which aspect—reliability or validity—is addressed by consistency within and between the sets of data.

Try This Activity

Comparing Two Acids

Purpose

Do all acids behave similarly? You will compare two acids that appear at different positions on the "Table of Acids and Bases."

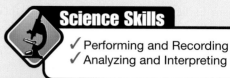

Science Skills

✓ Performing and Recording
✓ Analyzing and Interpreting

Materials

- 1.00-mol/L ethanoic acid
- 1.00-mol/L hydrochloric acid
- 2, 10-mL graduated cylinders
- 2 eyedroppers
- 2, 5-cm lengths of magnesium ribbon
- 2, 50-mL beakers
- 2 test tubes (capacity around 5 mL)
- pH paper (or pH meter)
- test tube rack
- scissors
- grease pencil (or waterproof marker)
- stopwatch (or clock)
- conductivity meter
- forceps or tweezers

 CAUTION!

Use gloves, safety glasses, and a lab apron for this activity.

Procedure

step 1: Prepare a data table with two columns. Use the names of the two acid solutions listed in the materials as the headings for your table.

step 2: Use the grease pencil to label one of the test tubes "Ethanoic Acid." Place the test tube into the test tube rack.

step 3: Transfer exactly 5.00 mL of ethanoic acid to one of the graduated cylinders. Use an eyedropper to ensure the meniscus is at the 5.00-mL mark on the cylinder.

step 4: Transfer the ethanoic acid in the graduated cylinder to the "Ethanoic Acid" test tube.

step 5: Transfer enough of the ethanoic acid from the test tube to cover the bottom of one of the 50-mL beakers. Use the conductivity meter to test the solution. Record your observations in your data table. Use the acid in the beaker to measure the pH. Place one of the strips of pH paper into the remaining solution, and record the pH of the solution in a data table. (If you are using a pH meter, you may have to use a larger volume of acid in the beaker to cover the electrode at the bottom of the meter. Ensure that you rinse the electrode before testing the pH of the second solution.)

step 6: Repeat steps 2 to 5 using the hydrochloric acid solution.

step 7: Place a strip of magnesium into each of the test tubes. Record the initial response of the magnesium to the acid and the length of time until a reaction no longer occurs in each of the test tubes. Estimate the amount of magnesium remaining in each test tube.

Analysis

Use the data collected to prepare a list of similarities and differences between ethanoic acid and hydrochloric acid.

Strong and Weak Acids

The differences in the behaviour of ethanoic acid and hydrochloric acid are representative of two groupings used to classify acids. In the "Comparing Two Acids" activity, you tested two acid solutions with identical molar concentrations. Despite this similarity, can you explain why the hydrochloric acid solution had a lower pH and higher conductivity than the ethanoic acid solution? Earlier in this lesson you discovered that solutions with lower pH values, like hydrochloric acid, contain higher concentrations of hydronium ions. The higher conductivity of the hydrochloric acid solution confirmed that it contained more ions. The results from these two tests suggest that hydrochloric acid behaves differently than ethanoic acid in an aqueous solution.

Reaction of Hydrochloric Acid and Water

$$HCl(aq) + H_2O(l) \rightarrow H_3O^+(aq) + Cl^-(aq)$$

acid · · · · · base · · · · · conjugate acid · · · · · conjugate base

---

Reaction of Ethanoic Acid and Water

$$CH_3COOH(aq) + H_2O(l) \rightarrow H_3O^+(aq) + CH_3COO^-(aq)$$

acid · · · · · base · · · · · conjugate acid · · · · · conjugate base

---

You might then interpret the lower conductivity and the higher pH of the ethanoic acid solution to mean that ethanoic acid produced fewer hydronium ions when it reacted with water.

Acids and bases can be categorized into two groups: strong and weak. The members of each group appear in the "Table of Acids and Bases."

TABLE OF ACIDS AND BASES

	Acid Name	Acid Formula	Conjugate Base Formula
STRONG ACIDS	hydrochloric acid	$HCl(aq)$	$Cl^-(aq)$
	sulfuric acid	$H_2SO_4(aq)$	$HSO_4^-(aq)$
	nitric acid	$HNO_3(aq)$	$NO_3^-(aq)$
	hydronium ion	$H_3O^+(aq)$	$H_2O(l)$
WEAK ACIDS	oxalic acid	$HOOCCOOH(aq)$	$HOOCCOO^-(aq)$
	sulfurous acid	$H_2SO_3(aq)$	$HSO_3^-(aq)$
	hydrogen sulfate ion	$HSO_4^-(aq)$	$SO_4^{2-}(aq)$
	phosphoric acid	$H_3PO_4(aq)$	$H_2PO_4^-(aq)$
	orange IV	$HOr(aq)$	$Or^-(aq)$
	nitrous acid	$HNO_2(aq)$	$NO_2^-(aq)$
	hydrofluoric acid	$HF(aq)$	$F^-(aq)$
	methanoic acid	$HCOOH(aq)$	$HCOO^-(aq)$
	methyl orange	$HMo(aq)$	$Mo^-(aq)$
	benzoic acid	$C_6H_5COOH(aq)$	$C_6H_5COO^-(aq)$
	ethanoic (acetic) acid	$CH_3COOH(aq)$	$CH_3COO^-(aq)$
	carbonic acid, $CO_2(g) + H_2O(l)$	$H_2CO_3(aq)$	$HCO_3^-(aq)$
	bromothymol blue	$HBb(aq)$	$Bb^-(aq)$
	hydrosulfuric acid	$H_2S(aq)$	$HS^-(aq)$
	phenolphthalein	$HPh(aq)$	$Ph^-(aq)$
	boric acid	$H_3BO_3(aq)$	$H_2BO_3^-(aq)$
	ammonium ion	$NH_4^+(aq)$	$NH_3(aq)$
	hydrogen carbonate ion	$HCO_3^-(aq)$	$CO_3^{2-}(aq)$
	indigo carmine	$HIc(aq)$	$Ic^-(aq)$
	water (55.5 mol/L)	$H_2O(l)$	$OH^-(aq)$

(right-hand labels: **WEAK BASES**, **STRONG BASE**)

As indicated earlier, the substances in the "Table of Acids and Bases" are arranged according to strength. It is important to note that strength refers only to the extent that an acid or base will react with water to produce hydronium ions or hydroxide ions, respectively.

As you saw, both the ethanoic acid and the hydrochloric acid tested had equal molar concentrations and both consumed the same amount of magnesium ribbon. It is important to remember that weak acids will transfer a hydrogen ion to a base similar to the way a strong acid will.

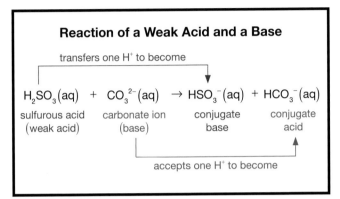

Reaction of a Weak Acid and a Base

transfers one H^+ to become

$$H_2SO_3(aq) \ + \ CO_3{}^{2-}(aq) \ \rightarrow HSO_3{}^-(aq) \ + \ HCO_3{}^-(aq)$$

sulfurous acid (weak acid)   carbonate ion (base)   conjugate base   conjugate acid

accepts one H^+ to become

The reaction between sulfurous acid and carbonate ions demonstrates that the deposition of a weak acid could react with carbonate ions—a substance found in many types of soil. From the "Comparing Two Acids" activity, you saw that a weak acid solution and a strong acid solution of identical concentration and volume produces the same overall effect. Now, recall that many acids are produced from emissions. Whether strong or weak, acids can still lower the pH of water and react with components in the soil. Can you predict the effect on chemical components of soil, like carbonate ions, when subject to long-term acid deposition?

Practice

45. List the acids produced from sulfur oxide and nitrogen oxide emissions. Use the "Table of Acids and Bases" to classify these acids as being either strong or weak.

46. Use the pH values you measured in the "Comparing Two Acids" activity to further support the notion that the two acids tested produce different concentrations of hydronium ions.

47. "Strong acids react almost completely with water to produce hydronium ions." Is this statement supported by the data you collected in the "Comparing Two Acids" activity? Support your answer.

48. Write the balanced chemical equation for the reaction between nitrous acid, $HNO_2(aq)$, and hydroxide, $OH^-(aq)$. Identify the acid, the base, the conjugate acid, and the conjugate base.

Titrations Involving Strong or Weak Acids and Bases

When you completed the "Comparing Two Acids" investigation, you may have been surprised to find that acids can vary in the extent to which they react with water. Earlier in this chapter you used pH measurements to measure acidity; but the results of the last investigation showed that pH is not the best way to determine the concentration of acid in a solution. When acid particles react directly with base particles, titration is the preferred method of determining the concentration of acid in a solution.

When designing a titration, you need to ensure that the acid will react with the base; so, when possible, a solution containing hydroxide ions (a strong base) is used. For a similar reason, solutions containing strong acids are most often used to titrate basic solutions. When selecting solutions for titration, you may want to refer to the "Table of Acids and Bases."

Regardless of the acid being titrated, the quantity (number of moles) involved in the reaction, not its strength, will determine the volume of base required. Example Problems 1.10 and 1.11, on pages 216 and 217, demonstrate calculations using data obtained from the titration of weak acids and bases. As you work through these problems, identify similarities in how these problems and the examples you completed earlier were solved.

Example Problem 1.10

A 25.00-mL sample of methanoic acid, HCOOH(aq), was titrated with a standard solution of 0.250-mol/L sodium hydroxide, NaOH(aq). If 17.5 mL of sodium hydroxide was required to react with the methanoic acid, calculate the initial concentration of the acid solution.

Solution

step 1: Write the balanced chemical equation of the reaction between the acid and the base.

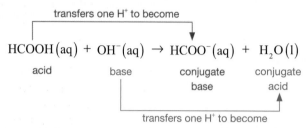

$$HCOOH(aq) + OH^-(aq) \rightarrow HCOO^-(aq) + H_2O(l)$$

acid   base   conjugate   conjugate
                       base   acid

Note: Only $OH^-(aq)$ is written because that is how this base appears on the "Table of Acids and Bases." Since $Na^+(aq)$ is neither an acid nor a base, it is not involved in this reaction and does not need to appear in the equation.

step 2: Confirm that the acid and base react in equal proportions using the coefficients from the balanced chemical equation.

Because the acid and base react in equal proportions,

$$n_{OH^-} = n_{HCOOH}$$

step 3: Use the data to determine the initial concentration of the methanoic acid.

$$C_{OH^-} = 0.250 \text{ mol/L}$$

$$V_{OH^-} = 17.5 \text{ mL} \times \frac{1 \text{ L}}{1000 \text{ mL}}$$

$$= 0.0175 \text{ L}$$

$$V_{HCOOH} = 25.00 \text{ mL} \times \frac{1 \text{ L}}{1000 \text{ mL}}$$

$$= 0.025\ 00 \text{ L}$$

$$C_{HCOOH} = ?$$

$$n_{OH^-} = n_{HCOOH}$$

$$C_{OH^-}V_{OH^-} = C_{HCOOH}V_{HCOOH}$$

$$C_{HCOOH} = \frac{C_{OH^-}V_{OH^-}}{V_{HCOOH}}$$

$$= \frac{(0.250 \text{ mol/L})(0.0175 \text{ L})}{(0.025\ 00 \text{ L})}$$

$$= 0.175 \text{ mol/L}$$

The initial concentration of the methanoic acid was 0.175 mol/L.

Example Problem 1.11

Calculate the volume of a 0.150-mol/L solution containing hydrogen carbonate ions required to react with the hydronium ions present in 75.5 mL of a 0.200-mol/L hydrobromic acid solution.

Solution

Write the balanced chemical equation for this reaction, and determine the proportion of base reacted to acid reacted.

$$H_3O^+(aq) + HCO_3^-(aq) \rightarrow H_2CO_3(aq) + H_2O(l)$$

Therefore, $n_{HCO_3^-} = n_{H_3O^+}$.

Determine the volume of carbonate ions needed to react with the hydrobromic acid.

$$C_{H_3O^+} = 0.200 \text{ mol/L}$$

$$V_{H_3O^+} = 75.5 \text{ mL} \times \frac{1 \text{ L}}{1000 \text{ mL}}$$

$$= 0.0755 \text{ L}$$

$$C_{HCO_3^+} = 0.150 \text{ mol/L}$$

$$V_{HCO_3^-} = ?$$

$$n_{HCO_3^-} = n_{H_3O^+}$$

$$C_{HCO_3^-} V_{HCO_3^-} = C_{H_3O^+} V_{H_3O^+}$$

$$V_{HCO_3^-} = \frac{C_{H_3O^+} V_{H_3O^+}}{C_{HCO_3^-}}$$

$$= \frac{(0.200 \text{ mol/L})(0.0755 \text{ L})}{(0.150 \text{ mol/L})}$$

$$= 0.101 \text{ L or } 101 \text{ mL}$$

To neutralize the hydrobromic acid, 101 mL of the hydrogen carbonate ion solution is required.

Practice

49. In a titration, 27.3 mL of a 0.0130-mol/L potassium hydroxide solution was required to neutralize 50.0 mL of a nitric acid solution. Calculate the concentration of the nitric acid solution.

50. A student titrates a solution containing an unknown concentration of sodium hydroxide with a standard solution of hydrochloric acid. If 33.6 mL of 0.0200-mol/L hydrochloric acid is required to neutralize a 25.0-mL sample of the basic solution, calculate the concentration of the sodium hydroxide in the basic solution.

51. A technician wants to predict the volume of a 0.150-mol/L sodium hydroxide solution required to neutralize 2.00 L of a 0.100-mol/L acidic solution. Calculate the volume of sodium hydroxide solution required.

Determining Buffering Capacity

Components in the soil or water can neutralize acid added as either wet or dry deposition. As you know, soils and lake water in different parts of Canada have different chemical components and, thus, vary in their ability to neutralize acids. As a result, measuring the buffering capacity of soil or lake water provides a great deal of insight into the ability of an area to withstand the effects of acid deposition.

Buffering, as the term suggests, refers to a sample's ability to be exposed to acid or base and not change in pH. The chemical components in soil can act as buffers because substances that can act as bases or as acids are present. You have examined the importance of the carbonate ion, $CO_3^{2-}(aq)$, as a buffer in soil. Because a carbonate ion has the ability to accept a hydrogen ion from an acid, the carbonate ion reacts with the acid, keeping the pH of the soil (or of the water) constant.

Sources of Buffering

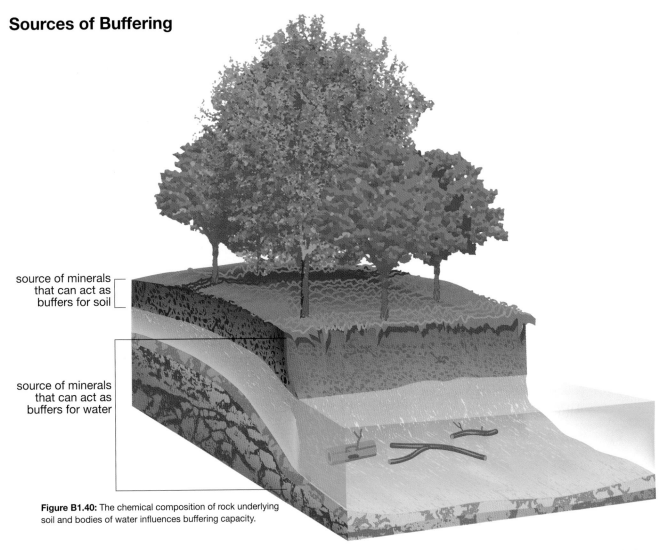

source of minerals that can act as buffers for soil

source of minerals that can act as buffers for water

Figure B1.40: The chemical composition of rock underlying soil and bodies of water influences buffering capacity.

Buffers exist in other biological systems. Blood contains two dissolved chemical substances: carbonic acid, $H_2CO_3(aq)$, and hydrogen carbonate, $HCO_3^-(aq)$. Each of these substances has the ability to react with and counteract the presence of either excess base or excess acid, respectively, that may be present in blood. Because a change in blood pH of over 0.5 can be fatal, this buffering mechanism is important to survival. Even when you are exercising and producing lots of CO_2 and lactic acid, the hydrogen carbonate ion in the blood counteracts the effects of CO_2 and lactic acid to maintain a constant pH.

Blood Buffering

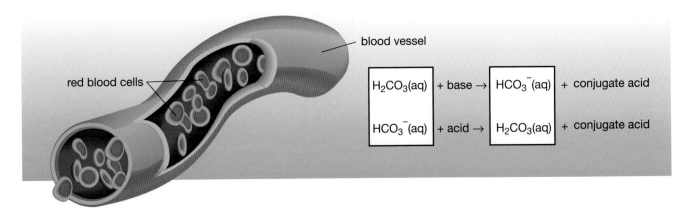

blood vessel

red blood cells

$H_2CO_3(aq)$ + base → $HCO_3^-(aq)$ + conjugate acid

$HCO_3^-(aq)$ + acid → $H_2CO_3(aq)$ + conjugate acid

The net effect of a buffer is to maintain the pH at a relatively constant level despite the addition of an acid or base. Can buffering last forever? From earlier studies, it appears that regions of eastern Canada have low natural buffering capacity; many areas have become overwhelmed by acid deposition. Is it possible to apply what you have learned about performing a titration and using the data collected to determine a value for the buffering capacity of a sample? In the next investigation you will develop an experimental procedure to address this question.

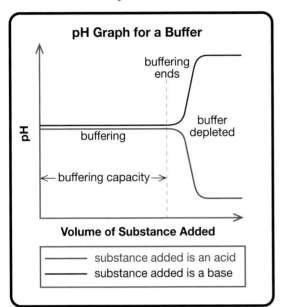

Figure B1.41: Buffers minimize the pH change for a system (e.g., soil or lake water). A sharp change to the pH of a sample being tested indicates that the acid or base being added is no longer being neutralized—the buffering capacity has been exceeded.

Investigation

Designing an Experiment to Determine Buffering Capacity

Background Information

So far in this unit you have learned about acid-base reactions, indicators, pH, titrations, and calculations involving chemical quantities of substances when dissolved in solution. You are encouraged to use your accumulated knowledge and skills to develop an experiment that could achieve the purpose of this investigation.

Science Skills

✓ Initiating and Planning

Purpose

You will develop a procedure to determine the amount (number of moles) of acid that can be buffered by a sample of lake water or by a sample of soil.

Other Ways of Monitoring Acid Deposition

In Lesson 1.1 you discovered that Alberta's Ministry of the Environment collects information about the condition of the atmosphere from a variety of monitoring stations throughout the province. In addition, a mobile monitoring station is available to travel to locations where additional testing is required. Recall that scientists examine biodiversity and changes to populations within an ecosystem as another source of information about the effects of acid deposition. You also looked at the traditional ecological knowledge of people within Canada's First Nations, Métis, and Inuit communities regarding changes that have been occurring within the environment. All of these sources provide valuable information and contribute to a better understanding of the impact human activity has on the environment.

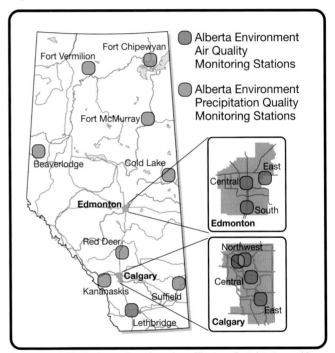

Figure B1.42: Monitoring stations throughout Alberta collect data to provide information about air quality.

Figure B1.43: This is one of many air monitoring stations around Alberta.

Assessing an Approach to Monitor the Effects of Acid Deposition

Science Skills

✓ Analyzing and Interpreting
✓ Communication and Teamwork

Purpose

You will evaluate the experimental design of a study developed to monitor the effects of acid deposition and the recovery of an area affected by acid deposition.

Background Information

The effects of acid rain were first noticed in the Great Lakes region of eastern Canada in the 1970s. Since that time, a great deal of study has been undertaken to identify factors and patterns of emissions and how they have affected the environment. Current studies involve the long-term collection of chemical and biological data to monitor a number of lakes in the region for signs of change. You should note that many of these lakes have been affected by acidification and are being monitored for changes to determine whether water quality and ecosystems are demonstrating improvement over time.

Procedure

step 1: Prepare a table with two columns. Add the heading "Positive Aspects" to the first column and the heading "Negative Aspects" to the second column.

step 2: Obtain the document "Acid Rain Biomonitoring in Ontario's Lakes" from the Science 30 Textbook CD.

step 3: Read the plan described in the document. Then use the Internet to conduct additional research on this plan.

step 4: Consider each aspect of the plan described in the document and those identified in the additional information you collected. Determine if the aspect is positive or negative. For each entry in the table, provide a justification.

step 5: Identify any aspects that are not being investigated in the plan, and place them in the appropriate column along with your justification.

step 6: Compare your table with those of other students. Identify any similarities and differences among the aspects and any similarities and differences among the justifications.

step 7: Develop a consensus within the group, and prepare a brief visual presentation identifying important strengths and weaknesses of the approach used to monitor the effects of acid deposition.

step 8: To use reliable methods and improve the validity of research, scientists often choose to use approaches developed by previous studies when planning a new study. Make a recommendation as to whether the plan you reviewed should be used as a framework for studies to monitor the effects of acid deposition in Alberta. If possible, indicate parts of the study that need to be modified or identify any additional tests that should be performed. Explain your reasoning.

1.4 Summary

In this lesson you analyzed and performed titrations to solve problems involving quantifying acids or bases. You also learned about the importance of buffering capacity to a biological system. Titration can be used to determine a value for buffering capacity. You also determined that acids and bases can be classified as being strong or weak, based on the extent to which they react with water.

Knowledge

1. Define the following terms.

   a. indicator   b. titration

   c. burette   d. Erlenmeyer flask

   e. endpoint   f. pH meter

2. Explain why a solution's pH cannot always be used to estimate the concentration of acid within a solution.

3. Write a list of the strong acids that appear on the "Table of Acids and Bases." Explain why strong acids are often used as standard solutions for titrations.

Applying Concepts

4. It takes 16.7 mL of 0.100-mol/L hydroxide ions to neutralize 10.0 mL of an acidic solution of unknown concentration.

   a. Calculate the hydronium-ion concentration of the acid.

   b. Determine the pH of the acid.

5. 60.0 mL of nitric acid with a molar concentration of 2.50 mol/L is accidentally spilled. The base, HCO_3^-(aq), from an acid-spill kit has a concentration of 0.145 mol/L. Determine the volume of base, HCO_3^-(aq), needed to treat the spill.

6. In a titration experiment, a 10.0-mL sample of vinegar, CH_3COOH(aq), is titrated with 0.108-mol/L sodium hydroxide, NaOH(aq). After three trials, it is determined that an average of 7.55 mL of NaOH(aq) is required to neutralize the solution. Determine the molar concentration of ethanoic acid in the vinegar solution.

7. Three 10.0-mL samples of hydrochloric acid with phenolphthalein were titrated with a 0.0567-mol/L solution of sodium hydroxide, NaOH(aq). The results obtained are summarized in the table.

Trial	Volume of Standard Solution (mL)			Endpoint Colour
	Final	Initial	Added	
1	13.61	1.72		light pink
2	25.68	13.67		light pink
3	37.55	25.64		light pink

   a. Calculate the average volume of NaOH(aq) used.

   b. Calculate the molar concentration of the hydrochloric acid tested.

8. Mikhail performed two series of titrations on 15.0-mL test samples. Here are his results.

TITRATION 1

Initial Reading (mL)	Final Reading (mL)	Difference (mL)
10.13	20.73	10.60
20.73	31.34	10.61
31.34	41.93	10.59

TITRATION 2

Initial Reading (mL)	Final Reading (mL)	Difference (mL)
10.15	19.96	9.81
19.96	30.68	10.72
30.68	41.87	11.19

   Which set of data would you be more confident with? Explain your reasons.

9. Explain at least two ways in which you can improve your titration technique to obtain more consistent results.

Figure B1.44: Sulfur stockpiles are the result of using technologies that remove sulfur from natural gas and other petroleum sources.

Thus far, you have seen that a great deal of knowledge, both chemical and general, is required to understand the issue of acid deposition. Earlier, you were asked to identify intended and unintended aspects of human activity and use of technology. When you think about preventing acid deposition, the obvious solution is to remove acid-forming substances from emissions. But what do you do with the products?

Sulfur is also stockpiled from oil sand refined near Fort McMurray. Each year, 15 million tonnes of sulfur is removed from oil sand. What is done with all that sulfur? Does sulfur removal actually help reduce acid deposition?

In this lesson you will discover how tackling the problem of acid deposition not only involves the use of technology, it also involves all parts of society: local and international governments, industries, and individuals.

Practice

52. It is estimated that up to 5% of the mass of oil sand mined is sulfur and that 15 million tonnes of sulfur each year are produced by sulfur-removal processes used in the oil sands. Estimate the mass (in tonnes) of oil sand mined yearly.

Reducing Acid Deposition

Theories about acid deposition and its effects on the environment have changed over time as new evidence has accumulated. At one time, it was believed that dispersing sulfur-dioxide emissions from the smelting of nickel higher in the atmosphere using a superstack (like the one in Figure B1.45) would decrease the occurrence of acid deposition. Unfortunately, the hypothesis was not supported when evidence of acid deposition began to appear in areas over 200 km from the smelter.

Currently, a variety of technologies are used to reduce emissions. Evidence collected from studies of lakes in Ontario and other regions affected by acid deposition have shown the following:

- Reducing emissions is necessary for areas exposed to extreme acid deposition to recover.
- Areas exposed to extreme levels of acid deposition will recover, but it is a long process.

Figure B1.45: The 380-m tall superstack in Sudbury, Ontario, was the world's tallest chimney when it was built in 1972.

Try This Activity

Catching Emissions

Purpose
You will determine a method of catching emissions.

Materials
- long, plastic tube (e.g., golf-club tube at least 30 cm long)
- electric hair dryer (at least 1000 W)
- plastic grocery bag
- metre-stick
- Styrofoam chips (or confetti or black pepper)
- 10-cm length of transparent tape (or elastic band)

Procedure

step 1: Hold one end of the plastic tube about 3 cm above a small pile of Styrofoam chips.

step 2: Use your other hand to turn on the hair dryer, and position the airflow across the top of the tube. Operate the hair dryer for one minute.

step 3: Observe the effect the air current has on the material at the other end of the tube.

step 4: Once the minute is up, turn off the hair dryer and inspect the inside of the tube.

step 5: Wrap the plastic bag around the end of the metre-stick to make a ball small enough to fit inside the plastic tube. Use the tape to fasten the bag to the metre-stick so the plastic bag stays in place.

step 6: Insert the end of the metre-stick with the bag attached into the plastic tube. Move the bag back and forth along the inside of the plastic tube for 1 min.

step 7: After 1 min, remove the metre-stick (and the plastic bag) from the plastic tube and repeat steps 1 to 3.

step 8: Clean the inside of the tube as instructed by your teacher, and return all materials to their proper place.

Analysis
1. Describe the effect that the air from the hair dryer had on the material at the lower end of the tube.
2. Describe the effect that moving the plastic bag through the tube had on the material located at the lower end of the tube when you repeated the procedure.
3. Provide an explanation of the results observed.

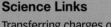

Science Skills

✓ Analyzing and Interpreting

Science Links
Transferring charges onto the surface of the plastic tube causes the charged particles drawn up the tube to be attracted to the inside walls, stopping the particles' movement. In Unit C you will learn more about electric charges and fields and how substances moving against each other often cause a transfer of electrons.

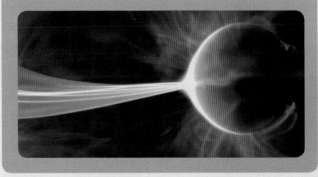

Reducing Emissions—Electrostatic Precipitation

Did you notice in the "Catching Emissions" activity that the material drawn into the tube stuck to the walls after the plastic bag was moved through the tube? What effect did transferring a charge onto the tube have on the particles drawn up the tube?

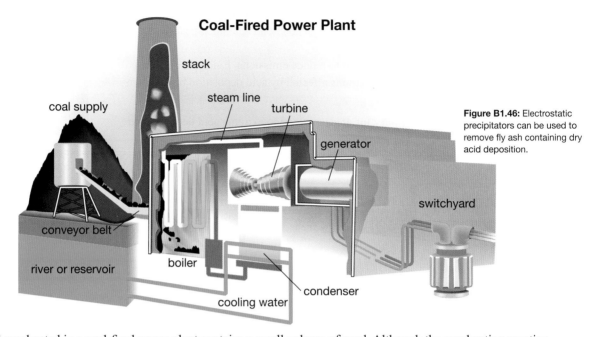

Coal-Fired Power Plant

stack

coal supply

steam line

turbine

generator

switchyard

conveyor belt

river or reservoir

boiler

condenser

cooling water

Figure B1.46: Electrostatic precipitators can be used to remove fly ash containing dry acid deposition.

The coal combusted in a coal-fired power plant contains a small volume of sand. Although the combustion reaction does not chemically change the sand, smaller particles of sand are released from the combustion chamber and leave the stack as **fly ash**. Recall that SO_2 and NO_x can be absorbed into the surface of substances, including fly ash. This makes fly ash a potential source of dry acid deposition.

In a process similar to the "Catching Emissions" activity, fly ash is removed from the gases that travel up the stack by an **electrostatic precipitator**. As the particles of ash move into the precipitator, they are exposed to two electrodes. Particles of fly ash become negatively charged as a result of their contact with the negative electrode. Once the fly ash is negatively charged, it will be attracted to and stick to the positively charged plates within the precipitator.

> **fly ash:** small particles of sand and other unburned material that remain suspended in the exhaust gases when pulverized coal is combusted

> **electrostatic precipitator:** a device that uses electric fields to collect fly ash from emissions

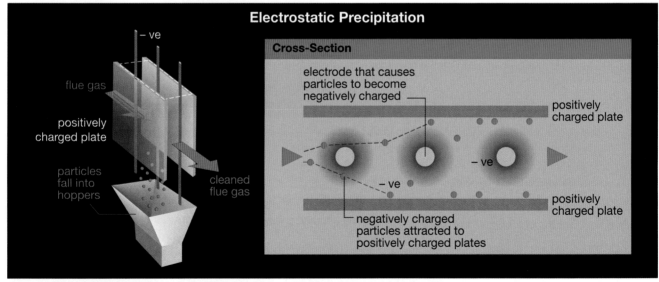

Electrostatic Precipitation

– ve

flue gas

positively charged plate

particles fall into hoppers

cleaned flue gas

Cross-Section

electrode that causes particles to become negatively charged

positively charged plate

– ve

– ve

positively charged plate

negatively charged particles attracted to positively charged plates

Figure B1.47: An electrostatic precipitator collects fly ash to reduce particulate emissions and acid deposition.

Electrostatic precipitators not only greatly reduce the release of dry acid deposition absorbed onto fly ash, they also reduce particulate emissions. Recently, greater attention has been paid to particulate emissions because evidence has shown that they are a cause of the increased numbers of cases of asthma and other breathing difficulties.

Reducing Emissions—Scrubbing Emissions

When the smoke from the combusted coal was bubbled into water, it rapidly changed the colour of the indicator in the water. **Scrubbing** is a process used to remove one or more gases from a mixture of gases. Scrubbers are used to remove $SO_2(g)$ produced by the combustion of coal.

What kind of substance would you place into the scrubber to remove $SO_2(g)$? Perhaps the next demonstration will help you answer this question.

▶ scrubbing: a process used to remove one or more components from a mixture of gases by passing it through substances that absorb and separate unwanted components

Testing Scrubbing Materials—Demonstration

Science Skills
✓ Analyzing and Interpreting

CAUTION!
The procedure should be performed by your teacher.

Purpose
You will watch a demonstration that tests the ability of substances to remove acid-forming compounds from smoke.

Materials
Set up the materials as shown in Figure B1.48.

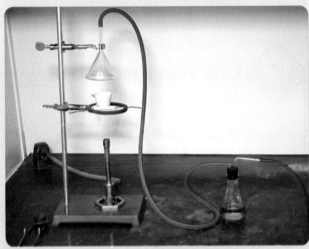

Figure B1.48

- 0.100-mol/L NaCl(aq)
- 0.100-mol/L NaOH(aq)
- 0.100-mol/L Na_2CO_3(aq)
- 0.100-mol/L NH_3(aq)
- $CaCO_3$(s)

Procedure
Observe and compare the results for each of the trials performed with the solutions listed. Observe and compare the results of the trial using the solid substance with the results obtained from the trials using the solutions.

Analysis

1. Explain how you were able to determine whether the substance tested was able to reduce the amount of acid-forming substances in the gas.

2. Rank the substances tested in terms of their decreasing ability to remove acid-forming substances from the gas collected.

3. Using your knowledge of chemistry, explain which type of substance appeared to be best at removing acid-forming substances.

4. If the solutions represent a wet-scrubbing process and the solid represents a dry-scrubbing process, compare the efficiency of wet and dry scrubbers at removing acid-forming substances from the gas collected.

5. Do you feel the procedure in this demonstration allowed for valid comparisons to be made among the substances tested and between the use of solutions and solids as materials for scrubbing? Support your answer by citing specific examples.

Many substances are capable of scrubbing or absorbing acid-forming emissions. Did you notice in the demonstration that the best scrubbers were bases—the substances containing hydroxide ions, carbonate ions, and ammonia? All of these substances are used in industrial scrubbers because of their ability to react with acids. Calcium carbonate is a popular scrubbing compound because of its abundance and because it is a weak base. Safety concerns associated with the use of hydroxides (e.g., highly corrosive) and ammonia (e.g., strong, pungent odour) restrict the use of these substances as scrubbers.

The design of a scrubber is quite simple. Refer to Figure B1.49. Exhaust gases enter the bottom of the tower. At the top of the tower, the liquid containing the material that will absorb components from the exhaust gases is added. The gases and the scrubbing compounds meet within the tower and the reaction between the two substances completes the scrubbing process.

Cross-Section of a Scrubber

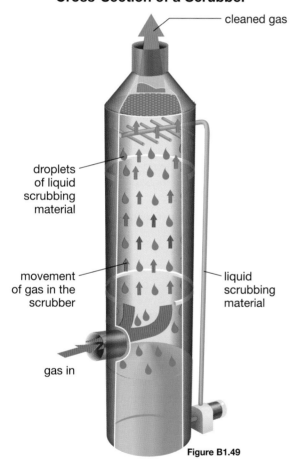

cleaned gas

droplets of liquid scrubbing material

movement of gas in the scrubber

liquid scrubbing material

gas in

Figure B1.49

Many of the materials used in scrubbers to remove SO_2 are related. The metal-refining industry depends highly on the use of scrubbers that contain lime (calcium oxide) to remove sulfur dioxide produced during the refining of metal ores. Lime (calcium oxide) is produced by the heating of calcium carbonate. Both substances also have basic properties. Kilns, like the one pictured in Figure B1.50, are used to heat calcium carbonate to produce lime.

?-DID YOU KNOW?-

Kilns measuring up to 200 m in length operate at temperatures above 1400°C to convert limestone into lime, which is used in the production of cement. To produce such high temperatures, a large quantity of coal or natural gas is required. The cement and other industries that utilize combustion processes use technologies, like scrubbers, to control emissions.

Figure B1.50: This kiln at Lehigh Inland Cement in Edmonton is over half the length of a football field and 4.2 m in diameter.

?-DID YOU KNOW?-

The reaction between SO_2 and limestone in a scrubber can be used to produce calcium sulfate, $CaSO_4(s)$, commonly known as gypsum. Gypsum is used in a variety of building materials, like drywall. Many industrial processes are being designed in such a way that waste materials may be used for other processes.

Reducing Emissions—NO_x

Recall that NO_x is an abbreviation for two oxides of nitrogen: $NO(g)$ and $NO_2(g)$. Because of differences in the chemical properties of these two compounds, it is difficult to remove both compounds using a scrubber. A more efficient method for removing NO_x compounds from the exhaust of combustion reactions involves the use of a **catalyst**.

The transportation industry, including automobiles, is a major source of acid deposition because of the NO_x emissions produced by the internal combustion engine. The high temperature at which combustion occurs within an engine causes a reaction between atmospheric nitrogen and oxygen that produces NO_x.

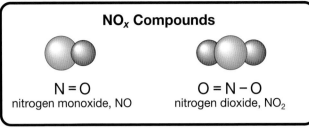

NO_x Compounds

$N = O$
nitrogen monoxide, NO

$O = N - O$
nitrogen dioxide, NO_2

Catalytic Converter

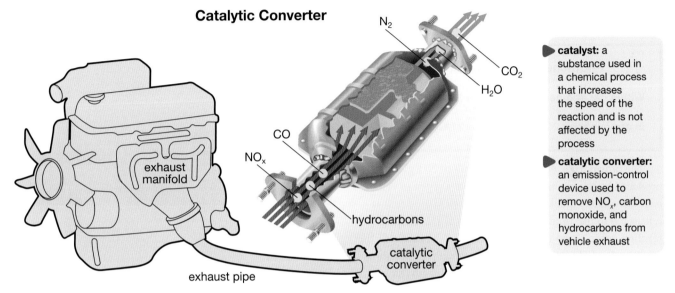

▶ **catalyst:** a substance used in a chemical process that increases the speed of the reaction and is not affected by the process

▶ **catalytic converter:** an emission-control device used to remove NO_x, carbon monoxide, and hydrocarbons from vehicle exhaust

One of the purposes of a **catalytic converter** is to change NO_x compounds into nitrogen. Automobile exhaust containing NO_x, carbon monoxide, and small hydrocarbon molecules undergoes reactions in the presence of the catalysts within the converter to produce $N_2(g)$, $CO_2(g)$, and $H_2O(g)$. Catalytic converters were first used in automobiles in the 1970s as a pollution-control device. Further development of the technology has resulted in converters becoming more efficient in removing pollutants from exhaust. Converters are used in vehicles fuelled by gasoline, diesel, propane, and natural gas.

Large industry also uses catalysts to remove NO_x compounds from emissions.

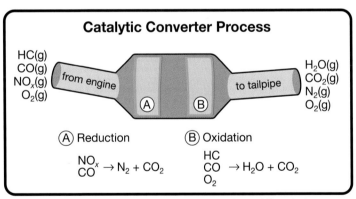

Catalytic Converter Process

HC(g)
CO(g)
NO_x(g)
O_2(g)
from engine

to tailpipe
H_2O(g)
CO_2(g)
N_2(g)
O_2(g)

Ⓐ Reduction

$\begin{matrix} NO_x \\ CO \end{matrix} \rightarrow N_2 + CO_2$

Ⓑ Oxidation

$\begin{matrix} HC \\ CO \\ O_2 \end{matrix} \rightarrow H_2O + CO_2$

Figure B1.51: The reactions within a catalytic converter change NO_x and other substances of concern into less harmful substances.

Figure B1.52: Concerns regarding emissions where vehicles are used indoors have prompted the development of catalytic converters for vehicles like this forklift, which operates on propane.

? DID YOU KNOW?

The actions of drivers can have a significant effect on emissions. When catalytic converters were first fitted on vehicles, concerns about the reduction in the horsepower cause many people to remove them from their vehicles. Even with more efficient models of catalytic converters, drivers cause significant levels of emissions by excessive idling, such as waiting in line at a drive-through.

Photochemical Smog

Imagine you've been sitting indoors all day. You are looking forward to getting outside and doing some sort of physical activity, whether it be playing soccer, running, or walking. But when you look out the window toward the horizon you notice a brownish haze in the sky. You may begin to wonder what that haze is and whether it is even safe to exercise outside.

The brownish haze is $NO_2(g)$ collecting in the **troposphere**. This brownish haze is often referred to as **photochemical smog**. Photochemical smog occurs most often in major cities, where higher levels of automobile exhaust and emissions of hydrocarbons and NO_x compounds occur.

Photochemical Smog Reaction 1

Within car engine: $N_2(g) + O_2(g) \rightarrow NO(g)$

In atmosphere: $2\,NO(g) + O_2(g) \rightarrow 2\,NO_2(g)$

The brown haze, $NO_2(g)$, is the result of $NO(g)$—produced by the reaction of nitrogen and oxygen in vehicle engines—that is quickly converted into $NO_2(g)$ once it is released into the atmosphere. The photochemical smog reaction doesn't stop at $NO_2(g)$. Sunlight can cause a further reaction. Sunlight is composed of wavelengths of radiation with different energies. Some of these wavelengths have sufficient energy to convert $NO_2(g)$ back into $NO(g)$ and a single oxygen atom.

Photochemical Smog Reaction 2

$$NO_2(g) \xrightarrow[\text{sunlight}]{\text{energy from}} NO(g) + \underset{\uparrow}{O}(g)$$

oxygen atom

Now, a single oxygen atom is highly reactive and will combine with oxygen in the troposphere to form ozone.

Photochemical Smog Reaction 3

$$O(g) + O_2(g) \rightarrow O_3(g)$$

Note: This reaction involves another substance, like $N_2(g)$, present in the atmosphere to act as a catalyst.

Normally, ozone is considered to be beneficial as a filter to protect Earth from ultraviolet radiation; but that is when it is located in the stratosphere, not the troposphere. Ozone is toxic to organisms at high concentrations. At lower concentrations, like those present in photochemical smog, it irritates your eyes, nose, and throat. Hot, windless days during summer can contribute to higher levels of ground-level ozone, causing asthma, bronchitis, coughing, respiratory infections, and decreased lung performance. On such days, smog advisories might be issued to inform you that exercising outdoors is not recommended.

Figure B1.53: Toronto (bottom) shows a thicker layer of photochemical smog than Calgary (top). The city of Calgary, along with many other highly populated urban areas is working hard to avoid the air-quality problems that the city of Toronto is experiencing.

▶ **troposphere:** the lowest region of the atmosphere that extends to approximately 18 km above Earth's surface; the region of the atmosphere where all weather occurs

▶ **photochemical smog:** a brownish-red haze produced by the reaction of sunlight and the components in automobile exhaust

? DID YOU KNOW?

Information about air quality, including ozone levels, can be obtained form a variety of sources, like the television or the Internet. Alberta Environment updates air-quality information hourly and makes this information available at

http://www3.gov.ab.ca/env/air/AmbientAirMonitoring/currentairquality.html

Figure B1.54: The colour change along the edge of the leaf and the spots on the leaf are indicators of damage caused by ozone.

Although ground-level ozone is invisible, you can see quite easily the evidence of its effects. Some plants are extremely sensitive to ozone concentrations in the atmosphere and are used as bio-indicators. Materials like rubber, plastics, and paint are also affected by exposure to ozone. You may recall that rubber is composed of unsaturated hydrocarbon molecules. Ozone reacts with the multiple bonds between carbon atoms in unsaturated molecules, changing the properties of the rubber and causing it to lose its elasticity.

Volatile organic compounds (VOCs), including the hydrocarbons in exhaust and other organic molecules present in the atmosphere, can react with NO_x and ground-level ozone to produce peroxyacetyl nitrate, often referred to as PAN. The presence of PAN in the air is a concern because it is a strong irritant to the respiratory system.

> ▶ **volatile organic compound (VOC):** a hydrocarbon or other organic molecule that vapourizes and exists as a gas in the air; sources include gasoline, solvents, paints, and other petroleum-based materials that vapourize

The catalytic converter is designed to reduce—not completely remove—hydrocarbons and NO_x emissions in vehicle exhaust. Since the occurrence of photochemical smog is directly related to automobile use, many major cities have initiated programs to reduce the number of vehicles on the road during morning and evening rush hour. These programs have made an impact on the severity of photochemical smog and the frequency of smog alerts in some areas.

Practice

53. Catalysts can become "poisoned" and lose their ability to function when exposed to certain substances. The catalyst within catalytic converters can be poisoned by the presence of lead and sulfur in gasoline. List other benefits that come from the removal of lead and sulfur from gasoline.

54. The pollution-reduction reaction that occurs within a catalytic converter is temperature sensitive. Better emissions reduction occurs when the catalytic converter operates at higher temperatures than at lower temperatures. Identify which driving behaviour listed below allows the catalytic converter to provide the best pollution reduction.

Driving Behaviours
  • starting a car's engine 10 min before driving on a cold winter day
  • waiting in the line at a drive-through with the engine running
  • parking the car and turning off the engine while waiting to pick up a friend
  • rapidly accelerating away from the curb after starting the vehicle

55. Explain how installing catalytic converters in vehicles that are used indoors can promote improved workplace safety.

56. During an emissions test, the function of an automobile's catalytic converter can be tested. To perform this test, probes are placed to detect the presence of substances in the vehicle's exhaust. One probe measures the amounts of substances in the exhaust before the catalytic converter, and the other probe measures the amounts of substances after the catalytic converter.

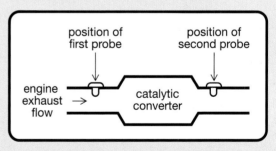

a. Identify whether the relative concentrations of CO, NO_x, and H_2O in the exhaust are high or low at the first and second probes.

b. In catalytic-converter testing, only a sensor that detects the amount of oxygen is normally used. Explain the rationale and the risks and benefits of using data regarding one substance in such a test.

Practice

57. Refer to Figure B1.55 when answering questions 57.a. to 57.d.

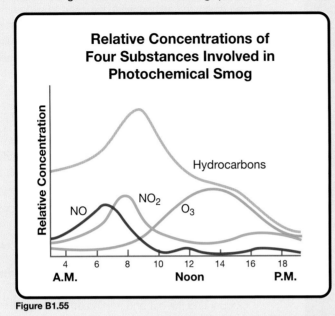

Relative Concentrations of Four Substances Involved in Photochemical Smog

Relative Concentration

Hydrocarbons

NO_2

NO

O_3

4   6   8   10   12   14   16   18
A.M.   Noon   P.M.

Figure B1.55

a. Explain the reason for the increase in the levels of NO and hydrocarbons early in the graph.

b. Explain why the highest concentration of NO_2 does not occur at the same time as the highest concentration of NO.

c. Explain why the concentration of O_3 rises in the afternoon when the concentrations of the other substances decrease.

d. Could a similar pattern of changing concentrations for these four substances occur in the late afternoon and evening after rush hour? Support your answer.

Reducing Emissions—Preventing the Production of SO_2, NO_x, and H_2S

Throughout your studies you may have asked yourself: "If sulfur in fuels is a source of acid deposition, is it possible to remove it before using the fuel?" Questions of this kind are very important when modifying existing technologies or designing improved technologies and processes to meet future societal demands. As you will soon see, there has already been a great deal of research and investment in developing technologies to remove sulfur from automobile gasoline and from coal.

Earlier, you learned about hydrogen sulfide, H_2S, that may be present in sour gas, natural gas, or petroleum deposits. Hydrogen sulfide is not only toxic, but it forms hydrosulfuric acid when dissolved in water. As you know, acids can contribute to the corrosion of metal. This creates additional problems at well sites. Many petroleum deposits begin to produce $H_2S(g)$ and, thus, become sour gas wells once they have been drilled. Research has identified that proper management of the water used at well sites can prevent wells from becoming contaminated with bacteria that converts the sulfur in the petroleum or natural gas which produces sour gas.

DID YOU KNOW?

Some species of bacteria can use the hydrocarbons in oil and natural gas as food. Oil companies support scientific research into the use of bacteria that consume petroleum and other hydrocarbons for cleanup and reclamation of sites where spills have occurred.

Emissions of NO_x can be prevented by altering conditions for combustion processes. You may recall that high temperatures within a furnace or combustion chamber of an automobile engine can provide sufficient energy for nitrogen and oxygen to combine. Two changes that have made considerable differences to NO_x emissions have been to

- use non-combustion processes where possible
- remove nitrogen from the combustion process by using oxygen instead of atmospheric air

Figure B1.56: Wind turbines are an example of a non-combustion process that can be used to produce electricity.

DID YOU KNOW?

Research enables modifications to the processes used to reduce emissions. The Claus process—invented over 100 years ago to remove sulfur from hydrogen sulfide to sweeten sour gas—has been modified many times. The SuperClaus process uses special catalysts to prevent the formation of SO_2. The Oxygen-Claus process uses pure oxygen to prevent the production of NO_x.

Recovering from Acid Deposition

Because ecosystems are so complex—involving the interaction of biotic and abiotic factors—recovery from acid deposition is expected to take a long time. Scientific data collected on lakes in Ontario that have experienced severe acidification demonstrated that the ecosystems have begun to show signs of recovery; but it is still a slow process.

▶ **liming:** adding a basic compound to soil or a body of water to neutralize acid deposition

One method to assist in the recovery of lakes and/or soil that have become acidified is **liming**. Lime is calcium oxide, which is a basic compound. Other basic compounds that can be used include calcium carbonate, calcium hydroxide, and magnesium carbonate. Adding lime neutralizes the accumulated acid in the soil or water. By neutralizing the accumulated acid, liming immediately changes the pH of soil or water. Despite this immediate effect, can you think of a reason why liming is considered only a short-term solution to acidic deposition? Another problem with liming is the amount required. Calculations to determine the amount of lime to add and careful management during its application are important to ensure that an excess of the base is not added. An excess of base—and resulting alkaline pH—could create other undesirable effects.

Practice

58. Write the chemical formula for the bases used for liming.
59. Write a balanced chemical equation for the reaction describing the reaction between hydronium ions in the soil with the following bases.
   a. magnesium carbonate
   b. calcium hydroxide

Evaluating Needs and Technologies

Thus far, you have studied processes and actions that can be used to reduce emissions that can cause acid deposition. In the next activity you will study how many of these methods can be used together to achieve a purpose.

Utilizing Technology

Risks and Benefits of Clean-Coal Technologies

Background Information

The vast majority of the electricity produced in Alberta comes form the combustion of coal. Alberta has extensive low-sulfur coal reserves, but coal is considered to be one of the dirtiest fuels. Currently, there is much discussion about the development of a technology to reduce emissions produced by the combustion of coal. Zero-emissions or clean-coal technologies could provide a means for ensuring future energy supplies, maintaining (or even improving) environmental standards. There would also be economic benefits from the possible sale of the technology to other countries.

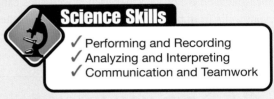

Science Skills

✓ Performing and Recording
✓ Analyzing and Interpreting
✓ Communication and Teamwork

Question

Will investment in developing clean-coal technology benefit all Albertans?

Purpose

You will perform a risk-benefit analysis on the development of technologies that reduce emissions.

Procedure

step 1: Read the "Reducing Emissions from Coal" handout from the Science 30 Textbook CD. This handout describes the steps involved in developing clean-coal technology.

step 2: Read the article *Clean-Coal Advocates Seek Federal Funding for $33M Pilot Project* on the Science 30 Textbook CD.

step 3: Use the Internet to research the following focus questions:

- Will coal be required as an energy source in Alberta, in Canada, and throughout the world in the future?
- What is the projected impact on the environment if coal continues to be used in the future?
- What other technologies could be used to produce electricity if coal was not to be used?
- Is it possible to develop zero-emissions coal? Where do the emissions go? Would this result in improved environmental standards?
- Does it make sense for governments to invest in the development of the technology so that Alberta can become a leader in the development of clean-coal technology?
- What would be the local, national, and international impact of being a leader in the development of this type of technology?

Analysis

1. Use the steps listed in "Decision-Making Skills and Risk-Benefit Analysis" on pages 590 and 591 to perform a risk-benefit analysis to address the question stated following the background information.

2. Prepare a brief summary outlining the results of your risk-benefit analysis and your position regarding the research question you investigated.

Thinking Smart—Not Creating New Problems

Methods to address acid deposition have often relied on using technology. Scrubbers and catalytic converters are examples of these technologies. However, as you have seen, if the processes that generate emissions continue, the technology may not be enough. Technology cannot always fix problems, but changing processes and behaviours can.

Using public transport to reduce the number of cars on the road, changing driving habits, or using vehicles and equipment that do not rely on a combustion process can reduce emissions.

Figure B1.57: Participating in a car pool reduces the number of cars on the road at rush hour and reduces emissions contributing to photochemical smog and acid deposition.

? DID YOU KNOW?

Plans for development prior to the 2010 Olympic Winter Games involve the use of 20 hydrogen-fuel-cell buses to service the Whistler area. After the Olympics, these buses will join the general fleet of buses, replacing the older diesel buses. Other plans to address environmental concerns associated with the development and hosting of the Olympics involve using fuel-cell-powered vehicles and building hydrogen filling stations between the major centres of Vancouver, Victoria, and Whistler.

Many major cities are using buses that utilize fuel cells—a technology you will study more in depth in Unit D. Fuel cells convert the chemical potential energy in hydrogen into electrical energy that powers an electric motor in the bus. This technology does not involve a combustion reaction and, therefore, does not produce emissions that contribute to acid deposition. However, there are questions regarding how hydrogen is produced and whether these methods make hydrogen a clean fuel.

Earlier, you saw a picture of the blocks of sulfur generated by the sulfur-removal processes used in refining oil sand. Some of the sulfur produced is sold to the manufacturers of fertilizers, pharmaceuticals, and other products; but a large excess cannot be sold. The stockpiles of excess sulfur have the potential to create environmental problems. Temperature extremes between winter and summer in the Fort McMurray area can cause the blocks of sulfur to erode and be carried by wind and deposit on surrounding soil. Deposited sulfur can be converted by bacteria in the soil into sulfuric acid. Possible negative effects such as soil acidification and possible changes to groundwater or surface water near the blocks are reduced by methods used to construct and monitor sulfur stockpiles.

Figure B1.58: Technicians use a variety of techniques, including video cameras, to determine the changes that occur to stockpiled sulfur.

Burying sulfur seems like an obvious solution to the problems caused by exposed sulfur piles, but careful study is required before burying sulfur is seriously considered as an option. Many factors, like temperature and moisture content of the ground and exposure to oxygen, can influence the growth of bacteria. Careful testing must ensure that proper conditions for storage occur. Both scientific and economic data for underground sulfur storage is being collected in order to make an informed decision regarding the use of this technology. How do you think scientific and economic data should be considered when making decisions about an environmental issue? You might want to look at the information that is available about this project and the scientific and economic data. You may also want to further discuss this issue with other students in your class.

International, National, and Individual Action

Throughout your study, you have seen that acid deposition is not only a problem in Canada. The United States and other industrialized countries have also been affected. Scientific evidence about substances that cause acidic deposition is quite clear—reducing emissions will result in a decrease in the occurrence of acid deposition and other environmental problems, like photochemical smog. Because wind currents can carry emissions across borders, international agreements between countries need to exist to protect the environment and people living in the countries affected.

Canada has participated in the development of a variety of international agreements relating to SO_2 and NO_x emissions. These include the

- 1985 United Nations Economic Commission for Europe Sulfur Protocol
- 1988 United Nations Economic Commission for Europe NO_x Protocol
- 1991 Canada-US Air Quality Agreement
- 1994 United Nations Economic Commission for Europe Sulfur Protocol

Since 1980, SO_2 emissions in Canada have been reduced by almost 50%, enabling Canada to meet its commitment to these international agreements. But, as you have seen, acid deposition is still a serious problem.

At the time this textbook was published, *The Canada-Wide Acid Rain Strategy for Post-2000* was the most recent document describing plans and actions to address acid deposition.

In Alberta, the development and use of plentiful fossil fuel resources has led to an increase in SO_2 and NO_x emissions, despite the extensive use of technologies that reduce emissions. Although this strategy acknowledges the opportunities for Alberta to develop these resources, it acts as a reminder of possible harm that may come to the environment. It may be only a matter of time before Saskatchewan and other provinces downwind of Alberta begin to demonstrate negative effects from acid deposition.

The strategy also identifies actions that each individual can take to help reduce SO_2 and NO_x emissions. Some of these actions include

- conserving energy by using public transport or alternative forms of transport, using more efficient automobiles, changing driving habits, and improving the insulation in your home

- supporting the development of technologies that produce electricity through non-combustion processes

- supporting processes that use technologies that reduce emissions

- recycling paper, metals, and plastics

1.5 Summary

In this lesson you discussed technologies used to reduce SO_2 and NO_x emissions. You also examined how the development of technology may indirectly cause other problems. You also discovered that solving the problem of acid deposition is a complex process that requires reductions in emissions to provide the opportunity for recovery. Canada's participation in international agreements and its development of a national strategy to address acid deposition have provided an opportunity for industry and individuals to take action to reduce emissions.

Knowledge

1. Make a list of activities that you and your family undertake that contribute to acid deposition.

2. Examine the list of personal actions that can be taken to reduce SO_2 and NO_x emissions on page 234. Explain how each of these actions could result in lower emissions.

3. Explain the conditions and substances necessary for the development of photochemical smog.

4. List the technologies that reduce SO_2 and NO_x emissions.

Applying Concepts

5. Use the following graphs to answer questions 5.a. to 5.e.

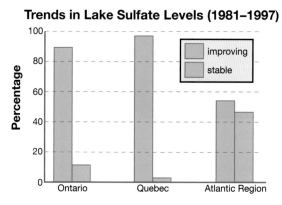

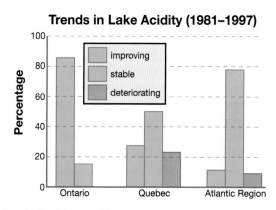

a. Explain why sulfate levels can be used as a means to assess the level of acid deposition.

b. During the period shown on the graphs, sulfur-reduction technologies were required to be used by industry in Canada. Identify which regions of eastern Canada appeared to benefit the most and which appeared to benefit the least from the use of these technologies. If possible, provide a possible explanation for the improvement and for the lack of improvement.

c. What information would you want to see before making any conclusions as to whether the area was recovering?

d. Explain what is meant by "Lake acidity is still deteriorating in some lakes" when referencing the "Trends in Lake Acidity (1981–1997)" graph.

e. Is there a correlation between the information shown on the two graphs? Support your answer.

6. From March to May 1993, Calgary was the first Canadian city to have a voluntary emissions-testing program for vehicles. The SMOG FREE (Save Money On Gas From Reduced Exhaust Emissions) program offered free emissions tests and coupons for discounts on products, repairs, and services.

a. List advantages and disadvantages of a program like SMOG FREE.

b. Suggest possible reasons for the program to no longer exist.

c. Predict whether a program like SMOG FREE would work today. Support your answer using examples.

7. Explain the benefits of being able to access current air-quality reports using the Internet or other technologies.

8. Use the Internet to determine the conditions necessary for a smog alert to be issued.

9. Is it necessary to invest funds on research and the development of technologies that reduce emissions to prevent acid deposition? Identify other ways the money could be spent.

Producing electricity, driving automobiles, and other processes important to society create emissions that can have adverse effects on the environment and human health. Your study in this chapter has enabled you to identify substances contained in emissions from processes involving combustion and explain how these emissions can lead to acid deposition and other negative environmental effects. You also examined the technologies and changes to behaviour that help reduce emissions.

Studying the effects of acid deposition on the environment involves conducting experiments and collecting data about chemical and biological changes in the environment. Additional data about environmental change can be gathered by consulting those with traditional ecological knowledge. In Chapter 2 you will continue your study of organic compounds and their impact on society and their effects on the environmental.

Summarize Your Learning

This chapter focused on a variety of technologies, chemical terms, and chemical reactions and their impact on the environment. As you may recall, there are many complex relationships between these aspects. Managing the complex information you learned is much easier if you take some time to identify relationships within the information and organize it into some sort of pattern. Now that you have come to the end of this chapter, this is an appropriate time to focus on the patterns within the things you have learned.

Since the pattern has to be in a form that is meaningful to you, you have some options about how you can create this summary. Each of the following options is described in the Reference Section.

Option 1: Draw a concept map or a web diagram.	Option 2: Create a point-form summary.	Option 3: Write a story using key terms and concepts.	Option 4: Create a colourful poster.	Option 5: Build a model.	Option 6: Write a script for a skit (a mock news report).

Chapter 1 Review Questions

Knowledge

1. Use the following information to classify each substance listed as either acidic, basic, or neutral.

   a. lake water with a pH of 7.9

   b. gastric acid with a pH of 2.0

   c. window cleaner with a hydronium-ion concentration of 2.23×10^{-10} mol/L

   d. rust remover with a hydronium-ion concentration of 5.72×10^{-3} mol/L

2. Indicators can be used to measure the pH of a solution.

   a. Explain how indicators can be used for this purpose.

   b. Explain the level of precision that is attainable using indicators to measure pH.

   c. Identify one technology that can be used to measure pH and provides better precision than indicators.

3. a. State the name of the theory that identifies acid-base reactions as involving the transfer of a hydrogen ion.

   b. Identify which substance donates a hydrogen ion and which substance accepts a hydrogen ion during an acid-base reaction.

Applying Concepts

4. Complete the following reactions. Label the acid, the base, the conjugate acid, and the conjugate base in each reaction.

  a. $HF(aq) + NH_3(aq) \rightarrow$

  b. $HNO_3(aq) + HCO_3^-(aq) \rightarrow$

  c. $H_3O^+(aq) + H_2BO_3^-(aq) \rightarrow$

  d. $OH^-(aq) + HCO_3^-(aq) \rightarrow$

  e. $CH_3COO^-(aq) + HS^-(aq) \rightarrow$

5. Methanoic acid is dissolved in water and produces a solution that has acidic properties.

  a. Write the balanced chemical equation for methanoic acid and water.

  b. Identify which product is responsible for the solution's acidic properties.

  c. List the properties an acidic solution would have when tested using the apparatus you used in the investigations throughout this chapter.

  d. Explain how empirical properties of acids and bases are useful when describing acids and bases.

6. Explain how rainwater can naturally have a pH of around 5.5.

7. Explain how rainwater can have a pH lower than 5.5.

8. Use the following information to complete the statement.

Solution	pH or $[H_3O^+(aq)]$
1	12.4
2	1.20×10^{-2} mol/L
3	4.5×10^{-9} mol/L
4	5.6

The four solutions in order from most acidic to least acidic are _____, _____, _____, and _____.

9. Refer to Figure B1.42 on page 219 to answer questions 9.a. to 9.e.

  a. Explain why many monitoring stations are used in Alberta.

  b. Review the locations of the precipitation-quality monitoring stations shown on the map. Identify monitoring stations that are located near activities that may have an effect on the environment.

  c. List the kinds of measurements that are made during precipitation-quality monitoring. Explain the significance of these tests.

  d. Explain how the locations of the monitoring stations provide information about acid deposition in Alberta.

  e. Explain how the monitoring stations in these locations may not provide sufficient data regarding the effects of acid deposition in Alberta.

10. Refer to the cartoon to answer questions 10.a. to 10.c.

  a. Identify the issue the cartoon is addressing.

  b. Use your scientific knowledge to explain the issue identified in the cartoon.

  c. Identify aspects of the cartoon that may be misleading.

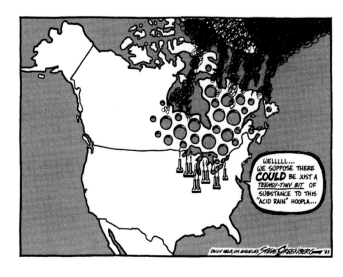

11. "The solution to pollution is dilution." Use your knowledge of acidic deposition to build an argument that either agrees or disagrees with this statement.

12. Describe some of the long-term effects acidic deposition might have within your local area.

13. Describe actions being taken by groups within your community to study or reduce emissions that could lead to acid deposition. Describe how the groups are determining whether these actions are having any effect.

14. Explain what takes place during chemical monitoring within the environment. Explain the importance of chemical data from monitoring stations to the study of acid deposition.

15. Define *biomonitoring*. Explain how biomonitoring is done within an ecosystem. Explain the importance of biomonitoring to the study of acid deposition.

16. Define *traditional ecological knowledge*. Explain the importance of traditional ecological knowledge to the study of acid deposition.

17. A student designs an experiment to investigate the effect of acid deposition on plants. Use the following information to answer questions 17.a. to 17.f.

Experimental Design

Obtain three healthy spider plants. Each plant will be watered daily, directly onto the soil, and using equal volumes of liquid. The first plant will be watered with a solution containing sulfuric acid that has a pH of 1; the second plant will be watered with a solution of ethanoic acid with a pH of 3; and the third plant will be watered with distilled water (pH 7). The plants will be observed each day for one week for signs of damage to leaves, loss of colour, and other changes to the appearance of the plant.

   a. Predict some of the changes to the plants you think you will see during the experiment.

   b. If you were able to perform chemical tests on the soil during the experiment, predict any changes you might expect to occur.

   c. Predict the effect that a potting soil with a high buffering capacity could have on the results of the experiment.

   d. Identify the controlled variables in the experiment.

   e. Identify the limitations of the experiment.

   f. Describe any modifications to this experiment that could improve both reliability and validity.

18. Closely examine the graphs titled "SO_2 Emissions in Canada (1980–2000)" and "NO_x Emissions in Canada (1980–2000)."

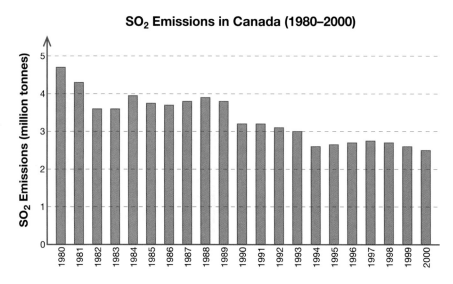

SO_2 Emissions in Canada (1980–2000)

NO$_x$ Emissions in Canada (1980–2000)

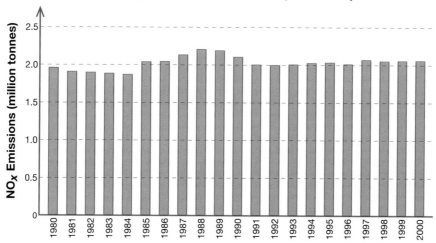

a. Determine the percentage change for each of SO$_2$ and NO$_x$ from 1980 to 2000 in Canada.

b. Account for the trend shown on each of the graphs.

c. Predict the effect that the change in emissions would have on the pH of rainfall.

d. Explain why data for SO$_2$ and NO$_x$ emissions from sources in the United States is important in developing a prediction regarding changes in the pH of rainfall in Canada.

e. Refer to the following maps.

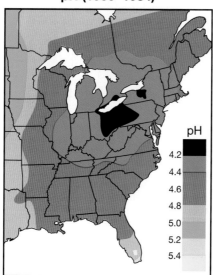

Five-Year Mean Rainfall pH (1980–1984)

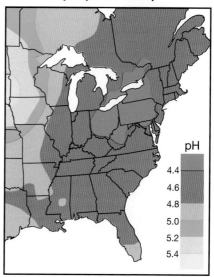

Five-Year Mean Rainfall pH (1996–2000)

Explain whether the data shown on these maps supports the predictions you made in your answer to question 18.c. What inference can you make from these maps regarding SO$_2$ and NO$_x$ emissions in the United States over the time given?

f. Is it possible to use the maps depicting a five-year mean pH for rainfall to conclude that a reduction in SO$_2$ and NO$_x$ emissions will reduce the severity of acid deposition? Support your answer.

Chapter 2 The Chemical Legacy of Human Activity

"A Touch of the Farm in the Heart of the City" is the slogan for the Old Strathcona Farmers' Market in Edmonton. Every Saturday, thousands of customers flock to the market to browse and buy from more than 130 vendors. Many people frequent the Farmers' Market for the crafts and the entertainment; but for the most part, people make the trip to Old Strathcona for the wide array of food available.

One type of food, in particular, that many people purchase is "certified organic" food. Many have expressed concern about "chemicals" used in the production of foods and other materials. But isn't all matter, technically, a chemical? Can chemical substances be classified as good and bad? What criteria would be used to do this?

In this unit you will consider the concerns people have about human practices and their impact on the environment. You will study substances used in agriculture, industry, and your home; and you will become aware that some of their properties may cause concern. You will also examine how science, industry, and government address concerns about the environmental impact of some human practices.

Try This Activity

Keeping Up with the News— Chemicals and the Environment

Purpose

You will collect information about environmental issues and determine whether each issue is the result of a single chemical substance or a group of substances.

Background Information

The term *chemical* is often misused. As a science student, you know that all matter, including water and oxygen, are chemicals. How is this term used or misused by the media? When are "chemicals" referred to and in what way?

Instruction

step 1: Prepare a table with the following headings: Title of News Item, Source of News Item, Chemical Substance Discussed, Source of Chemical Substance, and Issue Addressed. Leave room for three additional columns that you will add later.

step 2: As you study this chapter, collect news items (e.g., newspaper clippings, magazine articles, sound bites from radio or podcasts, and video segments) that discuss "chemicals" in the environment.

step 3: As you collect items, record the information in your table.

step 4: At the end of this chapter you will be given additional instructions about organizing the news items you collect.

2.1 Organic Compounds

Successful farming relies on more than selecting an appropriate crop to match soil conditions. Over the length of a growing season, farmers manage many factors that affect the health and growth of crop plants. Farming requires careful observation of the crop during key stages in its growth. Many farmers use fertilizers, herbicides, and pesticides at certain times of the growing season in hopes of producing a large, high-quality crop.

As many people in the agriculture industry will tell you, current farming practices that include the use of organic compounds are necessary for crop production. Scientific evidence collected from water and from the tissues of animals suggests that the use of organic compounds in farming and in manufactured materials may have an impact far beyond what they were originally intended for.

In this lesson you will study some of the substances used in agriculture and around your home, along with their intended and unintended effects. You will also examine how the chemical properties of organic compounds influence their behaviour in the environment.

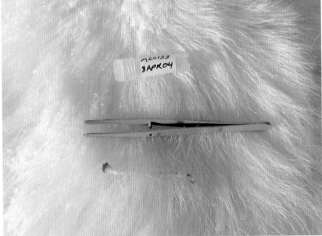

Figure B2.1: Fat samples taken from a polar bear can be used to detect presence of organic pollutants within arctic ecosystems.

Organic Compounds

In Science 20 you were introduced to organic chemistry—the study of compounds composed of carbon. The simplest types of organic molecules are hydrocarbons. The bonding between the carbon atoms in a hydrocarbon is significant. As demonstrated in Figure B2.2, a single, double, or even triple bond can exist between carbon atoms in a hydrocarbon.

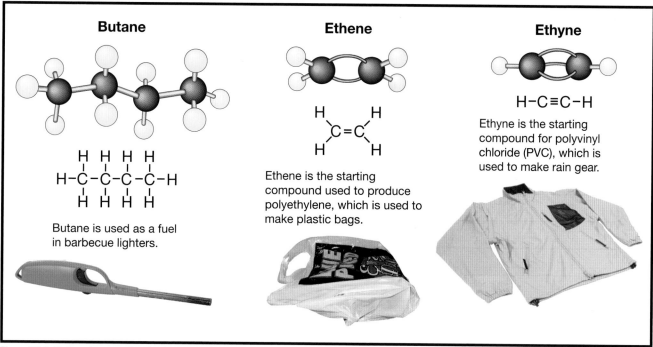

Butane

$$H-\overset{\overset{\displaystyle H}{|}}{C}-\overset{\overset{\displaystyle H}{|}}{C}-\overset{\overset{\displaystyle H}{|}}{C}-\overset{\overset{\displaystyle H}{|}}{C}-H$$

Butane is used as a fuel in barbecue lighters.

Ethene

$$\overset{\displaystyle H}{\underset{\displaystyle H}{}}C=C\overset{\displaystyle H}{\underset{\displaystyle H}{}}$$

Ethene is the starting compound used to produce polyethylene, which is used to make plastic bags.

Ethyne

$$H-C\equiv C-H$$

Ethyne is the starting compound for polyvinyl chloride (PVC), which is used to make rain gear.

Figure B2.2: Hydrocarbons are the simplest types of organic molecules.

You may recall that hydrocarbons with multiple bonds between carbon atoms are unsaturated and have a different name than saturated hydrocarbons. You will review the naming of hydrocarbons later in this lesson; but for now, use the next activity to review some of the concepts about the shape and other features of hydrocarbons.

Try This Activity

Building Models of Hydrocarbons

Science Skills
✓ Analyzing and Interpreting

Purpose
You will construct a molecular model for each hydrocarbon listed.

Background Information
Molecular models can be used to provide accurate information about the shape of the molecule and the types of bonds between carbon atoms in a hydrocarbon molecule.

Materials
• molecular model kit

Procedure
Build a model of each compound listed in question 1. Use your model kit to determine whether there are enough hydrogen atoms in the chemical formula to fill the spaces around each carbon atom. Use an additional spring to fill open spaces between carbon atoms to symbolize double bonds where necessary. Use only single or double bonds between carbon atoms when constructing models in this activity.

1. Copy and complete the following table. For each molecule you build, record information about the molecule.

Chemical Formula	Complete Structural Diagram	Bonds Between Carbon Atoms	Saturated or Unsaturated
C_5H_{12}		all single bonds no double bonds	saturated
C_5H_{10}			
C_5H_8			
C_6H_{14}			
C_6H_{12}			
C_6H_{10}			
C_6H_8			
C_6H_6			
C_6H_6 (circular)			
C_7H_8 (circular)			
C_8H_{10} (circular)			

Analysis

2. In Science 20 you learned that the general structure for hydrocarbon molecules was linear. Is this a correct description of the general shape for all hydrocarbons? Describe other arrangements that are possible.

3. If you reduce the number of hydrogens, describe the effect on the arrangement of carbons within a hydrocarbon.

4. Is it possible to have a saturated hydrocarbon that does not possess the maximum number of hydrogen atoms?

Naming System for Hydrocarbons

If you compare the molecules you constructed with those built by other students, you may notice that there are many possible correct formations. In order to communicate the precise arrangement of the atoms within organic molecules, a systematic naming system is used. Recall that the longest continuous chain of carbon atoms is considered to be the backbone for most organic molecules and features prominently in the name.

To review the systematic names for linear and branched hydrocarbon molecules, refer to the "Naming Hydrocarbons—Flowchart" handout from the Science 30 Textbook CD.

Practice

1. Write the systematic names for the following hydrocarbon compounds.

   a.

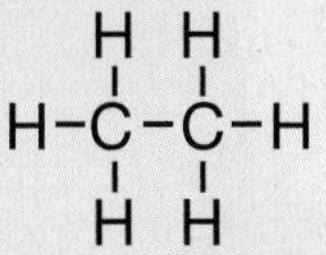

   ```
      H H
      | |
   H–C–C–H
      | |
      H H
   ```

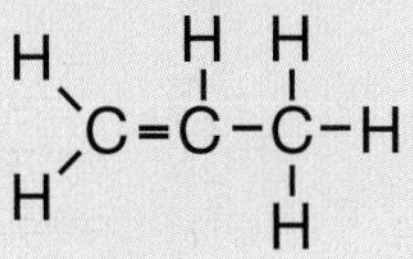

   b.

   ```
   H      H H
    \     | |
     C = C–C–H
    /        |
   H         H
   ```

   c.

   ```
      H
      |
   H–C–H
      |
      H
   ```

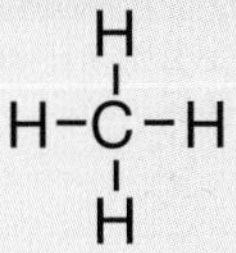

2. Draw the structural diagram for each compound given.

   a. 2,2-dimethylpropane

   b. 2-methylprop-1-ene

Hydrocarbons can come in many arrangements, including cyclic shapes. One arrangement for the carbon atoms is a hexagon, and one type of hexagonal hydrocarbon structure is a **benzene ring**. Benzene, C_6H_6, and other molecules containing this ring structure are a group of compounds that share similar physical and chemical properties that make them unique organic compounds. This structure can also be referred to as an **aromatic ring** or **phenyl ring**. Aromatic compounds, biphenyls, or benzene-based compounds that you may hear about in the news are all substances that contain this hexagonal structure.

Benzene

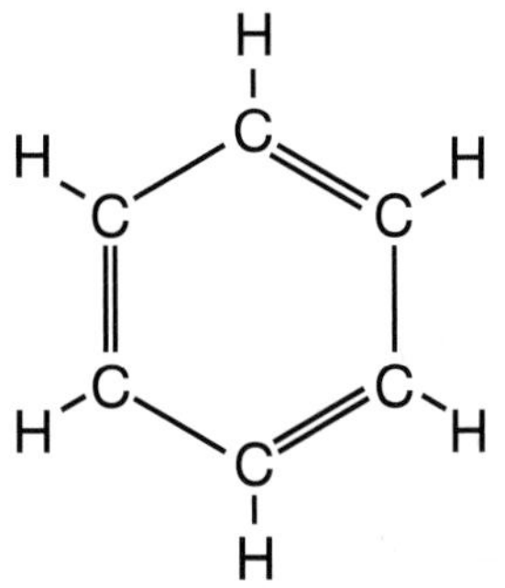

- found in gasoline
- used to make polystyrene

Toluene

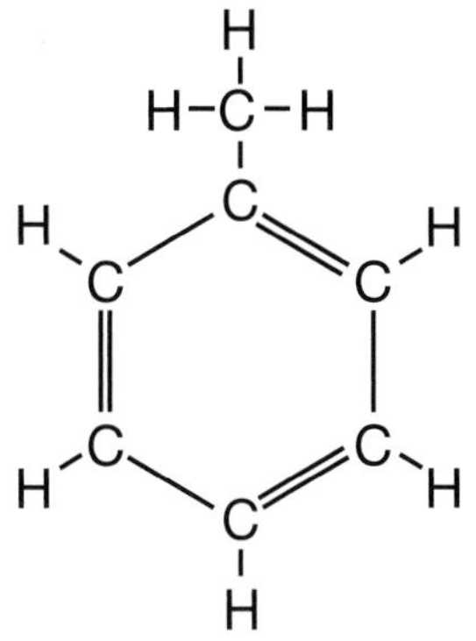

- found in high-octane gasoline
- used in glues for plastic

Xylene

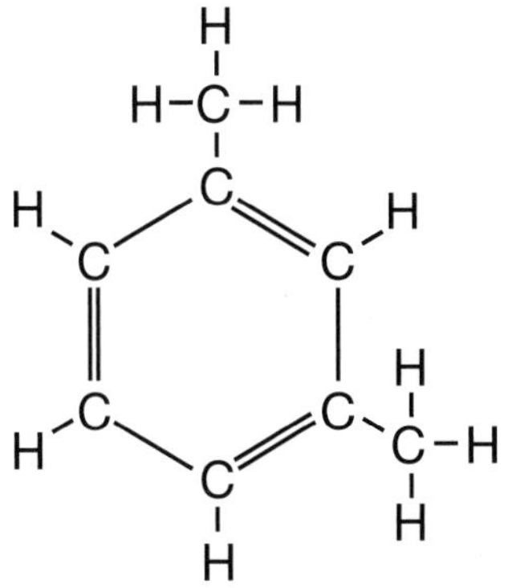

- found in high-octane gasoline
- used in rubber cement

Napthalene

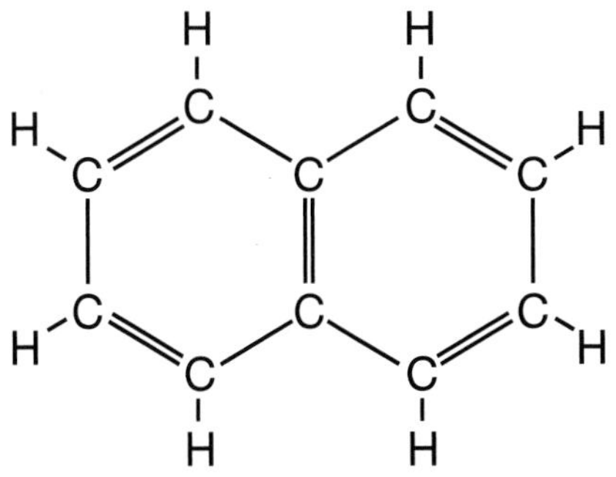

- found in water
- used as moth repellent and fungicide

▶ **benzene ring:** the hexagonal-ring-shaped chemical structure formed by six carbon atoms and six hydrogen atoms or other atoms

▶ **aromatic ring:** another name for a benzene ring

▶ **phenyl ring:** another name for a benzene ring

Benzene and Its Consequences

Aromatic compounds are naturally occurring compounds, present in natural resources like petroleum and coal. The gasoline or diesel fuel used in automobiles is a mixture of many hydrocarbons, including aromatic compounds. At one time, benzene and related aromatic compounds made up a large percentage of the hydrocarbons in gasoline. When scientific evidence first suggested that benzene was a carcinogen, action was taken by government and industry to reduce the concentration of benzene in gasoline. Legislation in Canada restricts the percentage of benzene permitted in gasoline.

Cleaning up gasoline that has leaked from an underground storage tank or cleaning up a fuel spill requires the removal of the contaminated soil from the site for treatment. Even though the densities of hydrocarbons are less than the density of water, some compounds in petroleum and gasoline are soluble in water. At spill sites there is often concern about the leaching of benzene and other aromatic hydrocarbons into sources of drinking water. This leaching can contaminate well water and ground water, threatening the health of animals and humans. Water-quality tests performed on well water and other sources of drinking water can identify whether any hydrocarbons are present (e.g., benzene).

The contaminated soil removed from a service station must be treated by a process called **remediation**. Remediation involves the removal or breakdown of hydrocarbons in the spilled gasoline. During remediation, linear hydrocarbons tend to be quickly broken down by the action of bacteria in the soil. Unfortunately, the remediation of molecules containing benzene rings is not as quickly achieved. As you learned earlier, the chemical stability of the benzene rings makes it more difficult for bacteria or chemical processes to break them down. The chemical stability of benzene-based molecules has resulted in their classification as persistent organic molecules, or **persistent organic pollutants** (POPs).

Figure B2.3: Service stations sometimes have to replace their underground fuel tanks with new tanks to keep hydrocarbons in gasoline from leaching into soil because of corroded containers.

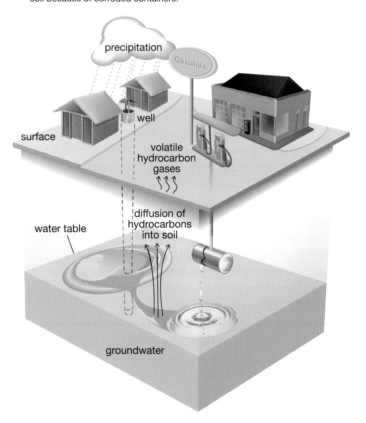

▶ **remediation:** the removal of pollutants from soil, groundwater, or surface water

▶ **persistent organic pollutant (POP):** an organic compound that is resistant to being broken down by biological or chemical means

You may recall that the presence of double bonds can influence a molecule's shape and chemical reactivity. If the benzene ring consists of three double bonds, you would expect that aromatic compounds would be very reactive, like unsaturated hydrocarbons. Despite the prediction that three double bonds are present in a benzene molecule, substances containing benzene rings are very stable unlike saturated hydrocarbons. Analysis of the structure of the benzene ring demonstrates that bonds between carbon atoms that form the ring are not similar to the double bonds between the carbon atoms in other hydrocarbons. Aromatic compounds have a reactivity similar to compounds with single bonds, but do not have a structure like those with single bonds.

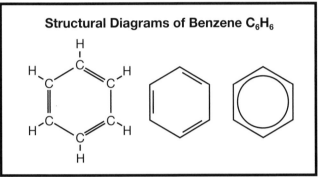

Structural Diagrams of Benzene C_6H_6

Figure B2.4: Aromatic rings are represented using alternating single and double bonds or using a circle inside the ring to represent resonance.

Carbons in a benzene ring demonstrate a unique bonding arrangement called **resonance**. Within an aromatic ring, extra electrons become shared by all the carbon atoms. A circle placed inside the hexagon in the structural diagram indicates this special bonding in the benzene ring. This unique bonding is believed to be responsible for the high degree of chemical stability and the flat shape of the benzene ring structure.

> **resonance:** a concept used to describe the true structure for certain compounds that cannot be accurately represented using any one type of bonding structure

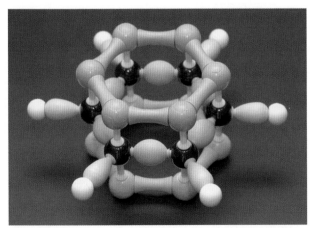

Figure B2.5: The purple and pink rings above and below this model for benzene represent the bonding of the six carbon atoms in the ring to the extra electrons.

The temperature at which combustion occurs in motor vehicles is not sufficient to break apart the aromatic compounds in the fuel. Concern about the presence of benzene in tailpipe emissions was a major factor in the development of legislation to reduce the concentration of aromatic hydrocarbons in gasoline.

Practice

3. Draw three diagrams used to represent a benzene ring.
4. Write two names, other than benzene, that describe the chemical structures in question 3.

> **polycyclic aromatic hydrocarbon (PAH):** a compound that contains multiple benzene rings produced by the incomplete combustion of organic substances, like oils, gasoline, diesel, wood, garbage, and plastics

Figure B2.6: High grill temperatures and flames are used to charbroil foods.

Many people love the taste of charbroiled foods, but the incomplete combustion of oils from the food can produce **polycyclic aromatic hydrocarbons** (PAHs). Like the particles that form the charred layer on a steak, PAHs are particulate emissions contained in motor vehicle exhaust or the smoke from forest fires. Recent research has indicated that polycyclic aromatic hydrocarbons, like benzopyrene, have the ability to interact with deoxyribonucleic acid (DNA) and form structures that may result in mutations. Because emissions from diesel automobiles are a major source of PAH emissions, many major cities are investigating means to reduce particulate emissions from diesel engines, including those in cars, buses, and trucks. When you cook food using a barbecue, you may want to use a low-temperature grill to reduce flare-ups and the PAHs present in your food.

Chemical Structure of Benzopyrene

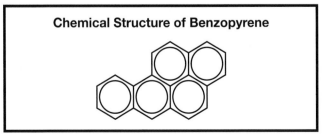

Figure B2.7: Benzopyrene is an example of a polycyclic aromatic hydrocarbon.

5. The City of Edmonton tested filters on diesel-powered buses to determine whether they were able to reduce particulate-matter emissions.

a. Use the Internet or other sources to identify the characteristic used to classify particulate-matter emissions.

b. Prepare a table that identifies the two groups of particulate-matter emissions and their sources. Include two examples of processes that produce each type of particulate-matter emission.

6. Obtain the handout "Diesel Particulate Filter (DPF) Demonstration" from the Science 30 Textbook CD. Read the handout, and answer the questions that follow.

  a. State the problem being investigated by this study.

  b. What do you think the term *local environmental conditions* refers to? Why is this such an important consideration?

  c. List the controlled variables used in the study.

7. Gasoline is a mixture of many hydrocarbons. A few of the many components found in gasoline are listed in a table in the "Some Components of Gasoline" handout on the Science 30 Textbook CD. Use the Internet to find the chemical formula and chemical structure for the components listed. Identify which of the substances in the list are alkanes, alkenes, aromatic compounds, hydrocarbons, and organic compounds.

? DID YOU KNOW?

Many naturally occurring compounds, like tobacco, contain molecules with benzene rings. The low-temperature combustion of tobacco that occurs while smoking produces carcinogens that include benzene, C_6H_6, and a PAH called benzo(c)phenanthrene.

? DID YOU KNOW?

You have a greater likelihood of being exposed to benzene inside your home than outdoors. Glues, paints, and solvents are common sources. Benzene is also present in tobacco smoke and vehicle exhaust.

Science Links

The three-dimensional shape of the benzene ring is similar to the shape of some parts of the DNA molecule. The ability of PAH and other molecules to form bonds to the nitrogen bases in a DNA molecule may result in the development of mutations. The structure of DNA and mutations and their effect on cells are covered in more detail in Unit A.

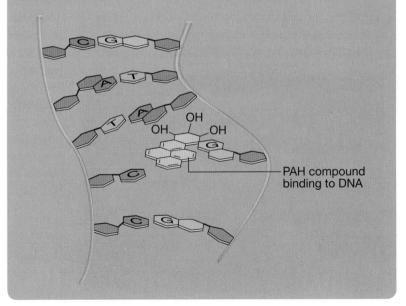

PAH compound binding to DNA

Functional Groups

The petrochemical industry in Alberta involves other processes in addition to the extraction of oil and natural gas. Hydrocarbons, as you may recall, can be used as fuel or as a raw material for the production of plastics or other **synthetic organic molecules** (as shown in Figure B2.8).

▶ **synthetic organic molecule:** a human-made compound containing carbon

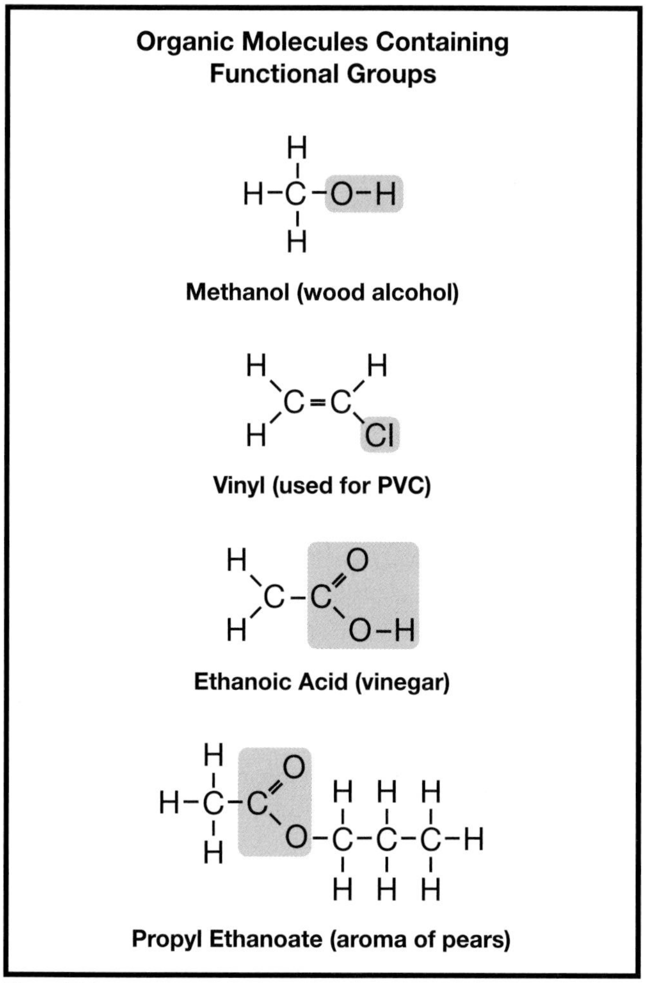

Organic Molecules Containing Functional Groups

H–C–O–H

Methanol (wood alcohol)

C=C with H, H, H, Cl

Vinyl (used for PVC)

C–C with H, H, O, O–H

Ethanoic Acid (vinegar)

H–C–C with O, O–C–C–C–H

Propyl Ethanoate (aroma of pears)

Figure B2.8

Modifications to naturally occurring hydrocarbons can involve the addition of carbon side chains or the addition of atoms other than carbon or hydrogen, creating organic molecules containing a **functional group**.

Halogenated Hydrocarbons

September 23 is an important day for environmental scientists. It's not a birthday; it is the first day of spring in the southern hemisphere. On this day, the first rays of sunlight illuminate the South Pole, which has been in total darkness throughout its winter. The end of winter is an important time for atmospheric scientists. It provides an opportunity to assess the extent of damage to the layer of ozone in the stratosphere above the South Pole.

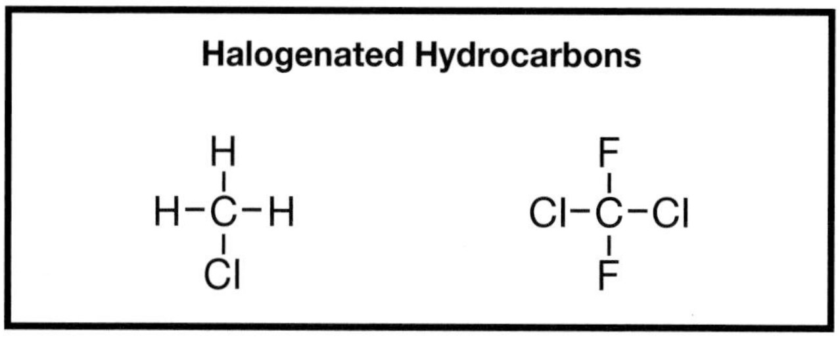

Halogenated Hydrocarbons

H–C–H with H, Cl

Cl–C–Cl with F, F

Chlorofluorocarbons—commonly referred to as CFCs—were invented in the late 1920s to replace ammonia, $NH_3(g)$, sulfur dioxide, $SO_2(g)$, and other gases used in air-conditioning and refrigeration systems. Because CFCs are non-flammable and non-toxic, their use in commercial and residential refrigerators and air-conditioning systems became widespread. Although the worldwide use of CFCs in refrigeration systems and other chemical processes has had many benefits, there is evidence that their use has had harmful consequences for the ozone layer.

▶ **chlorofluorocarbon (CFC):** a synthetic organic molecule in which hydrogen atoms are replaced with chlorine and fluorine atoms; also called Freon

Figure B2.9: Many CFCs, or Freons, are used in refrigeration systems.

▶ **functional group:** an arrangement of single atoms or groups of atoms, other than carbon or hydrogen, attached to an organic molecule

Chlorofluorocarbons are part of a larger group of organic molecules called **halogenated hydrocarbons**. Halogenated hydrocarbons are synthetic organic compounds formed by reactions that substitute hydrogen atoms on a hydrocarbon

> **halogenated hydrocarbon:** a hydrocarbon molecule that has one or more hydrogen atoms replaced by atoms of chlorine, fluorine, bromine, or iodine

with atoms from the halogen family of elements—chlorine, fluorine, bromine, or iodine. The term *chlorofluorocarbon* (CFC) describes the molecule as having both chlorine and fluorine atoms replacing hydrogen atoms in the chemical structure.

Try This Activity

How Does a Refrigerant Work?

Purpose

You will investigate a physical change of matter and study its potential for use in a refrigeration system.

CAUTION!

Butane is flammable. Perform this activity only under the supervision of a teacher and in a room in which there are no open flames or sparks. Do not open the bags containing the butane unless you are told to do so by your teacher.

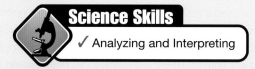

Science Skills

✓ Analyzing and Interpreting

Background Information

Butane, C_4H_{10}, has a boiling point of $-0.5°C$. If compressed, gaseous butane can be converted into its liquid form. In this activity you will observe the energy change that accompanies the change in state as liquid butane becomes gaseous butane.

Materials

- handouts from the Science 30 Textbook CD
  - "Schematic of a Refrigerator"
  - "MSDS: Ammonia"
  - "MSDS: Butane"
- liquid butane (Ask your teacher for this.)
- plastic, zipper-lock sandwich bag
- fume hood
- plastic drywall anchor (#4)
- scissors

Procedure

step 1: Read the entire procedure before starting the experiment. Prepare a suitable data table for recording your observations.

step 2: Read the information on the MSDS for butane. Highlight or underline sections of the MSDS that identify safety concerns regarding the use of butane.

step 3: Obtain a small sample of liquid butane in a zipper-lock sandwich bag from your teacher. Quickly observe how expanded the bag feels and how hot or cold the outside of the bag feels to the touch. Don't record your observations until you have completed step 4.

step 4: Locate where the liquid butane is in the bag. Place your fingers around the outside of the bag in an area where liquid butane is located. Observe the effect the heat from your hand has on the liquid butane and any changes to the amount the bag has expanded. Record your observation to steps 3 and 4 in the data table you prepared earlier.

step 5: Put all the equipment away, and properly dispose of the butane as instructed by your teacher.

Analysis

1. Explain how heat energy from the air surrounding the bag and your hand caused a phase change in the butane. Write the chemical reaction for this change.

2. Explain how the phase change could be used to cool the contents of food placed in a refrigerator.

3. Complete the "Schematic of a Refrigerator" handout by adding the following labels:
   - location of butane in the refrigerator system
   - states of butane at the positions A, B, and C
   - directions of the flow of thermal energy in the coils outside the refrigerator and in the coils inside the refrigerator

4. The compressor motor is an important component of a refrigerator. It forces the gaseous refrigerant to undergo a phase change back into a liquid. Identify the energy change that occurs to the compressed gas when it changes from a gas to a liquid. Explain the function for the coils outside the refrigerator.

5. Compare the safety concerns you identified for butane in step 1 of the procedure to the MSDS provided for ammonia. Based on the information, identify which substance—ammonia or butane—would make a safer refrigerant. Provide a justification for your choice. Identify any additional information you would want to have before making a final choice.

Naming Halogenated Hydrocarbons

The naming system used previously for hydrocarbons can be modified slightly to include hydrogenated hydrocarbons. Halogen atoms present in a molecule are indicated, like hydrocarbons, using the appropriate prefixes. These prefixes are listed in the "Halogen Prefixes" table. The end result will be to name the hydrocarbon part of the molecule first and, then, use prefixes to identify halogen atoms and their location.

HALOGEN PREFIXES

Halogen	Prefix
fluorine	fluoro
chlorine	chloro
iodine	iodo
bromine	bromo

To determine the systematic name for halogenated hydrocarbons, use the method for naming hydrocarbons and add the following steps.

step 1: Name the parent chain.

This is the same as naming the parent chain of a hydrocarbon.

step 2: Find all halogen atoms in the molecule.

You may find it easier if you circle these atoms.

step 3: Determine the appropriate prefixes to represent the halogens.

Each type of halogen atom is referenced using its appropriate prefix. (Refer to the "Halogen Prefixes" table.) If the same halogen atom appears in the molecule more than once, use the same prefixes that indicate the number of branches in a hydrocarbon chain (e.g., *di-* and *tri-*). For example, if two chlorine atoms are present, the prefix is *dichloro*.

step 4: Communicate where each halogen atom appears in the parent chain.

For example, 2-*fluoro* means that there is a fluorine atom on carbon 2 of the parent chain. Also, 2,2-*difluoro* means that there are two fluorine atoms on carbon 2 of the parent chain. If more than one halogen atom appears on the molecule, list them in alphabetical order.

Example Problem 2.1

One of many refrigerants developed by Thomas Midgley was CF_4. Write the systematic name for CF_4.

Solution

step 1: Name the parent chain.

F
|
F–C–F   only 1 carbon
|
F

The parent chain is methane.

step 2: Find all halogen atoms in the molecule.

F
|
F–C–F
|
F   There are 4 fluorine atoms.

step 3: Determine the appropriate prefixes to represent the halogens.

Because there are 4 fluorine atoms, the prefix is *tetrafluoro-*.

step 4: Communicate where each halogen atom appears in the parent chain.

Since there is only 1 carbon in the parent chain, there is no need to communicate where each fluorine atom appears.

Therefore, the systematic name of CF_4 is tetrafluoromethane.

Figure B2.10: Proper maintenance of an air conditioning unit involves checking the refrigerant level.

DID YOU KNOW?

Deaths attributed to leaked refrigerants led Thomas Midgley to develop CFCs. Midgley demonstrated the safety of his discovery to other scientists by inhaling a lung full of the Freon gas and then blowing out a candle flame with the exhaled gas.

Midgley—a scientist for General Motors Corporation— also worked on developing fuel additives and leaded gasoline.

Example Problem 2.2

Teflon—a polymer commonly used on frying pans and valued for its non-stickiness and ability to resist damage from high heat and other chemicals— is produced by the reaction of many molecules of 1,1,2,2-tetrafluoroethene. Draw the molecular structure of a single 1,1,2,2-tetrafluoroethene.

Solution

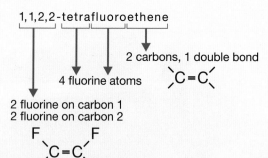

1,1,2,2-tetrafluoroethene

2 carbons, 1 double bond $\begin{matrix} \diagdown \\ C=C \\ \diagup \end{matrix}$

4 fluorine atoms

2 fluorine on carbon 1
2 fluorine on carbon 2

$$\begin{matrix} F & & F \\ \diagdown & & \diagup \\ & C=C & \\ \diagup & & \diagdown \\ F & & F \end{matrix}$$

There are no empty bonds to fill with hydrogens. Therefore, the structure of 1,1,2,2-tetrafluoroethene is

$$\begin{matrix} F & & F \\ \diagdown & & \diagup \\ & C=C & \\ \diagup & & \diagdown \\ F & & F \end{matrix}$$

Example Problem 2.3

CFC-113 is a solvent used in the manufacture of computers and electronic components. It is also used in dry cleaning where it replaced the use of CCl_4. Write the systematic names for these two halogenated hydrocarbons.

$$\begin{matrix} Cl & F \\ | & | \\ F-C-C-Cl \\ | & | \\ Cl & F \end{matrix} \qquad \begin{matrix} Cl \\ | \\ Cl-C-Cl \\ | \\ Cl \end{matrix}$$

CFC-113   **CCl_4**

Solution

CFC-113	CCl_4
$\begin{matrix} Cl & Cl \\ \| & \| \\ F-C-C-F \\ \| & \| \\ Cl & F \end{matrix}$	$\begin{matrix} Cl \\ \| \\ Cl-C-Cl \\ \| \\ Cl \end{matrix}$
Determine the parent chain.	
ethane	methane
Determine the prefixes.	
trichloro- trifluoro-	tetrachloro-
Show where each halogen appears (if necessary).	
1,1,2-trichloro- 1,2,2-trifluoro-	N/A
Put it all together.	
1,1,2-trichloro-1,2,2-trifluoroethane	tetrachloromethane

Practice

8. The first CFC produced by Thomas Midgley was dichlorodifluoromethane. Draw the chemical structure for this compound.

9. Obtain the "Halogenated Hydrocarbons" handout from the Science 30 Textbook CD. On this handout, you will see some halogenated hydrocarbons listed. Complete this table.

DID YOU KNOW?

The chemical formula for a chlorofluorocarbon (CFC) or a hydrochlorofluorocarbon (HCFC) can be determined from its number.

- Add 90 to the CFC or HCFC number, and write out the resulting number.
- The first number tells you the number of carbon atoms in the molecule.
- The second number tells you the number of hydrogen atoms in the molecule.
- The third number tells you the number of fluorine atoms in the molecule.
- The remaining bonds to the carbon atoms are filled with chlorine atoms.

Example: CFC-11

$$11 + 90 = 101$$

1 C   O H   1 F

A carbon has four bonds, and only one bond is used by fluorine. Therefore, 3 chlorine atoms must be bonded to the carbon atom. The chemical formula is $CFCl_3$.

Use this method to determine the chemical formula for CFC-12, HCFC-22, HCFC-124, and HCFC-134a. Would it be possible to have a CFC-15?

Ozone and Concerns Regarding CFCs

The energy from the Sun is a collection of different forms of radiation. Some of the forms of energy in sunlight include ultraviolet and infrared radiation and visible light. Ultraviolet radiation can cause damage to living tissue because it possesses greater energy than many other forms of radiation found in sunlight. As you have learned, energy from sunlight can excite molecules and initiate chemical reactions in the atmosphere. Oxygen molecules in the **stratosphere** are exposed to ultraviolet radiation, which initiates the development of ozone, $O_3(g)$. The **ozone layer** is a portion of the stratosphere that protects Earth from exposure to excessive levels of ultraviolet radiation. The reactions involving the production and decomposition of ozone that form the ozone cycle absorb the components of ultraviolet radiation—most harmful to human skin and eyes—protecting life on Earth from its harmful effects. The importance of the ozone layer to life on Earth has made it a popular focus for scientific research.

▶ **stratosphere:** the portion of the atmosphere between 10 km and 50 km above Earth's surface

▶ **ozone layer:** the portion of the stratosphere, where the highest concentrations of ozone occur

Some of the first scientific work on ozone involved identifying the ozone cycle and estimating the quantity of ozone that should be present in the ozone layer. Later—once it became possible to make measurements—it was determined that the actual amount of ozone in the stratosphere was less than the amount predicted. This observation further raised the interest of many scientists who began to work toward identifying a reason for the difference.

Although investigations had shown that some substances reacted with ozone, the demonstration that nitrogen oxides could decompose ozone attracted even more interest toward investigating the effects of human-made emissions on the ozone layer. The role of CFCs in ozone depletion became clearer when key findings from a variety of different research projects studying CFCs and the reactivity of free chlorine atoms were interpreted together.

Evidence had shown that CFCs were stable molecules in the troposphere, where they were exposed to low levels of UV radiation. Once data became available that CFC molecules were present in all levels of the atmosphere, scientists became concerned about the stability of these molecules, since they are exposed to greater levels of UV higher in the stratosphere.

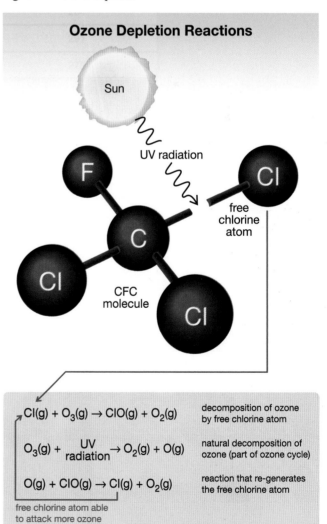

Ozone Depletion Reactions

Sun

UV radiation

F

Cl

free chlorine atom

C

Cl

Cl

CFC molecule

$Cl(g) + O_3(g) \rightarrow ClO(g) + O_2(g)$	decomposition of ozone by free chlorine atom
$O_3(g) + \underset{\text{radiation}}{\text{UV}} \rightarrow O_2(g) + O(g)$	natural decomposition of ozone (part of ozone cycle)
$O(g) + ClO(g) \rightarrow Cl(g) + O_2(g)$	reaction that re-generates the free chlorine atom

free chlorine atom able to attack more ozone

The Process of Ozone Depletion (simplified)

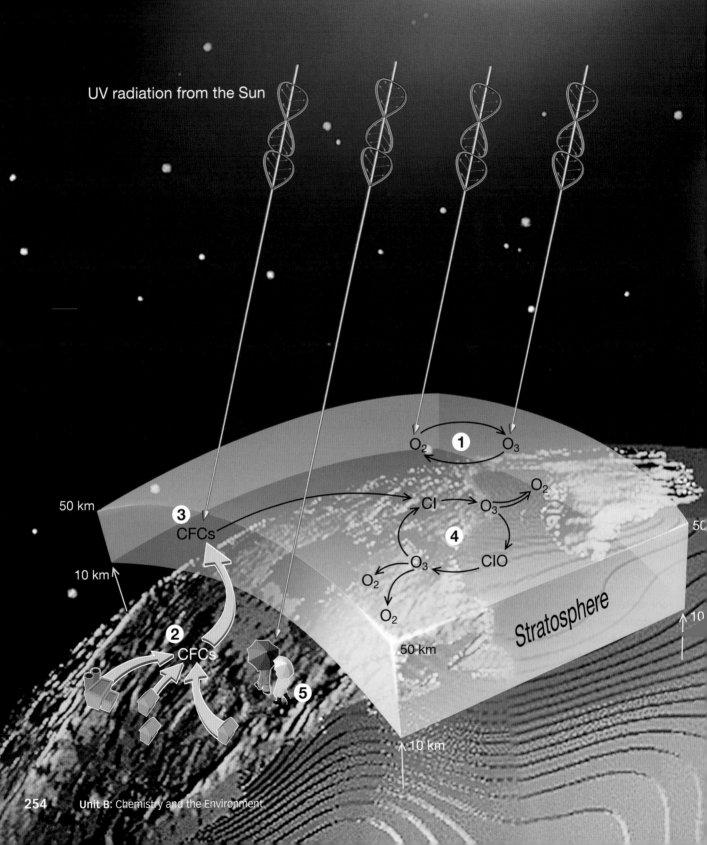

UV radiation from the Sun

50 km

10 km

① O_2 O_3

③ CFCs

② CFCs

④ Cl O_3 O_2 ClO O_3 O_2 O_2

⑤

Stratosphere

50 km

10 km

50

10

1. **Natural Ozone Cycle:** UV radiation collides with oxygen, $O_2(g)$, and ozone, $O_3(g)$, molecules. Energy from this radiation is absorbed and breaks chemical bonds, creating a cycle. The ozone cycle is the only mechanism to produce stratospheric ozone. Absorption of UV radiation by $O_2(g)$ and $O_3(g)$ prevents harmful forms of radiation from reaching Earth's surface.

2. **CFCs Released:** CFCs are stable below the stratosphere. Winds carry CFCs into the stratosphere.

3. **CFCs Broken Down:** CFCs are exposed to higher levels of UV radiation in the stratosphere. Collisions between CFCs and UV radiation produce chlorine atoms.

4. **Ozone Broken Down:** A reaction between chlorine atoms and ozone occurs. The chlorine atoms are regenerated and attack thousands of ozone molecules. The natural balance in the ozone cycle is disrupted.

5. **Increased UV at Surface:** Harmful forms of UV can reach Earth's surface because there is less stratospheric ozone.

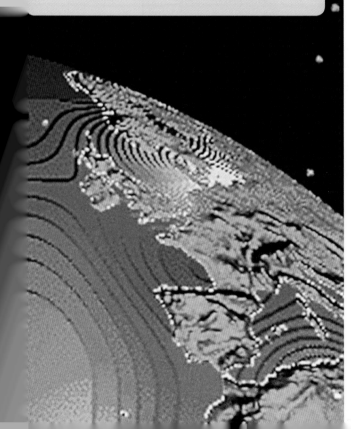

Results from experiments demonstrated that UV radiation caused the removal of chlorine atoms from CFC molecules in the stratosphere and that the free chlorine atoms could react to destroy ozone. CFCs that were first demonstrated by Midgley as a miracle chemical became an even greater cause for concern when additional evidence demonstrated that chlorine atoms could be regenerated by reactions occurring in the atmosphere. Regeneration provides the opportunity for a single chlorine atom to bring about the destruction of many ozone molecules.

Science Links

Ultraviolet radiation—a form of energy released by the Sun—can produce free radicals in cells, resulting in their damage. Units A and C expand on the intensity and forms of energy released by the Sun, including ultraviolet radiation and its effects on living systems.

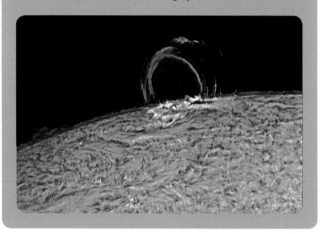

? DID YOU KNOW?

In 1995—more than 20 years after alerting the world to the impact that CFCs produced by human activity were having on the ozone layer—Paul Crutzen, Mario Molina, and F. Sherwood Rowland won the Nobel Prize in chemistry. Crutzen was acknowledged for his work on the effect of nitrogen oxides on the ozone layer, a crucial discovery that enabled Molina and Rowland to determine that CFCs also destroyed stratospheric ozone. The publication of Molina and Rowland's discovery increased society's attention to environmental issues. Government action in the late 1970s and early 1980s led to restrictions on the use of CFCs as aerosol propellants and resulted in increased attention by government, industry, and scientists toward environmental issues.

Free Radicals

The addition of UV radiation to a CFC can result in the formation of free radicals of chlorine in the atmosphere. You may have heard or read advertisements warning about the effect free radicals can have on your body. You may have heard that free radicals cause aging and can cause damage to parts of the body.

Free radicals are chemical species that have an unpaired electron in their valence shell. You may recall that substances with unpaired electrons seek out other substances they can combine with to fill their valence shell. In the body, exposure to radiation, or substances within food, may result in the production of a variety of oxygen-containing free radicals. Despite their origin, you have seen that free radicals are very reactive and bring about chemical change. Concern about free radicals in people's diet is based on evidence that they can react with lipids (a major component of the cell wall), proteins, and DNA. Damage to any of these components can affect the function of cells and may result in tissue damage.

Vitamin E (α-tocopherol)

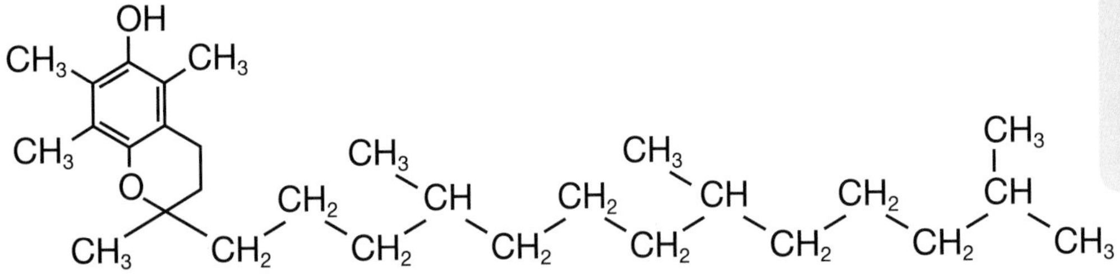

> **antioxidant:** a substance that prevents the oxidation of another substance; a substance present within the body or other materials that reacts with free radicals to protect important components

Figure B2.11: Vitamin E

There is no way to completely avoid free radicals, but it is possible to reduce exposure through food choices containing **antioxidants**. Vitamins E and C, beta-carotene, and lycopene are well-known antioxidants. All of these antioxidants are available from vegetables. If you are concerned about the amount of antioxidants in your diet, consult Canada's Food Guide, a dietician, or other appropriate sources.

Holes in the Ozone Layer

The ozone layer over Earth varies in thickness. The thickness of the ozone layer is measured in Dobson units (DU). One Dobson unit is equivalent to a thickness of 0.01 mm of ozone gas at a standard temperature and pressure (0 °C and 100 kPa). As you can see in Figure B2.12, some regions have significantly higher levels of ozone. Areas with low levels of ozone are called ozone holes.

Total Ozone in Dobson Units (2006/10/24)

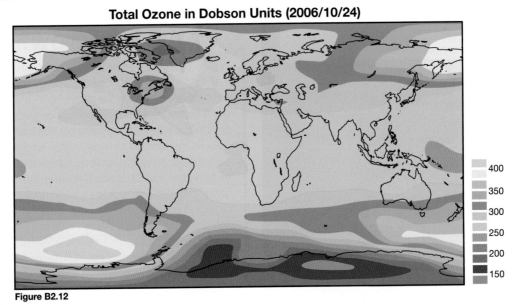

Figure B2.12

The thickness of the ozone layer can be measured daily. One of the most important evaluations of the thickness of the ozone layer occurs at the end of winter. You have learned that the reaction that produces chlorine radicals requires UV radiation. UV radiation is also required for the reaction to produce ozone. Research on the ozone layer tends to focus on the thickness of ozone over Earth's poles. Measurements taken around the end of winter for each hemisphere—September 23 for the South Pole and March 23 for the North Pole—provide scientists with the opportunity to assess the damage done to the ozone layer during the previous year and to compare the data to other years.

10. The thickness of the ozone layer at an Antarctic research station in 1956 was 321 DU. Calculate the percentage loss in ozone between 1956 and 1997, when the thickness was 139 DU.

11. In Figure B2.12, determine the locations where the thickness of the ozone layer is the lowest.

12. Use the Internet to find a recent world ozone map. Compare this map with Figure B2.13. Identify any similarities and any differences.

13. Graph the following data. Account for the fluctuation in the thickness of the ozone layer during the time for which data is shown.

AVERAGE THICKNESS OF OZONE LAYER OVER ANTARCTICA (2005–2006)

Month	Ozone Thickness (DU)
August	207
September	158
October	155
November	253
December	290
January	298
February	284
March	291
April	278

14. Predict the trend for the average monthly ozone layer thickness over the North Pole over the same time period as shown in question 13.

Monitoring Ozone

The thickness of the ozone layer is determined by data collected both from satellites and from measurements made by devices that travel into the stratosphere by weather balloon. Many satellites use spectrometers and other equipment to measure reflected UV radiation and atmospheric temperatures to determine the amount of ozone.

Balloon measurements use an ozone sonde—a device that draws in ozone as the balloon rises in the atmosphere. The concentration of ozone present at various levels in the atmosphere determines the strength for a radio signal that is sent from the sonde to a detector on the ground.

Figure B2.13: The Aura satellite, launched in 2004, is used to monitor the ozone layer.

15. Use the Internet to determine the names for the abbreviations TOMS and OMI. These devices are used in the measurement of Earth's ozone layer.

16. Measurements of Earth's ozone layer are made using satellites and balloon sondes. Because of the differences between conditions in space and on Earth, different instruments are used. Explain how the use of different instruments to study the ozone layer can improve the interpretation of the data collected.

17. Atmospheric measurements for ozone concentration are expressed as parts per million (ppm), whereas measurements for the free radical chlorine monoxide, ClO(g), are expressed as parts per billion (ppb). Explain the difference between the magnitudes of these two units for concentration. Explain how a change in the concentration of chlorine monoxide in the atmosphere could affect the concentration of ozone.

International Agreements to Protect the Ozone Layer

The scientific evidence that demonstrated the effects of CFCs and other halogenated hydrocarbons on the environment supported the need for action to protect the environment. In 1987, an international treaty called *The Montreal Protocol on Substances That Deplete the Ozone Layer* was developed. Under this agreement, countries commit to phase out the production and use of ozone-depleting substances. As of 2006, the number of countries committing to the Montreal Protocol had grown from its initial group of 40 to 190.

Figure B2.14: Montreal at night

To meet the requirements of the Montreal Protocol, governments are demanding that changes be made to previous practices. In most cases, alternatives to ozone-depleting chemicals must be found or new processes must be developed. Because chlorine atoms (radicals) released from CFCs cause damage to the ozone layer, other halogenated hydrocarbon alternatives to CFCs have been developed. HCFCs (hydrochlorofluorocarbons)—which contain fewer chlorine atoms in their chemical structures—and HFC (hydrofluorocarbons)—which do not contain any chlorine in their chemical structure—cause less damage. Target dates for the reduction of these substances and other ozone-depleting substances are shown in the table.

Ozone-Depleting Substance	Target Date for Elimination Under the Montreal Protocol
Halons	1994
CFCs, HBFCs (hydrobromofluorocarbons), tetrachloromethane	1996
bromomethane	2010
HCFCs	2030

You may wonder whether international agreements like the Montreal Protocol are successful, especially when you see the length of time required for target dates to become effective. Although the process to eliminate ozone-depleting substances appears to take a long time, many people consider the Protocol a success given the large number of countries that have committed to meeting these targets. In some cases, countries have managed to meet target dates ahead of schedule. Reasons that may account for the success of this agreement may include

- a consensus among countries regarding the scientific evidence identifying a threat to the ozone layer by CFCs and other halogenated hydrocarbons

- problem chemicals can be restricted to a few types that can be controlled or for which alternatives can be found

- changes in behaviours regarding the use of ozone-depleting substances that are not costly or do not otherwise affect countries economically

In some cases, even though scientific evidence demonstrates that a compound causes ozone depletion, it is not included in the list of substances to be phased out by the Montreal Protocol. This is because exemptions can be made for substances if there are no alternatives and their use is critical. For example, although scientific evidence has demonstrated that some halogenated hydrocarbons containing bromine have a greater capacity to deplete ozone than CFCs, these substances are not prohibited by the Protocol. Halon-1211 (also known as bromochlorofluoromethane) and Halon-1301 (or bromotrifluoromethane) have a significantly higher ability to deplete ozone when compared to CFCs. Controversy existed at the time the Protocol was drafted because these compounds were used in fire extinguishers in airplanes. Due to the unique conditions and specifications required to contain fires in this environment, few alternatives existed; so to maintain safety, the use of these compounds was allowed under even stricter control. Since then, suitable alternative fire retardants have been found.

One compound for which a suitable alternative has yet to be found is bromomethane (also called methylbromide). Methylbromide is a pesticide used in agriculture to fumigate soil. A great deal of concern has been expressed by farmers, especially in the United States, that no suitable alternative exists to protect sensitive crops from pests.

In order to demonstrate agreement with the Montreal Protocol, countries applying for critical-use exemptions must justify why they need to continue to produce or import restricted substances.

Other Halogenated Compounds

In addition to CFCs, many other synthetic halogenated organic compounds exist. Plastics, fire retardants, paints, solvents, cleaning supplies, pesticides, and herbicides are all examples of the types of products that may contain halogenated hydrocarbons.

Dichlorodiphenyltrichloroethane (DDT)

This is used for mosquito control.

Toxaphene

This is a pesticide. **Note:** The exact positions of the chlorine atoms are not known.

Polychlorinated Biphenyl

This is used in some older electric transformers.

Dioxin

This is a by-product of some chemical processes where chlorine is used.

Furan

This is a by-product of some chemical processes where chlorine is used.

Biomagnification

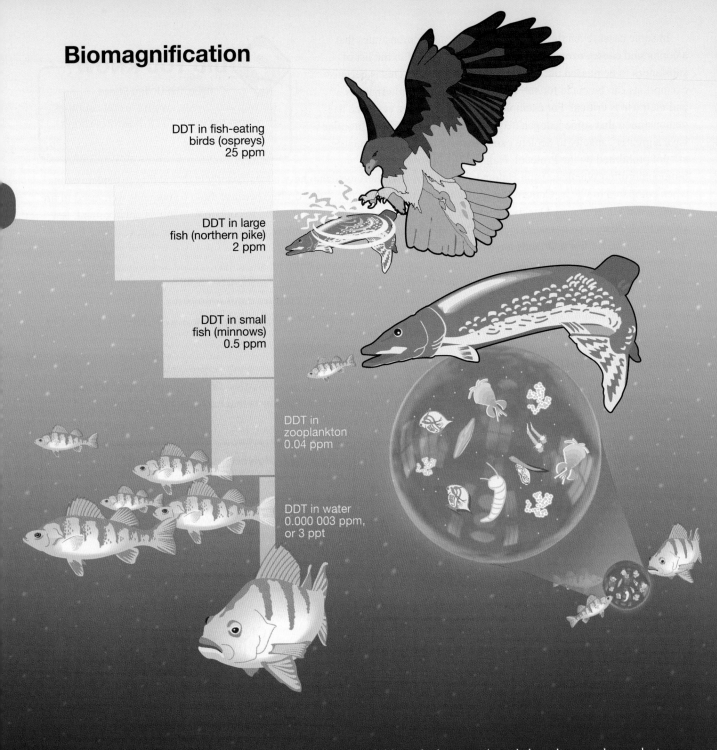

DDT in fish-eating
birds (ospreys)
25 ppm

DDT in large
fish (northern pike)
2 ppm

DDT in small
fish (minnows)
0.5 ppm

DDT in
zooplankton
0.04 ppm

DDT in water
0.000 003 ppm,
or 3 ppt

The only sources of halogenated hydrocarbons are human activities, whether as an intended result or as a by-product. Some, like CFCs and polychlorinated biphenyls (PCBs), were developed for use in a variety of applications because of their chemical stability. However, this characteristic has caused them to be a problem to living organisms. Chlorinated hydrocarbon compounds, like DDT and toxaphene, have been shown to biomagnify precisely because of their tendency not to break down in food chains and affect higher-level organisms within ecosystems, like the peregine falcon, other birds of prey, and humans.

Dioxins and furans are halogenated hydrocarbons produced as a by-product of the chlorine bleaching process for wood pulp and from the low-temperature incineration of chlorinated organic compounds (e.g., plastics). Dioxins, furans, and even pesticides used thousands of kilometres away from the Arctic have been detected in the tissues of organisms in all levels of

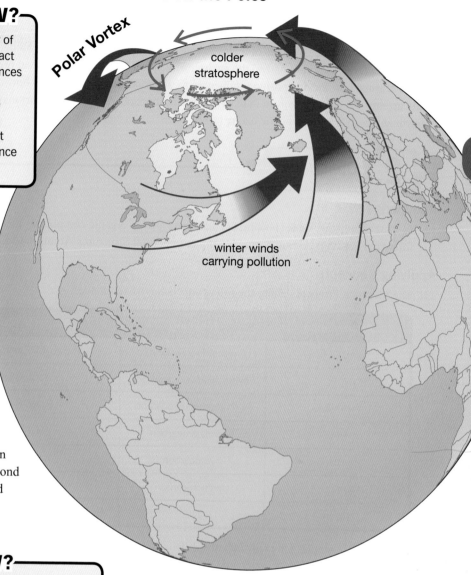

? DID YOU KNOW?

Because of the large number of chemical substances you come in contact with, it is difficult to identify the substances that can present the greatest risk. Epidemiology is the branch of medicine that looks at the occurrence of disease and attempts to identify similarities that may exist between people that experience certain forms of disease.

Many herbicides and pesticides contain halogen atoms. As a result, concern exists regarding the effect pesticides can have on human health. When you eat, can you be sure your food doesn't contain traces of pesticides or herbicides that may have been used in its production?

Apart from environmental persistence, halogenated hydrocarbons are a health concern because they target important parts of the body: the central nervous system, heart, liver, and kidneys. As you learned earlier, chlorine compounds can be broken down. Chlorine radicals are also able to bond to organic compounds in these tissues and cause damage.

? DID YOU KNOW?

Alberta's Swan Hills Hazardous Waste Treatment Facility uses temperatures of 1200°C or higher to combust and break down the highly stable benzene ring in aromatic compounds. This facility is one of few sites in Canada capable of treating CFCs and other halogenated hydrocarbons like PCBs.

Earlier in this lesson you learned that organic compounds, like CFCs and other halogenated hydrocarbons, are detected in the tissues of arctic animals. Halogenated hydrocarbons, as you have seen, are used by industry and agriculture at lower latitudes and can be transported by prevailing wind patterns toward the polar regions.

Like all winds, the polar vortex is produced by the unequal heating of air. The winds that create the polar vortex are located higher in the atmosphere than other wind currents. Conditions exist to create a vortex at both the North Pole and South Pole. It is believed that these winds have drawn pollutants from industrialized areas toward the poles.

The collection of these compounds in the atmosphere, along with the cold temperatures that occur during winter, create polar stratospheric clouds. Much of the research on the atmosphere in the Arctic and Antarctic focuses on the chemical reactions that occur within these clouds and how these reactions affect the ozone layer and other phenomena.

2.1 Summary

In this lesson you studied the uses of hydrocarbons—aromatic compounds and halogenated hydrocarbons—by society as well as the impact these uses have had on the environment. You examined the chemical properties of these classes of compounds and you learned how the composition influences these properties. You then saw how these substances can be transported by wind currents and can be involved in reactions in the atmosphere. Their transport may have greater consequences for all parts of Earth and even the stratospheric ozone layer.

2.1 Questions

Knowledge

1. Prepare a summary table showing the different types of organic compounds that were introduced in this lesson. Use the following headings: Group Name, Example, Important Structures/Atoms, and Environmental Concerns.

Applying Concepts

2. The Montreal Protocol defines the following classes of substances.

Abbreviation	Meaning	Atoms in Molecule
CFC	chlorofluorocarbon	Cl, F, and C
HCFC	hydrochlorofluorocarbon	H, Cl, F, and C
HBFC	hydrobromofluorocarbon	H, Br, F, and C
HFC	hydrofluorocarbon	H, F, and C
HC	hydrocarbon	H and C
PFC	perfluorocarbon	F and C
Halon	N/A	Br, Cl (in some), F, H (in some), and C

Provide two examples for each class of substances. For each example, draw a structural diagram, write its chemical formula, and determine its systematic name. (Your examples should differ in the number of carbon atoms.)

3. Describe the difference between CFCs and HCFCs.

4. Suggestions have been made to replace the use of CFCs and HCFCs with hydrocarbons, like butane, and other compounds, like ammonia. Identify risks associated with the use of these suggested alternatives.

5. Describe how the action of winds within the polar vortex could contribute to the reduction in ozone at the North Pole and South Pole.

6. 1,1,1,2,3,3,3-heptafluoropropane (FM-200) and 1,1,1,3,3,3-hexafluoropropane (HFC-236fa) are replacements for halogenated bromine compounds (Halons) used in fire extinguishers in aircraft.

   a. Draw the chemical structures for these two compounds.

   b. Identify properties of these compounds that would make them suitable alternatives to Halons.

7. Explain why free radicals are reactive substances.

8. Use the Internet to locate information and then prepare a table that lists the antioxidants identified in this lesson and the food sources that contain these substances.

9. Use the Internet to find five examples of naturally occurring and synthetic compounds that contain aromatic rings. Indicate their source or importance.

10. List concerns about aromatic compounds identified in this lesson. Explain how these concerns can be attributed to the chemical properties of the aromatic ring.

In Lesson 2.1 you briefly studied Earth's ozone layer and its ability to absorb harmful wavelengths of ultraviolet radiation. Concerns about the thinning ozone layer and the possibility of developing skin cancer have more people thinking about using sunscreens to protect themselves from the Sun. All sunscreens contain substances that absorb UV radiation; but with so many products to choose from, which is the best choice?

You may know someone who has an allergy to a certain brand of sunscreen or even to antibiotics prescribed to fight a bacterial infection. Exposure to certain chemical substances can cause an allergic reaction. In Unit A you discovered that the body's immune system responds to antigens, the chemical substances the body identifies as foreign.

What causes substances with such different purposes to have a similar effect on the body? In this lesson you will learn more about the structure of three groups of organic compounds: alcohols, carboxylic acids, and esters. You will identify these molecules by their functional groups, and you will identify some of the chemical and physical properties demonstrated by these groups of compounds.

Alcohols

It was a nasty cold snap. In fact, it was ten straight days of temperatures below −20°C. Although you saw many stalled cars on your way to school, your family's car seemed to start just fine. It may surprise you to know that one of the reasons your family's car was able to continue to operate despite the cold conditions was the addition of a few millilitres of a certain alcohol when the car was last filled up with gasoline.

Figure B2.15: Methanol, a component of gas-line antifreeze, can be used to prevent the formation of ice in the fuel line to an automobile's engine.

Alcohols are a group of organic molecules that possess a **hydroxyl functional group**. Although the hydroxyl functional group consists of two atoms, it replaces a single hydrogen atom on a carbon atom. As you may have noticed, alcohols are also indicated by the suffix *-ol* in their names. Alcohols are one of the most important classes of organic molecules and have many uses.

> **hydroxyl functional group:** a chemical structure found in organic molecules that consists of an oxygen atom bonded to a hydrogen atom; often represented as R–OH, where R represents a hydrocarbon or an organic molecule

Methanol

$$H-\overset{\displaystyle H}{\underset{\displaystyle H}{C}}-O-H$$

Ethanol

$$H-\overset{\displaystyle H}{\underset{\displaystyle H}{C}}-\overset{\displaystyle H}{\underset{\displaystyle H}{C}}-O-H$$

Isopropanol

$$H-\overset{\displaystyle H}{\underset{\displaystyle H}{C}}-\overset{\displaystyle O-H}{\underset{\displaystyle H}{C}}-\overset{\displaystyle H}{\underset{\displaystyle H}{C}}-H$$

Figure B2.16

SOME ALCOHOLS AND THEIR USES

Example	Use
methanol	solvents, fuels, production of pharmaceuticals, disinfectants
ethanol	solvents, fuels, alcoholic beverages, production of pharmaceuticals, disinfectants
glycol	solvents
isopropanol	disinfectants

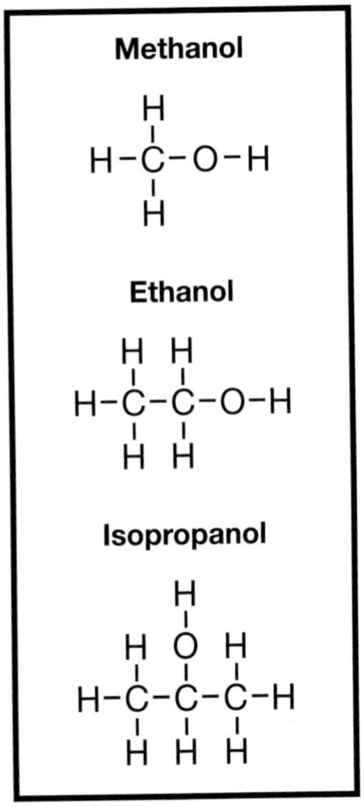

Earlier, you learned that hydrocarbons have very low solubility in water. The presence of a hydroxyl group on a hydrocarbon increases the compound's solubility in water. You also learned that the solubility of substances in water is a result of their ability to attract water molecules. In gas-line antifreeze, the polarity of the hydroxyl group of methanol acts to attract water molecules present in the fuel or within the fuel system. The attraction of the water to the methanol molecule prevents the formation of ice, which can block the fuel line.

Nomenclature of Alcohols

The systematic naming of alcohols involves the use of the suffix *-ol* to indicate the hydroxyl functional group. Other parts of the name that precede the functional group can include numbers to describe the position of the hydroxyl group and/or the prefixes and numbers used in naming the hydrocarbon portion of the molecule.

To determine the systematic name for an alcohol, use the following steps. The end result will be to name the hydrocarbon part of the molecule followed by the suffix *-ol* that identifies the hydroxyl group and its location. Alcohols, such as methanol and ethanol shown in Figure B2.16, contain a single hydroxyl functional group located on the first carbon in the parent chain. When the hydroxyl group is in this position, the number 1 is not required.

step 1: Find the hydroxyl functional group on the molecule and circle it.

step 2: Determine the parent chain of carbon atoms, starting at the end nearest the hydroxyl group.

step 3: Use the method of naming hydrocarbons to determine the initial part of the name.

For example, if the parent chain contains two carbon atoms, the initial part of the name will be *ethan-*.

step 4: Communicate the location of the hydroxyl group on the parent chain, and add the suffix that represents the presence of a hydroxyl group.

For example, *2-ol* means the hydroxyl group is on carbon 2. Also, *1,2-diol* means there are two hydroxyl groups: one on carbon 1 and one on carbon 2 of the parent chain.

Example Problem 2.4

Gas-line antifreeze contains what is sometimes referred to as methyl alcohol or wood alcohol (shown on the right). Determine the systematic name of this structure.

Methyl Alcohol

$$H-\overset{\overset{\displaystyle H}{|}}{\underset{\underset{\displaystyle H}{|}}{C}}-O-H$$

Solution

step 1: Find the hydroxyl functional group on the molecule, and circle it.

$$H-\overset{\overset{\displaystyle H}{|}}{\underset{\underset{\displaystyle H}{|}}{C}}-\boxed{O-H}$$

There is one hydroxyl group.

step 2: Determine the parent chain of carbon atoms, starting at the end nearest the hydroxyl group.

The parent chain consists of 1 carbon.

step 3: Use the method of naming hydrocarbons to determine the initial part of the name.

Because there is only 1 carbon in the parent chain, the initial part is of the name is *methan-*.

step 4: Communicate the location of the hydroxyl group on the parent chain, and add the suffix that represents the presence of a hydroxyl group.

Because there is only 1 hydroxyl group and 1 carbon in the parent chain, add the suffix *-ol*.

Therefore, the systematic name of methyl alcohol, or wood alcohol, is methanol.

Example Problem 2.5

Isopropyl alcohol is commonly sold in stores as a disinfectant. Use the chemical structure provided to write the systematic name for isopropyl alcohol.

Isopropanol

$$H-\overset{\overset{\displaystyle H}{|}}{\underset{\underset{\displaystyle H}{|}}{C}}-\overset{\overset{\displaystyle O}{|}}{\underset{\underset{\displaystyle H}{|}}{C}}-\overset{\overset{\displaystyle H}{|}}{\underset{\underset{\displaystyle H}{|}}{C}}-H$$

Solution

$$H-\overset{\overset{\displaystyle H}{|}}{\underset{\underset{\displaystyle H}{|}}{C}}-\overset{\overset{\boxed{\displaystyle O}}{|}}{\underset{\underset{\displaystyle H}{|}}{C}}-\overset{\overset{\displaystyle H}{|}}{\underset{\underset{\displaystyle H}{|}}{C}}-H$$

← hydroxyl group on carbon 2

↗ 3 carbons on parent chain

The systematic name of isopropyl alcohol is propan-2-ol.

Example Problem 2.6

Propanol, $CH_3CH_2CH_2OH$, is used as a grease remover in some cleaning products. Draw the chemical structure for propanol.

Solution

$$H-\overset{\overset{\displaystyle H}{|}}{\underset{\underset{\displaystyle H}{|}}{C}}-\overset{\overset{\displaystyle H}{|}}{\underset{\underset{\displaystyle H}{|}}{C}}-\overset{\overset{\displaystyle H}{|}}{\underset{\underset{\displaystyle H}{|}}{C}}-O-H$$

18. Draw the chemical structure and write the systematic names for two alcohol molecules each containing 3 carbon atoms, 7 hydrogen atoms, and 1 hydroxyl functional group.

19. The accumulation of cholesterol is associated with the blockage of coronary blood vessels that can result in a heart attack.

Cholesterol

a. Identify the structure on the cholesterol molecule that is similar to alcohols.

b. Identify the portion of the name that identifies cholesterol as a molecule that possesses this functional group.

20. Ethan-1,2-diol, also known as ethylene glycol, is a solvent used in the production of paint and is a major component of automobile antifreeze. Use the systematic name to draw the chemical structure for ethylene glycol.

Carboxylic Acids

For many people, vinegar is a welcome ingredient when cooking or seasoning food. From your studies earlier, it may not surprise you that the sour taste of vinegar is due to the presence of an acid. Whether your favourite vinegar is balsamic, malt, or white, the tangy taste is due to the presence of ethanoic acid. Ethanoic acid is produced naturally by the conversion of ethanol by certain kinds of bacteria. Ethanol-containing substances, like wine and cider, have been used for centuries to make many kinds of vinegars.

The Conversion of an Alcohol to a Carboxylic Acid

$$H-\overset{\overset{\displaystyle H}{|}}{\underset{\underset{\displaystyle H}{|}}{C}}-\overset{\overset{\displaystyle H}{|}}{\underset{\underset{\displaystyle H}{|}}{C}}-O-H \quad \rightarrow \quad H-\overset{\overset{\displaystyle H}{|}}{\underset{\underset{\displaystyle H}{|}}{C}}-C\overset{\displaystyle =O}{\underset{\displaystyle O-H}{}}$$

Ethanol   **Ethanoic Acid**

Figure B2.17: The functional groups for the reactant and product show that oxygen has a significant role in this reaction.

Carboxyl Functional Group

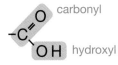
carbonyl

hydroxyl

Figure B2.18: The carboxyl functional group is the combination of two functional groups: a carbonyl functional group and a hydroxyl functional group.

The **carboxyl functional group** contains two oxygen atoms joined to the same carbon atom. By examining Figure B2.18, you will notice that the carbon atom in the carboxyl group is attached to a single oxygen atom by a double bond; this is the **carbonyl functional group**. This same carbon is also attached to the oxygen of a hydroxyl group. All carboxylic acids contain this combination of functional groups, often represented as R-COOH and with the suffix -*oic acid* in their names.

▶ **carboxyl functional group:** the organic chemical structure composed of a carbonyl functional group and a hydroxyl functional group chemically joined to the same carbon atom

▶ **carbonyl functional group:** the functional group formed by the joining of an oxygen atom to a carbon atom by a double bond

In Chapter 1 you examined the empirical properties of acids and discovered that acids undergo a reaction with water that produces hydronium ions. Carboxylic acids demonstrate the same empirical properties as other acids. Hydronium ions are produced by the reaction between the hydrogen located on the hydroxyl group and water.

Ethanoic Acid Reacting with Water

$$CH_3COOH(aq) + H_2O(l) \rightarrow H_3O^+(aq) + CH_3COO^-(aq)$$

acid   base   conjugate   conjugate
                                acid   base

In an earlier investigation, you tested the conductivity and pH of ethanoic acid and hydrochloric acid solutions with identical concentration. It was discovered that the ethanoic acid solution had a lower conductivity and a higher pH compared to the hydrochloric acid solution. This is because organic acids do not react completely with water and, thus, are categorized as weak acids.

Lactic acid is the common name for a carboxylic acid produced by the body during physical exertion. Strenuous exercise usually results in the accumulation of lactic acid inside muscle cells. The fatigue you experience while exercising is often due to the accumulation of hydronium ions—resulting in a small change in the pH within your muscles—produced by the reaction of lactic acid with water. If lactic acid were a strong acid, a greater change in pH would occur within your muscle cells.

How does the body respond to changes in pH within its cells? As you know, humans, as well as all organisms, do not respond well to large changes in pH. Cells, as well as the blood, contain substances to neutralize excess hydronium ions. Hydrogen phosphate ions and dihydrogen phosphate ions present in muscle cells act as a buffering system to maintain a relatively constant pH within muscle cells even during physical exertion.

Practice

21. Copy the structure of lactic acid into your notebook.

Lactic Acid

a. Use differently coloured pens or pencils to draw circles that identify the hydroxyl, carbonyl, and carboxyl functional groups.

b. Use a balanced chemical equation to show how the reaction between lactic acid and water produces a hydronium ion.

c. Explain how the presence of hydrogen phosphate or dihydrogen phosphate could act to buffer the accumulation of hydronium ions that occurs during strenuous exercise.

Some Chemical Structures That Cause Allergic Reactions

Previously, you learned that some people have concerns about the substances present in sunscreens. PABA, short for para-aminobenzoic acid, is a molecule formed by the attachment of two functional groups—one being a carboxyl group—to a benzene molecule. The chemically stable benzene ring is able to absorb UV radiation, serving to protect skin layers beneath the sunscreen. Unfortunately for some people, exposure to

PABA causes an allergic reaction. People with sensitivity to PABA tend to be sensitive to other medicines. Some sunburn and sore-throat medications, along with certain antibiotics, can be broken down by the body to produce PABA or a chemical structure very similar to PABA. The body's contact with these compounds triggers the immune system to respond.

For people who are highly sensitive to an antigen, there is a risk that exposure could cause an **anaphylactic reaction**. For some people, the choice of products they use is very important.

> **anaphylactic reaction:** a life-threatening, severe reaction of the immune system to an antigen that results in severe swelling and may affect the muscles involved in breathing

Figure B2.19: People with extreme sensitivity to certain chemical compounds often wear jewellery that informs medical personnel of their allergy.

?–DID YOU KNOW?–

Rashes, itchy skin, or hives can be an indication that your body is having a mild allergic reaction. Swelling and difficulty breathing are often signs of severe allergic reactions and, thus, require immediate medical attention.

Naming Carboxylic Acids

Writing systematic names for carboxylic acids involves similar steps to those used to name alcohols. The end result will be to name the hydrocarbon part of the molecule followed by the suffix *-oic acid*, which identifies the carboxyl group.

Example Problem 2.7

Propanoic acid is used to prevent some foods from spoiling.

a. Use the systematic name to draw the chemical structure for propanoic acid.

b. State whether it is possible to have the carboxyl functional group on the second carbon in the parent chain of propanoic acid.

Solution

a. **propanoic acid**

Ⓐ Ⓑ
Ⓒ

Ⓐ indicates that there are 3 carbons in the parent chain

Ⓑ indicates that the compound is a carboxylic acid—contains a carboxyl functional group

Ⓒ no number indicates that the carboxyl group is attached to the first carbon

Therefore, the chemical structure is

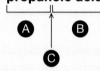

b. The carboxyl functional group requires three bonds. A carbon atom within a chain has only two bonds available, since two of the four bonds are needed for the adjacent carbon atoms. Therefore, it is not possible for a carboxyl functional group to appear in the middle of the parent chain.

Practice

22. Prepare a table that lists the chemical structures and the systematic names for the carboxylic acids that contain one, two, and three carbons, respectively.

Household Cleaning Products

Many people use vinegar for purposes other than food preparation. Many properties of acids make them ideal for a variety of purposes, but can they be used as cleaning products in your home? In the next activity you will examine the cleaning products used in your home and consider the risks and benefits of using vinegar for cleaning.

Utilizing Technology

Risks and Benefits of Household Cleaning Products

Purpose

You will identify issues associated with the use of common household cleaning products and to evaluate the use of alternative products.

Science Skills

✓ Performing and Recording
✓ Analyzing and Interpreting
✓ Communication and Teamwork

Background Information

Regular household cleaning often involves the use of many products. Apart from the instructions for using the product and the safety information listed on the label, most people are unaware of possible risks associated with **direct exposure** to these products. Concerns also exist regarding whether the substances in household cleaning products are **biodegradable** or whether they will have negative, unexpected effects on the environment.

Problem

Is vinegar a safe and suitable replacement for many liquid household cleaners?

▶ **direct exposure:** contact with a chemical substance that occurs while using it or by being present in an area where it has been used

Procedure

step 1: Prepare a list of the liquid cleaning products used during a routine cleaning of your home and the homes of other people in your class. Identify the intended use for each product (glass cleaner, disinfectant, stain remover, etc.). Also, identify the size of the container and the cost of each cleaning product.

step 2: Use the product label, the Internet, and/or other sources of information to identify risks associated with the use of the cleaning products listed. Collect information about the

- safety concerns regarding the storage of the product
- safety concerns when using the product
- harmful effects to humans or pets from direct exposure to the product
- information about the product's biodegradability

▶ **biodegradable:** ability to be broken down by natural mechanisms

step 3: Use the Internet to prepare a list of where vinegar can be used as an appropriate cleaner. Also, indicate situations where it is not recommended to use vinegar as a cleaner.

step 4: Use the product label and/or the Internet to collect information about risks associated with the use of vinegar.

step 5: Determine the quantity of each substance used during a regular household cleaning session. Add this information to the list prepared in step 1.

step 6: If possible, perform an experiment to determine whether vinegar is a suitable replacement for a cleaning product used in your home.

Analysis

1. Identify cleaning products that could be replaced by using vinegar.

2. Calculate a price per millilitre for each liquid cleaning product used during the regular household cleaning session. Calculate the total cost for all the liquid cleaning products used in the cleaning session. You may find it helpful to use a spreadsheet or graphing calculator to calculate and display this information in a table.

3. Use the information you collected to estimate the quantity of vinegar required to complete the cleaning session. Use resources available to you to determine the cost of using vinegar to complete the routine cleaning session.

4. Prepare a risk-benefit analysis of using vinegar as a replacement for the liquid cleaners.

5. Evaluate the list of risks and benefits you prepared and develop a response to the problem stated at the start of this activity. Use one or more of the following perspectives in supporting your answer: scientific (or technological), ecological, and economic.

Esters

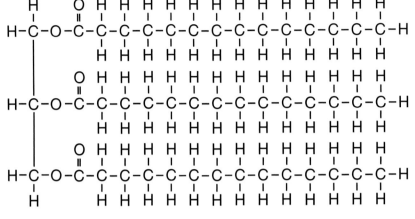

Fat Molecule

Methyl Salicylate

Esters are organic compounds formed by the chemical reaction of a carboxylic acid with an alcohol. Esters may be naturally occurring or synthetic products. In previous science courses you may have heard about fatty acids and fats. Fats and oils are examples of naturally occurring esters produced by your body. The synthesis of fats involves chemically joining three carboxylic acid molecules, called fatty acids, to the hydroxyl groups on a glycerol molecule.

The food and cosmetics industry dedicates a great deal of time to identifying naturally occurring esters and developing synthetic methods to produce these molecules to enhance their taste or aroma.

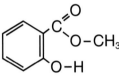

Figure B2.20: Esters are used to provide a desired flavour or odour to a food product like red licorice.

Structure and Formation of Esters

Components of a Fat Molecule

Esters contain a functional group that is a combination of the functional groups of a carboxylic acid and an alcohol. The reaction that forms an ester also forms a second product: a water molecule. The elimination of the water molecule is necessary to enable the chemical joining of the carboxylic acid to the alcohol.

The reaction that synthesizes an ester occurs between the functional groups, leaving the parent chain of both reactants unaffected. Since the other parts of the reactant molecules are unaffected, the components of an ester can be identified and a systematic process can be used to name esters.

Naming Esters

As you have seen, naming other organic compounds with functional groups containing oxygen involves the use of a suffix that identifies the functional group. For esters, the suffix is *-oate*. The remainder of the name identifies the alcohol and the carboxylic acid used in its synthesis.

Naming an ester involves either knowing both the alcohol and carboxylic acid used in its synthesis or analyzing its chemical structure to determine these components.

Example Problem 2.8

A chemical reaction occurs between propanol and ethanoic acid. Use a structural diagram to show the reactants and products for this reaction.

Solution

To determine the systematic name for an ester from a structural diagram, use the following steps:

step 1: Find the ester functional group, and draw a box around it. Then circle each chain of carbon atoms that extend from the functional group.

step 2: Locate the chain of carbon atoms that is attached to the functional group by a single bond to an oxygen atom.

This is the part of the molecule derived from an alcohol.

step 3: Identify the number of carbons in this chain.

If the chain contains one carbon, the prefix *methyl* is used.

step 4: Count the number of carbon atoms in the chain, starting with the carbon that contains a double bond to an oxygen atom.

This is the portion of the ester that is derived from a carboxylic acid.

step 5: Identify the number of carbons in this chain.

For example if the chain contains one carbon, *methan-* is used in this part.

step 6: List the parts identified in steps 3 and 5, followed by the suffix *-oate*.

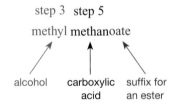

Example Problem 2.9

The ester depicted here produces an aroma similar to that of raspberries. Write the systematic name for this ester.

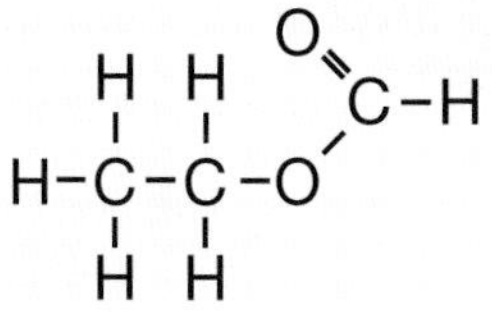

Solution

Follow the steps of systematically naming an ester. First, isolate the three parts of the ester; then identify the alcohol part of the name (steps 1 to 3).

Steps 1 to 3

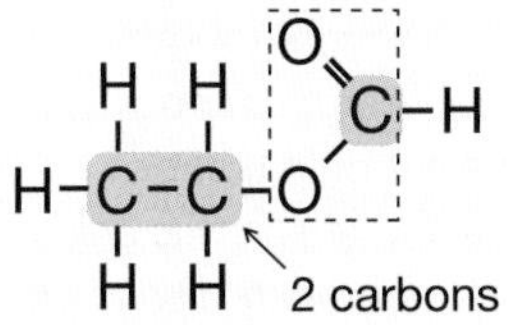

Since there are 2 carbons in the alcohol part, the first part of the name of this ester is *ethyl*.

Now, identify the carboxylic acid part of the name (steps 4 and 5).

Steps 4 and 5

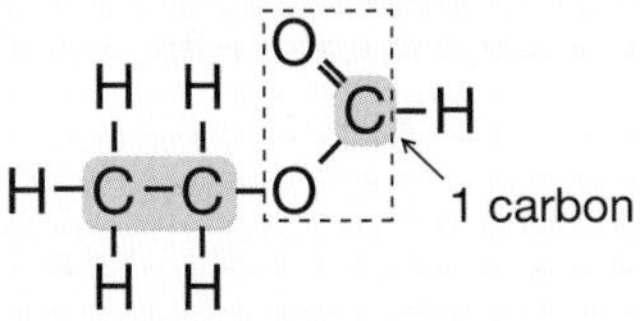

Since there is only 1 carbon in the carboxylic acid part, the middle part of the name of this ester is *methan-*.

Therefore, when you add the suffix *-oate* (step 6) for an ester, the systematic name of this ester is ethyl methanoate.

Practice

23. Benzocaine is an organic compound that is able to dull the sensation of pain by acting on parts of the nervous system. Benzocaine is used in a variety of products, including lotions and ointments used to treat mouth sores, insect bites, and sunburns.

Benzocaine

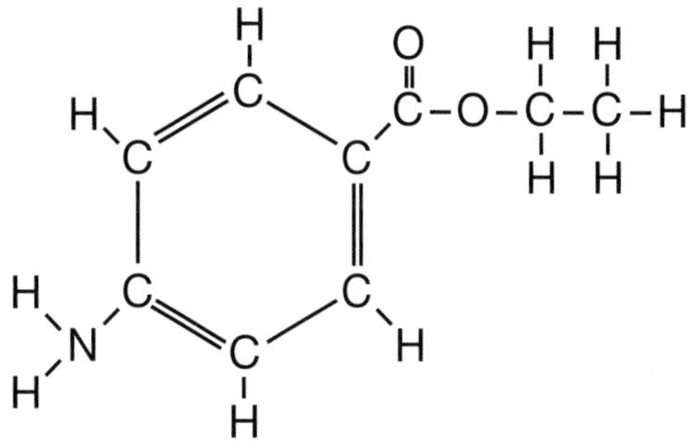

a. Copy the structure of benzocaine into your notebook, and draw a box around the ester functional group.

b. Circle and label the part of the benzocaine molecule that is derived from an alcohol and the part that is derived from a carboxylic acid.

c. State the name of the alcohol used in the production of benzocaine.

d. Explain why people who have allergies to sunscreens containing PABA may also demonstrate a sensitivity to benzocaine.

24. Draw the structural diagrams for the products of the following reactions. Where possible, write the names for the chemical substances involved.

a.

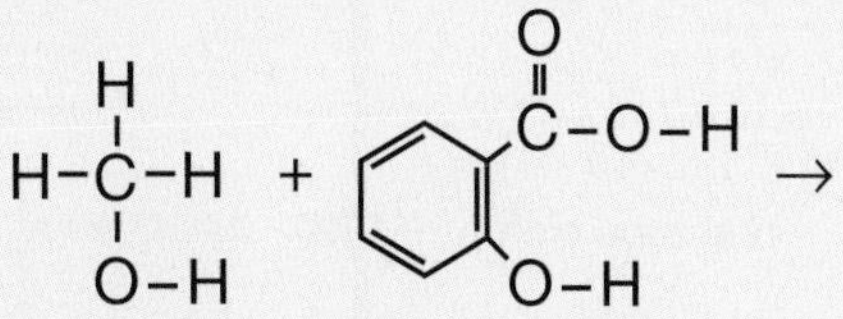

methanol   salicylic acid

b. $CH_3CH_2OH(l) + HCOOH(l) \rightarrow$

c. ethanol + ethanoic acid $\rightarrow$

? DID YOU KNOW?

Acetylcholine—an important molecule in the action of nerves—is an ester. The ester group of an acetylcholine molecule is continually broken apart and reformed as nerve cells function to recycle this important molecule.

Purpose

You will prepare a synthetic, organic compound—an ester.

Pre-Lab Activity

Obtain the handout "Making Esters" from the Science 30 Textbook CD, and closely study the table to see which scents are produced from the reaction of the carboxylic acid and the alcohol. Also, obtain from your teacher a list of the alcohols and carboxylic acids available to you for this investigation.

1. Write the reactions and expected results for three esters that can be synthesized using the alcohols and carboxylic acids available to you. Determine the systematic name for each ester. Show your reactions to your teacher.

Materials

- tap water
- 25 mm × 250 mm test tubes (or larger) (1 for each reaction)
- 2, 250-mL beakers
- 3, 10-mL graduated cylinders
- weighing boat
- lab stand
- test tube clamp (or utility clamp)
- reflux apparatus (one-hole stopper with inserted glass tubing)
- alcohols and carboxylic acids made available by your teacher
- dropper bottle containing concentrated sulfuric acid (handled only by your teacher)

- hot plate
- thermometer
- thermometer clamp
- laboratory tongs
- laboratory scoop
- electronic balance
- a vial of salicylic acid
- evaporating dish (1 per reaction)
- test tube rack
- tray or large beaker containing ice

CAUTION!

Use gloves, safety glasses, and a lab apron for this activity. Sulfuric acid is corrosive; use extreme caution.

Procedure

step 1: Assemble a water bath by placing a 250-mL beaker, half-filled with tap water, onto the hot plate. Place the water bath close to the lab stand. Attach the thermometer clamp to the lab stand and position the thermometer inside the clamp in such a way that it measures the temperature of the water inside the water bath. Attach the test tube clamp to the lab stand.

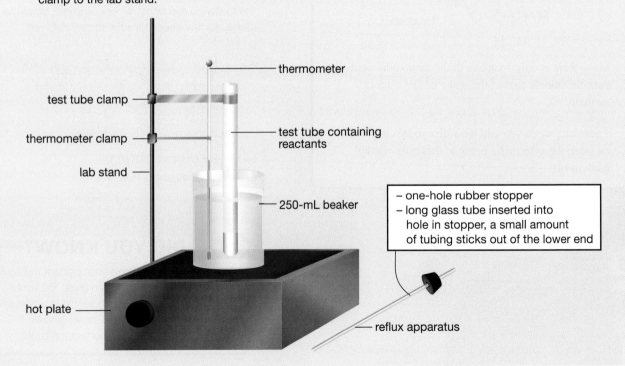

- thermometer
- test tube clamp
- thermometer clamp
- lab stand
- test tube containing reactants
- 250-mL beaker
- one-hole rubber stopper
- long glass tube inserted into hole in stopper, a small amount of tubing sticks out of the lower end
- hot plate
- reflux apparatus

step 2: Transfer approximately 4 mL of the carboxylic acid you have chosen and approximately 5 mL of the alcohol you have selected into separate graduate cylinders. **Note:** If you use salicylic acid, measure approximately 2 g of the salicylic acid crystals into a weighing boat.

step 3: Transfer the contents from the graduated cylinders to the test tube. Fasten the test tube to the test tube clamp attached to the lab stand in such a way that the reactants in the test tube are below the surface of the water bath.

step 4: Use a clean graduated cylinder to measure 2 mL of concentrated sulfuric acid. Add this to the contents of the test tube.

step 5: Attach the reflux apparatus to the test tube. Turn on the hot plate, and begin heating the water bath. Monitor the temperature of the water bath during the experiment to maintain the temperature of the water bath between 70°C and 80°C. Allow the contents of the test tube to heat for 15 min.

step 6: Remove the test tube from the water bath, and allow the contents to cool for 5 min; then place the test tube into a second water bath containing cold or ice water water for 5 min.

step 7: Pour the cooled contents into an evaporating dish. Gently waft the vapour from the dish containing the synthesized ester toward you. Record the odour detected in the appropriate place in your table.

step 8: Repeat steps 2 to 7 for your two other esters.

step 9: Follow your teacher's instructions regarding the disposal of liquid waste. **Be careful not to spill or splash the esters. These mixtures may contain unreacted sulfuric acid.**

step 10: Disassemble, wash (if needed), and return the equipment to its appropriate place.

Analysis

2. Compare the observed odours with the scents listed in the "Making Esters" handout. Were you able to create the ester you intended to synthesize? Use the evidence from the experiment to support your answer.

3. Compare your results with those of other students in your class. Were some esters more difficult to make than others?

4. Is the creation of an ester a fast or slow reaction? Give a reason for your answer.

5. Is this method to create esters reliable and valid?

Polyesters

Enjoying the outdoors may require more than just sunscreen. The pieces of equipment used by wakeboarders, for example, are composed of many different kinds of **plastics**. Most plastics in manufactured materials are **polymers**. One common type of plastic is **polyester**. It is created from the reaction of many alcohols and carboxylic acids, forming long chains or filaments. These filaments are used to make such things as towropes, straps for personal flotation devices (PFDs), and some of the everyday T-shirts in your dresser.

> **plastic:** material that can be shaped or moulded with or without the application of heat

> **polymer:** a large molecule formed by the chemical joining of many smaller molecules

> **polyester:** a polymer containing many ester functional groups

To form the long chains of ester bonds, both the carboxylic acid and alcohol must have two functional groups. For these molecules, chemical reactions occur at both functional groups. This enables the molecule to grow in both directions, producing a filament. Bonding that occurs within and between filaments is responsible for the strength of the plastic, making polyesters like Dacron a useful material in many applications.

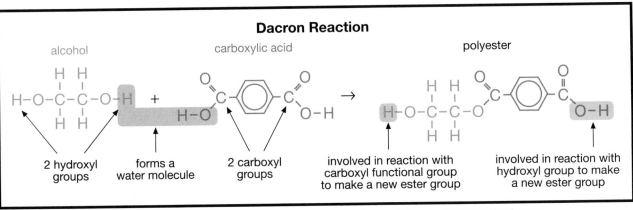

Figure B2.21: A common polyester, called Dacron, is formed by the reaction of an acid and an alcohol, each with two functional groups.

Bioplastics

A major problem with the use of plastics is that they are not biodegradable. Although recycling is one way of reducing the amount of waste sent to landfills, many plastics used today that make their way to landfills will not break down.

> **bioplastic:** an organic polymer produced by plants or bacteria that can be used in place of synthetic polymers to form materials

Bioplastics are a group of compounds that can be used to produce a wide range of materials and have the added advantage of being completely biodegradable. Plastic cups, cutlery, plates, and store bags may be formed from a variety of naturally produced compounds. Bioplastics are produced by extracting a polyester compound from the tissues of plants (such as corn, soy, and even hemp) or from the cells of certain bacteria. The naturally occurring compounds used as bioplastics can be decomposed by bacteria within the soil, often within a few months if properly disposed. Bioplastics are being considered for use in materials like dissolvable sutures and other medical applications.

Bioplastics

Question

How do products made from bioplastics compare to the same products made from synthetic plastics?

Researching the Issue

Use the Internet to prepare a list of different types of bioplastics. For each type of bioplastic, list products that are made from that bioplastic.

Choose one product made from bioplastic, and design a series of experiments that will compare the properties of the product formed from the bioplastic to the same product formed from a synthetic plastic. Show your teacher the designs for the experiments you wish to conduct. If possible, perform the experiments. Use the data collected from your experiments and the results from your research to demonstrate the uses of materials composed from bioplastics.

Science Skills

✓ Performing and Recording
✓ Analyzing and Interpreting
✓ Communication and Teamwork

2.2 Summary

In this lesson you studied organic compounds that have functional groups containing oxygen atoms. Alcohols, carboxylic acids, and esters represent three important groups of compounds that can be identified by the suffixes in their respective systematic names. Compounds within these groups have significance in biological systems and are often used in all aspects of people's lives, including food, building materials, and manufactured products.

2.2 Questions

Knowledge

1. Complete the following table.

Type of Organic Compound	Drawing of Functional Group	Name of Functional Group	Suffix Used During Naming
alcohol			
carboxylic acid			
ester			

2. Prepare a list of some of the common uses for alcohols, carboxylic acids, and esters.

3. State the empirical properties shared by all acids, including carboxylic acids.

Applying Concepts

4. Folic acid is one of the B vitamins essential to human health. People must obtain folic acid through their diet. Bacteria are able to produce folic acid when provided PABA (para-aminobenzoic acid).

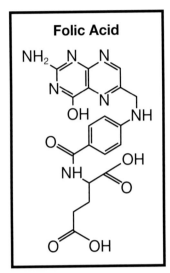

a. Identify the hydroxyl functional groups present in the structure of folic acid.

b. Identify the carboxyl functional groups present in the structure of folic acid.

5. Sulfanilamide is an antibiotic used to treat bacterial infections. Doctors must check their records to ensure that patients do not have an allergy to PABA before prescribing sulfanilamide.

a. Identify similarities between the chemical structures of sulfanilamide and PABA.

b. Explain the significance of any similarities in structure between these two compounds and its importance to a patient's treatment.

c. Explain why it is important for doctors to know about a patient's sensitivity to PABA, or other compounds, when prescribing drugs.

6. The chemical structures for a type of bioplastic are shown here. The first structure represents a single unit, and the other represents two joined units that form part of the polymer. Use these diagrams to answer the following questions.

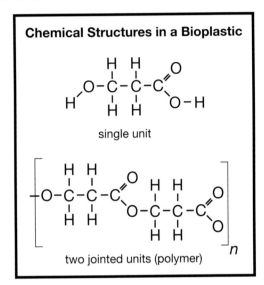

a. Copy the chemical structure for the single unit into your notebook. Circle each functional group, and identify the name.

b. Identify the type of functional group in the polymer.

c. Use structural diagrams to explain how the polymer can be formed from the combination of two single-unit molecules.

d. Use structural diagrams to show the polymer formed from the combination of four single-unit molecules.

e. Write the balanced chemical equation for the process explained in question 6.d.

Congratulations, you've landed a great summer job! Not only will you be able to work outside, you might even get the opportunity to play lots of golf as well. Maintaining the condition of the fairways, greens, and other parts of a golf course is a complex job that requires the superintendent and crew to utilize a variety of chemical substances, including fertilizers, herbicides, insecticides, and pesticides. As part of the grounds crew, you will be required to handle and use many of these substances. Which substance should you be concerned about the most? What actions can you take to reduce your concerns?

In this lesson you will learn more about some of the substances that are present in your environment. Considering that you spend a great deal of time both indoors and outdoors, the choices you make about the substances you use in your daily activities and how you handle them influence what you will be exposed to.

off-gassing: the release of volatile organic compounds from building materials

indoor air quality: an evaluation of the air within a room or structure

Painting is probably one of the many tasks you will be asked to complete, whether at home or while on the job. Imagine you were given permission to decorate your room in any style you choose. Think of all the choices! Renovating a room, an apartment, or a house involves many decisions. Not only are there colours to consider, there are so many different materials from which to choose. The smell of fresh paint is very distinct; it is also an indication of the presence of volatile organic compounds (VOCs) released by the paint through a process called **off-gassing**. Flooring, along with other materials used in decorating, can release VOCs through off-gassing as well. Because of the amount of time people spend inside, **indoor air quality** and exposure to VOCs from off-gassing is a concern for many people.

Science Links

In addition to VOCs, the air inside a room may contain mould, carbon monoxide, ozone, and even pesticides. People with asthma and allergies are especially sensitive to the air quality and substances present. Dust, mould, and insects in a room can trigger allergic reactions. To prevent the accumulation of allergens, smooth, washable surfaces are recommended along with frequent cleaning of floors, walls, and shelves. Have you included information about any substances you are allergic to or perhaps that you have asthma in your personal health file you started in Unit A?

Concerns Regarding Off-Gassing

One way to prevent off-gassing is to use products that do not contain volatile organic compounds (VOCs). Paint and related products that do not contain VOCs—like ethan-1,2-diol (ethylene glycol) or 1,2-dichloroethane (a halogenated hydrocarbon)—are available from many manufacturers.

As paints or solvents dry, the compounds identified as VOCs evaporate and mix into the air in the room, where it can be inhaled. People who spend many hours indoors—in hospitals, day-care facilities, and schools—tend to have a higher level of exposure to VOCs. Reduced-odour paint provides one alternative that reduces exposure. People who work or live in newly-painted rooms experience only a short-term exposure. On the other hand, painters, who work with paint daily, experience long-term exposure. In addition to carefully choosing paint, simple practices like wearing gloves and clothing to protect skin from direct contact can also help reduce exposure.

Figure B2.22: Odourless paint and paint supplies do not contain VOCs.

Building Materials Can Limit Environmental Impact

Figure B2.23: Labels often provide instructions on how to access additional information about a product, including its effect on indoor air quality.

In addition to paint, other building materials like lumber, flooring, and floor and wall covering materials can be manufactured from recycled materials or from materials developed that use alternative technologies. Labels can indicate that a product has met national standards. When buying building materials and other products that are environmentally friendly, you are supporting companies that use processes that reduce the amount of material sent to landfills and use alternatives to toxic chemicals. Because of your decision, you may find yourself walking on a carpet containing plastic recycled from pop bottles, hanging a picture on a wall built from wood produced by a quick-growing variety of tree that absorbs carbon dioxide from the atmosphere at a high rate, or using wood that was not treated with toxic substances. Information about most building products is available on the Internet or at stores that stock the product.

In the next activity you will consider materials you could use for redecorating your room.

Practice

25. Draw the chemical structure of the VOC 1,2-dichloroethane. Identify one environmental concern associated with halogenated hydrocarbons.

26. Explain how removing halogenated hydrocarbons from paint could address the environmental problem identified in question 25.

Science Links

Safety gear, like protective suits, gloves, and masks to filter inhaled air, prevents exposure to chemicals used in automobile paint. Short- or long-term exposure to certain substances may affect the body. Similarities exist between exposure to radiation and to certain chemicals. For more information about sources of radiation you may be exposed to, go to Unit C.

Utilizing Technology

Risk-Benefit Analysis of Renovation Materials

Background Information

In this activity you will plan a renovation for a room in your home. A risk-benefit analysis involves considering many factors before you start the project. You will conduct research on some options that exist for the materials you plan to use to complete the renovation. You will also evaluate your renovation plan by considering technological, ecological, and economic factors.

Purpose

You will investigate and evaluate the use of products that decrease the release of synthetic organic compounds into the environment.

Procedure

step 1: Sketch the room you intend to renovate. In your sketch, include measurements of the dimensions of the room as well as the number and size of windows and doors.

step 2: List the materials required to complete the renovation you proposed. You may wish to use a spreadsheet to organize the information you collect in the steps that follow. Consult your teacher as to how extensive your renovation plan can be (e.g., paint, draperies, flooring, and mouldings).

step 3: Use the room measurements and, if necessary, the Internet to research information about the amount of each material listed in step 2. For example, some websites can estimate the amount of paint required. Record the amount of each material required in your spreadsheet.

Science Skills

✓ Performing and Recording
✓ Analyzing and Interpreting

step 4: Use the Internet to research an environmentally friendly paint or an alternative to painting. Identify characteristics that enable these products to be designated as "environmentally friendly."

step 5: Visit some local businesses that sell the materials you need to complete your plan. Identify the products you would like to use. List the technological, economic, and ecological aspects of the product in your spreadsheet. These aspects may include ingredients or substances used in its construction, durability, performance, texture, look, limitations, and cost.

step 6: Collect information about environmentally friendly alternatives to the products you have chosen in step 5. Collect information about the environmentally friendly products for your spreadsheet that will allow for a comparison. Use the information in your spreadsheet to compare the products.

Analysis

1. Calculate the cost for completing the renovation project using environmentally friendly materials and the other alternative products.

2. Compare the environmentally friendly materials with the other alternative products in terms of technological, economic, and ecological factors.

3. Finalize your renovation plan, and list the products you would use. Defend your choices.

Targeting Toxic Chemicals

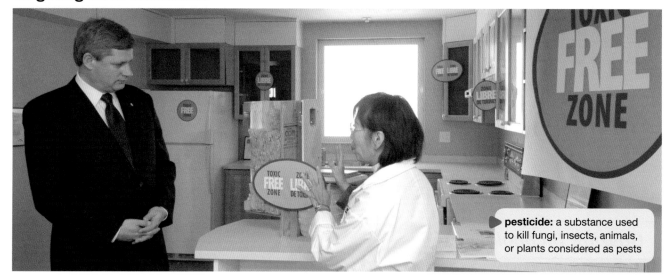

pesticide: a substance used to kill fungi, insects, animals, or plants considered as pests

Choices about products other than paint can influence which chemicals you are exposed to. In Lesson 2.2 you evaluated the use of vinegar as a cleaning product. Are there other substances you are exposed to?

At a golf course, or possibly at home, one or more forms of **pesticide** are used. The term *pesticide* is a very general one, since so many different types of pests exist. The "Pesticides" table lists some of the pesticides used by homeowners.

PESTICIDES

Type	Purpose	Types of Organic Compounds
insecticide	to remove insects that may cause damage or disease in domestic locations, agriculture, and forestry	halogenated hydrocarbons and various organic compounds
herbicide	to remove unwanted plants that compete for nutrients and sunlight, affecting the growth of desired plants	various organic compounds
fungicide	to protect crop plants and animals from fungi that can cause disease; can also be used to prevent the growth of moulds in food or within homes	phenols

? DID YOU KNOW?

Other types of pesticides commonly used include acaricides (kill mites and ticks), rodenticides (kill small mammals like mice and gophers), algicides (kill algae in ponds or swimming pools), and disinfectants (kill micro-organisms).

Constructing a Database of Pesticides Used in the Home

Purpose
You will prepare a database of pesticides used around your home.

Procedure
Search your home, garage, or other buildings for household and garden products used to remove pests. Prepare a database of the products you find. Include the following information about each product in your database:

- product name
- intended use
- type of pesticide (herbicide, insecticide, etc.)
- name of ingredient used as killing agent in product

Check your database by searching for a name of a compound within it or by sorting the information alphabetically by product name.

Analysis
1. Identify a purpose for the database of pesticides in your home.
2. Identify additional information you would add to the database along with a justification.

Considerations When Using Pesticides—Specificity

Chemical technologies, like pesticides, act as tools to achieve a desired purpose. On a golf course, farm, or in your yard or garden, herbicides may be used to control the growth of weeds. Careful selection of a substance that is appropriate for a pest involves knowing the pesticide's **target specificity**.

When the correct tool is selected for a job, there is a better chance of success. As you may have noticed from the database you constructed in the preceding activity, you probably have a variety of products in your home, each designed to control a specific type of pest. Some pesticides have high target specificity and are designed to act on a small range or even just one type of insect or plant. A **broad-spectrum pesticide** is a product that has low target specificity and will act more generally, affecting many species. Can you identify the pesticides in your database that have high target specificities? Can you identify those that can act on a broad spectrum?

An example of a highly selective herbicide is 2,4-D, which is short for (2,4-dichlorophenoxyethanoic acid). This herbicide is one of the more popular herbicides used in Alberta. Similarities between the chemical structure of 2,4-D and hormones that control the growth of the plant allow the herbicide to be taken to the stem and root tips, where it interferes with the plant's growth. Dandelions, clover, thistle, and other broad-leaved plants are most affected by 2,4-D, whereas narrow-leaved grasses and crop plants (e.g., wheat) are less affected.

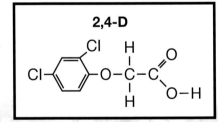

2,4-D

Prior to using a pesticide, it is important to consult information about the **toxicity** of the product. This information may not always be available on the product label, but it can be obtained using the Internet or from the site of purchase.

> **target specificity:** the range of organism(s) affected by a pesticide
> **broad-spectrum pesticide:** a chemical substance that can control the population of a large variety of organisms
> **toxicity:** the ability of a substance to cause damage to living tissue, impair the function of a body system, or cause death when ingested, inhaled, or absorbed through the skin

LD$_{50}$ and LC$_{50}$

Tests to determine toxicity of a pesticide focus on more than the target species. The most common ways to express information about the toxicity are **LD$_{50}$** and **LC$_{50}$**. These values state concentrations at which a significant killing effect on an organism is observed. LD$_{50}$ values are often expressed in milligrams of chemical substance per kilogram of animal tested. A substance with an LD$_{50}$ value below 43 mg/kg is considered to be highly toxic. Since pesticides often end up in bodies of water (lakes, pools, etc.), LC$_{50}$ is often used to express the concentrations at which toxic effects on aquatic organisms occur. Products with low LD$_{50}$ values for the target organism are popular choices for use in pest control because, in theory, smaller amounts of pesticide will be required to control the pests. Broad-spectrum pesticides should also have low LD$_{50}$ values, but this will often be for a variety or pests.

▶ **LD$_{50}$:** the dosage of a chemical substance, given all at once, that kills half (50%) the population tested within a specified time

▶ **LC$_{50}$:** the concentration of a chemical substance in air or water that kills half (50%) the population tested within a specified time

Regardless of target specificity, pesticides should not affect non-target organisms. When looking at toxicity data, you may note that LD$_{50}$ values are stated for many non-target organisms, often at different stages in their lifecycle. Prior to licensing a product, the Government of Canada requires that sufficient testing be completed to ensure that a pesticide will have minimal impact on non-target organisms at various levels in the food chain. It is important to note LD$_{50}$ values for mammals that are tested because this data may provide information about what concentrations may be toxic to humans.

SOME LD$_{50}$ AND LC$_{50}$ DATA FOR 2,4-D

Organism	LD$_{50}$ or LC$_{50}$
Daphnia (aquatic invertebrate)	25 mg/L
rainbow trout	358 mg/L
frog	359 mg/L
earthworm	350 mg/kg soil
quail	668 mg/kg
mallard duck	2000 mg/kg
mouse	370 mg/kg
rat	375–666 mg/kg

? DID YOU KNOW?

Estimates on the financial impact of pesticide use suggest that for every dollar spent on pesticides, there is a return of $4 due to greater productivity.

Practice

27. Describe an advantage and disadvantage of using the following.
   a. a pesticide that can kill only one type of insect
   b. a pesticide that can kill many types of insects

28. Scientists testing 2,4-D and an ester of 2,4-D compared LC$_{50}$ values.

LC$_{50}$ VALUES FOR 2,4-D AND 2,4-D ESTER

Organism		LC$_{50}$	
		2,4-D	2,4-D Ester
chinook salmon	3 months to 1 year old	1.250 mg/L	0.246 mg/L
rainbow trout	3 to 5 days old	0.642 mg/L	0.329 mg/L
	3 months to 1 year old	1.555 mg/L	0.342 mg/L

   a. Use the information in the table to identify the substance that has the greater toxicity.
   b. State reasons why experiments are performed to determine the LD$_{50}$ and LC$_{50}$ values for a variety of organisms.
   c. Use a structural diagram of 2,4-D to indicate how it could be modified into an ester.

29. Explain whether LD$_{50}$ and LC$_{50}$ test the effects of short-term or long-term exposure to a substance.

Considerations When Using Pesticides—Combined Effects

When looking at the labels of pesticides found in your home, you may have noticed that the products are often a mixture of compounds and may include trace amounts of by-products. Toxicity data is not routinely collected for commercial products; therefore, there are concerns regarding the effects that combinations of organic compounds used in pesticides may have on the environment and on humans.

? **DID YOU KNOW?**
    Absorption of some pesticides through the skin is higher when sunscreens are worn. Despite this information, the use of sunscreens is encouraged.

Studies testing the toxicity of commercial pesticides suggest that surfactants and other compounds in the products alter the level of toxicity.

Considerations When Using Pesticides—Drift, Grasshopper Effect, and Persistence

Spraying is one way to ensure direct contact between the pest and the pesticide; but weather and even the properties of the pesticide can affect contact. Spraying on a windy day can cause herbicides or insecticides to **drift** onto neighbouring crops or bodies of water. As you discovered earlier in this unit, the solubility of organic compounds in water can result in aquatic invertebrates, amphibians, fish, and other species in these ecosystems becoming exposed to the pesticide. Also, a rainfall after spraying may result in pesticides being transported into the soil with rainwater or into bodies of water in runoff.

> **drift:** the transfer of a pesticide by wind or air currents from the location where it is sprayed
>
> **grasshopper effect:** the transport of pesticides that results from their evaporation in warmer climates and condensation and deposition in colder climates
>
> **persistence:** the resistance of a chemical substance being broken down by biological or chemical means

The volatility of many organic compounds may result in pesticides travelling in wind currents from the site where they were applied. Pesticides detected in the Arctic are believed to have been transported by the **grasshopper effect**.

Modifications, such as synthesizing esters of 2,4-D, change the volatility of a compound and the performance of the pesticide. As you might predict after completing the "Making Esters" investigation in Lesson 2.2, an ester of 2,4-D would have an increased volatility and a greater tendency to drift or be transported larger distances by the grasshopper effect if used in very warm climates.

Pesticides containing halogenated hydrocarbons and organic compounds containing benzene rings often demonstrate **persistence** in the environment. Soil micro-organisms can act on pesticide molecules—using them as a source of carbon for their own growth—resulting in low persistence. Without the action of soil micro-organisms or chemical reactions that occur by exposure to sunlight, the molecules remain unchanged. Pesticides are designed to be applied at specific times during a growing season to co-ordinate with the life cycle of insects, the germination time of seeds, or the times of rapid growth in plants. Problems occur when pesticides remain in the air, soil, or water or when they are present in the tissues of other organisms in an ecosystem. As you saw with the heavy metal mercury and the persistent pesticide DDT, biomagnification results in toxic effects appearing in organisms higher up the food chain. Given the position of humans in the food chain, prolonged exposure to pesticides containing persistent organic compounds, even at low levels, may have negative health effects over a lifetime.

? **DID YOU KNOW?**
    Inhalation is a major route by which pesticides can enter your body. Directions for use for many pesticide products suggest that the area be avoided immediately after spraying to allow the substance to settle.

The Grasshopper Effect

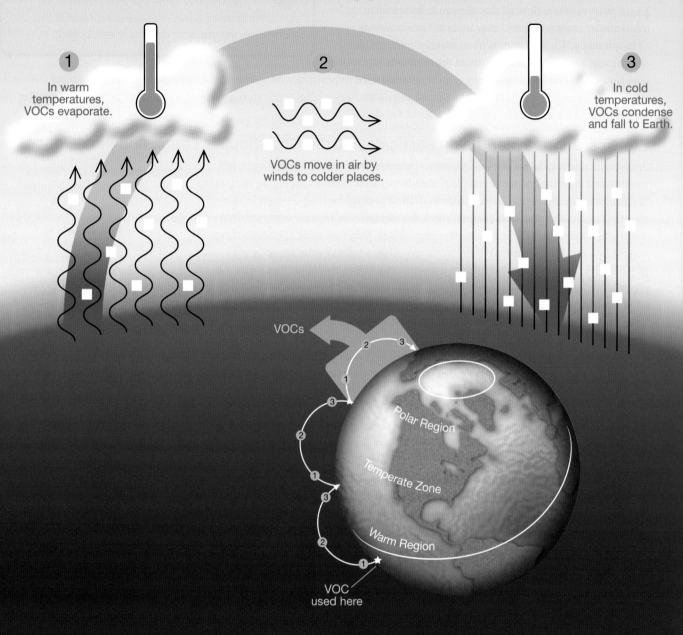

1 In warm temperatures, VOCs evaporate.

2 VOCs move in air by winds to colder places.

3 In cold temperatures, VOCs condense and fall to Earth.

VOCs

Polar Region

Temperate Zone

Warm Region

VOC used here

Considerations When Using Pesticides—Water Quality

Try This Activity

Hypothesizing Patterns for Water Quality

Background Information

Tests performed on water samples include the detection of organic compounds. Assume you are working for Alberta Environment and plan to conduct a study that monitors the frequency at which different pesticide compounds are found in surface waters throughout the province. Surface water may be located in a variety of forms:

- lakes
- rivers
- creeks
- wetlands
- irrigation canals and drains
- urban creeks

Purpose

You will formulate a hypothesis about pesticide use over a year in Alberta and describe how such a study can be conducted.

Questions

1. Prepare a table that lists the forms of surface water from which you collect water samples. In the table, indicate whether the pesticides originate from agricultural, industrial, and/or domestic use.

2. Obtain the handout "Predicting Pesticide Use" from the Science 30 Textbook CD. Sketch a line that describes the expected trend for pesticide concentration in all water samples collected each month during a one-year study. Provide an explanation for the pattern, including any peaks or troughs that may be shown.

3. Sketch a second line that identifies the expected trend for the number of different pesticides that would be detected each month during a one-year study. Provide an explanation for the pattern, including any peaks or troughs that may be shown.

Figure B2.24: A location on the Bow River in winter and summer.

Fertilizers and Organic Matter—Effect on Water Quality

In parts of this unit you studied the effects on water quality of acid deposition and persistent organic compounds. The leaching of metal ions and persistent organic compounds used as pesticides are not the only substances that can affect the quality of surface water sources. Contaminating bodies of water with **fertilizers** or **organic matter** can also negatively impact aquatic ecosystems.

Figure B2.25: Tests are conducted to determine water quality.

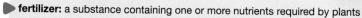

fertilizer: a substance containing one or more nutrients required by plants

organic matter: waste or decaying material from plants or animals

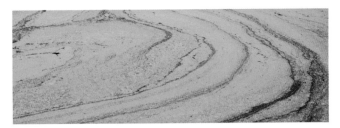

Have you ever had a day at a lake affected by the presence of a thick layer of algae growing over its surface? An **algal bloom** can be a common occurrence in many prairie lakes. Rapid growth of algae is the result of high nutrient content in the lake's water. Many prairie lakes are considered to be **eutrophic**. They can be considered examples of well-developed ecosystems in which a rapid conversion of nutrients occurs.

Domestic and agricultural fertilizers commonly contain nitrogen and phosphorous—essential plant nutrients. As stated earlier, leaching is a common mechanism for removing substances that were sprayed onto a crop.

Figure B2.26: Irrigation canal amid fields of crops

The leaching of fertilizers and organic matter rich in nitrogen and phosphorous from fields into surface water adds additional nutrients. A rapid growth of algae and other plants is a natural response to this abundance of nutrients.

Toxins produced by species of blue-green algae that are present within an algal bloom can affect the health of humans and livestock. Symptoms of exposure to these toxins include skin irritation, rashes, sore eyes, swollen lips, and allergic reactions similar to hay fever. In some cases, severe illness and death of livestock has occurred from the consumption of water containing these toxins.

The decomposition of algae from an algal bloom can produce a dramatic change to the quantity of oxygen dissolved within a body of water. During winter months, the layer of ice over the surface prevents the absorption of oxygen from the atmosphere. Many processes occurring within the lake require oxygen. In addition to the oxygen needed for the respiration of fish and other organisms, oxygen is required for the decomposition of organic matter. In the winter following an algal bloom, additional oxygen is used by micro-organisms involved in the decomposition process. **Winterkill** occurs when the concentration of dissolved oxygen falls below the levels necessary to support fish species within the lake.

A **biochemical (biological) oxygen demand (BOD)** test is a measure of the effects of organic matter and other substances present within a water sample will have on dissolved-oxygen concentration. This test consists of comparing the dissolved-oxygen concentrations of a sealed water sample at the beginning and end of the test period (often five days). A decrease in the concentration of dissolved oxygen within the sample occurs when micro-organisms decompose organic matter. Water samples containing higher levels of organic matter (high BOD) tend to demonstrate a large reduction in dissolved-oxygen concentration.

Water contaminated by organic matter from human or animal waste may have a high BOD or may serve as a source of nitrogen and phosphorous that promote algal blooms. Despite these possibilities, the greatest concern regarding the release of **sewage** directly into water systems is the possible exposure to disease-causing viruses and bacteria. The World Health Organization estimates that water-borne diseases are the leading cause of death in the world. Contaminated water containing a strain of the bacterium *E. coli* (*Escherichia coli*) produces a toxin that severely affects humans.

Higher nutrient levels and the presence of bacteria from human and animal waste in Alberta lakes and waterways have resulted in a greater concern about water quality. Individual homes, settlements, and municipalities with insufficient water-treatment systems are required to boil their water before use to remove harmful bacteria. Some First Nations settlements in Alberta concerned about the use of chlorine as a disinfectant to treat water are investigating the use of chemical-free water-treatment systems.

- **algal bloom:** a rapid increase in the population of algae
- **eutrophic:** of a body of water having excessive plant growth due to a rich supply of nutrients
- **toxin:** a substance that can have harmful effects
- **winterkill:** the death of water organisms caused by the depletion of oxygen in an ice-covered body of water
- **biochemical (biological) oxygen demand (BOD):** a measure of the amount of oxygen required for the decomposition of organic matter
- **sewage:** waste matter often carried in sewers

?> DID YOU KNOW?

The deaths of seven people in Walkerton, Ontario, was caused by the ingestion of water contaminated with bacteria from cattle manure.

30. Use the following information to complete questions 30.a. and 30.b.

	Dissolved-Oxygen Concentration (mg/L)		
	Sample A	Sample B	Sample C
Start	10	9	5
End	8	2	2

a. Use the values for dissolved oxygen to rank the water samples from lowest to highest with respect to BOD.

b. Match each water sample with one of the possible sources listed in the table.

Possible Source	Sample
raw sewage	
river water upstream of major city	
river water downstream of major city	

Considerations When Using Pesticides—Resistance

Rodent pests, like gophers and prairie dogs, can cause considerable damage to a golf course. Some farmers are concerned about their farm animals getting injured by stepping in holes made by rodents. Many people, at some point or another, have worried about being exposed to a virus carried by mice (e.g., hantavirus). There are many reasons for people to use pesticides well beyond those associated with maintaining high crop productivity. However, this broad use of pesticides can result in the development of **resistant populations**.

> **resistant population:** a group of organisms not affected by a pesticide

Recall from Unit A that genetic principles, including mutation, create variation within a population. Variation can result in some members of the population possessing resistance to a pesticide. After application, only resistant individuals remain in the population and are able to thrive as a result of reduced competition. Since genetic traits are inherited by offspring, the population of resistant organisms increases. You may also recall that breeding between resistant and non-resistant pest populations tends to result in offspring that are resistant, further reducing the effect of existing pesticides.

It may seem like a contradiction, but pest-management practices designed to kill higher percentages of the pest population often result in the fastest development of resistant pest populations.

Warfarin is a chemical compound that acts as an anticoagulant—preventing the action of platelets, which are responsible for the clotting of blood. Warfarin was first used in the 1950s to control rodent populations. Currently, warfarin and a variety of related compounds, called first-generation anticoagulants, are ineffective on many rodents because of the development of resistance to these chemical compounds. Effective rodent control in many situations now requires the use of second-generation anticoagulants.

The development of pesticide-resistant populations may be the result of poor pest-management practices, including relying too heavily on one product. By alternating the type of pesticide used or using alternative procedures, you increase the ability to control pests resistant to one pesticide.

Figure B2.27: Traps and pesticide-laden seeds are both effective methods of controlling mice.

Have you ever noticed signs of mice present in your garage or in your home? If so, you have a variety of choices. First, you need to determine whether they are a pest and whether they present any reason for concern. For some people, co-existing with mice presents no real problem. For others, minimizing contact may be a priority. A variety of alternatives to control mice exist, but which would you choose? If the problem is due to only a small number of mice, then trapping or the short-term use of a poison may be all that is required. Removing the pesticide once there are no further signs of mice reduces the risk of selecting individuals in the population that may be resistant and the risk of accidental exposure to pets. If the level of infestation is more severe or the mice do not seem to be affected by the methods you have used, a pest-control specialist may need to be consulted.

Practice

31. Explain how leaving pesticide-laden seeds or other poisons in traps for an extended period of time might increase the possibility of developing resistance to a pesticide within a population of pests.

32. Use the Internet to add information about the target specificity, LD_{50}, persistence, and development of resistance to the pesticides listed in the database you developed earlier in this lesson.

Chemical Inventory—Toxic Substances List

Earlier, you completed an activity and prepared a database of pesticides used in your home. Your database provides information about the substances used and other information, like safety and instructions for proper use. Lists like this are important resources for information about substances people are exposed to.

Federal, provincial, and municipal levels of government in Canada are involved in the management of chemical substances. These substances may be used in consumer products, by industry, or in the maintenance of parks and recreation areas. Currently, federal legislation restricts the use of more than 1000 chemical compounds, with an additional 23 000 compounds that have been assessed for their impact on humans and the environment.

DID YOU KNOW?

To view the Toxic Substances List and to see how dangerous substances have been classified, visit the following website:

http://www.ec.gc.ca/CEPARegistry/subs_

Substances appearing on the Toxic Substances List have been organized using the following categories:

- Persistent Substances
- Bioaccumulative Substances
- Inherently Toxic to the Environment

Two additional categories in this database are used to identify health concerns for humans from exposure to substances. These categories are

- Greatest Potential for Exposure
  - indicates how often a substance is used and the possibility for exposure
- Inherently Toxic to Humans
  - substances known or suspected of having harmful effects on humans

DID YOU KNOW?

It is estimated that $300 million will be required to complete the research needed to update the Toxic Substances List.

33. Evaluate the categories used in the Toxic Substances List by indicating both good and bad points about the categories.

34. DDT is a substance on the Toxic Substances List and is not permitted for use in Canada. Use the Internet to identify the evidence used to place DDT on the list. Use this evidence to determine under which categories DDT would appear.

Utilizing Technology

Updating Canada's Toxic Substances List—Debate

Chemical technologies often result in the production of new chemical compounds. Over time, additional information about exposure to and the environmental effects of existing substances can be collected and evaluated. An update to the Toxic Substances List would involve the use of funds collected from taxes to allow for the required testing of new and existing substances.

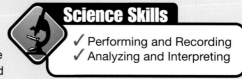

Science Skills

✓ Performing and Recording
✓ Analyzing and Interpreting

Question

Should government funds be spent to update Canada's Toxic Substances List?

Procedure

step 1: Read each of the following articles from the Science 30 textbook CD:

- *List of Toxic Chemicals Tests Tories on Environment*
- *Gov't Targets Toxic Chemicals*
- *Scientists Call for Tougher Rules on Toxic Chemicals*

step 2: Identify which stakeholders are represented by the information presented in the articles. Identify other stakeholders who may be affected by this issue. These may include other levels of government, industry, agriculture, or the public. Use the Internet to collect information that represents the position of the other stakeholders about this topic.

step 3: Choose a debate position—either for or against—to the question stated.

step 4: If necessary, conduct additional research the aspects or impact of the Toxic Substances List. Determine how this information could be used to support your position in a debate.

step 5: Use information collected during your research to state and defend your position in a debate on this issue.

Using Chemical Knowledge to Understand the Effect of Exposure

Substances can be added to the Toxic Substances List after they have been used in commercial products or chemical processes, provided that sufficient scientific evidence demonstrating harmful effects has been collected. Earlier in this unit you discovered that CFCs and benzene are examples of compounds that were restricted once evidence about their harmful effects on the environment and to humans had been demonstrated. Reasons for studying environmental chemistry include gaining a better understanding of chemical interactions in the environment and becoming better able to predict and prevent adverse effects from the chemical substances used by society.

One way to predict possible environmental effects is to group substances by similarities in chemical structure. You have already learned that a common problem associated with halogenated hydrocarbons and synthetic organic compounds containing benzene rings is their persistence in the environment.

estrogen
(female sex hormone)

This dioxin is a by-product of processes where chlorine is used.

2,3,7,8-tetrachlorodibenzodioxin
(2,3,7,8-TCDD)

This is used in the manufacturing of plastics.

bisphenol-A

By-products of 2,4-D production can include chlorinated dioxin compounds. Although these compounds are found at levels that are barely detectable, chlorinated dioxins are associated with a number of adverse health effects in humans, such as decreased immune-system function, interference with hormonal systems, and linkages to some forms of cancer. Similarities between the chemical structure and shape of the female sex hormone estrogen and synthetic organic compounds, like dioxin, are believed to allow dioxins to stimulate cells in a manner similar to that of estrogen. Estrogen-mimicking compounds, like bisphenol-A (used in the manufacture of plastics), is suspected of influencing the development of sexual characteristics in males and females in various organisms. Synthetic organic compounds that influence the levels of sex hormones can effect reproductive cycles, fertility, and behaviour in a variety of organisms. These observations have increased interest focused on identifying and studying endocrine-disrupting compounds present in the environment.

When Does Exposure Happen?

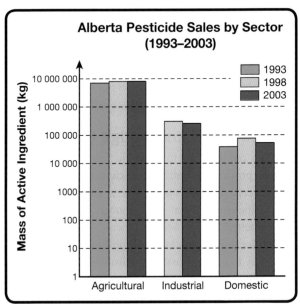

You can reduce your exposure to organic chemicals in pesticides by wearing coveralls and gloves and following the procedures described for safe handling and use of the pesticide. Recall that the volatility and solubility of organic compounds results in their transfer into air and water.

All species are exposed to a variety of synthetic organic compounds in air, water, soil, and food. Many scientific studies have resulted from concerns about human health and focused on "how much" and "for how long." Some studies have demonstrated a connection between high levels of exposure or prolonged exposure and certain diseases. To maintain good health, humans have a responsibility to make wise decisions about materials they use and their effect on themselves and on the environment.

Alberta Pesticide Sales by Sector (1993–2003)

You have learned the importance of organic compounds in society. The use of pesticides—whether used in agriculture, industry, or your home—indicates that they are an important class of synthetic organic compounds. As the "Alberta Pesticide Sales by Sector (1993–2003)" graph indicates, pesticide use in Alberta has changed very little over the ten-year period. The pattern of use and reliance on pesticides by society results in continual exposure to these compounds.

Tests on samples of drinking water in Alberta found trace levels of pesticides in more than 25% of the water supplied by water-treatment facilities. Recall that estrogen-mimicking compounds can also be present in other sources of drinking water. The presence of these compounds in water sources demonstrates the inability of water-treatment processes to remove them. Acceptable levels for organic compounds, including pesticides in drinking water, have been established, and routine testing of source water and drinking water is important to minimize exposure. Routine sampling and testing can also be used to identify sources of pollution.

Exposure can be the result of practices people follow. What do you do with the clothes you wear after handling pesticides? Is it possible to be exposed to substances used in your yard or garden when you are inside your home? Whether working on the golf course or at home, you need to be conscious of the safety instructions provided with each product. These instructions were developed in accordance with the properties of the particular organic compounds.

Simple actions—like washing your hands and clothes—in addition to following safety precautions reduce exposure.

? DID YOU KNOW?

Some pesticides and other organic compounds can be present on the foods you eat. Washing fruits and vegetables with water containing a mild detergent before use can help remove residues from some products.

Practice

35. Refer to the "Alberta Pesticides Sales by Sector (1993–2003)" graph on page 292.

a. Determine the mass of active ingredient of pesticides used by agriculture and domestic users in 2003.

b. Calculate the factor difference between the mass used by agriculture as compared to the mass for domestic use.

c. Comment on the labelling of the vertical axis for this graph.

Reducing Exposure—Actions Making a Difference

? DID YOU KNOW?

Skin rashes can be a result of exposure to pesticides. Pesticides absorbed into the fabric of hats, coveralls, and other clothes concentrate over time and become a source of exposure when worn again.

One change people can make to reduce exposure to pesticides is to carefully consider not only the choice of products available, but why a pesticide is being used, and whether it is controlling the pest population. This may require consulting experts at garden centres or other knowledgeable people. Selecting the right product not only results in efficiently controlling pests, but has additional benefits, like minimizing the amount used, thereby reducing your personal exposure.

In your garden and flower beds, you may choose to control pests using alternative strategies. Selecting plants that demonstrate resistance to pests or selecting plants that require less chemicals to support their growth are two such strategies. Alternatively, routinely caring for plants by removing weeds and insect eggs as they appear can directly control many pests and reduce the need to use pesticides.

Integrated pest management is a comprehensive approach to controlling pests that involves all available strategies including

- using natural predators, parasites, and biological agents for controlling target pests
- using crop varieties resistant to pests
- carefully managing habitat using strategies like flooding or burning to deter the growth of pests
- carefully monitoring crop condition and number of pests
- using pesticides only when necessary

Canola farmers in Alberta might be quite familiar with the bertha armyworm. The larva of this insect is responsible for damage to canola and other crops. Adapting an integrated pest-management strategy to control bertha armyworms involves the practices listed in the "Controlling Bertha Armyworms" table.

CONTROLLING BERTHA ARMYWORMS

Practice	Effect on Bertha Armyworm
tilling (ploughing fields after harvest) and removing stubble from fields	• prevents accumulation of snow • exposes insect eggs to lower temperatures during winter • decreases protection for newly hatched larva
biological control strategies (e.g., introducing viruses and other insects)	• reduces bertha armyworm population by causing disease (virus) or weakening the organism (parasitic wasps)
planting alternative crops	• reduces available food for armyworms, thus reducing their population
using selective pesticides (if needed)	• kills insect population

It should be noted that the information about controlling bertha armyworms encourages farmers to evaluate the extent of infestation of their crops and its economic effect before spraying. As you have been encouraged to do throughout this course, identifying risks and benefits from ecological, economic, as well as other perspectives is an important part of decision making.

Some strategies for pest reduction focus on the use of naturally occurring compounds. The toxin produced by the soil bacteria *Bacillus thuringiensis* (Bt) can kill certain insect species. Since the toxin is harmless to humans, spraying the toxin on infested crops provides temporary control of some pests. To permit pest control during the entire life of corn and some other crop plants, the gene responsible for toxin production was used to produce genetically modified varieties of crop plants. As you might expect, resistance to Bt toxin has already begun to develop in some species of insects.

Science Links

Crops that produce the Bt toxin are examples of transgenic organisms. A process used to move genes from one organism into another and how genetic resistance can develop is explained in Unit A.

Practice

36. Explain why observation is an important aspect of pest-control strategies.
37. Identify which strategies listed at the top of the page could act to reduce the use of synthetic organic compounds in pest management.
38. Briefly explain a process by which a resistant insect population to Bt toxin could develop.
39. Match the practices used to control bertha armyworms to the strategies identified as part of integrated pest management.

Proper disposal of unused products and their containers, regardless of the quantity, can prevent the transfer of pesticides and other organic compounds into the soil and water sources. Many cities have special waste-handling facilities that permit the separation of materials containing persistent organic substances, like paint and pesticides. Taking the time to identify and transport materials to a handling facility prevents toxic materials from ending up in your household garbage where it might negatively affect the environment.

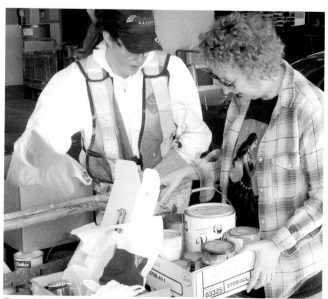
Figure B2.28: A waste-handling facility in Edmonton

Practice

Some roads are designated routes for the transport of dangerous goods.

40. Identify a roadway in your local area that is designated as a dangerous goods route. Use a map or describe the location of this route within your local area. List the risks and benefits with the route chosen.

Try This Activity

Current Opinions on the Use of 2,4-D

Background Information

2,4-D was first introduced as a herbicide in 1944. Although a great deal of testing and scientific data exists about its properties and behaviour in the environment, controversy exists over its use. Recently, the use of 2,4-D was brought into question and investigated by federal, provincial, and municipal governments in Canada.

Science Skills

✓ Analyzing and Interpreting
✓ Communication and Teamwork

Problem

What is the current position of your local municipality regarding the use of herbicides containing 2,4-D? What scientific authority is used to support the decision regarding the level of use of 2,4-D by the municipality?

Procedure

Investigate the questions stated in the problem by accessing relevant and reliable sources of information that exist within and outside your community. Prepare a presentation that summarizes the results from your investigation and makes explicit reference to scientific data and the sources of information collected.

DID YOU KNOW?

Waste-handling facilities can accept containers of unidentified chemicals. Unknown and highly toxic materials may be transported to the Swan Hills Waste Treatment Centre for processing.

At the beginning of your study in this unit, you completed the "Detection Limits" activity. In this activity you considered how important it is to be able to detect chemicals present in the environment. Given what you have learned about the concerns regarding exposure to persistent organic compounds, the detection of chemical substances, even at low concentrations, is important for certain compounds.

Many environmental samples are analyzed using a gas chromatograph mass spectrometer (GCMS). In the next activity you will investigate how this device operates and how it is used by scientists studying the environmental impact of organic compounds.

Utilizing Technology

Detecting Organic Compounds Using a GCMS

Background Information

Throughout this unit, you have become aware that many of the substances in air, water, soil, and animal tissues may be present in very small concentrations. The gas chromatograph mass spectrometer (GCMS) is an important apparatus used in the study of environmental science. This device detects and identifies substances present in quantities as low as a picogram.

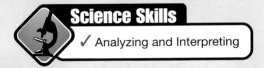

Science Skills

✓ Analyzing and Interpreting

Purpose

You will analyze data collected using a GCMS and determine if bioremediation of a crude oil component has occurred.

Procedure

step 1: Obtain the handouts "GCMS—Diagram" and "GCMS—Data" from the Science 30 Textbook CD.

step 2: Use the Internet to find a diagram or animation of the parts of a GCMS and their functions.

step 3: Label the parts of the GCMS and their functions on your copy of the diagram.

step 4: View the applet "Using the GCMS and Bioremediation" from the Science 30 Textbook CD.

Analysis

1. Compare the mass of 1 pg (picogram) to 1 mg.
2. Use the diagram of the GCMS to identify where the separation of compounds occurs.
3. Explain how the GCMS provides information on the quantity of each compound in a sample.
4. Refer to the "GCMS—Data" handout. Did the bacterial culture in the flask affect the dibenzothiophene present in the sample? Explain how you used the GCMS spectra to support your answer.

❓ DID YOU KNOW?

The detection of caffeine in surface water samples is an indicator of pollution from human sewage. The water qualities of popular lakes are often monitored for caffeine and other indicators of pollution from human sources.

POPs in the Arctic

In this chapter you learned about mechanisms like the grasshopper effect and the polar vortex that have drawn molecules identified as persistent organic pollutants (POPs) toward the Arctic. Given the climate, the potential for the breakdown of these molecules by bioremediation is very low. Scientists examining the tissues of organisms in arctic food chains have identified bioaccumulation of persistent compounds. In addition to the work done by scientists, observations made by the Inuit, including changes to the numbers of offspring and breeding behaviours of animals, suggest that something present in the environment might be having an effect. The contributions of the traditional ecological knowledge of the Inuit and the data collected by scientists may provide an opportunity for a deeper understanding of the changes occurring.

Investigating the Effects of POPs in the Arctic

Background Information

Observing how the issue of climate change is being addressed by the Inuit community and scientists provides an opportunity to determine how other environmental issues could be studied in a way that involves the communities affected. At the end of this activity, you should be able to

- describe information that could be classified as traditional ecological knowledge
- explain how the consideration of traditional ecological knowledge could contribute to greater scientific understanding

Purpose

You will write a research proposal that describes how you would investigate the impact of persistent organic pollutants in the arctic ecosystem.

Preparation

You may find that as you watch the video, important information appears quickly. Before you watch the video, think of strategies you may need to use so you can identify, extract, and, if necessary, go back and find important information. Before you view the video, read the Analysis questions. Prepare a table to record information as you view the video.

Procedure

View the video "Sila Alangotok—Inuit Observations on Climate Change" from the Science 30 Textbook CD. View the video once in its entirety; then, review specific sections as needed. Use the information from the video to answer the Analysis questions.

Analysis

1. Prepare a list of several changes to the environment that have been observed by the residents of Banks Island.

2. What research question were the scientists investigating?

3. Why did the scientists ask the people of Banks Island to describe their observations?

4. Using examples, describe how the observations of the residents of Banks Island demonstrate a holistic view of ecosystems.

5. Are the residents of Banks Island asked to express opinions or describe observations? Support your answer.

Science Skills

✓ Initiating and Planning
✓ Analyzing and Interpreting
✓ Communication and Teamwork

6. Do you feel the contribution of the residents of Banks Island is being respected? Support your answer.

7. Review the parts of a scientific study.

   Parts of a Scientific Study

   (1) collection of background information

   (2) development of a hypothesis

   (3) development of a problem statement

   (4) development of a design for experimental work

   (5) collection of data

   (6) analysis of data

   (7) interpretation of data

   (8) sharing of conclusions

   Identify the parts of a scientific study where the contribution of traditional ecological knowledge may benefit the scientific process. Provide support for your answers.

8. How does the oral tradition of First Nations impact the ability to access traditional ecological knowledge?

9. Describe possible benefits that could come from consulting Aboriginal populations in this study or in other studies.

10. Describe possible risks that could come from consulting Aboriginal populations in this study or in other studies.

11. Identify the main concern about climate change expressed by the residents of Banks Island.

Communication and Teamwork

12. Write a research proposal that describes how you would investigate the impact of persistent organic compounds in the arctic ecosystem. In your proposal, accurately define what you wish to study and how you intend to study it. List and justify the experiments and other investigations you intend to carry out. Indicate the equipment necessary for your study and explain why it must be used. If possible, justify the use of traditional ecological knowledge by describing how you will collect this type of data and why this type of information would be useful to the goals of your study.

The Dirty Dozen

The "dirty dozen" are twelve persistent organic pollutants (POPs) that were identified by the Stockholm Convention—the first international agreement on POPs held in 2001. Due to the polar vortex, many of the substances in the "dirty dozen" have migrated from lower latitudes to the Arctic and have been detected within arctic food chains.

THE DIRTY DOZEN

Chemical Substance	Purpose
Aldrin	pesticide
Endrin	pesticide
Dieldrin	pesticide
hexachlorobenzene (HCH)	pesticide
Chlordane	pesticide
Heptachlor	pesticide
Mirex	pesticide
Toxaphene	pesticide
DDT	pesticide
PCBs	industrial processes
Dioxins	industrial processes
Furans	industrial processes

2.3 Summary

Exposure to low concentrations of synthetic organic compounds present in the environment may be long term or short term. Pesticides and building materials are two of the many possible examples of how these organic compounds are used. Some persistent organic compounds include halogenated hydrocarbons. Biomagnification of persistent compounds in ecosystems is an environmental problem in many ecosystems, including the Arctic. Assessing the need to use synthetic chemical technologies and finding alternatives are important steps to reducing negative effects from exposure to these compounds.

Knowledge

1. State one type of substance released during off-gassing.

2. Define *toxicity*.

3. Describe a benefit of having data from LD_{50} or LC_{50} tests.

4. List a source and two health effects that result from exposure to dioxins.

5. Identify the group of organic molecules to which dioxins and furans belong.

Applying Concepts

6. Explain the rationale for testing the LD_{50} for a pesticide in many organisms that form a food chain within an ecosystem.

7. Write the chemical structures that correspond to the red, blue, and green parts of the systematic name for the herbicide 2,4-D.

   2,4-dichlorophenoxyethanoic acid

8. Predict the effect the following weather conditions would have on the concentration of a pesticide in air, surface water, and soil in the area in which it is sprayed.

   a. a rain shower that occurs within an hour after spraying the pesticide

   b. spraying occurs on a hot day

9. Explain, in terms of reducing personal exposure to pesticides, why it is important to consult with local experts before use and to observe the effect of a pesticide after its use.

10. Review the principles of organic farming practices.

    Principles of Organic Farming Practice

    • Protect the environment, minimize soil degradation and erosion, decrease pollution, optimize biological productivity, and promote a sound state of health.

    • Maintain long-term soil fertility by optimizing conditions for biological activity within the soil.

    • Maintain biological diversity within the system.

    • Provide attentive care that promotes the health and meets the behavioural needs of livestock.

    • Prepare organic products, emphasizing careful processing and handling methods in order to maintain the organic integrity and vital qualities of the products at all stages of production.

    Identify how the use of synthetic compounds as pesticides or as fertilizers is not consistent with the practices listed.

11. Explain a situation in which you would choose to use chemical pesticides as part of an integrated pest-management strategy.

12. Describe how the development of a Bt genetically modified crop plant may lead to the development of insect populations resistant to the Bt toxin.

In this chapter you studied different classes of organic compounds, including their use and impact on the environment. You identified and named halogenated hydrocarbons, alcohols, carboxylic acids, and ester compounds. You also examined the structure and properties of benzene rings and the importance of aromatic and polycyclic aromatic compounds.

Organic molecules were developed for many purposes. Throughout the chapter you were introduced to the uses of different types of organic molecules and, in some cases, their unexpected effects. Some by-products of organic reactions, including dioxins and furans, are examples of harmful persistent organic compounds that can cause mutations and even cancer.

Exposure to pesticides and other substances can have negative health effects; but actions taken by individuals and by society can reduce the presence of these substances in the environment. You also examined techniques for conducting studies and you became aware of the importance that detecting organic compounds in the environment has in studying their effects.

Summarize Your Learning

In this chapter you covered a number of chemical terms, types of organic compounds, chemical reactions, and a great deal about the impact that the development and use of chemical compounds has had on the environment. You may have collected news articles about chemical issues and the environment. You will have a much easier time recalling the application of the information you learned if you take some time to organize it into a pattern. Now that you have come to the end of this chapter, this is an appropriate time to focus on the patterns in the things you have learned.

Since the pattern has to be in a meaningful form to you, there are some options about how you can create this summary. Each of the following options is described in "Summarize Your Learning Activities" in the Reference Section.

Option 1: Draw a concept map or a web diagram.	Option 2: Create a point-form summary.	Option 3: Write a story using key terms and concepts.	Option 4: Create a colourful poster.	Option 5: Build a model.	Option 6: Write a script for a skit (a mock news report).

Chapter 2 Review Questions

Knowledge

1. State the suffix used when naming organic compounds with each of the following functional groups: hydroxyl, carboxyl, and ester.
2. State the reactants necessary to synthesize an ester.
3. Match each name with the chemical structures given.

I. 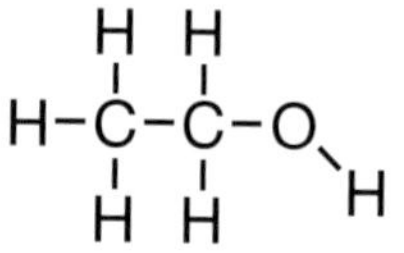

II. 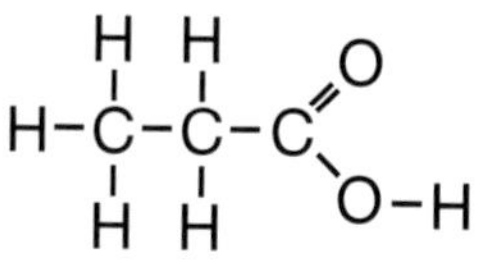

III. 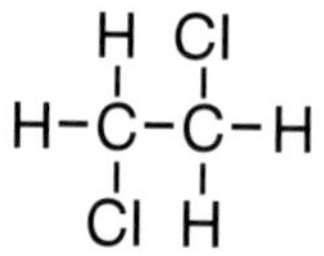

IV. 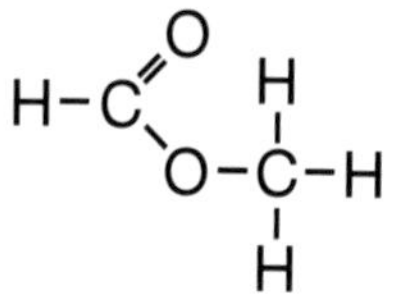

a. 1,2-dichloroethane

b. methyl methanoate

c. ethanol

d. propanoic acid

4. Use the list of chemical structures to identify parts of each molecule given. **Hint:** More than one structure may be identified in each molecule.

Chemical Structures

i. benzene ring
ii. hydroxyl functional group
iii. carboxyl functional group
iv. ester functional group
v. halogen atom

a. **Acetylsalicylic Acid (ASA)**
(anti-inflammatory drug)

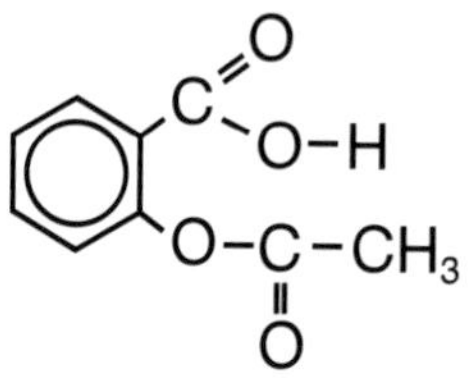

b. **Ibuprofen**
(anti-inflammatory drug)

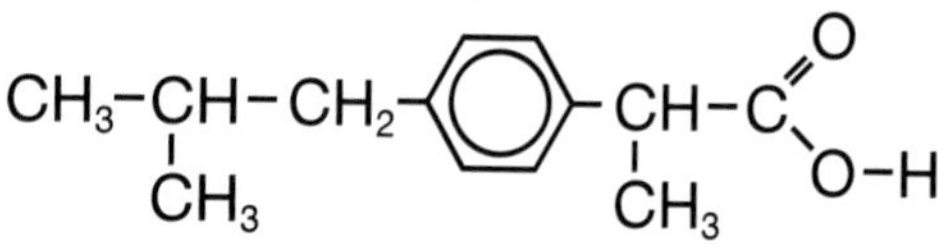

c. **Naproxen**
(anti-inflammatory drug)

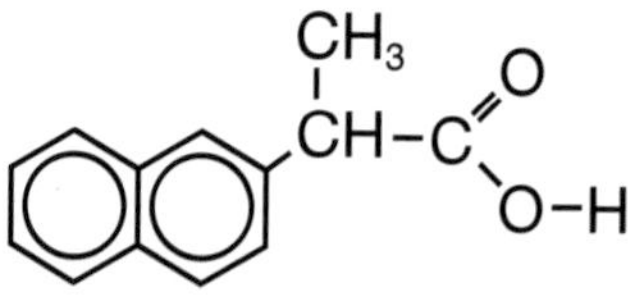

d. **Halothane**
(anaesthetic gas)

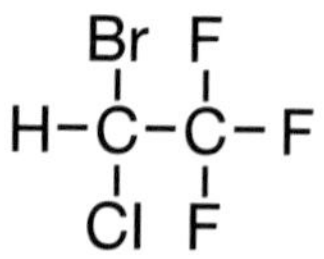

e. **Sucralose**
(artificial sweetener)

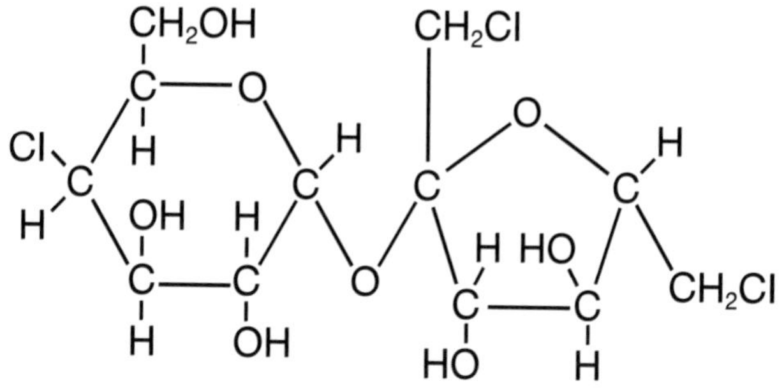

5. State a technology or application for each type of organic compound given.

   a. halogenated hydrocarbon

   b. alcohol

   c. carboxylic acid

   d. ester

6. Define *persistence*. State two examples of organic compounds considered to be persistent substances.

Applying Concepts

7. List similarities and differences between the hydroxyl, carboxylic acid, and ester functional groups.

8. Describe the effect that the leaching of fertilizers used in agriculture can have on a body of water.

9. List some products that contain volatile organic compounds (VOCs). Explain how exposures to VOCs occur in outdoor and indoor settings. State health risks associated with VOCs.

10. Explain how bioremediation can be used to remove organic compounds from soil and water.

11. List some water-borne diseases. Describe processes that can reduce the incidence of water-borne diseases.

12. Define *BOD*. What does a water sample with a high BOD indicate? Explain why surface water with a high BOD is undesirable.

13. Why do chlorinated hydrocarbons remain in the soil and water for such a long time?

14. List the advantages and disadvantages of using chemical pesticides.

15. Use the following graph to answer questions 15.a. to 15.d.

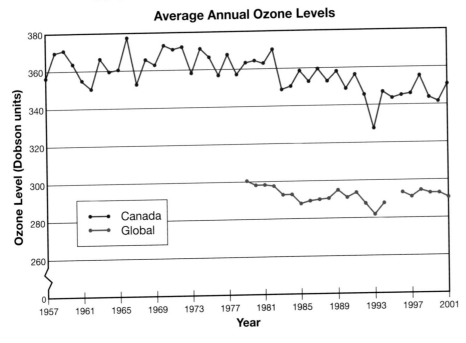

Average Annual Ozone Levels

   a. Determine the year in which the largest drop in stratospheric ozone occurs.

   b. Explain why stratospheric ozone concentration is not expected to increase in the near future.

   c. List the consequences of ozone depletion.

   d. Identify regions of Earth where ozone depletion is greatest. Explain why some regions of Earth experience greater ozone depletion than others.

16. A long-term study investigating synthetic organic compounds in the environment was conducted using the eggs of cormorants, a fish-eating bird, in an area surrounding a major lake. The concentration of DDE (the main breakdown product of the pesticide DDT) and PCBs are shown in the following graph.

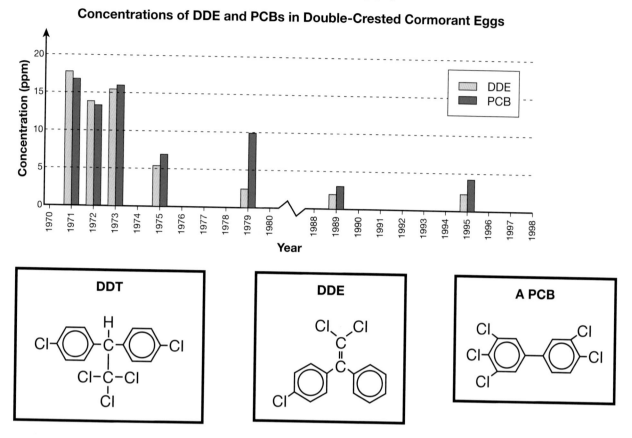

Concentrations of DDE and PCBs in Double-Crested Cormorant Eggs

a. Identify parts of the chemical structure of DDT and PCBs that suggest that these compounds might be persistent in the environment.

b. DDE present in organisms comes from the body's action to absorb DDT. DDE has been shown to have toxic effects on the immune and nervous systems and the thickness of eggshells in birds. Evaluate this information, and justify whether it is appropriate to show DDE concentrations on the graph and to use these levels to make conclusions about the presence of DDT in the environment.

c. Explain how the data shown in the graph demonstrate that DDT—an insecticide banned in Canada since 1974—and PCBs—industrial chemicals that have been highly restricted since 1977—are persistent organic compounds.

d. Describe sources of persistent organic pollutants in the environment.

Unit B Conclusion

Human activity has made an impact on the environment. In this unit you learned about the impact of many important parts of Alberta's economy, including electricity generation, oil and natural gas production, agriculture, and the production and use of consumer products involving organic compounds. You also examined the processes involved in the production of acid deposition, ground-level ozone, volatile organic compounds, and persistent organic pollutants. From your study, you should be able to identify concerns associated with the presence of these substances in the environment and with the technologies and changes that serve to reduce their production.

Exposure to certain chemical compounds can have negative effects on human health, causing mutations to DNA—a topic developed in Unit A. Radiation, described in Unit C, that reaches Earth's surface due to damage to the ozone layer as a result of the release of chlorofluorocarbons can also cause mutations.

Studying the environmental effects caused by substances released into the environment is essential to preventing further harm in the future.

Career Profile

Executive—Oil and Gas Resource Development

"Since we are made from the same source and elements, humans should feel a greater connection to the environment," states Elmer Ghostkeeper. Wisdom, defined by Elmer, is the combination of the experience, knowledge, spirit, mind, and emotion a human being can serve as a guide when considering activities that might effect the environment.

As president of Métis Moccasin Resources Inc.—a majority Métis-owned oil and natural gas company—Elmer urges the use of practices that attempt to minimize negative environmental impacts to the parts of the ecosystem we can see and to those parts that we cannot see. Consideration of possible "invisible" effects includes changes to the composition of soil, air, and water. Practices that result in the pollution of "air, water, and soil demonstrate disrespect for the environment and ourselves," states Elmer when referring to many current practices that reduce environmental quality and the need humans have for fresh air and water.

Making connections has been an important part of Elmer's life. As Regional Manager for Aboriginal Health Services for the Capital Health Aboriginal Wellness program, he helped patients connect and partner Aboriginal healing practices with the use of insulin. For Elmer, connections also played an important role in his learning, proudly stating that he still keeps in touch with his grade 7 and 8 teacher. As a learner, Elmer feels that interactions with fellow students and teachers build knowledge and provide the opportunity for additional experiences that attach additional meaning to knowledge, which develops wisdom.

As an instructor of anthropology at Portage College in Lac La Biche, Elmer encourages his students to think about the benefit of what they are being asked to learn. This often requires them to consider how the material is connected to other knowledge and how thinking about connections serves to develop a greater level of understanding. In his published works, Elmer has demonstrated how Aboriginal wisdom and Western scientific knowledge can connect to form a partnership that will benefit both cultures. Elmer has a passion for learning and is planning to further his research into the greater significance of water to other Aboriginal and world cultures.

1. Distinguish between the terms *acid deposition* and *acid rain*.

2. In general terms, describe the stages of change that occur within a body of water that has been exposed to acid deposition over a long period of time.

3. Use the following graph to answer questions 3.a. to 3.d.

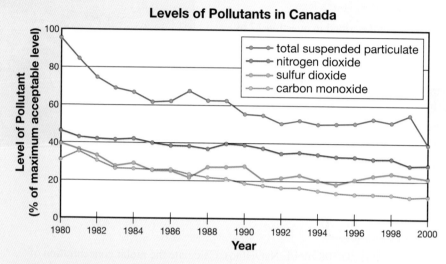

Levels of Pollutants in Canada

- total suspended particulate
- nitrogen dioxide
- sulfur dioxide
- carbon monoxide

(y-axis: Level of Pollutant (% of maximum acceptable level), x-axis: Year)

   a. State possible sources for each air pollutant shown.

   b. Describe the environmental impact or the effect on human health that results from each pollutant shown.

   c. State one technology used to reduce the level of each pollutant shown.

   d. The graph shows an overall reduction in emissions for all substances in Canada. Suggest reasons why Alberta may not follow this trend.

4. Identify some contaminants that can affect the quality of surface water, and state the source of each contaminant identified.

5. Buffering and bioremediation are examples of processes that minimize negative impacts on ecosystems.

   a. Identify the substances that each process acts upon to minimize environmental impact.

   b. Explain how buffering and bioremediation act to minimize the negative impact on an ecosystem.

   c. Identify situations where these processes are unable to minimize negative environmental effects.

6. List some chemical impurities present in rainwater. Describe the effect that these impurities can have on the properties of rainwater.

7. List the empirical properties of acidic, basic, and neutral solutions.

8. Explain the behaviour of acids and bases during a chemical reaction.

9. List two ways a body of water can become acidic.

10. Why is water that is exposed to acid deposition especially toxic to fish?

11. Electrostatic precipitators, scrubbers, and increasing the efficiency of processes are examples of technologies used to reduce acid deposition. Describe how each of these technologies acts to decrease emissions that cause acid deposition.

12. Identify the chemical component present in rock that neutralizes acid deposition. State the name of the mineral present in rocks that reacts with the acidic components of wet or dry deposition.

13. Use a balanced chemical equation to demonstrate the neutralization of a hydronium ion, $H_3O^+(aq)$, by the component identified in question 12.

14. Describe an experiment in which three acid-base indicators are used to confirm that the pH of a sample of rainwater is between 5.5 and 6.0. State possible indicators and expected results from the test.

15. Explain the relationship between a solution's pH and the hydronium-ion concentration within the solution.

16. Explain how liming can restore the pH of a lake that has become acidified.

17. Describe an experiment that could be performed that will approximate the amount of liming compound needed to restore the pH of a lake.

18. Justify the need for performing the experiment described in question 17 by indicating the consequences if too little or too much liming compound is used.

19. Complete the following table.

$[H_3O^+(aq)]$ (mol/L)	pH	Acidic, Basic, or Neutral
1.00×10^{-5}		
	8.23	
2.5×10^{-11}		
	2.250	

20. A sample of industrial effluent was titrated against 0.0500-mol/L NaOH(aq). Calculate the molar concentration of hydronium ions in a 10.0-mL sample of effluent if 27.3 mL of NaOH(aq) were required to complete the titration.

21. Describe the similarities and differences between strong and weak acids.

22. Use the following information to answer questions 22.a. to 22.c.

LD_{50} VALUES FOR SOME SYNTHETIC ORGANIC COMPOUNDS

Substance	LD_{50} for Rats (mg/kg)
TCDD (a dioxin)	0.01
Aldicarb (insecticide)	0.8
strychnine (rodenticide)	30
2,4-D (herbicide)	370

a. Rank the substances from most toxic to rats to least toxic to rats.

b. Explain the significance of the position of strychnine, a substance found in rat poison, in your ranking.

c. Suggest a reason why other compounds in the list are not used as rat poison.

23. Write the chemical structures that correspond to the coloured parts of the systematic name for the herbicide mcPA, 2-methyl-4-**chlorophen**oxyethan**oic acid**

24.

The chemical structure given is often referred to as an ester of 2,4-D.

a. Circle the ester functional group in the molecule.

b. Identify the part of the molecule that corresponds to the alcohol used in the synthesis of this compound.

25. Explain how dumping sewage into a river increases the BOD (biochemical or biological oxygen demand) of the river water. Identify negative consequences that arise from dumping sewage into surface water.

26. Eutrophication—the stimulation of the growth of algae by nutrients in a body of water—can be a problem in some lakes.

a. Identify the nutrients most likely to stimulate the growth of algae.

b. Identify sources for these nutrients that come from agriculture or other human activities.

c. Describe a negative consequence of eutrophication.

d. Describe an experiment, or series of experiments, that could be used to collect data to demonstrate that eutrophication is occurring in a body of water. In your description, indicate tests that could be performed and the type of data that would need to be collected.

27. Identify substances that are by-products of processes that use chlorine. Describe the general attributes and properties of these by-products with respect to their behaviour in the environment.

28. Photochemical reactions can have significant effects on the environment.

a. Define *photochemical reaction*.

b. Identify **two** examples of photochemical reactions. State the effect that light has in the reaction and the consequence of each reaction to the atmosphere.

c. Identify a component of solar radiation that can be involved in a photochemical reaction.

29. Explain the chemical term *radical*. In general terms, describe **two** examples of chemical reactions that involve radicals. **Note:** Chemical reactions are not necessary.

30. State some risks associated with using underground tanks for storing gasoline and other hydrocarbons.

31. Define *VOC* and *POP*.

32. List technologies that can be used to reduce the presence of VOCs and POPs in consumer products and in the environment.

33. Ozone is a significant substance in the atmosphere.

a. Indicate the atmospheric layer in which ground-level ozone and the ozone layer can be found.

b. Identify sources of ground-level ozone.

c. Explain how the location of ozone in the atmosphere can influence its interpretation as good or bad.

34. Identify major sources of hydrocarbons in polluted air.

35. Explain the rationale behind reducing sulfur in gasoline and diesel fuel.

Unit C Electromagnetic Energy

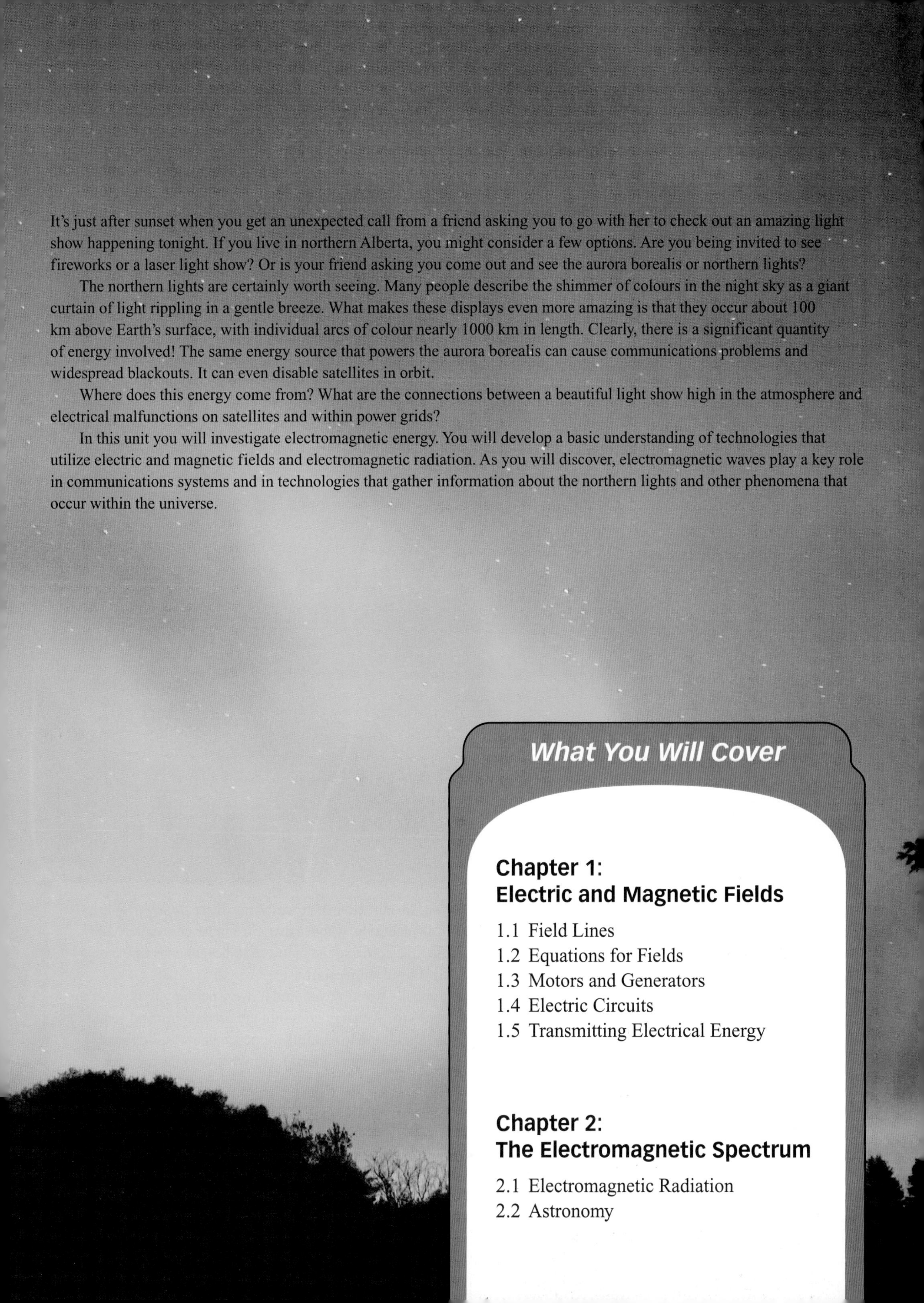

It's just after sunset when you get an unexpected call from a friend asking you to go with her to check out an amazing light show happening tonight. If you live in northern Alberta, you might consider a few options. Are you being invited to see fireworks or a laser light show? Or is your friend asking you come out and see the aurora borealis or northern lights?

The northern lights are certainly worth seeing. Many people describe the shimmer of colours in the night sky as a giant curtain of light rippling in a gentle breeze. What makes these displays even more amazing is that they occur about 100 km above Earth's surface, with individual arcs of colour nearly 1000 km in length. Clearly, there is a significant quantity of energy involved! The same energy source that powers the aurora borealis can cause communications problems and widespread blackouts. It can even disable satellites in orbit.

Where does this energy come from? What are the connections between a beautiful light show high in the atmosphere and electrical malfunctions on satellites and within power grids?

In this unit you will investigate electromagnetic energy. You will develop a basic understanding of technologies that utilize electric and magnetic fields and electromagnetic radiation. As you will discover, electromagnetic waves play a key role in communications systems and in technologies that gather information about the northern lights and other phenomena that occur within the universe.

What You Will Cover

Chapter 1:
Electric and Magnetic Fields

1.1 Field Lines
1.2 Equations for Fields
1.3 Motors and Generators
1.4 Electric Circuits
1.5 Transmitting Electrical Energy

Chapter 2:
The Electromagnetic Spectrum

2.1 Electromagnetic Radiation
2.2 Astronomy

Chapter 1 Electric and Magnetic Fields

The great thing about portable sound systems is you can take your favourite tunes virtually anywhere. Many people find this especially convenient while exercising because the music makes the whole experience more enjoyable. MP3 players are so small that they can be strapped to your arm, leaving the cord and the lightweight headphones as the only reminders that you are carrying around a complete library of all your favourite songs.

Have you ever wondered how these portable sound devices actually work? If you find it overwhelming to think of the whole system, consider just one component: the headphones. If electrical energy goes into the headphones and sound energy comes out, how is the energy conversion accomplished? If you were to carefully dissect a pair of headphones, what parts would you expect to find inside? What accounts for the difference in sound quality between inexpensive headphones and more expensive ones? Can the inappropriate use of headphones damage your hearing? Are some people more susceptible to these risks than others?

In this chapter you will investigate answers to these questions by exploring the basic properties of electric and magnetic fields. You will apply these properties as you learn about the designs of electromagnetic devices, such as headphones, motors, and generators. By the end of this chapter you will understand that all of these devices have one essential thing in common with electric circuits—their ability to convert energy from one form into another.

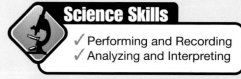

Try This Activity

Observing Magnetic and Electrical Effects

Purpose

You will observe and record the effects of electricity and magnetism on test objects.

Materials

- bar magnet
- ebonite rod and fur
- 1 m of thread
- retort stand and utility clamp
- 3-inch common nail
- pith ball
- tape

Science Skills

✓ Performing and Recording
✓ Analyzing and Interpreting

Procedure

step 1: Using the thread, suspend a pith ball from the retort stand, as shown in Figure C1.1.

Figure C1.1

step 2: Rub the ebonite rod several times with fur. Carefully bring the ebonite rod close to the pith ball, without allowing any contact between them. Record your observations.

step 3: Briefly touch the ebonite rod to the pith ball and then separate them. After doing so, carefully bring the ebonite rod close to the pith ball, again without allowing any contact between them. Record your observations.

step 4: Replace the pith ball with the iron nail. Suspend the nail so it is parallel to the lab bench and can swing freely from side to side, as shown in Figure C1.2.

Figure C1.2

step 5: Carefully bring a bar magnet close to the head of the nail, without touching it. Record your observations.

step 6: Briefly allow the bar magnet and the nail to touch; then separate them.

step 7: Again, carefully bring the magnet close to the pointed end of the nail, without touching it, and observe.

step 8: Hold the head of the nail and gently stroke the surface of the nail at least ten times with one end of the bar magnet. Always stroke the nail in the same direction, from the head to the point.

step 9: Bring the north end of the bar magnet to the head of the suspended nail. Record your observations.

Analysis

1. Use your observations to identify the similarities and differences between electrical effects and magnetic effects.

2. You observed forces acting between two objects even though the objects were not touching. How was this able to occur?

Figure C1.3: Lightning travels across the sky at speeds of over 100 km/s.

Think back to the last time you saw a sky like this. Can you remember what the weather was like that day? At first, this may seem like a ridiculous question, but it is not coincidence that most thunderstorms occur late in the afternoon or evening of a very hot, humid summer day. The reason for this is that it takes the intense summer sun to make the air hot and rich in water vapour. Warm air floats up in cooler surrounding air—like a cork in water. As it rises, the water vapour starts to condense and forms a cloud. The condensation releases energy, which causes the air parcel to get even warmer and rise even higher. Sometimes the top of a thundercloud can reach 12–20 km above the ground!

As a column of warm water vapour rushes up, it comes in contact with a column of condensed water droplets that are descending. Since the water droplets more readily hold on to their electrons than the rising water vapour does, electrons are transferred from the rising water vapour to the descending water droplets. The result is that the bottom of the cloud has an excess of electrons, so it is **negatively charged**. The top of the cloud has lost electrons, so it is **positively charged**. Recall from previous courses that objects with opposite charges attract each other, while objects that have the same type of charge repel one another.

▶ **negatively charged:** having more electrons than protons, creating an imbalance

▶ **positively charged:** having fewer electrons than protons, creating an imbalance

As the cloud passes over buildings and other tall objects on the ground, how will the electrons in these objects respond? Since like charges repel, the electrons within the objects on the ground are forced to move away from the cloud. The presence of the large negative charge at the bottom of the cloud, in turn, causes the separation of charges on Earth's surface—the surface becomes positively charged and below the surface becomes negatively charged. Finally, pockets of ionized air molecules in the atmosphere can form a conductive path for the electrons in the cloud to jump to the large, positive surface of Earth, resulting in a lightning strike.

The reason that a lightning strike can be so dangerous is because the number of electrons transferred is huge—around 10^{18} to 10^{20} electrons. To make it easier to describe and study these effects, scientists use a special unit for charge called the **coulomb**, named after Charles Coulomb, one of the first researchers in the study of electricity. The symbol for this unit is C. One coulomb is equivalent to the transfer of 6.25×10^{18} electrons. If one object gains this number of electrons, it is said to have a charge of -1.00 C; and if a second object loses this many electrons, it is said to have a charge of $+1.00$ C. Since the symbol for charge is q, this would be communicated as follows:

$$\text{charge on object } 1 = q_1 = -1.00 \text{ C}$$
$$\text{charge on object } 2 = q_2 = +1.00 \text{ C}$$

The quantity of charge that you normally encounter is much less than one coulomb.

coulomb: an SI unit for charge; one coulomb is equivalent to the transfer of 6.25×10^{18} electrons

If you scuff your feet while walking across a carpet on a dry day, you can acquire a charge of $-55\ \mu C$.

a. Use the charge to determine whether you gained or lost electrons.

b. Explain why is it essential for another object to have a charge of $+55\ \mu C$. Identify this object.

c. Use the fact that $1.00\ C = 6.25 \times 10^{18}$ electrons to set up a conversion factor that would enable you to determine the number of electrons gained or lost while scuffing your feet.

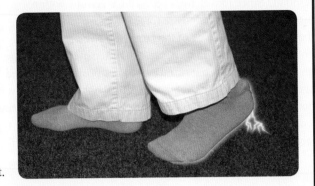

Solution

a. The negative sign on the charge indicates that you gained electrons.

b. Electrons cannot be created nor destroyed; so, if you gained electrons, something else must have lost them. In this case, the carpet must have lost a number of electrons equivalent to a charge of $+55\ \mu C$.

c. **step 1:** Set up a conversion factor.

$$1.00\ C = 6.25 \times 10^{18}\ electrons$$

$$\text{Therefore, } 1 = \frac{6.25 \times 10^{18}\ electrons}{1.00\ C}$$

To convert from coulombs to electrons in the next step, coulombs are placed in the denominator.

step 2: Convert from coulombs to number of electrons.

charge on the person, $q_{person} = 55\ \mu C$

$$= 55 \times 10^{-6}\ \cancel{C} \times \frac{6.25 \times 10^{18}\ electrons}{1.00\ \cancel{C}}$$

$$= 3.4 \times 10^{14}\ electrons$$

While scuffing your feet across the carpet, you would gain 3.4×10^{14} electrons.

Practice

1. Pockets of ionized air in the atmosphere are not evenly spaced; instead, they tend to be randomly distributed. Use this information to explain why lightning strikes tend to have a jagged appearance instead of being perfectly straight.

2. It's been said that humidity is the fuel of a thunderstorm. The higher the humidity, the greater the possibility of having a large-scale storm.

    a. Explain why an updraft within a thundercloud will tend to rise higher if the air has a higher moisture content.

    b. Explain the role of the air's moisture content in producing the positive and negative charges within a thundercloud.

3. While completing the "Observing Magnetic and Electrical Effects" activity in the beginning of the chapter, a student rubbed an ebonite rod with fur, transferring about 1.4×10^{10} electrons from the fur to the ebonite rod.

    a. Determine whether the ebonite rod has a negative or positive charge.

    b. Use a conversion factor to determine the charge (in coulombs) on the ebonite rod.

Voltage

As shown in Example Problem 1.1, your body can acquire a charge from the environment. This frequently happens as one object slides past another, such as when you scuff your feet across a carpet and reach out to open a door. By the time you reach the other side of the room, you may have acquired so much charge that when you get very close to the doorknob, the excess charge jumps across a few millimetres of air, creating a spark. This can be painful because the spark is hot. There clearly is energy involved here.

$$
\begin{array}{ccccc}
\text{work done moving} & & \text{potential energy} & & \text{energy transferred} \\
\text{electrons from} & = & \text{stored in the excess} & = & \text{through your} \\
\text{carpet to your body} & & \text{electrons on your body} & & \text{fingertip in a spark}
\end{array}
$$

Prior to touching the doorknob, work was done removing electrons from the carpet, causing the electrons to gain potential energy relative to other objects, such as the doorknob at the other end of the room. Since the doorknob is a **conductor**, as soon as your hand gets close enough for the electrons to jump the tiny air gap, a spark is produced. In other words, the potential energy stored in the electrons is converted mostly to thermal energy, which causes the pain in your finger, and partially to light and sound energy as the spark produces a tiny flash and a snapping sound.

Measuring this energy is a challenge because it is transferred through the action of electrons, and the sheer number of electrons is huge. One approach to this problem is to describe the energy transfer in terms of the change in electric potential energy per unit of charge, or the **electric potential difference**. The unit for electric potential difference is the unit for energy, the joule, divided by the unit for charge, the coulomb. This combination has been given a special name, the **volt**. In everyday speech, many people use the unit to identify the quantity, so they simply refer to electric potential difference as **voltage**.

voltage or electric potential difference $\longrightarrow V = \dfrac{\Delta E_p}{q}$ ← change in electric potential energy

← charge

Units: $1 \text{ volt} = \dfrac{1 \text{ joule}}{\text{coulomb}}$

$1 \text{ V} = 1 \text{ J/C}$

> **conductor:** a material in which some of the electrons can move freely, allowing the material to conduct an electric current
>
> **electric potential difference:** the change in potential energy per unit of charge
>
> **volt:** the unit for electric potential difference; $1 \text{ V} = 1 \text{ J/C}$
>
> **voltage:** another term for *electric potential difference*

Example Problem 1.2

While scuffing your feet across the carpet, you do about 0.25 J of work to acquire $-55~\mu\text{C}$ of charge. Determine your voltage.

Solution

$\Delta E_p = W$

$\quad = 0.25 \text{ J}$

$q = -55~\mu\text{C}$

$\quad = -55 \times 10^{-6} \text{ C}$

$V = ?$

$V = \dfrac{\Delta E_p}{q}$

$\quad = \dfrac{0.25 \text{ J}}{55 \times 10^{-6} \text{ C}}$ ← The sign of the charge is not included.

$\quad = 4.5 \times 10^3 \text{ J/C}$

$\quad = 4.5 \times 10^3 \text{ V}$

After scuffing your feet across the floor, your voltage is 4.5×10^3 V.

Example Problem 1.3

An appliance in your kitchen is plugged into a socket that can provide the appliance with 120 V and up to 15 C of charge every second. If the cord for this appliance became frayed and you grabbed it with wet hands, calculate the energy that could be transferred to you in 1 s.

Solution

$V = 120 \text{ V}$

$q = 15 \text{ C}$

$\Delta E_p = ?$

$V = \dfrac{\Delta E_p}{q}$

$\Delta E_p = Vq$

$\quad = (120 \text{ V})(15 \text{ C})$

$\quad = (120 \text{ J/C})(15 \text{ C})$

$\quad = 1.8 \text{ kJ}$

The energy that could be transferred to you in 1 s is 1.8 kJ—a dangerous quantity that could be lethal.

The Combination of Energy and Charge

Voltage is probably the one quantity of electricity people are most familiar with. Many portable devices are powered by cells that are rated at 1.5 V. What exactly does that value mean? For most students, the best answer comes from translating the units: 1.5 V means 1.5 J of electric potential energy per coulomb. If you apply this same thinking to the results of Example Problem 1.2, the results might seem a little alarming: 4.5×10^3 V means 4500 J/C. Isn't this a high value? If there was a sign on the doorknob that said "4500 V," would you still touch it?

The important thing to remember is that voltage indicates the joules of energy transferred by every coulomb of charge. So, if you don't have many coulombs of charge, the total energy transferred may not be a very big concern. If the sign on the door said "0.25 J," you may be much less concerned. However, if the number of coulombs involved is very large, you have to be especially careful. In Example Problem 1.3, the appliance's frayed cord was connected to a 120-V source, which at first might appear to be much safer than the 4500 V between you and the doorknob. However, since the number of coulombs involved is much larger, the energy that can be delivered is actually much greater. A lightning strike can be extremely dangerous because both the voltage and the quantity of charge involved are large.

Practice

4. A lightning strike transferred about 15 C of charge from a cloud to a building. The voltage between the cloud and the building was 1.50×10^8 V.

   a. Calculate the energy delivered in the lightning strike.

   b. A typical home in Alberta uses 3×10^9 J of electrical energy every month. Compare your answer to question 4.a. with this value.

Hiking Through Fields

People who enjoy outdoor activities, like hiking, camping, and rock climbing, have to pay close attention to the conditions in their environment. Much of the data from the environment is easily observable, such as the types of cloud formations and the temperature. Other factors, such as changes in humidity or atmospheric pressure, require special instruments in order to be observed. In this section you will learn about three aspects of the environment that can only be observed indirectly through their effects on other objects.

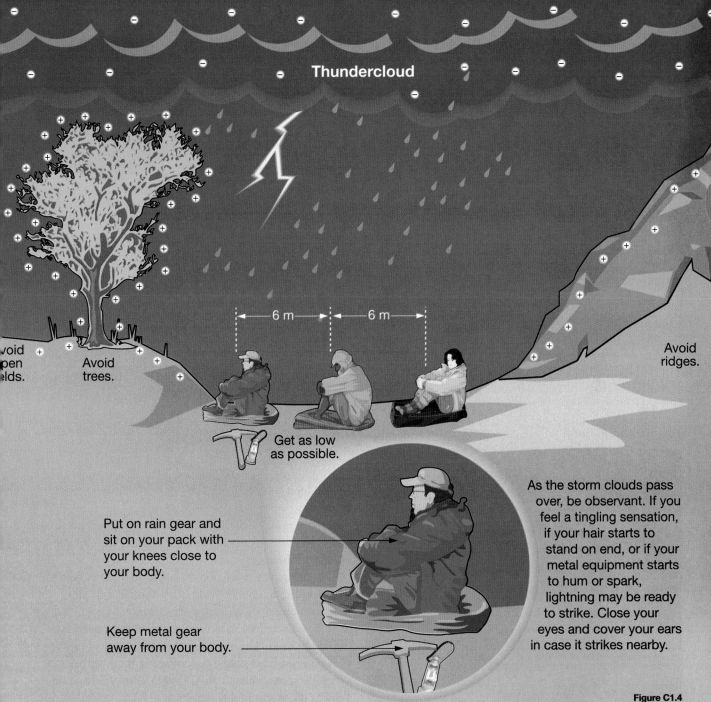

Thundercloud

6 m   6 m

Avoid open fields.

Avoid trees.

Avoid ridges.

Get as low as possible.

Put on rain gear and sit on your pack with your knees close to your body.

Keep metal gear away from your body.

As the storm clouds pass over, be observant. If you feel a tingling sensation, if your hair starts to stand on end, or if your metal equipment starts to hum or spark, lightning may be ready to strike. Close your eyes and cover your ears in case it strikes nearby.

Figure C1.4

The Electric Field

Hikers and rock climbers have to be especially careful of the potential hazards presented by thunderstorms. If you are in a forested area, the dense cover of trees can make it very difficult to see the sky and watch for approaching clouds. Thunder can echo through canyons, making it very difficult to know the direction a storm is approaching from. If you are in steep terrain, storm clouds can suddenly blow overhead from a nearby ridge, giving you only minutes' notice that a storm is approaching. If you were hiking in the mountains and were surprised by a thunderstorm's sudden approach, what would you do?

The suggestions shown in Figure C1.4 are the recommended preventative measures to avoid being hit by lightning. Note the list of things to watch for. The thundercloud may be several kilometres above you, yet the huge negative charge on the bottom of the cloud is still capable of making your skin tingle, your hair stand on end, or your metal equipment hum and spark. All this can occur before the lightning strikes. How is the cloud, which may be thousands of metres above the ground, able to exert forces on objects on the ground below? A meteorologist would answer this question by saying that the charge on the bottom of the cloud is surrounded by an **electric field**. The three hikers cannot see the electric field itself because it is invisible. They can only observe the effects that the field has on charges within the field.

> **electric field:** a property of the space around a source charge that enables the source charge to exert forces on other charges that enter this region

For example, one of the hikers might notice that loose threads on a frayed part of a jacket are starting to stand on end. Even though the threads are **insulators**, and cannot pass an electric current, the charge within the threads can be rearranged so that the threads respond to the electric field. The threads are not the electric field, but rather they provide evidence that the field is present. Since a thread provides a way of testing if a field is present, it is called a **test body**. Test bodies are observable objects that experience a force due to the presence of a field. Other test bodies in this situation could include the hair on the hiker's head or the ions within nerve endings that produce a tingling sensation in the hiker's skin.

Thunderclouds are not the only sources of electric fields. In general, any charged object will surround itself with an electric field. A tiny circuit charges the wires in a portable bug zapper, shown in Figure C1.6, to create a strong electric field close to the wire mesh. This field is then used to exert lethal forces on insects that are close to the mesh grid.

Figure C1.5: The charges within the fibres of the threads shift slightly, allowing the threads to respond to the electric field.

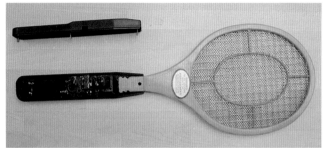

Figure C1.6: Bug zappers use strong electric fields.

insulator: a material in which none of the electrons can move freely, preventing the material from being able to conduct an electric current

test body: an observable object that can experience a force due to the presence of a field

The Magnetic Field

If the hikers take all the recommended precautions, they could make it through the storm unharmed. The wind would soon carry away the thunderclouds and the massive charge that created the dangerous electric field. But this is not the end of the hikers' experience with fields. After taking off their rain gear, they might decide to resume their trek and check their bearings with a compass.

The compass needle soon swings around and indicates which direction is north. What exerts this force on the compass needle? If you look at the compass, you will see that there does not appear to be anything touching it other than the hiker's hand. The hand cannot be the source of the force because if the hiker holds the compass in the other hand or sets the compass on the ground, it still points the same way. What is the source of this force?

A geologist would say that Earth's **magnetic field** exerts the force on the compass needle. Once again, you cannot see the magnetic field itself—it's invisible. You can only observe the effects of the magnetic field on the appropriate test body (in this case, the tiny magnet that forms the compass needle).

magnetic field: a property of the space around a magnet or an electric current that enables the magnet or electric current to exert forces on other magnets, such as compass needles, and electric currents that enter this region

Earth's magnetic field is thought to originate from electric currents deep within the planet. In general, magnetic fields are produced by electric currents and magnets. This is why compass needles may not function properly close to electric motors or speakers. These devices produce their own magnetic fields that can interfere with the compass's ability to align itself with Earth's magnetic field.

The Gravitational Field

Rock climbing is an outdoor activity that requires specialized equipment, skills, and careful training. Once these things are in place, the only other requirement is a safe and interesting place to climb. As climbers inch up a rock face, they move themselves farther from the centre of Earth, overcoming the force of gravity the whole way up.

? DID YOU KNOW?

Archaeologists suspect the first compass originated in China thousands of years ago. The ancient Chinese compasses used a piece of iron oxide, $Fe_3O_4(s)$, that happened to be naturally magnetized. Over time, the design was refined to use a small iron needle. Magnetic iron oxide was still needed to periodically remagnetize the smaller needle using a process similar to the one you used in the "Observing Magnetic and Electrical Effects" activity.

Figure C1.7: A traditional Chinese compass

The descent can be just as dangerous as the climb up. The tension in the rope is balancing the downward force of gravity as the climber descends. How is Earth able to exert such a large force on the climber? If the contact with the rope supplies the upward force, what is the contact with the planet that supplies the downward force?

The contact between Earth and the climber is the **gravitational field** of Earth that pulls the climber toward Earth's centre. Just like electric and magnetic fields, the gravitational field of Earth is invisible—it can only be observed through the forces that it exerts on test bodies. The test bodies for gravitational fields are other objects with mass. Examples would include the climber, a penny in the climber's pocket, or even a satellite in orbit hundreds of kilometres above the climber. Earth exerts a gravitational force on each of these masses through the gravitational field that surrounds the planet.

▶ **gravitational field:** a property of the space around a source mass that enables the source mass to exert forces on other masses that enter this region

▶ **field lines:** lines that describe the direction of a field by the way they point, and the strength of a field by their density

Although Earth's gravitational field is invisible, it can be represented by **field lines**. The field lines point in the direction that a test mass would be forced if it were brought close to Earth—toward the centre of the planet. The density of the field lines communicates the strength of the gravitational field. Close to the surface, the field lines are highly concentrated, indicating that the field is stronger than it is farther from the planet, where the field lines are farther apart. Field-line diagrams are useful because they can communicate the overall pattern and shape of the field.

Earth is not the only object that surrounds itself with a gravitational field. The Moon, the other planets, and the Sun each have their own gravitational field. In general, any object with mass will be surrounded by a gravitational field; however, only very massive objects, like planets, produce gravitational fields with observable effects.

Image of Earth from Space with Gravitational Field Lines Added

Although Earth's gravitational field is present, it is invisible.

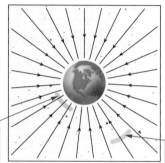

The lower concentration of field lines indicates that the field is weaker here.

The higher concentration of field lines indicates that the field is stronger here.

5. Although air is not normally a conductor of electricity, under the extreme circumstances of a thunderstorm, it can provide a conducting path for lightning. In general, lightning tends to follow a shorter path rather than a longer one.

   a. Refer to Figure C1.4, on page 317 to explain why hikers should avoid open fields, trees, and ridges during a storm.

   b. Explain the rationale for the recommended location and body position of the hikers.

6. In addition to magnetic fields, compass needles also respond to metals that contain iron, cobalt, and nickel. Refer to the concept of a magnetic field to explain why it is important to stand clear of these metals when determining which way is north.

7. The strength of Earth's gravitational field is slightly less at a mountain's peak than it is at the base of the same mountain. Refer to field lines as you explain this effect.

8. Copy and complete the following table. Leave enough room for your responses as you complete it.

Type of Field	General Description of Sources for This Field	General Description of Test Bodies for This Field	Two Examples of a Source for This Field
electric			
magnetic			
gravitational			

Describing Fields with Diagrams

The technique of describing a field with a field-line diagram does not just apply to gravitational fields. As you will see in the following investigations, this technique can also be used to describe electric fields and magnetic fields.

Before starting the investigation "Observing Magnetic Field Lines," it is important to quickly review some fundamental ideas about magnets that you have learned in previous courses.

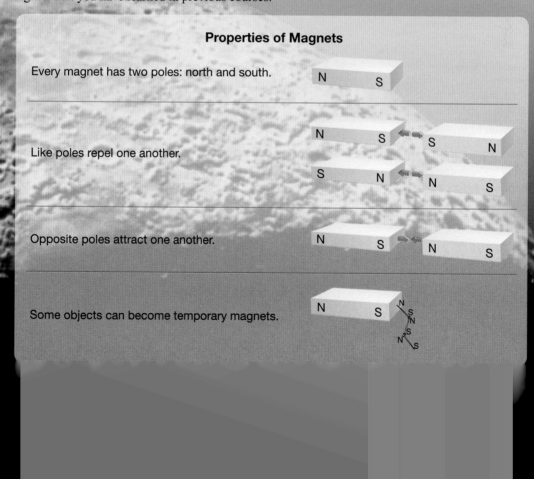

Properties of Magnets

Every magnet has two poles: north and south.

Like poles repel one another.

Opposite poles attract one another.

Some objects can become temporary magnets.

Investigation

Observing Magnetic Field Lines

Purpose

You will sketch the patterns produced by test bodies when they are placed in magnetic fields.

Materials

- ceramic or iron bar magnet
- iron filings in a container with a removable lid that allows the filings to be sprinkled
- compass
- lid of a shoebox with one end open
- cookie sheet that is ferromagnetic (A magnet will stick to it.)
- 2 books that are the same thickness (Both must be thicker than the bar magnet.)
- "Placement of a Compass Around a Bar Magnet" handout from the Science 30 Textbook CD

Part A: Using Iron Filings as Test Bodies

Procedure and Observations

step 1: Set up the apparatus as shown in Figure C1.8.

Science Skills

✓ Performing and Recording
✓ Analyzing and Interpreting

 CAUTION!

Iron filings should be handled with care.

- If the filings come in contact with a magnet, they are very difficult to remove.
- If the filings come in contact with your clothing, permanent staining is a possibility.
- Avoid spills.

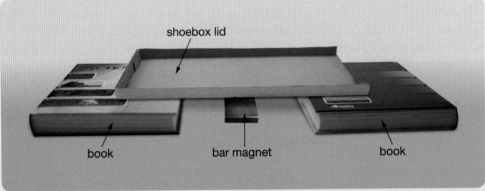

shoebox lid

book   bar magnet   book

Figure C1.8

step 2: Observe the empty lid of the shoebox. Is there any evidence of a magnetic field being present?

step 3: Lightly sprinkle iron filings into the lid of the shoebox. Be careful not to allow any filings to spill outside the lid. Gently tap the tops of the two books with your fingers for a few seconds until the filings form a pattern.

step 4: Observe the pattern of filings from above. Sketch a diagram to record your observations.

step 5: Observe the filings by looking from the side, just over the edge of the shoebox. Sketch a diagram to record your observations.

step 6: Carefully pour the iron filings back into the container.

step 7: Set up the apparatus as shown in Figure C1.9, and repeat steps 3 to 6.

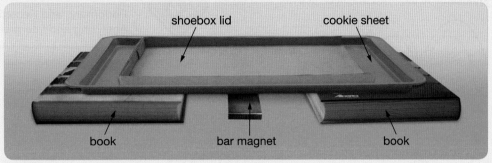

Figure C1.9

Analysis

1. Use your observations from step 2 to explain the importance of test bodies when observing magnetic fields.

2. Collect your observations from steps 4 and 5, when only the shoebox lid was between the magnet and the filings. Use these observations to answer the following questions.

   a. Identify the regions of the magnet where the magnetic field lines are most concentrated.

   b. Determine whether the magnetic field lines are restricted to the flat (two-dimensional) surface of the shoebox lid or whether they exist in the three-dimensional space beyond the shoebox lid.

3. Collect your observations from step 7, when both the cookie sheet and the shoebox lid were between the magnet and the filings. Use these observations to answer the questions 3.a. and 3.b.

   a. Describe how the cookie sheet changed the pattern of filings.

   b. Many sensitive electronic devices do not perform well if exposed to strong magnetic fields. Suggest a way to shield these devices from strong magnetic fields.

Part B: Using a Compass as a Test Body

Procedure and Observations

step 1: Check your compass to ensure that it points to magnetic north.

step 2: Obtain the handout "Placement of a Compass Around a Bar Magnet." Note that the positions for the compass on this handout follow from the observations with the iron filings in Part A.

step 3: Position the bar magnet where shown on the handout, and place the compass at the other end of the table.

step 4: Working quickly and efficiently, momentarily place the compass in each of the positions shown on the handout. In each position, do the following:

   • Observe which way the north end of the compass needle points.
   • Move the compass to the other end of the table.
   • Draw an arrow on the handout to record your results.

Analysis

4. Use your observations to determine which end of the magnet is the south end and which end is the north end.

5. In Part A you were able to observe the pattern formed by many field lines. In Part B you were able to observe the direction that the north end of a compass needle would point along two field lines. Combine your results from Parts A and B by producing a diagram that includes the direction of many field lines surrounding a magnet.

CAUTION!

The sensitive magnet in a compass needle is easily damaged if exposed to strong magnetic fields for an extended length of time.

   • Do not store compasses in the same location as strong magnets.

   • Do not allow compasses to touch strong magnets.

   • If a procedure requires that a compass be momentarily brought close to a strong magnet, quickly make the observation and then return the compass to a safe distance from the magnet.

Key Ideas About Magnetic Fields

Magnetic field lines show the way the north end of a compass needle would point. These lines always leave the north end of a magnet and form a loop that enters the south end of a magnet. You can confirm your understanding of these ideas by using a computer simulation in the "Two Magnets" activity.

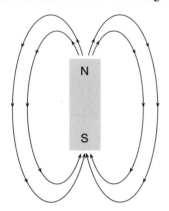

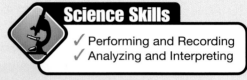

Science Skills

✓ Performing and Recording
✓ Analyzing and Interpreting

Purpose

You will use the computer simulation "Two Magnets" from the Science 30 Textbook CD to explore the pattern of magnetic field lines between two magnets.

Procedure

Follow the instructions in the computer simulation and complete the activity.

Summary

Record four statements to summarize what you have learned in this activity.

Investigation

Observing Electric Field Lines

Purpose

You will sketch the patterns produced by test bodies when they are placed in electric fields.

Science Skills

✓ Performing and Recording
✓ Analyzing and Interpreting

Background Information: Using Grass Seeds as Test Bodies

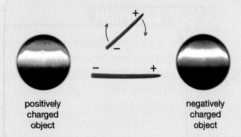

positively charged object

negatively charged object

CAUTION!

This investigation requires the use of high-voltage devices to create the electric fields you will be studying. Be sure to follow all the recommendations of your teacher regarding the safe use of this equipment.

Although grass seeds are insulators, the small number of charges on the grass seed can be separated slightly. Grass seeds floating in mineral oil can be used to demonstrate the presence of electric fields. Because one end of a grass seed is slightly positive and the other is slightly negative, the seed will twist as each end is pulled in an opposite direction. The seed stops twisting when it is aligned with the electric field. Grass seeds that sink to the bottom of the mineral oil are not able to align with the electric field, so these should be ignored as you look for patterns.

Materials

- high-voltage DC power supply (at least 500 V DC)
  (An inexpensive, handheld bug zapper can be modified to become a high-voltage power supply.)
- 200 mL of mineral oil
- latex or vinyl gloves
- waste bucket to recover mineral oil
- large Petri dish (100 mm by 15 mm)

- 10 mL of grass seed
- variety of objects to become charged in the Petri dish
  - straight-line sources ($\frac{1}{2}$-inch copper plumbing tees)
  - point sources ($\frac{3}{4}$-inch copper plumbing coupling)
  - variable-shaped sources (large hex nuts or eyebolts)
  - 2 strips of thin metal sheeting (2 cm by 15 cm each)
    (inexpensive metal flashing used for roof repair)

Procedure

step 1: Put on the latex or vinyl gloves.

step 2: Pour mineral oil into the Petri dish until the layer of mineral oil is about 3 mm deep. Pouring slowly helps prevent bubbles.

step 3: Obtain the "Observing Electric Fields: Sources" handout from the Science 30 Textbook CD.

step 4: For the first arrangement of sources shown in the handout, do the following:

- Place the sources in the Petri dish as shown in the handout. Make sure the sources are no more than 2 cm apart.
- With the high-voltage power supply switched off, connect the sources.
- Switch on the high-voltage power supply. Before adding the grass seeds, observe the region between the sources for any evidence of an electric field.
- Carefully add a few grains of grass seed in the space between the sources.
- If you notice that the floating grass seeds are starting to line up in the mineral oil, add a few more grass seeds to the areas where the lines appear to be going.
- Once the pattern formed by the floating grass seed is visibly distinct, switch off the high-voltage power supply. It may help to form the pattern if you repeatedly switch the power supply on and off.
- Sketch the pattern of electric field lines shown by the floating grass seeds in the corresponding space on the handout.
- Remove the sources from the Petri dish. Carefully empty the mineral oil and grass seeds from the Petri dish into the empty waste bucket.

step 5: Repeat step 4 for each of the other sources on the "Observing Electric Fields: Sources" handout.

step 6: Obtain the "Observing Electric Fields: Lightning Safety" handout from the Science 30 textbook CD. Follow the instructions on this handout to bend the two metal strips into the required shapes.

step 7: Repeat step 4 using the metal shapes you created in step 6.

Analysis

1. Recall what you observed between the sources when the high-voltage power supply was turned on but the grass seed was not yet added. Explain the importance of test bodies when it comes to observing fields.

2. Identify the sources that tended to produce patterns of electric field lines that were evenly spaced. Which ones produced patterns that were concentrated?

3. Refer to your answer to question 2 and your observations from step 7. Use the patterns in the field lines to explain the safest location for hikers during a thunderstorm.

Adding Direction to Electric Field Lines

Although the grass seeds in the "Observing Electric Field Lines" activity provided an opportunity for you to sketch electric field lines, there was no way to indicate the direction in which the lines were pointing. The direction of an electric field is determined by the direction of the force on a positive test body. This is why electric field lines always point toward negative sources and away from positive sources—this is the way a positive test charge would go.

Under a typical thundercloud, the electric field can become very intense, especially around pointed objects that project high into the air. The electric field lines point up because this is the way that positive charges would move as they are attracted to negative charges in the cloud. Since the excess electrons in the bottom of the cloud are negatively charged, they move in the opposite direction to the electric field—down toward Earth's surface.

Using this thinking, good advice to a hiker caught in a thunderstorm would be to seek a low region where the electric field lines are not as intense and, therefore, where the lightning is less likely to strike.

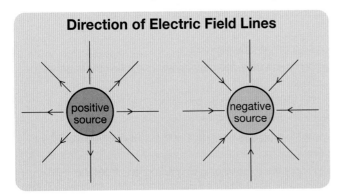

Direction of Electric Field Lines

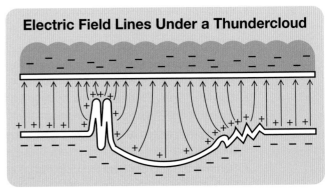

Electric Field Lines Under a Thundercloud

1.1 Summary

Objects can become charged when electrons are transferred. Positively charged objects are the result of losing electrons, while negatively charged objects are the result of gaining electrons. Charge is measured in coulombs—a huge unit, since 1 C corresponds to a transfer of 6.25×10^{18} electrons. An uncomfortable spark from scuffing your feet across the carpet might be a few microcoulombs, while a single lightning strike could be 10 C to 30 C. Lightning is dangerous, not only because of the huge quantity of charge that is transferred, but also because this charge transfers incredible amounts of energy. The ratio of the change in electric potential energy to the charge transferred is called the potential difference or voltage and is measured in volts.

A field is an invisible connection between a source and a test body. The electric field that exists between the bottom of a thundercloud and the ground below can be detected by small charged objects below the cloud. The magnetic field produced by a strong magnet can be detected by another magnet, such as a compass needle. Gravitational fields produce noticeable effects on test bodies when the source is very massive—like a planet, a moon, or a star. Even though all of these fields are invisible, their effects on test bodies can be observed and recorded in field-line diagrams.

1.1 Questions

Knowledge

1. Define the following terms.

   a. negative charge

   b. positive charge

   c. coulomb

   d. electric potential difference

   e. voltage

   f. volt

   g. electric field

   h. magnetic field

   i. gravitational field

   j. test body

   k. field lines

2. Compare and contrast characteristics of electric, magnetic, and gravitational fields.

3. Explain the importance of test bodies when studying fields.

Applying Concepts

4. Each of the following objects is the source of a field.

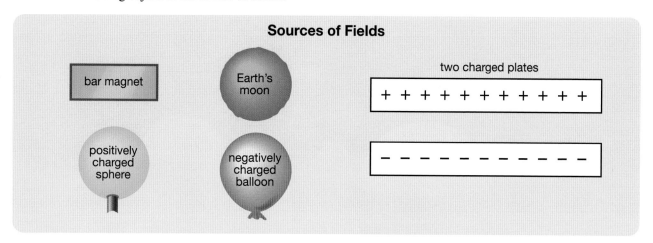

Sources of Fields

bar magnet

Earth's moon

two charged plates

+ + + + + + + + + + +

– – – – – – – – – – –

positively charged sphere

negatively charged balloon

 a. Sketch each object in your notebook. Be sure to leave enough room to add the field lines.

 b. Under each of your sketches, identify the type of field you sketched.

Use the following information to answer question 5.

As a child goes down a plastic playground slide, the plastic surface tends to remove electrons from the child's clothing. When the child reaches the bottom of the slide, it is common for her to have developed enough charge to become the source of an electric field. Note the field lines indicated by the child's hair in the photograph. It is possible for children to acquire a voltage of over 20 000 V in these circumstances, creating a nasty shock when their feet touch the ground!

Many young children with impaired hearing use a special electronic device called a cochlear implant. The circuitry within these tiny devices is very sensitive to the buildup of static electricity on the user's body. Unfortunately, if a child using such a device slides down a plastic playground slide, the sudden discharge of static electricity at the bottom of the slide will often erase the specific programming on the microprocessor, causing the cochlear implant to fail.

5. a. Determine whether the child became positively or negatively charged.

 b. Sketch a field-line diagram to represent the electric field around the child's head.

 c. The high voltage is sufficient to affect the circuitry in a cochlear implant. Beyond this effect, explain why the high voltage does not present a health hazard to most children who use the slide.

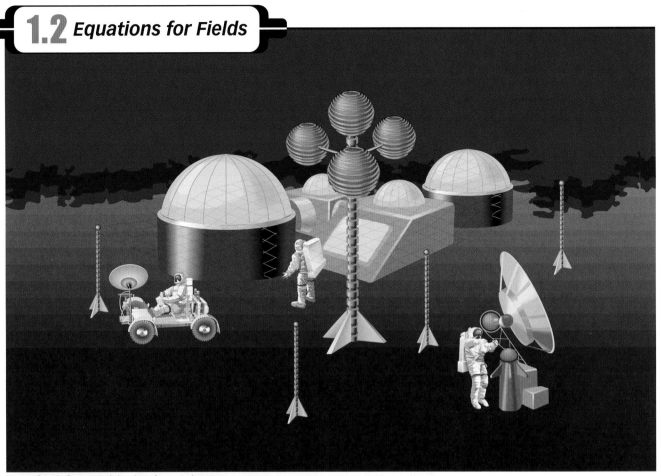

Figure C1.10: Conceptual drawing of a moon base

Do you think that students could one day be going to school on Mars? Could people move beyond the solar system and eventually have colonies on planets that orbit stars other than the Sun? Many scientists and engineers who have been thinking about these questions suggest the first step in exploring these possibilities would be to set up a base on the Moon. This would provide an opportunity to improve space technologies closer to Earth. A moon base could also be a convenient "stepping off point" for other space exploration.

Although people have already visited the surface of the Moon, the Apollo missions were quite short in duration. A moon base could allow people to live on the Moon for years instead of days, which is why the moon base would need a shield to protect its inhabitants from the charged space particles that bombard the lunar surface. Some of these particles are electrons,

protons, and nuclei of helium atoms emitted from the Sun. The flow of these particles emitted from the Sun is called the **solar wind**. Larger, positively charged particles are also emitted from stars in distant parts of the galaxy. These emissions from beyond Earth's solar system are called **cosmic rays**. Long-term exposure to these types of radiation presents a real hazard to unprotected astronauts, who face an increased probability of developing cancer. When particles from the solar wind or cosmic rays collide with cells, parts of the cell may become ionized, often killing the cell. If the cell survives but segments of DNA are ionized, the cell may produce other abnormal cells that may become cancerous.

> **solar wind:** a stream of high-speed, ionized particles ejected from the Sun, consisting mainly of electrons, protons, and helium nuclei

> **cosmic rays:** a stream of high-speed, ionized particles ejected from the objects beyond the solar system, consisting mainly of atomic nuclei

How would the large spheres in Figure C1.10 protect astronauts from the solar wind and cosmic rays? If Earth is a giant spaceship travelling rapidly around the Sun, it is exposed to these radiations as well. How are you protected from these hazards? What do fields have to do with the answers to these questions and with space exploration in general? You will have an opportunity to answer these questions in this lesson.

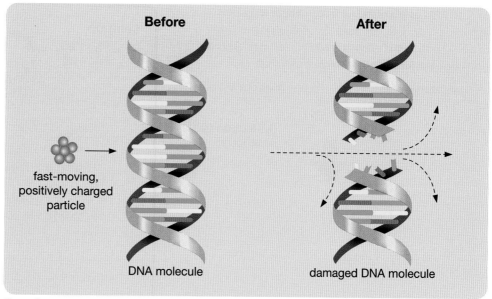

Before **After**

fast-moving, positively charged particle

DNA molecule

damaged DNA molecule

Figure C1.11: The high-energy, positively charged particles from cosmic rays have the potential to break both strands in a DNA molecule during a collision. This kind of damage is more difficult for a cell to repair than a single-strand break.

Practice

9. In general terms, explain how the presence of a positively charged particle could cause the ionization of other molecules, leading to the breakage of chemical bonds.
10. Explain why it is more difficult for cells to repair damage to DNA molecules if both DNA strands have been affected.

Gravitational Field Strength

Before considering the design of space stations, it is necessary to deal first with the challenges of leaving the surface of Earth. Think back to the last time you climbed a number of stairs. Each step required you to exert a force to overcome the natural tendency of Earth's gravitational field to pull you back down to the surface. With a space-shuttle launch, the rocket engines not only supply the force to overcome the force of gravity, they also accelerate the shuttle and its contents to high speeds—about 8 km/s for low-Earth orbit. It is the combination of high speed and gravitational field that defines a stable orbit. Without these high speeds, satellites would be pulled back to Earth by the planet's gravitational field.

In order to calculate the speed necessary for a satellite to maintain a certain orbit, and to determine the amount of rocket fuel required to achieve that orbit, an equation is needed to predict the **gravitational field strength**.

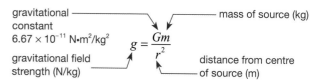

gravitational constant 6.67×10^{-11} N•m²/kg² ⟶ mass of source (kg)

$$g = \frac{Gm}{r^2}$$

gravitational field strength (N/kg) ⟶ distance from centre of source (m)

Note that the key variables on the right side of the equation are m, the mass of the object that is the source of the field, and r, the distance from the centre of the source. The gravitational constant, G, is not a variable—its value, 6.67×10^{-11} N•m²/kg², never changes. The gravitational constant is needed to ensure that when the value for source mass is entered in kilograms and the value for distance is entered in metres, the result of the calculation will give the correct value for gravitational field strength in newtons per kilogram.

> **gravitational field strength:** the number of newtons per kilogram a test body will experience at a given location from a source mass

The units of gravitational field strength reveal an important feature of this quantity. Multiplying the mass of a test body by the gravitational field strength gives the **gravitational force** that acts on that test body.

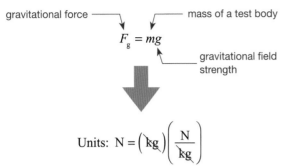

gravitational force ⟶ ⟵ mass of a test body

$$F_g = mg$$

⟵ gravitational field strength

Units: $N = \left(kg\right)\left(\dfrac{N}{kg}\right)$

Example Problem 1.4 illustrates how these ideas can be applied.

> **gravitational force:** the force exerted on a test body by a gravitational field; calculated by multiplying the mass of the test body by the gravitational field strength

Example Problem 1.4

Earth's radius has an average value of 6.37×10^6 m, while Earth's mass has a value of 5.98×10^{24} kg.

a. Calculate the value of the gravitational field strength at Earth's surface.

b. A person with a heavy backpack has a mass of 100 kg and can be considered a test body for the gravitational field. Use the value from part a. to predict the force of gravity Earth would exert on this person.

continued

Solution

a. $r = 6.37 \times 10^6$ m

$m_{source} = 5.98 \times 10^{24}$ kg

$g = ?$

$$g = \frac{Gm_{source}}{r^2}$$

$$= \frac{\left(6.67 \times 10^{-11} \text{ N} \cdot \text{m}^2/\text{kg}^2\right)\left(5.98 \times 10^{24} \text{ kg}\right)}{\left(6.37 \times 10^6 \text{ m}\right)^2}$$

$$= 9.829\ 878\ 576 \text{ N/kg}$$

$$= 9.83 \text{ N/kg}$$

The strength of the gravitational field at Earth's surface is 9.83 N/kg.

Note: The following keystrokes summarize a typical entry for many calculators:

Consult your calculator owner's manual for more information.

b. $g = 9.829\ 878\ 576$ N/kg

$m_{test} = 100$ kg

$F_g = ?$

$$F_g = m_{test}g$$

$$= \left(100 \text{ kg}\right)\left(9.829\ 878\ 576 \text{ N/kg}\right)$$

$$= 983 \text{ N}$$

Using the value from part a., Earth's gravitational field will exert a force of 983 N on the person with the backpack.

Note: The unrounded value for g is used as an input in part b., but the final answer is recorded to three significant digits, consistent with the given values.

The calculation in part b. of Example Problem 1.4 reveals an important aspect of gravitational field strength: it provides a convenient way to predict the amount of force a test body would experience in the field. The only caution is not to mix up gravitational field strength with gravitational force. Many students use units to help keep this clear.

- Force of gravity is measured in newtons (N).
- Gravitational field strength is measured in newtons per kilogram (N/kg).

The value calculated in part a. of Example Problem 1.4 is based on the average value for the radius of Earth and ignores the effects of Earth's spin. So, it follows that the gravitational field strength is also an average value for Earth. In Alberta, the gravitational field strength is 9.81 N/kg. Does this number look familiar? In previous courses you used 9.81 m/s² as the value for acceleration due to gravity. As the following analysis of units reveals, this is not a coincidence—the units for acceleration due to gravity and gravitational field strength are equal. The value for the gravitational field strength of Earth varies from a low of 9.79 N/kg at the equator to a high of 9.83 N/kg at the poles. This variation is due to Earth's spin and to the flattening of Earth at its poles.

This new interpretation of the value of g helps to answer some important questions that may not have been answered in previous courses, such as why does the Moon's surface have a different value for the acceleration due to gravity than the surface of Earth does? Example Problem 1.5 provides insight into the answer to this question.

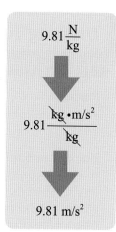

Example Problem 1.5

The Moon has an average radius of 1.74×10^3 km and a mass of 7.35×10^{22} kg.

a. Calculate the gravitational field strength of the Moon.

b. Explain why the Moon has a different value for gravitational field strength than Earth does.

c. An astronaut in a new lightweight spacesuit has a mass of 100 kg and could be considered a test body for the gravitational field of the Moon. Determine the force of gravity exerted on the astronaut by the Moon's gravitational field.

Solution

a. $r = 1.74 \times 10^3 \text{ km} \times \dfrac{1000 \text{ m}}{1 \text{ km}}$

     $= 1.74 \times 10^6$ m

Note: Kilometres are converted to metres before the values are substituted in the equation.

$m_{\text{source}} = 7.35 \times 10^{22}$ kg

$g = ?$

$g = \dfrac{Gm_{\text{source}}}{r^2}$

   $= \dfrac{\left(6.67 \times 10^{-11} \text{ N} \cdot \text{m}^2/\text{kg}^2\right)\left(7.35 \times 10^{22} \text{ kg}\right)}{\left(1.74 \times 10^6 \text{ m}\right)^2}$

   $= 1.619\ 252\ 874$ N/kg

   $= 1.62$ N/kg

The strength of the gravitational field at the Moon's surface is 1.62 N/kg.

b. Gravitational field strength depends upon two key variables: m, the mass of the source, and r, the distance from the centre of the source. Since both of these values are significantly different from the values for Earth, the Moon has a different value for gravitational field strength.

c. $g = 1.619\ 252\ 874$ N/kg

$m_{\text{test}} = 100$ kg

$F_g = ?$

$F_g = m_{\text{test}} g$

   $= \left(100 \text{ kg}\right)\left(1.619\ 252\ 874 \text{ N/kg}\right)$

   $= 162$ N

Using the value from part a., the Moon's gravitational field will exert a force of 162 N on the astronaut.

Compare the solution to part b. of Example Problem 1.4 to the solution to part c. of Example Problem 1.5. The mass of the test body was the same in both cases (100 kg), but the force of gravity was different. How would you explain this? Look at the values of gravitational field strength in both locations. Even though the masses of the test bodies were the same, the differences in gravitational field strength resulted in different forces.

Utilizing Technology

Plotting the Gravitational Field Strength of Venus

Purpose

You will use a graphing calculator to calculate, graph, and identify trends in gravitational field strength values for Venus.

Science Skills

✓ Performing and Recording
✓ Analyzing and Interpreting

Background Information

Due to similar values for mass and radius, it was once thought that Venus was very similar to Earth. Early astronomers referred to Venus and Earth as "sister planets." However, the conditions on the surface of Venus are dramatically different from those on Earth.

Venus's atmosphere is so thick with carbon dioxide that the "greenhouse effect" makes the surface temperatures as hot as an oven on "self-clean": 482°C. Figure C1.12 shows the thick clouds of sulfuric acid drops that blanket Venus. The photograph was taken by a probe that was sent to explore Venus in 1979.

Figure C1.12: Venus

Figure C1.13: *Venus Express*

More recent exploration of Venus began in 2006 with the European Space Agency's probe, *Venus Express*. The orbit of this probe will be modified over the course of the mission, depending upon the data that needs to be collected. Planning for a stable orbit means that both the speed of the probe and the strength of the gravitational field at various locations around Venus will have to be determined.

Materials

• graphing calculator   • "Plotting the Gravitational Field Strength of Venus" handout

Procedure

Obtain the "Plotting the Gravitational Field Strength of Venus" handout from the Science 30 Textbook CD. Follow the steps described in the handout.

1. Plot a graph of your results in the space provided in the handout. Draw a smooth curve to connect the data points.

Analysis

2. Compare the data for trial 5 with the data for trial 1.

   a. How does the distance value for trial 5 compare to the distance value for trial 1?

      Answer by completing this sentence:

      To get the distance for trial 5, multiply the distance value for trial 1 by _____.

   b. How does the gravitational field strength value for trial 5 compare to the gravitational field strength for trial 1?

      Answer by completing this sentence:

      To get the gravitational field strength for trial 5, multiply the gravitational field strength for trial 1 by the decimal _____ (rounded to three digits) or by the fraction _____.

3. Repeat the analysis of question 2 for the values in trials 2 and 7.

4. Repeat the analysis of question 2 for the values in trials 3 and 9.

5. Describe the pattern that emerges from your answers to questions 2, 3, and 4.

6. Use the equation for gravitational field strength to explain the pattern that you identified in your answer to question 5.

The Effect of $\frac{1}{r^2}$ on Gravitational Field Strength

The position of r in the denominator of the gravitational field strength equation means that as distance from the source increases, the value of gravitational field strength decreases. This trend is compounded by the fact that the value of r is squared. Figure C1.14 shows how these ideas apply to the gravitational field of Mercury, one of the smaller planets in the solar system.

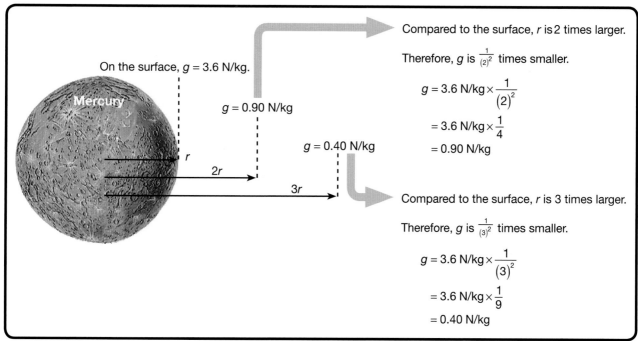

On the surface, $g = 3.6$ N/kg.

$g = 0.90$ N/kg

$g = 0.40$ N/kg

r

$2r$

$3r$

Compared to the surface, r is 2 times larger.

Therefore, g is $\frac{1}{(2)^2}$ times smaller.

$$g = 3.6 \text{ N/kg} \times \frac{1}{(2)^2}$$

$$= 3.6 \text{ N/kg} \times \frac{1}{4}$$

$$= 0.90 \text{ N/kg}$$

Compared to the surface, r is 3 times larger.

Therefore, g is $\frac{1}{(3)^2}$ times smaller.

$$g = 3.6 \text{ N/kg} \times \frac{1}{(3)^2}$$

$$= 3.6 \text{ N/kg} \times \frac{1}{9}$$

$$= 0.40 \text{ N/kg}$$

Figure C1.14

Students who like mathematics find that the patterns shown in Figure C1.14 are a convenient shortcut that reduces the need for always doing long calculations. For example, given the information in Figure C1.14, how strong would the gravitational field strength be at a location ten times farther away than the surface of Mercury? Since the distance is ten times farther away, the gravitational field strength should be $\frac{1}{(10)^2}$ or $\frac{1}{100}$ times larger, or 0.036 N/kg.

Practice

11. Before you begin solving problems, it is a good idea to review how to enter these calculations into your calculator. Enter the data for part a. of Example Problem 1.4 and part a. of Example Problem 1.5 into your calculator and confirm the answers. A common data-entry error is forgetting to square the value for distance, r. Would this error generate gravitational field strength values that are too large or too small?

Use the following information to answer questions 12 to 15.

The following illustration shows a typical path for a space vehicle on a mission to the Moon.

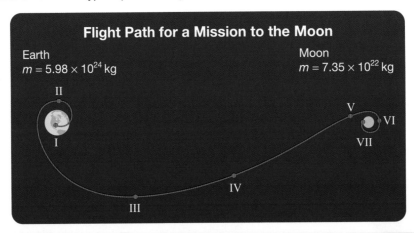

Flight Path for a Mission to the Moon

Earth
$m = 5.98 \times 10^{24}$ kg

Moon
$m = 7.35 \times 10^{22}$ kg

Location	Description	Distance from Centre of Earth (m)	Distance from Centre of Moon (m)
I	launch site on Earth	6.37×10^6	
II	high-Earth orbit	2.00×10^7	
III	about $\frac{1}{4}$ of distance to Moon	1.00×10^8	
IV	about $\frac{1}{2}$ of distance to Moon	2.00×10^8	
V	point of equal gravitational attraction	3.457×10^8	3.83×10^7
VI	low-Moon orbit		1.84×10^6
VII	landing site on Moon		1.74×10^6

12. Calculate the gravitational field strength of Earth at locations II, III, IV, and V.

13. Calculate the gravitational field strength of the Moon at locations V and VI.

14. Refer to the values you calculated for gravitational field strength at location V in questions 12 and 13. One of these values is the gravitational field strength of Earth. The other is the gravitational field strength of the Moon.

    a. Sketch a diagram of Earth and the Moon with location V indicated.

    b. Add an arrow to your diagram to indicate the size and direction of the gravitational field of Earth at location V.

    c. Add an arrow to your diagram to indicate the size and direction of the gravitational field of the Moon at location V.

    d. Explain why location V is referred to as the point of equal gravitational attraction.

    e. If a space vehicle comes to rest and turns off its engines at location V, it will not accelerate toward the Moon or Earth. Explain why.

15. Note the following observations in your answers to question 12:

    • observation 1: Location IV is two times farther from Earth than location III, and the gravitational field strength at location IV is $\frac{1}{4}$ the gravitational field strength at location III.

    • observation 2: Location IV is ten times farther from Earth than location II, and the gravitational field strength at location IV is $\frac{1}{100}$ the gravitational field strength at location II.

    a. Use the equation for gravitational field strength to explain observation 1.

    b. Use the equation for gravitational field strength to explain observation 2.

positive particles
from solar wind
and cosmic rays

Electric Field Strength

At the beginning of this lesson, it was explained that the large spheres in the illustration of the space station help to protect astronauts from ionizing effects of charged particles in the solar wind and in cosmic rays. The spheres are able to deflect these particles away from the space station by generating strong electric fields. To ensure that the electric fields are sufficient to protect the people working below, an equation is needed to predict the **electric field strength**.

electric field strength: the number of newtons per coulomb that a test body will experience at a given location from a source charge

The equation for electric field strength is very similar in structure to the equation for gravitational field strength.

electric field strength (N/C) — coulomb constant 8.99×10^9 N•m²/C²

$$|\vec{E}| = \frac{kq}{r^2}$$

charge on source (C)

distance from centre of source

Just like the equation for gravitational field strength, this equation involves a constant to ensure that the equation works for the given units. In this case, the coulomb constant is a large value: $k = 8.99 \times 10^9$ N•m²/C². This is because, overall, electric forces and fields are more significant than gravitational fields. Gravitational effects are only noticeable when one of the objects happens to have the mass of a planet, a moon, or a star. Electrical effects, on the other hand, can be observed among very ordinary objects.

Another unique feature of this equation is the notation. The symbol for the vector electric field is $\vec{E}$. Since this equation is just for the magnitude or strength of the electric field, it might be tempting to simply drop the vector arrow and use E, but this is already used as the symbol for energy. So, the absolute value signs were added to the vector electric field symbol, indicating that direction is not involved in this equation—it only describes the strength of the electric field.

The equation for electric field strength is an important tool for the NASA engineers who are drafting early plans for the protective spheres on the moon base. Each sphere has to be highly charged in order to generate a field that can exert forces on harmful particles from the solar wind and cosmic rays.

Example Problem 1.6 illustrates how the equation for electric field strength is applied to this situation. As was the case for solving gravitation problems, you have to be careful not to confuse the force with the field that exerts the force. Again, many students find that units help to keep them from getting mixed up:

electric force: the force exerted on a charged test body by an electric field; calculated by multiplying the electric field strength by the charge on the test body

- **Electric force** is measured in newtons (N).
- Electric field is measured in newtons per coulomb (N/C).
- Multiplying the electric field by the charge on a test body indicates the electric force on that test body.

Units: $N = \left(\dfrac{N}{C}\right)(C)$

electric force — electric field strength

Equation: $F_e = |\vec{E}| q$ ← charge on a test body

Example Problem 1.6

One of the charged spheres being developed to protect a base on the Moon has a charge of $+0.0200$ C.

a. Determine the strength of the electric field 20.0 m from the centre of this sphere.

b. The centre of one sphere is about 20.0 m from the next. Consider a second sphere that is also charged at $+0.0200$ C to be a test body for the first sphere. Calculate the force the electric field of the first sphere will exert on the second sphere.

c. Consider your answer to part b. Explain the implications of this answer for the designers and engineers at NASA.

Solution

a. $q_{source} = +0.0200$ C

$r = 20.0$ m

$|\vec{E}| = ?$

$$|\vec{E}| = \frac{kq_{source}}{r^2}$$

$$= \frac{\left(8.99 \times 10^9 \text{ N•m}^2/\text{C}^2\right)(0.0200 \text{ C})}{(20.0 \text{ m})^2}$$

$$= 449\ 500 \text{ N/C}$$

$$= 4.50 \times 10^5 \text{ N/C}$$

The electric field 20.0 m away from the sphere would be 4.50×10^5 N/C.

b. $q_{test} = +0.0200$ C

$|\vec{E}| = 449\ 500$ N/C

$F_e = ?$

$$F_e = |\vec{E}| q_{test}$$

$$= (449\ 500 \text{ N/C})(0.0200 \text{ C})$$

$$= 8.99 \times 10^3 \text{ N}$$

The force exerted by the electric field of the first sphere on the second sphere is 8.99×10^3 N.

c. The forces the spheres exert on each other would have to be balanced by the forces of the structure that holds them together. Since these forces are large, the supports holding the spheres together would have to be strong enough to hold the entire structure together.

Example Problem 1.6 illustrates how large the electric field would be around the charged spheres. It also illustrates a key challenge for the engineers—since each sphere would generate an electric field that would exert a large repulsive force on the others, the spheres would have to be well-supported. Given this challenge, you might wonder why it's not possible to use one large sphere instead of a cluster of smaller ones. The thinking here is that the electric fields of the smaller spheres would overlap, creating one very large electric field to repel the incoming positive particles.

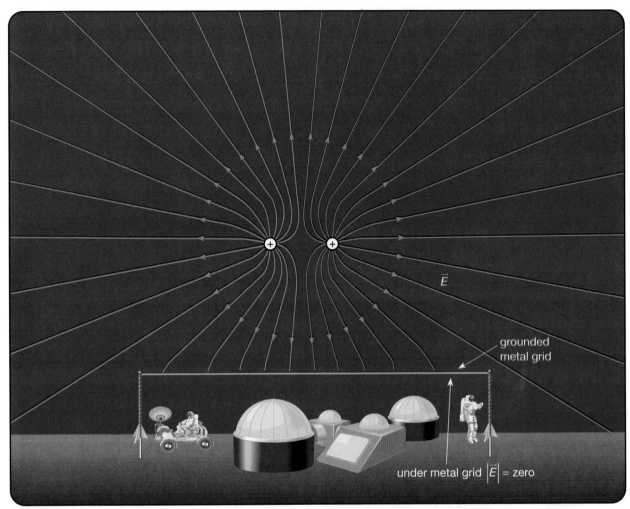

Figure C1.15

NASA estimates over 100 million volts will be required to maintain a field this strong above the lunar base. Clearly, the structures supporting the spheres would have to be made from non-conducting material. Recalling what you learned about lightning in Lesson 1.1, consider how hazardous it is for humans to work in an environment where there are large amounts of charge separated at high voltages. The metal grid above the base would be **grounded**, providing a safe conducting path for any stray or excess charges to flow to the ground below. The metal grid would also shield the people at the base from the strong electric fields, since the electric field strength is zero below the grid.

> **grounded:** connected to the ground; providing a safe conducting path for stray or excess charges; having zero electric potential energy

16. Refer to Figure C1.15, which shows the two charged spheres above the lunar base. The distance between the centres of the spheres is 20.0 m, and each sphere has a charge of +0.0200 C. There is a point midway between the spheres, the midpoint, that is exactly 10.0 m from the centre of each sphere.

   a. Calculate the electric field strength at the midpoint due to the sphere on the left.

   b. Determine the direction of the electric field at the midpoint due to the sphere on the left.

   c. Use your answers to questions 16.a. and 16.b. to determine the strength and direction of the electric field at the midpoint due to the sphere on the right.

   d. Explain why the sum of the electric fields at the midpoint is zero.

Electric Fields and You

Figure C1.16

Whether you are pulling clothes out of the dryer or combing your hair with a plastic comb on a dry day, you encounter the effects of electric fields on a daily basis. A simple demonstration of electric fields involves rubbing a balloon through your hair on a dry winter day. As each individual hair loses electrons to the balloon, the balloon acquires a negative charge and the individual hairs become positive test bodies. As shown in Figure C1.16, the positive test bodies respond to the electric field of the negatively charged balloon. In these circumstances, the balloon probably picks up only a few nanocoulombs of charge, but the electric field strength can still be determined.

Example Problem 1.7

A balloon is given a charge of −4.5 nC.

   a. Determine the electric field strength 30 cm from the centre of the balloon.

   b. Sketch a diagram of the electric field lines around the balloon.

Solution

a. $q_{source} = -4.5$ nC

   $\qquad = -4.5 \times 10^{-9}$ C

   $d = 30 \text{ cm} \times \dfrac{1 \text{ m}}{100 \text{ cm}}$

   $\quad = 0.30$ m

   $|\vec{E}| = ?$

   The negative sign is not used in the equation. The negative sign is used to determine direction in part b.

   $|\vec{E}| = \dfrac{kq_{source}}{r^2}$

   $\qquad = \dfrac{\left(8.99 \times 10^9 \text{ N} \cdot \text{m}^2/\text{C}^2\right)\left(4.5 \times 10^{-9} \text{ C}\right)}{\left(0.30 \text{ m}\right)^2}$

   $\qquad = 4.5 \times 10^2$ N/C

   The electric field strength 30 cm from the balloon's centre is 4.5×10^2 N/C.

b. Since the direction of the electric field is determined by the force on a positive test body, the electric field lines are directed toward the negatively charged balloon.

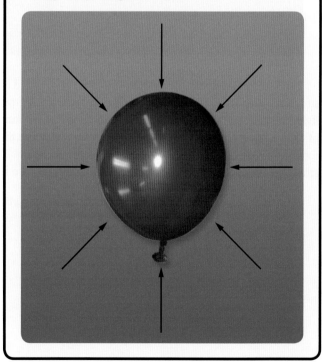

17. Figure C1.17 shows the set-up of a demonstration you can try in a very dry room. Given how dry it is inside most buildings in Alberta in the winter, this demonstration works best if it is done in December, January, or February.

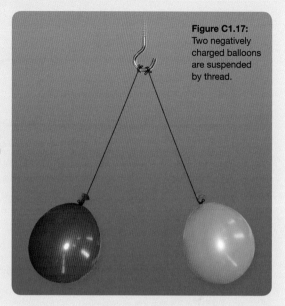

Figure C1.17: Two negatively charged balloons are suspended by thread.

a. Sketch a diagram showing the two balloons and the electric fields around them.

b. Assume each balloon has a charge of -5.0 nC. If the distance between the centres of the balloons is 44 cm, the midpoint is 22 cm from the centre of each balloon. Perform the necessary calculations and analysis to demonstrate that the electric field strength is zero at the midpoint.

DID YOU KNOW?

When working with computer circuit boards, it is important to ensure they are properly grounded. A grounding wire connected to your wrist allows stray amounts of charge that may accumulate on your body to be conducted to the ground instead of passing through sensitive electronic components. The charge accumulated on your body by simply walking across a room could be enough to seriously damage a new sound card for a computer. Warning labels remind you to ground yourself before handling sensitive components.

Moving Charges and Magnetic Fields

In considering NASA's plans for a moon base, you saw how an arrangement of positively charged spheres can protect the base from the bombardment of positively charged particles that are key components of cosmic rays and the solar wind. The solar wind also contains negatively charged particles—high-speed electrons. Since this form of radiation also has the ability to ionize matter, the high-speed electrons represent a health hazard to the astronauts working at the base. Given that the positively charged spheres would exert forces to attract these high-speed electrons toward the base, there would need to be another component of the design to deflect these particles as well as the positively charged particles from cosmic rays and the solar wind.

NASA's plans call for the positively charged spheres to be partially wrapped in insulating wire carrying a large **electric current**. The flow of moving charges through the coils of wire would exert a force on the incoming electrons before they reached the base, so a field must be involved. What kind of field is produced by the electric current? Can this effect be demonstrated here on Earth? You will have a chance to answer these questions in the next investigation.

Figure C1.18: Insulated wires carrying an electric current surround the positively charged sphere.

▶ **electric current:** the flow of electric charge from one point to another

Using a Coil to Deflect an Electron Beam

Science Skills

✓ Performing and Recording
✓ Analyzing and Interpreting
✓ Communication and Teamwork

Purpose

You will build a small coil and then pass a current through the coil for a few seconds at a time. At the moments when the current is passing through the coil, you will observe the effects the current has on a compass needle and on a beam of electrons.

Materials

- 1 cardboard cylinder, about 4 cm in diameter and 10 cm in length (empty toilet-tissue roll)
- 10 m of 26- or 28-gauge enamelled magnet wire
- 4 AA cells in a plastic battery pack
- 2 test leads with alligator clips at each end
- access to an operating CRT monitor (conventional TV or computer monitor)
- small knife or 1 piece of fine sandpaper
- tape
- compass
- "Magnetic Field Surrounding a Small Coil" handout

CAUTION!

This investigation involves briefly passing a current through a coil. The coil will become warm and remain that way for a few seconds after the current has passed. If the coil is left connected for more than a few seconds, it will become uncomfortably warm and will unnecessarily drain the batteries. Allow the current to pass through the coil for only a few seconds at a time.

Part A: The Magnetic Field Lines Around a Current-Carrying Coil

Procedure and Observations

step 1: Wrap 10 m of enamelled magnet wire around the cardboard cylinder to make a small coil. Leave about 10 cm of wire free at each end of the coil to act as contacts. Use adhesive tape to hold the contacts and coils in place. Use a small knife or sandpaper to carefully scrape the enamel coating from the last 5 cm of each contact, as shown in Figure C1.19.

Figure C1.19

step 2: Obtain the "Magnetic Field Surrounding a Small Coil" handout from the Science 30 Textbook CD. Without connecting the coil to the AA cells, arrange the equipment as shown in the handout. Adjust the position of the coil so its axis is aligned in the east-west direction.

step 3: Carefully connect one of the coil's contacts to the AA cells with a test lead. While watching the north end of the compass needle, make a brief connection between the coil's other contact and the AA cells. Break the connection as soon as you can tell which way the compass needle is pointing when the current is flowing. Record which way the north end of the compass needle pointed for the corresponding compass position on the handout.

step 4: Repeat step 3 with the compass in each of the other positions indicated on the handout. Record your observations on the handout.

Analysis

1. On the handout, connect the arrows you drew to show the compass needle's directions to create a magnetic field-line diagram. Identify another situation where you have seen a pattern of magnetic field lines like the one produced by the coil.

2. Compare your results to those of several other groups of students.

   a. Identify the common feature of the results from all groups.

   b. How do you account for the two possible different outcomes?

Part B: Observing the Deflection of an Electron Beam

Background Information

Conventional televisions and old computer monitors produce an image by shooting beams of electrons toward the screen from the back. The inside of the screen consists of thin stripes of three different phosphor compounds. One glows red when electrons strike it, the second glows green, and the third glows blue. Each thin phosphor stripe is targeted by one of the three electron beams.

If you look very closely at a TV screen, you should be able to see the light emitted by the tiny red, green, and blue bars. To ensure the TV picture has accurate colours, each electron beam is aimed to precisely hit the bar of the proper colour. In the next part of this investigation, you will carefully examine the effects of the magnetic field produced by your coil on the ability of the electrons to strike the correct phosphor stripe.

step 1: Turn on the TV and switch to a channel that has stationary (still) vertical lines dividing areas that have different colours. If you have cable television, the channel that displays the list of programs works well.

step 2: Without connecting the coil to the AA cells, arrange the equipment as shown in Figure C1.20.

step 3: Connect one end of the coil to the AA cells. Look across the top of the coil at the TV screen to find a tiny area of phosphor stripes on the boundary between the two regions of colour. While carefully observing the boundary between the phosphor stripes, make a very brief connection between the other contact and the AA cells. Observe which way the colours seemed to shift on the screen. Was it to the right or to the left? Make and break the connection several times until you can tell which way the colours seem to shift when the current flows in the coil. Record your results.

step 4: Reverse the connections of the coil to the AA cells and repeat step 3. Record your results.

Analysis

3. The tiny stripes of phosphor are unable to move because they are bonded to the inside of the TV screen. Using the information in the background information, how do you account for the observed shift in the colours in step 3?

4. Many speakers are built with powerful magnets. Based upon what you have observed in this investigation, suggest a reason why speakers that are built for use with televisions that utilize electron beams are magnetically shielded.

5. Conventional televisions are very heavy for several reasons, but one reason is that the glass used in their screens contains 2 kg to 4 kg of lead. Explain why it is important to send electronic components, like televisions and old computer monitors, to specialized electronics recycling centres instead of to landfills.

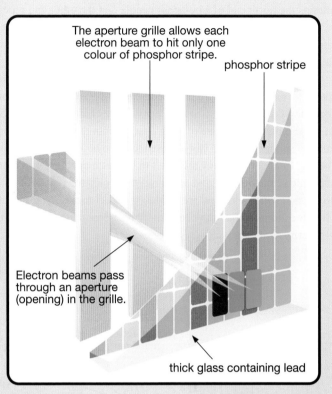

The aperture grille allows each electron beam to hit only one colour of phosphor stripe.

phosphor stripe

Electron beams pass through an aperture (opening) in the grille.

thick glass containing lead

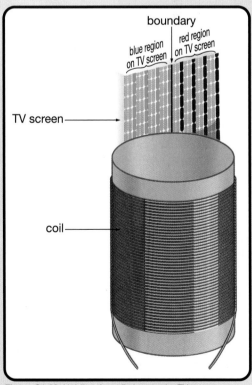

boundary

blue region on TV screen

red region on TV screen

TV screen

coil

Figure C1.20: Holding the coil close to the TV screen causes the colours in the picture to shift.

Moving Charges Generate All Magnetic Fields

As shown in Figure C1.21, an electric current passing through a coil of wire can generate a magnetic field with the same shape as the magnetic field around a bar magnet. Note that the symbol for a magnetic field is $\vec{B}$. Since the magnetic field at one end of the coil attracts the north end of a compass needle and the other end repels it, the ends of the coil can be labelled north and south. You might be surprised to know that this is not a coincidence because the magnetic field produced by a bar magnet is also due to electric currents.

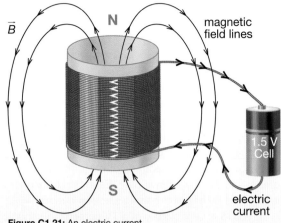

Figure C1.21: An electric current can generate a magnetic field.

Figure C1.22 shows that electrons within atoms are in constant motion—each electron orbits the nucleus of the atom and also spins like a top on its own axis. Since electrons are charged and since both of these motions involve a moving charge, both the orbital motion and the spinning motion can be considered to be an electric current flowing in a loop. So, why aren't all materials magnetic? In most substances, the orbiting and spinning of the electrons do not align, so the magnetic fields that are produced cancel themselves out. In substances like iron, cobalt, and nickel, it is possible to align the atoms so that the magnetic fields generated by the spinning and orbiting electrons reinforce one another. The result is a permanent magnet.

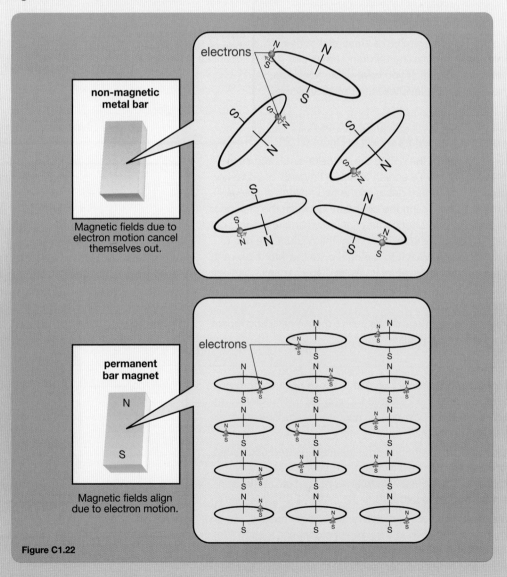

Figure C1.22

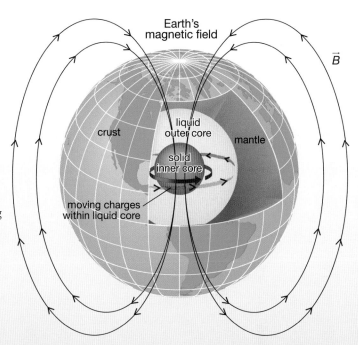

Earth's magnetic field

crust
liquid outer core
mantle
solid inner core

$\vec{B}$

moving charges within liquid core

Even Earth's magnetic field is a result of moving charges. You will recall from previous courses that deep within the planet is a core of molten material. Although it is not completely understood, many geologists suspect that within the liquid outer portion of Earth's core, matter becomes charged and separated into layers. Since this material is spinning along with everything else comprising the planet, the moving charges form an electric current that generates Earth's magnetic field.

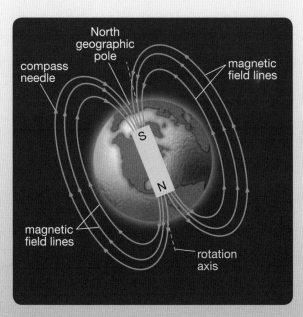

North geographic pole

compass needle

magnetic field lines

S

N

magnetic field lines

rotation axis

Note that since the north end of a compass needle always points toward the south pole of a magnet, the magnetic south pole of Earth is actually in the northern hemisphere. When people talk about going to the North Pole, they are referring to the geographic North Pole of Earth.

Practice

18. Explain the following statement:

    All magnetic fields are generated by moving charges.

19. Obtain the handout "Labelling the Magnetic Field Around a Current-Carrying Coil" from the Science 30 Textbook CD. Follow the instructions on this handout and supply the missing labels.

Moving Charges Experience Forces in Magnetic Fields

In the "Using a Coil to Deflect an Electron Beam" investigation, you observed the deflection of an electron beam by the magnetic field of a small coil carrying an electric current. This idea is the basis for the design NASA has proposed to protect the moon base from the bombardment of negative particles.

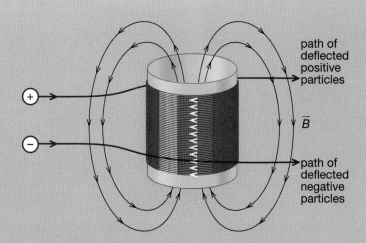

path of deflected positive particles

$\vec{B}$

path of deflected negative particles

By wrapping the large positive spheres with current-carrying wire, each sphere becomes a large coil. Although the electrons are attracted to the sphere due to the presence of the positive charge, the magnetic field that is generated by the coils is able to deflect the small but fast-moving electrons away from the base.

The positive particles bombarding the Moon's surface would also experience a deflecting force due to the magnetic field. However, because these ions are many thousands of times more massive than electrons, it is more difficult to change the direction of these positive particles using the magnetic field alone—hence the need for the positive charge on the spheres.

NASA's proposal is not without criticism. It has been pointed out that this scheme would be very energy-intensive because the electric current in the coils would have to be very large, and the voltage between the spheres and the lunar surface would likely have to be over 50 000 000 V. If this shielding method is found to be impractical, some other method will have to be used because the hazards associated with prolonged exposure to ionizing radiation are very real.

Just like the Moon, Earth is a massive body travelling through space, and it is exposed to the same sources of radiation: cosmic rays and the solar wind. What protects Earth's inhabitants from these fast-moving particles? You'll be glad to know there are two shields protecting you!

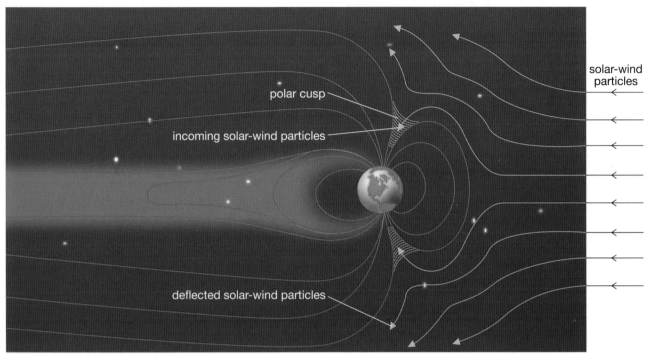

Figure C1.23: Solar-wind particles are deflected around Earth's magnetic field.

The first shield is Earth's magnetic field. It is an effective barrier against about one-third of the cosmic radiation and very nearly all of the solar wind. Note how the solar wind distorts the shape of Earth's magnetic field. As shown in Figure C1.23, most of the solar-wind particles are deflected around Earth's magnetic field. However, there are funnel-like openings called polar cusps that allow some of the solar-wind particles to pass through the magnetic field to the upper atmosphere.

The atmosphere is Earth's second shield. Figure C1.24 shows one of the results of solar-wind particles colliding with the atmosphere—the northern lights. If the collisions involve high-energy electrons with molecular nitrogen, purple light is emitted. Red and green light is emitted from collisions with atomic oxygen. When the solar wind is unusually strong, the charged particles can create giant electric currents in the upper atmosphere. These huge currents create their own magnetic fields. This has powerful effects that can be felt down on Earth—compass needles show incorrect directions and power surges can occur in electrical transmission lines, causing blackouts.

The atmosphere is able to absorb the energy from much of the radiation from cosmic rays. A fraction of the cosmic-ray particles are able to penetrate to the planet's surface. There are likely cosmic-ray particles

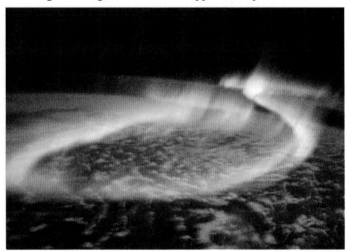

Figure C1.24: The northern lights are the result of solar-wind particles that enter the atmosphere.

passing through your body as you read this page! These particles are not a cause for alarm, as they form part of the natural background radiation. People who spend a lot of time at very high altitudes, such as the flight crew on a jet airliner, will receive a slightly higher dose of cosmic radiation in their lifetimes than other people because they spend their working days above part of the atmospheric shield. At this time, the health risks associated with this extra exposure to cosmic rays are thought to be minimal.

The magnetic field is represented by the symbol $\vec{B}$. No equation for magnetic field is used in Science 30. Unlike gravitational and electric field lines, magnetic field lines form closed loops. In all cases, these looping magnetic fields are established by electric currents. The easiest example of this is a simple coil of current-carrying wire, which surrounds itself with magnetic field lines—setting up one end of the coil as the north pole and one end as the south pole. Electric currents deep within Earth's core are thought to be the source of Earth's magnetic field, which works with the atmosphere to shield the planet from the solar wind and cosmic rays.

Practice

20. In this lesson you were introduced to NASA's plans for shielding a moon base with charged spheres wrapped in current-carrying wire. Identify the major challenge engineers will face in making this plan a reality.

21. Identify the two shields that protect Earth's inhabitants from the charged particles of the solar wind and cosmic radiation.

1.2 Summary

The strength of the gravitational field at the surface of Earth, the Moon, or any other object can be calculated using the equation $g = \frac{Gm}{r^2}$, where m is the mass of the source and r is the distance from the centre of the source. The unit for gravitational field strength is newtons per kilogram (N/kg). This serves as a reminder that gravitational field is not the same as gravitational force, which is measured in newtons (N). The equation for gravitational field strength can be combined with the fact that gravitational field lines always point toward the source mass to solve problems where a vector approach is required.

Electric fields are slightly more complicated because the direction of the field lines is determined by the direction of the force on a positive test body. Electric field lines are directed toward negative sources and away from positive sources. Nevertheless, electric field strength can be calculated using the equation $\left|\vec{E}\right| = \frac{kq}{r^2}$, where q is the charge on the source and r is the distance from the centre of the source. Once again, units are a very helpful guide to prevent mix-ups between electric field strength, which is measured in newtons per coulomb (N/C), and electric force, which is measured in newtons (N).

1.2 Questions

Knowledge

1. a. Calculate the gravitational field strength on the surface of each of the following objects:

      - Mars has a mass of 6.42×10^{23} kg and an average radius of 3.40×10^3 km.
      - Io, one of Jupiter's moons, has a mass of 8.94×10^{22} kg and an average radius of 1.82×10^3 km.

    b. Sketch diagrams of the gravitational field lines surrounding Mars and Io.

    c. Determine the force of gravity of an astronaut on the surfaces of Mars and Io if the mass of the astronaut is 100 kg.

    d. Identify the key features of each object that account for the differences in your previous answers.

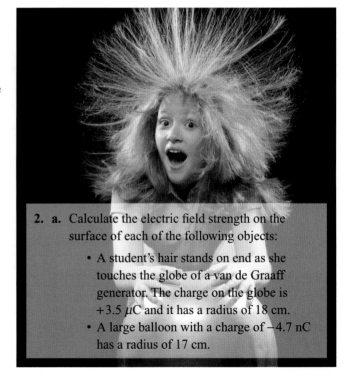

2. a. Calculate the electric field strength on the surface of each of the following objects:

      - A student's hair stands on end as she touches the globe of a van de Graaff generator. The charge on the globe is $+3.5\ \mu C$ and it has a radius of 18 cm.
      - A large balloon with a charge of -4.7 nC has a radius of 17 cm.

b. Sketch a diagram of the electric field lines around each of the objects.

c. A small speck of dust with a charge of -3.5×10^{-12} C comes into contact with the surface of each object. Determine the magnitude and the direction of the electric force on the dust speck in each case.

3. All magnetic fields have a similar shape. Draw a simple diagram to illustrate how this statement applies to each of the following sources of magnetic fields.

    a. a current-carrying coil

    b. a permanent magnet

    c. Earth

Applying Concepts

Use the following information to answer questions 4, 5, and 6.

On August 25, 1997, the *Advanced Composition Explorer* (*ACE*) satellite was launched. *ACE* was designed to monitor the stream of particles from the solar wind and cosmic rays that constantly bombard Earth. From its vantage point at about 1% of the distance between Earth and the Sun, the sensors onboard can provide advanced warning of sudden changes in the flow of charged particles toward Earth. The instant the sensors detect an increase in solar-wind activity, a signal is sent to the United States government's National Oceanic and Atmosphere Administration (NOAA). This organization tracks hurricanes and other large-scale

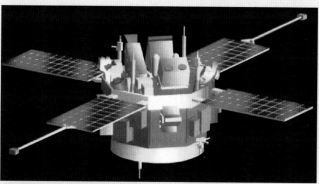

Figure C1.25: NASA's *ACE* satellite

weather events. Some refer to the data from *ACE* as monitoring "space weather." From the moment a warning from *ACE* arrives, the ground teams have about 50 minutes to warn the operators of satellites and electrical power grids.

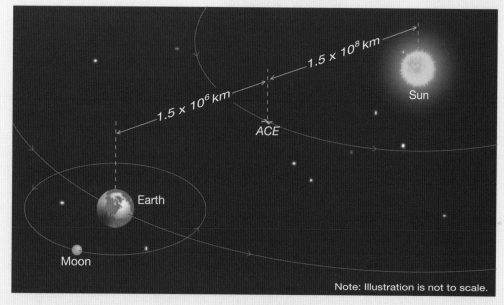

    NOAA has given public access to the data from *ACE*. If you enter *ACE Real-Time Solar Wind + NOAA* into a search engine, you can find the NOAA website that displays the current state of the solar wind. If you explore the other links on this site, you can find out more about *ACE* and current research into the solar wind.

4. The location of *ACE* between Earth and the Sun has been precisely chosen so *ACE* will take exactly the same length of time to orbit the Sun as Earth does. This ensures that *ACE* will always be between Earth and the Sun to monitor the solar wind. Normally, objects that are closer to the Sun move faster and complete their orbit around the Sun in less time. The unique location of *ACE* means that the gravitational field of Earth (outward) can act to reduce the gravitational force exerted by the Sun (inward), so the satellite stays aligned with Earth.

   a. Describe the direction of the gravitational field of the Sun at the location of *ACE*.

   b. Describe the direction of the gravitational field of Earth at the location of *ACE*.

   c. Combine your answers to questions 4.a. and 4.b. to explain how the gravitational field of Earth acts to reduce the effects of the gravitational field of the Sun.

5. If *ACE*'s instruments determine that an increase in solar activity is occurring, operators of other commercial satellites will immediately be notified so that they can temporarily "power down" the many electrical devices on the satellites to make them less susceptible to damage.

   Figure C1.26 shows a component on a communications satellite that has been charged by high-energy solar-wind particles.

   a. Describe the direction of the electric field lines around this component.

   b. If the electric field becomes strong enough, electrons on nearby components could suddenly move in response, creating a damaging electric current. Determine the direction in which the electrons would flow.

   c. Compare the directions in questions 5.a. and 5.b. Do these answers contradict one another?

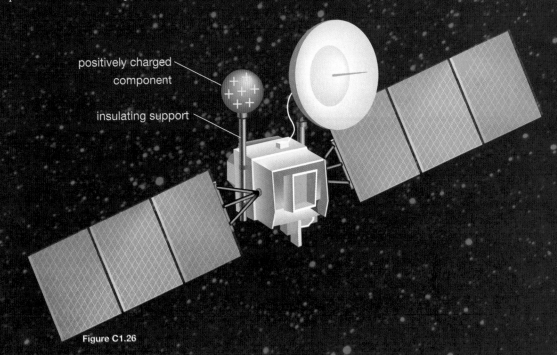

positively charged component

insulating support

Figure C1.26

6. In places like Fort McMurray, in northern Alberta, several tour companies take people out in the wilderness to view the northern lights. Explain how the information from the *ACE* website could be useful to these groups.

When your friends aren't nearby, what's the best way to communicate with them? You could give them a phone call; send them a text message with your cellphone; or, if you were close to a computer, you could use the latest instant-messaging software. Many communication technologies require the use of an integrated headset that combines a microphone with headphones.

Multiplayer computer games also use headphone and microphone technology. Websites that provide technical support to gamers include recommendations for accessories as well as suggestions for getting started if it's your first time using voice communication while gaming. One such website suggests that if you don't have a microphone for your computer, you can plug a set of headphones into the computer's microphone input and then speak into the headphones as if they were a microphone. The website goes on to explain that although headphones may be a little inconvenient to use and the sound quality may not be as good as a microphone, they can provide acceptable results until you get a proper microphone.

Figure C1.27: Many multiplayer computer games allow participants to communicate with each other using headphones and a microphone.

Figure C1.28: Headphones can be used as a microphone.

What processes enable a set of headphones to be used as a microphone? Does this work equally well with all headphones, or are some better suited to this conversion than others? In this lesson you will have an opportunity to complete investigations that will enable you to answer these questions. The essential components involve magnets and coils of wire carrying electric currents—things you investigated in the previous lesson. However, now you must also consider the conversions that occur between **electrical energy** and **mechanical energy**.

Recall from previous science courses that mechanical energy is a quantity used to describe objects, like tennis balls, that can be directly observed. A tennis ball that is hit high into the air has both kinetic energy, because it is moving, and gravitational potential energy, due to its height.

> **electrical energy:** the energy made available by the movement of charge

> **mechanical energy:** the energy possessed by an observable object due to motion or its position; the sum of the kinetic energy and potential energy of an object

Electrical energy is more challenging to study because it is due to the movement of charges in fields. Since neither charges nor fields are directly observable, electrical energy is easiest to investigate indirectly through its conversion to other forms of energy, such as sound, light, thermal energy, or mechanical energy. The electric motor is a great place to begin looking at this energy conversion because the mechanical energy can be measured and because there are so many interesting applications.

Practice

22. Sound is considered a mechanical wave because matter is given both kinetic and potential energy as the sound wave passes through. Often these vibrations occur too rapidly to see, but you can detect the vibrations with your sense of touch. Provide an example of a sound vibration in which you may be unable to see the matter vibrating but you can feel the vibrations with your fingertips.

23. Headphones and microphones both involve conversions between electrical energy and mechanical energy. A key difference between the two devices is the order of the energy conversion.

    a. Describe the order of the energy conversion for a microphone and for a headphone.

    b. Your sense of hearing involves an energy conversion as the vibrations of matter are converted into a signal that is sent to your brain. Describe the order of the energy conversion in your sense of hearing.

Electric Motors

Think of all the tasks you have to do in a typical day. How many of them involve electric motors? Preparing food, doing laundry, using tools, and even drying your hair can all be done using the spinning motion of a motor. If you have a chance to look inside some of these devices, you will see the same basic parts arranged in slightly different ways, depending upon the task.

The student-built motor in Figure C1.29 includes all the key components. The part of the motor that spins is called the **armature**. Electric current flows into the armature through the **commutator** to the turns of wire that form the coil. When the coil rotates, the **shaft** also rotates since these parts are connected. As the shaft rotates, it does the useful work the motor was designed to accomplish. In a hair dryer, the rotating shaft turns the blades of a fan to generate a stream of fast-moving air.

The lower section of Figure C1.29 includes all parts of the motor that do not move. The voltage source provides electrical energy to charges so that an electric current can be formed. The electric current enters the armature through each **brush** that gently makes contact with the commutator. Before the moving charges pass back through the commutator and return to the voltage source, they must circulate through the loops of wire in the coils of the armature. But how exactly is electrical energy converted into mechanical energy in this design? You will have an opportunity to answer this question in the next investigation.

armature: the section of a motor or generator that rotates, consisting of a coil of wire, a rotating shaft, and a commutator

commutator: a part of a motor or generator found on the armature that provides electrical contact, allowing current to flow to the rotating coil

shaft: a part of a motor or generator that supports the coil of the armature, providing an axis for the rotation of the armature

brush: a stationary part of a motor or generator that makes electrical contact with the rotating commutator

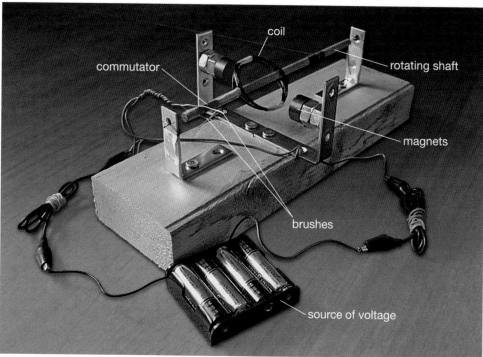

Figure C1.29: A student-built motor

Building an Electric Motor

Purpose

You will build a working electric motor and test its ability to function as a spooling machine or as a miniature crane.

Materials

- 4 AA cells in a plastic battery pack with leads
- 3, 5.0-cm bolts
- 2 test leads
- 2, 0.50-m pieces of solid, insulated 20-gauge connecting wire
- block of wood (3.5 cm by 9 cm by 30 cm)
- 2 metal angle brackets with predrilled holes (each side about 5.0 cm long)
- 2 metal angle brackets with predrilled holes (each side about 6.3 cm long)
- 4 wood screws (about 5.0 cm long)
- 4 hex nuts ($\frac{7}{16}$-inch thread size)
- 6 ceramic disc magnets (about 1.8 cm in diameter and 1 cm thick)
- piece of wood dowelling (about 6 mm in diameter and exactly 20.0 cm long)
- 5 m of 26-gauge enamelled magnet wire
- cylindrical glassware with a diameter of 3–4 cm
- scissors
- "Building the Armature" handout

Science Skills

✓ Performing and Recording
✓ Analyzing and Interpreting
✓ Communication and Teamwork

- 2 straight pins (2.5 cm long)
- 4 m of black thread
- 10 small paper clips
- ring stand
- large "bulldog" paper clamp
- transparent adhesive tape
- sharp knife
- wire cutters
- wire strippers
- pliers
- screwdriver
- digital multimeter or a voltmeter
- fine sandpaper
- "Building the Stationary Parts" handout

CAUTION!

Be sure to disconnect the cells from the motor when it is not running. This prevents the cells from draining unnecessarily. Also, the small coil of wire can become warm to the touch if an electric current runs through it when the armature is not turning.

Part A: Building the Armature

Obtain the handout "Building the Armature" from the Science 30 Textbook CD. Follow the steps outlined on this handout to assemble the armature of the motor.

Part B: Building the Stationary Parts

Obtain the handout "Building the Stationary Parts" from the Science 30 Textbook CD. Follow the steps outlined on this handout to assemble the stationary parts of the motor.

Part C: Getting the Motor to Run

step 1: Use the digital multimeter to ensure your battery of AA cells is producing 6.0 V of voltage.

step 2: Turn the armature so that the coil is vertical and the brushes do not make contact with the commutator. Use the test leads to connect the voltage source to the end leads of the connecting wire. Gently move the armature with your finger until contact is made between the brushes and the coil. Your motor should start to spin.

If it does not spin, disconnect the voltage source and begin to troubleshoot.

- A poor connection between the brushes and the commutator is the most common problem. When the coil is in a horizontal position, the exposed copper wires of the commutator should be contacting the brushes.
- If there is too much pressure between the wires that form the brushes, the armature will not spin well. If there is too little pressure, there will be poor contact and current will not flow through the coil.

step 3: Adjust the components of the motor so that the armature turns as rapidly and as smoothly as possible.

Reminder: While troubleshooting, only connect the motor to the voltage source for a few seconds at a time. If an electric current flows through the coil for a long time, the coil will get warm to the touch and the cells will become drained.

step 4: Attach the black thread to the end of the shaft on the end opposite from the coil. A ring stand set up beside the motor can be used to create a "looping path" for the thread that goes from the floor, up to a bulldog clamp on the ring stand, and then down to the shaft of the motor. Ensure that the thread can be easily pulled along this path with very little resistance.

step 5: Use your motor to spool the thread onto the rotating shaft of the armature. Once the end of the thread has been reached, disconnect the voltage source and gently pull the thread back through its path until some of the thread lies loose on the floor again.

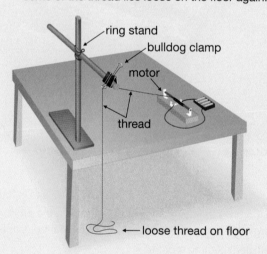

ring stand
bulldog clamp
motor
thread
loose thread on floor

step 6: Note that the motor will naturally tend to wrap the thread in a particular direction as it spins. Did you know that you can reverse the direction of the armature's rotation if you wish to wrap the thread in the opposite direction?

Devise two different adjustments you can make to the components of the motor that will cause the thread to reverse the armature's direction of rotation. Test each of these adjustments by seeing which way the thread spools each time.

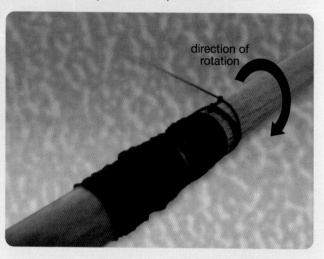

direction of rotation

Analysis

1. Describe the adjustments you made to the components of the motor to cause the thread to spool in a different direction.

2. Produce a number of labelled diagrams to explain why each of the adjustments you described in question 1 was able to cause the motor to reverse its direction of rotation.

Part D: Improving Energy Efficiency

Background Information

What do ribbon, movie film, and industrial wire all have in common? Each of these products is put on spools by a motor. In each case, it makes good business sense to operate the spooling motor using as little electrical energy as possible. In this part of the investigation you will try to minimize the voltage required by the motor to spool the thread.

The battery of four AA cells can be adapted so it can run on fewer cells. Every time you replace a cell with a 5.0-cm screw, you decrease the voltage output by 1.5 V. In this part of the investigation you will spool the thread with your motor using as little electrical energy as possible.

step 1: Replace one of the AA cells in the battery pack with a screw, as shown in Figure C1.30. Use the digital multimeter to confirm that the voltage is now 1.5 V less than it was before.

step 2: Gently pull the thread back through its path until there is again some loose thread on the floor.

step 3: Using the proper procedure, set up your motor and run it. Is the motor still able to spool the thread? Make any necessary adjustments so that the motor is able to spool the thread with the reduced voltage.

step 4: If the motor was able to spool the thread in step 3, continue testing to see whether a further reduction in voltage is possible. Repeat steps 1 through 3.

step 5: Repeat step 4.

Figure C1.30: A screw replaces one of the AA cells in the battery pack.

Analysis

3. Describe the adjustments you made to the motor so it could perform the task of spooling the thread with less voltage.

4. Each of the adjustments you described in question 3 helped your motor to run more efficiently by reducing the production of unwanted forms of energy. Identify the type(s) of unwanted energy that were reduced due to each of your adjustments.

5. List the benefits a business might experience by running more-efficient electric motors.

Part E: Improving the Motor's Ability to Do Work

Dockside cranes lift heavy cargo to and from ships. As the massive load is raised in the air, work is done and the cargo gains gravitational potential energy. If this is the output energy for the crane, what is the input energy? Usually, cranes such as these use electrical energy to drive their powerful motors.

In this part of the investigation you will make more adjustments to your motor so that it will be able to lift a load of paper clips while it is reeling in the thread.

Procedure

step 1: Use the digital multimeter to test that your battery of four AA cells is producing 6.0 V.

step 2: Gently pull the thread back through its path until there is some loose thread on the floor again. Make a small loop in the end of the thread and attach one paper clip.

step 3: Using the proper procedure, set up your motor and run it. Is the motor still able to spool the thread and lift the paper clip from the floor to the top of the ring stand? Make any necessary adjustments so that the motor is able to act as a crane and lift the paper clip. As soon as the paper clip reaches the top of the ring stand, disconnect the battery pack.

> **Remember:** You can replace the hex nuts acting as spacers with additional magnets. Just remember to ensure that the magnets on opposite sides are oriented so that they will attract one another.

step 4: Repeat steps 2 and 3 by adding additional paper clips until the motor is no longer able to successfully lift the paper clips from the floor to the top of the ring stand. Record the maximum number of paper clips your motor was able to lift.

step 5: Once you have determined the maximum number of paper clips your motor is able to lift, observe what happens if you disconnect the battery pack when the load of paper clips is at the top of its path. If you have been successful at reducing the frictional losses within your motor, the paper clips should be able to unwind the thread and turn the armature as they fall to the floor. If your motor is unable to do this, add a few more paper clips to the end of a raised load so that the dropping load is able to unwind the thread and turn the armature.

Analysis

6. Describe the adjustments you made so the motor could lift the maximum number of paper clips.

7. Using the same basic design, think of ways in which the motor could be modified to be more powerful. Describe some of the possible modifications that would likely enable the motor to lift even more paper clips.

8. Describe the energy conversion that occurs when the load of paper clips drops to the floor.

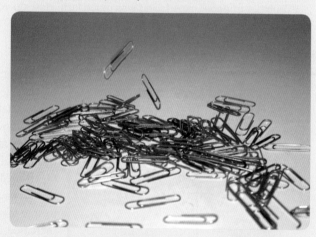

Part F: Converting the Motor into a Generator

Background Information

In the introduction to this investigation, it was explained that a motor is a device that converts electrical energy into mechanical energy. Do you think it is possible to reverse this process and convert mechanical energy into electrical energy?

In Part E of this investigation, you were able to get the falling paper clips to unwind the thread and turn the armature. In this part of the investigation you will look for evidence that electrical energy is produced as the coil is forced to turn through the field of the permanent magnets.

Procedure

step 1: Using the proper procedure, use your motor to lift the maximum number of paper clips to the top of the ring stand.

step 2: Once the load has reached the top, disconnect the battery pack at the same instant that a partner holds the paper clips so they do not fall.

step 3: Replace the battery pack with a digital multimeter set up as a voltmeter, as shown in Figure C1.31.

step 4: Set the meter to the most sensitive scale so that it is capable of reading a few millivolts.

step 5: While carefully observing the number of millivolts on the display, ask your partner to let the paper clips fall to the floor. Note the maximum number of millivolts displayed as the armature is forced to turn.

step 6: Determine the effect on the value for the maximum output voltage if you reduce the number of magnets.

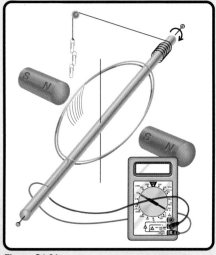

Figure C1.31

Analysis

9. Describe the energy conversions that occur in this part of the investigation.

10. The voltage required to raise the maximum number of paper clips was 6.0 V. The voltage generated by the same number of paper clips falling was much less. How do you account for the difference between these two values?

The Role of Electric Current

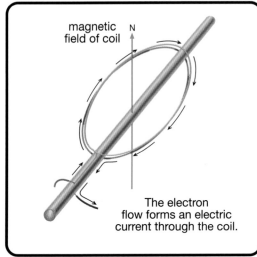

magnetic field of coil   N

The electron flow forms an electric current through the coil.

Figure C1.32

The motor you studied in the "Building an Electric Motor" investigation was able to operate because of the interactions between the armature and the stationary magnets. At the heart of this interaction is the electric current flowing through the coil. Figure C1.32 represents electric current with tiny arrows to show the direction in which electrons flow around the loop of the coil. You were able to vary the amount of electric current that flowed through the loop by changing the number of AA cells in the battery pack. As the number of cells increased, the armature was able to spin faster, suggesting that the electric current through the loop had increased. A better way to describe electric current is to use an equation.

$$\text{electric current (A)} \longrightarrow I = \frac{q}{t} \begin{array}{l} \longleftarrow \text{electric charge (C)} \\ \longleftarrow \text{time interval (s)} \end{array}$$

$$\text{Units: } 1 \text{ ampere} = \frac{1 \text{ coulomb}}{1 \text{ second}}$$

Electric current is measured in amperes, which is often shortened to "amps" in everyday speech. When one ampere of electric current is flowing, one coulomb of charge is passing a point in a wire every second. If more charges are able to pass a point in a wire in a given time interval, the value of the electric current is larger, as shown in the following diagrams and calculations.

4.0 C pass this point in 2.0 s.

$$I = \frac{q}{t}$$
$$= \frac{4.0 \text{ C}}{2.0 \text{ s}}$$
$$= 2.0 \text{ A}$$

8.0 C pass this point in 2.0 s.

$$I = \frac{q}{t}$$
$$= \frac{8.0 \text{ C}}{2.0 \text{ s}}$$
$$= 4.0 \text{ A}$$

Example Problem 1.8

A refrigerator is an appliance designed to transfer heat from the food inside the refrigerator to the environment outside the refrigerator. This movement of heat is accomplished with a fluid called a refrigerant. An electric motor is used to compress the refrigerant from a gaseous state to a liquid state as it moves through a set of heat-exchange pipes. The humming sound you hear when your refrigerator is running is the sound of this motor working to compress the refrigerant. The electric current required to run the refrigerator motor depends upon the size and efficiency of the refrigerator.

Refrigerators are needed because the activity of bacteria is slowed dramatically at lower temperatures. For example, the bacteria naturally present in milk will cause a glass of milk to spoil in three or four hours if the milk is left out on the kitchen table at room temperature. This same milk can be stored for over a week in the low temperatures of a refrigerator.

a. One model of refrigerator requires about 3.8×10^3 C of moving charge to flow through the coils of the compressor motor over a time interval of 15 min. Calculate the electric current required by this motor.

b. Sometimes a food item is placed in a refrigerator in a way that prevents the door from closing properly. Explain how people who eat the food from this refrigerator could develop food poisoning if this situation were to go unnoticed for several days.

Solution

a. $q = 3.8 \times 10^3$ C

$t = 15 \, \cancel{\text{min}} \times \dfrac{60 \text{ s}}{1 \, \cancel{\text{min}}}$

$= 9.0 \times 10^2$ s

$I = ?$

$I = \dfrac{q}{t}$

$= \dfrac{3.8 \times 10^3 \text{ C}}{9.0 \times 10^2 \text{ s}}$

$= 4.2$ C/s

$= 4.2$ A

The electric current required by this motor is 4.2 A.

b. If the refrigerator door does not close properly, the space inside the fridge becomes warmer as cool air from inside is exchanged with warm air from the room. As the temperature increases, the number of bacterial cells present on the food increases. When this food is eaten, the number of bacteria that enter the body is much larger than usual. This overwhelms the body's ability to kill the bacteria, causing food poisoning.

Practice

24. The compressor motor of a large refrigerator requires about 1.12×10^4 C of charge to pass through a segment of wire on one of its coils while it runs for 30 min. Determine the electric current that passes through the wire segment as the motor is running.

25. Countries in warm climates often struggle with issues of food storage. Developing countries lack the infrastructure to provide adequate food-storage facilities. Explain how an adequate supply of electrical energy would be advantageous to centralized food-storage facilities in a developing country, especially in a warm climate.

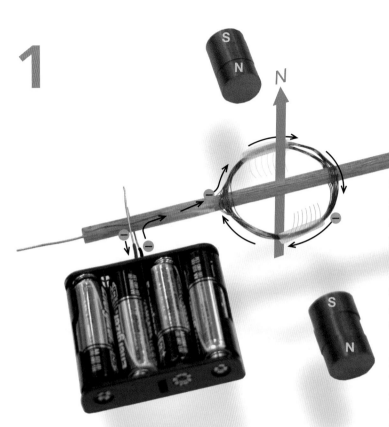

Understanding How Motors Work

In this position, the electron flow from the battery is able to pass from the brush to the commutator and momentarily pass through the coil of wire on the armature. Although this connection lasts only a tiny fraction of a second, a large current flows and a large magnetic field is generated around the coil. If the electrons flow in the direction indicated, the top of the coil becomes the north pole.

The north pole of the coil is repelled by the north pole of the bar magnet on the left and is attracted to the south pole of the bar magnet on the right. The result of this attraction is rotation. As the armature turns, the section of the coil that is highlighted in light blue is raised by the turning armature.

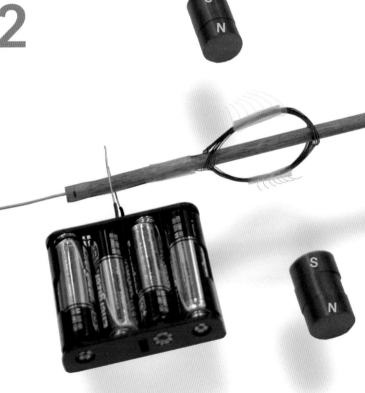

Even though there is no contact between the brush and the commutator, the force provided in the previous step causes the rotation to continue. This is a consequence of Newton's first law of motion, which states that in the absence of a net force, an object in motion will tend to remain in motion.

The forces opposing the rotation of the armature, mainly friction, have not been completely eliminated. Nevertheless, if the force provided in the previous step is great enough, and if the opposing forces are small enough, the rotation of the armature will be enough to rotate the highlighted section of the coil through a half-turn.

3

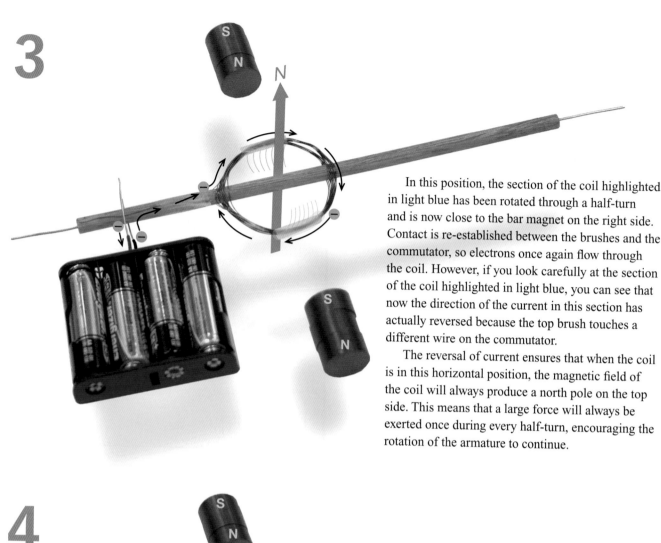

In this position, the section of the coil highlighted in light blue has been rotated through a half-turn and is now close to the bar magnet on the right side. Contact is re-established between the brushes and the commutator, so electrons once again flow through the coil. However, if you look carefully at the section of the coil highlighted in light blue, you can see that now the direction of the current in this section has actually reversed because the top brush touches a different wire on the commutator.

The reversal of current ensures that when the coil is in this horizontal position, the magnetic field of the coil will always produce a north pole on the top side. This means that a large force will always be exerted once during every half-turn, encouraging the rotation of the armature to continue.

4

The rotation of the armature continues as the section of the coil highlighted in light blue swings down to its lowest position. As was the case with step 2, even though no current is flowing in the coil and no forces are being exerted, the rotation continues. Eventually, the coil reaches the point where this whole process began and the cycle repeats.

Most commercially built motors increase the force on the coil by wrapping the coils around an iron core. You may have used this same idea in previous courses when you built an electromagnet by wrapping wire around an iron nail. The presence of an iron core concentrates the magnetic field lines within the coil, turning the coil into a stronger magnet.

26. Obtain the handout "Motor Analysis" from the Science 30 Textbook CD. Describe the direction of rotation for each motor on this handout.

Obtain the handout "Motor Dissection" from the Science 30 Textbook CD. Use the information on this handout to answer questions 27 to 30.

27. Describe the energy transformations that occur within this device.

28. In step 4, the inside of the casing and the inside surface of the magnets are shown. Describe the magnetic poles on the inside surface of each magnet.

29. In step 5, coils are shown mounted on an axle.
    a. Identify the name of this whole piece.
    b. Identify the name of the three separated contacts at one end of the axle.
    c. Suggest the function of the iron core for each coil.
    d. The student-built motor studied earlier had only one coil. Suggest the advantages of using three coils.

30. In step 6, a small plastic end cap supports thin metal contacts that connect the motor to the battery pack that runs the motor.
    a. Identify the proper name of these metal contacts.
    b. Suggest a reason why these contacts have been made from thin material that is light and spring-like.

From Motors to Generators

In the last part of the "Building an Electric Motor" investigation, the motor was converted into an electric generator. As the load of paper clips dropped, the unwinding thread caused the armature to rotate through the magnetic field of the permanent magnets.

The motor and generator both had the greatest forces exerted on the armature when the wires in the coil were moving at right angles to the magnetic field. Unfortunately, the loop is only in this optimum position for a very short time. The problem is compounded by the fact this is the only time when electric current is able to flow from the coil to the multimeter, due to the very brief connection between the brushes and the commutator. The graph in Figure C1.33 shows the output from this generator. Note the occasional spikes in voltage.

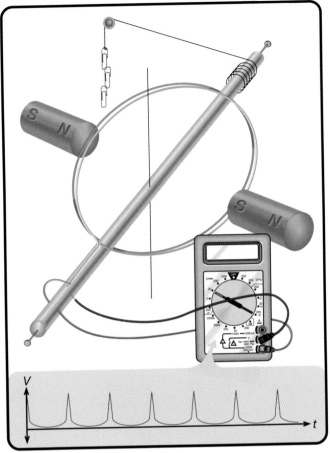

Figure C1.33

This graph explains why the value displayed on the multimeter was so low in the last part of the investigation. The meter displayed long intervals of zero output from the generator punctuated with momentary spikes every half-turn. Although this design was a convenient conversion from the motor, it is clearly not effective at producing useful electrical energy. How could the design be improved?

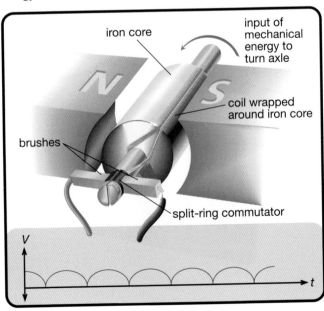

Figure C1.34

Wrapping the coils around an iron core helps to concentrate the effects of the magnetic field lines. Another useful improvement would be to change the commutators from small prongs of wire to a split-ring design that increases the contact time with the brushes. This change allows the electrical energy to be generated for a longer period of time. Note that this same thinking can be applied to the wrap-around shape of the magnets. This ensures that the armature coils are closer to the magnet, where the magnetic field is more intense. The output from this generator shows the effects of these improvements, as shown in Figure C1.34.

Further improvement is possible by positioning more coils at different orientations around the armature, with each one attached to its own commutator. This design means that during any part of a rotation, one of the coils is always in a position to deliver its maximum output. Although the voltage output of this generator design is not completely free of ripples, it is now a useful source of electrical energy. This kind of output from a generator is called **direct current**, or **DC** for short. The name reflects the fact that the value of the electric current generated is constant and that the current flows in only one direction. The ultimate in ripple-free DC sources is a fresh battery because there are no moving parts to create ripples.

> **direct current (DC):** a flow of charges that does not increase or decrease and flows in a single direction

> **alternating current (AC):** a flow of charges that reverses directions at regular intervals

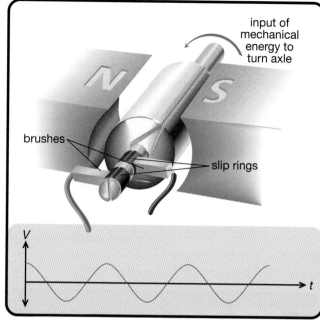

Figure C1.36

As you can appreciate from your work with building a motor, the speed of rotation of the armature can make it very challenging to learn more about a generator as it is operating. Computer animation is a great tool in these circumstances because you can adjust the rate of rotation and see the connections between the motion of the armature and the pattern of electric current produced.

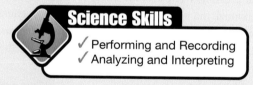

Utilizing Technology
DC and AC Generators

Science Skills
✓ Performing and Recording
✓ Analyzing and Interpreting

Purpose

You will use computer animations to compare and contrast the design and function of a DC generator with that of an AC generator.

Procedure

Obtain the handout "Properties of DC and AC Generators" from the Science 30 Textbook CD. Follow the instructions in the handout as you interact with the applet "The Simple Generator," which can also be found on the Science 30 Textbook CD.

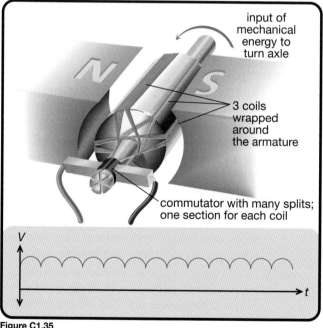

Figure C1.35

Despite the smooth output of well-designed DC generators, their use is not widespread. The most commonly used generators produce **alternating current**, or **AC**. Rather than try to remove any ripples from the output, an AC generator is designed to do exactly the opposite—to produce an electric current that makes one smooth sine wave, as shown in Figure C1.36.

The Importance of AC Generators

As you read this book right now, are you using daylight from a window or an electric light source? If you're using an electric lamp of some kind, it's easy to take for granted that somewhere far from where you are sitting, the energy for that lamp is in some other form—coal, natural gas, or perhaps moving air. In each case, a generator is used to help convert one form of energy into the electrical energy that powers your lamp. Generators are the essential first step in making all your electrically powered modern conveniences possible. Without generators there could be no late-night TV, no microwave popcorn, and no cold drinks in the refrigerator. Later in this chapter you'll learn why the whole system for the transmission of electrical energy depends upon AC generators, which is why any device you plug into a wall is designed to run on alternating current.

Your previous work with the motor revealed key factors that maximize the motor's energy output. Since a generator involves the same basic components, these same factors also make for an efficient generator design. To maximize the energy output of a generator, you need to

- increase the number of turns of wire on the armature
- ensure that the armature is spinning as quickly as possible
- use strong magnets outside the armature
- place an iron core within the coils on the armature

Manufacturers of commercial generators incorporate all these features into their designs.

Using Headphones as Microphones

This lesson began with the unusual suggestion that a pair of headphones could be used as a makeshift microphone. Now that you know the basics about the connections between motors and generators, you should be ready to unravel this mystery.

Investigation

Connections Between Headphones and Motors

Science Skills

✓ Performing and Recording
✓ Analyzing and Interpreting
✓ Communication and Teamwork

Purpose

You will determine whether an efficient set of headphones can be used as a microphone. You will explore the process that makes this possible by disassembling a pair of inexpensive headphones.

Materials

- set of headphones that are efficient (capable of reproducing loud sound at low volume)
- inexpensive set of headphones to be disassembled
- access to a computer with speakers and a microphone input
- 4 AA cells in a plastic battery pack
- 2 test leads
- digital multimeter
- small slot screwdriver
- probe from a dissection kit
- portable music system (CD player, MP3 player, radio)
- "Disassembling Inexpensive Headphones" handout

Part A: Using Efficient Headphones as a Microphone

Procedure

step 1: Turn on the computer and test to see that the speakers are working by playing something that has a soundtrack.

step 2: Test that the efficient headphones work by connecting the headphones to the computer. Note that on most computers, the speakers connect through an output jack on the back that is identified with a label or a green colour-code. When you are sure the headphones are working, reconnnect the speakers and test them again to ensure you have reconnected them properly.

step 3: Locate the input jack for the microphone. This input is usually identified with a label or is colour-coded pink or red. Plug the headphones into this input.

step 4: Locate the "Sound Hardware Test" menu for the computer. On many computers, the process for finding this menu goes like this:
Start → Control Panel → Sounds, Speech, and Audio Devices → Adjust the System Volume → Voice → Sound Hardware Test

---

step 5: Follow the instructions on this menu to see if headphones really can function as a microphone. Remember, the headphones were not really designed to work this way, so you may have to speak loudly for this to work.

Part B: Disassembling Inexpensive Headphones

CAUTION!

- Inexpensive headphones can be purchased for only a few dollars, whereas the efficient headphones used in Part A may be significantly more expensive. Make sure you have not mixed up the two pairs before you begin disassembling the inexpensive pair.

- The inexpensive headphones still have to function as headphones after you have removed the outer bits of plastic. Work carefully and gently so as not to damage key internal parts.

- After the investigation, reassemble the inexpensive headphones if possible. Otherwise, place the headphone parts in a container marked "For Recycling of Electronics."

Procedure

Obtain the handout "Disassembling Inexpensive Headphones" from the Science 30 Textbook CD. Follow the steps outlined on this handout to carefully disassemble an inexpensive set of headphones.

Analysis

1. Sketch the disassembled headphones and label the thin plastic diaphragm, the coil of fine wire, and the magnet assembly.

2. Determine whether headphones are designed to work more like a motor or more like a generator.

Part C: Testing the Disassembled Headphones

Procedure

step 1: Connect the headphones to a portable music system to ensure they still work.

step 2: Connect one end of the battery pack to the headphone plug with test leads, as shown in Figure C1.37.

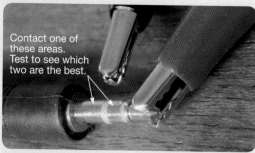

Contact one of these areas. Test to see which two are the best.

Figure C1.37

step 3: Make brief, intermittent contact with the other test lead connected to the battery pack. Observe the effect on the thin diaphragm.

step 4: Reverse the connections to the battery pack and repeat step 3.

Analysis

3. The diaphragm in each earpiece is supposed to vibrate back and forth. Sound waves are produced as these vibrations are transferred through the air. Combine this information with your previous observations to determine whether a pair of headphones is an AC or a DC device.

Part D: Using Disassembled Headphones as a Microphone

step 1: Set the digital multimeter to its most sensitive voltage setting so it is capable of measuring a few millivolts. Connect the disassembled headphones to the digital multimeter, as shown in Figure C1.38.

Contact one of these areas. Test to see which two are the best.

Figure C1.38

step 2: Very gently, using the tip of your finger, push the diaphragm up and down as you observe the output on the multimeter. Note your observations.

Analysis

4. As sound waves strike the thin diaphragm of a microphone, the diaphragm is forced to vibrate, moving the coil up and down relative to the magnet assembly. Combine this information with your previous observations to determine whether a microphone is designed to act more like a motor or more like a generator.

Motors and generators are devices that enable the conversion of mechanical energy into electrical energy. In the case of motors, the input is electrical energy and the output is mechanical energy. Generators reverse this process. In both cases, it is the motion of a conducting coil of wire through a magnetic field that makes this conversion possible. Most generators produce an alternating current (AC) instead of a direct current (DC). All of the electrical devices that plug into a wall outlet in your home are AC devices.

1.3 Questions

Knowledge

Use the following diagrams to answer questions 1 and 2.

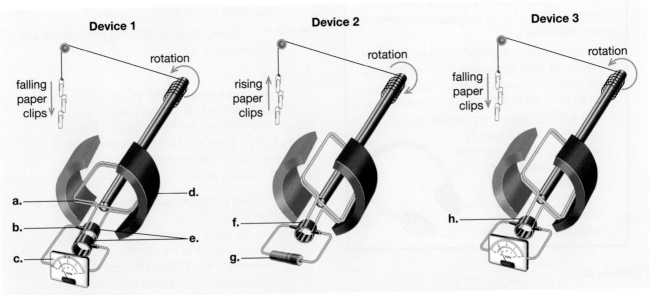

Device 1   Device 2   Device 3

1. Determine which of these three devices is best described as a DC motor, a DC generator, and an AC generator.

2. Note that the key parts of each device are labelled with letters. Choose from the following list to identify each part.

   - rotating coil
   - voltmeter
   - brush
   - voltage source
   - slip rings
   - permanent magnet
   - split-ring commutator

Applying Concepts

3. Copy the following diagram into your notes. Add the words *headphones* and *microphone* in the appropriate places.

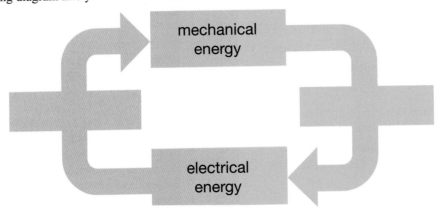

mechanical energy

electrical energy

Use the following diagram to answer questions 4 and 5.

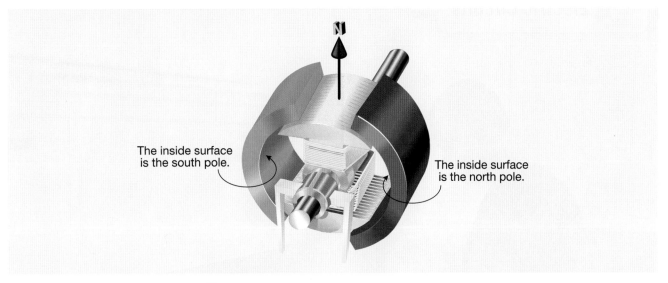

The inside surface is the south pole.

The inside surface is the north pole.

4. Determine which way this motor will turn.

5. Explain why this motor will continue to turn in the same direction.

Use the following diagram to answer question 6.

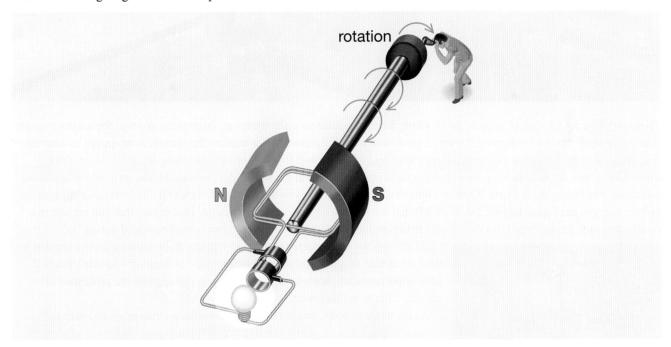

rotation

N

S

6. Sketch a graph of the voltage produced versus time for this device.

7. Show how the graph would change if the number of armature rotations per minute is increased.

Preparing food for a bunch of people can be a little frantic because so many things are happening at once: the toaster oven is heating up some snacks for dipping, the microwave oven is melting cheese over nachos, the blender is whipping up a frothy fruit drink, and the kettle has just been plugged in to boil water for tea. If you happen to be doing all of this in an older kitchen, you may not be able to operate so many different appliances at the same time. As soon as you turn on one appliance too many, everything shuts down. When this happens, a fuse blows or you hear the loud click of a circuit breaker tripping. In either case, you have gone beyond the limits of what the kitchen circuit can safely handle. This means that you are placing unsafe demands on the circuit. It's time to use fewer appliances at the same time or update the household wiring.

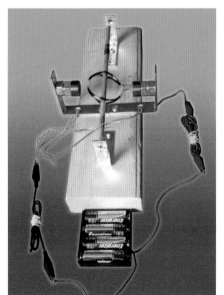

What happens within a circuit to cause the fuse to blow or the circuit breaker to trip? What role do fuses and circuit breakers play in keeping you safe? You will have opportunities to answer these questions as you explore the properties of electric circuits in this lesson.

As the name implies, an electric circuit involves a circle or closed loop for moving charges that form an electric current. What causes charges to move from one point in a circuit to another?

In your previous work with motors, a battery pack was the source of energy for the electric current that flowed through the rotating coil of the armature. The battery pack produced an electric field within and parallel to the wire that connected to it. The electric field exerted a force on free electrons within the wire, causing the electrons to move. As long as contact was made with the battery pack, the electric field was maintained within the wire and charges flowed, creating an electric current.

This lesson will take things a step further as the circuits will include other devices in addition to the wires and a source of voltage. In the next investigation you will use small light bulbs as you identify the characteristics of electric circuits.

Purpose
You will build simple circuits that will allow two small light bulbs to glow.

Science Skills

✓ Performing and Recording
✓ Analyzing and Interpreting

Materials
- 4 AA cells in a plastic battery pack
- 4 test leads
- 2 mini light bulbs with bases

Procedure
step 1: Use the materials to build a simple circuit that allows both bulbs to emit light energy. Sketch this circuit.

step 2: Without removing batteries from the battery pack, build a new circuit that causes the bulbs to emit a different amount of light than in step 1. Sketch this circuit.

Analysis
1. List the three essential parts that must be present in all electric circuits.
2. When things are arranged one after the other, it is often called a series. Identify which of your circuits used a series connection between the bulbs by adding the label "series connection" to that diagram.
3. Lines on loose-leaf paper are parallel to one another. Identify which of your circuits used a parallel connection between the bulbs by adding the label "parallel connection" to that diagram.
4. Suggest a reason why one circuit causes the bulbs to emit more light than the other.

Series and Parallel Connections

As demonstrated in the "Building Simple Circuits" activity, the best way to learn about electric circuits is to build and test them yourself. As you build circuits in this lesson, you will sometimes be asked to make a **series connection** or a **parallel connection**. Series connections involve the components being arranged one after the other so that the electric current has only one path to follow. Parallel connections provide multiple pathways so that the electric current has to divide and flow through each branch of the circuit.

The first place you will use the ideas of series and parallel connections is with the use of a digital multimeter to measure voltage and electric current in a circuit. Note that when a multimeter is set up to measure voltage, it can be called a **voltmeter** because it is measuring the number of volts. Similarly, when a multimeter is set up to measure electric current, it can be called an **ammeter** because it is measuring the number of amperes.

Series Connections

input · device 1 → device 2 → device 3 → device 4 · output

Parallel Connections

input · device 1 · device 2 · device 3 · device 4 · output

series connection: a single path available for electric current, where the charges flow through one device before passing through to the next

parallel connection: more than one path available for electric current, where the electric current divides, allowing each portion of the current to simultaneously pass through separate devices

voltmeter: an instrument that measures the voltage across two points in a circuit

ammeter: an instrument that measures the electric current flowing through a component in a circuit

Working with Electric Meters

Purpose

You will use computer software to review the use of a digital multimeter to measure electric current and voltage.

Procedure

step 1: Locate the applet "Working with Electric Meters" on the Science 30 Textbook CD.

step 2: Complete all parts of the applet by following the instructions and by answering the questions provided.

Analysis

1. Describe the proper way to connect a voltmeter to a device in a circuit.

2. Describe the proper way to connect an ammeter to a device in a circuit.

Science Skills

✓ Performing and Recording
✓ Analyzing and Interpreting

Measuring Voltage and Current

A digital multimeter is a useful tool because this one device can measure both voltage and current values in an electric circuit. The convenience of having one machine that can measure a number of different values does have its disadvantages, though. You have to be clear about which quantity you are measuring—current or voltage. Then you have to make sure that the following three things are properly adjusted:

- The dial on the meter is set to measure the desired quantity (current or voltage).
- The test leads of the meter are correctly positioned to measure the desired quantity.
- The circuit has the meter in series to measure current or in parallel to measure voltage.

If you forget one of these details, you may not be able to make accurate measurements and you could blow a fuse in the multimeter.

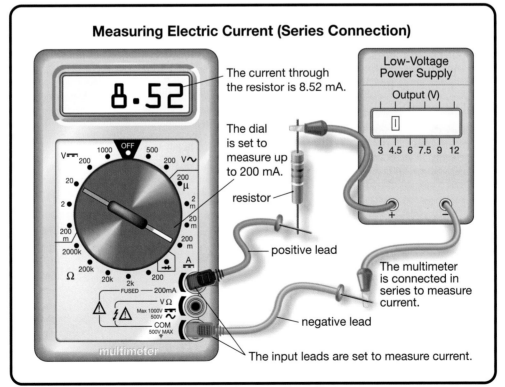

Figure C1.39: Use a series connection to measure electric current with a multimeter.

Measuring Voltage (Parallel Connection)

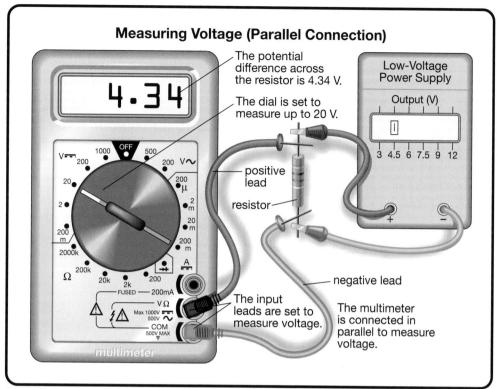

The potential difference across the resistor is 4.34 V.

The dial is set to measure up to 20 V.

positive lead

resistor

Low-Voltage Power Supply

Output (V)

3 4.5 6 7.5 9 12

negative lead

The input leads are set to measure voltage.

The multimeter is connected in parallel to measure voltage.

multimeter

Figure C1.40: Use a parallel connection to measure voltage with a multimeter.

Practice

31. Obtain the handout "Multimeter Troubleshooting" from the Science 30 Textbook CD. For each of the set-ups shown on the handout, describe the changes that must be made to correctly make the desired measurement.

Resistance

In modern electronic devices, you will likely find a number of tiny striped cylinders like those shown in Figure C1.41. These devices can serve a number of purposes, but they are usually used to reduce the current that is sent to some other part of a circuit. Since these devices resist the flow of electric current, each one is called a **resistor**. In some circumstances, the resistor is used to ensure that the current sent to some other device is within safe limits. In the case of motors, resistors connected in series with the motor can be used to regulate the speed of the motor.

Resistors are rated in terms of the voltage it takes to cause a quantity of current to flow. The ratio of the voltage applied across the ends of a device to the current that flows through the device is called **resistance**. This is one quantity where the name nicely describes what is going on—if it takes a larger voltage to cause a certain amount of current to flow, then there must be a greater resistance to the flow of charges. The equation for resistance makes this even clearer.

> **resistor:** an electronic component that resists the flow of electric current in a circuit

> **resistance:** the ratio of the voltage across a device to the current flowing through it

resistance of a device (Ω) → voltage across the device (V)

$$R = \frac{V}{I}$$

← electric current flowing through the device (A)

Units: $1 \text{ ohm} = \dfrac{1 \text{ volt}}{1 \text{ ampere}}$

Note: The symbol for the ohm is the Greek letter *omega*, Ω.

Figure C1.41: Resistors

The unit for resistance is named after George Ohm, a German scientist who did much of the early research into the ability of different types of wire to carry electric current. Ohm discovered that some materials maintain a constant ratio of voltage to current over a considerable range of values. If this is the case, then the equation for resistance becomes a useful tool for predicting the behaviour of the material. In these cases, the resistance equation is usually rearranged and called Ohm's law.

Ohm's Law
$$V = IR$$

Example Problem 1.9

A headlight in an automobile draws a current of 5.0 A from the car's 12.0-V battery.

a. Is the current passing through the headlight AC or DC?

b. Determine the resistance of the headlight while it is operating.

Solution

a. Since the source of the electric current is the car's battery, this is an example of direct current, or DC.

b. $I = 5.0$ A
   $V = 12.0$ V
   $R = ?$

   $V = IR$
   $R = \dfrac{V}{I}$
   $= \dfrac{12.0 \text{ V}}{5.0 \text{ A}}$
   $= 2.4$ V/A
   $= 2.4\ \Omega$

The resistance of the headlight while it is operating is 2.4 Ω.

Materials will offer resistance to the flow of charges whether they travel in one direction, the opposite direction, or back and forth through the material. That's why resistance can be calculated for both components in direct current (DC) and alternating current (AC) circuits.

Example Problem 1.10

A light bulb in a typical lamp is connected to the 120-V wall outlet. When the bulb is operating, it has a resistance of 240 Ω.

a. Is the current passing through the bulb AC or DC?

b. Determine the value of the electric current that is passing through the bulb.

Solution

a. All household circuitry is designed around alternating current. Therefore, the current through the bulb is AC.

b. $V = 120$ V
   $R = 240\ \Omega$
   $\quad = 240$ V/A
   $I = ?$

   $V = IR$
   $I = \dfrac{V}{R}$
   $\quad = \dfrac{120 \text{ V}}{240 \text{ V/A}}$
   $\quad = 0.500$ A

The current passing through the bulb is 0.500 A.

Practice

32. A low-intensity light bulb illuminates the numbers on the outside of a house. The bulb is operated by one of the 120-V household circuits and draws 0.25 A.

    a. Is the current passing through the bulb AC or DC?

    b. Determine the resistance of the bulb while it is operating.

33. The four cells in a flashlight form a battery with a total voltage of 6.0 V. When the flashlight is switched on, the resistance of the bulb is 8.0 Ω.

    a. Is the current passing through the bulb AC or DC?

    b. Determine the value of the current passing through the bulb.

Why are wet locations, like hot tubs, bathrooms, laundry rooms, and kitchen sinks, the typical places for people to get accidental electric shocks?

The dangerous effects of an electrical shock are the result of a current passing through your body. The magnitude of the current depends on the voltage applied by the energy source and the resistance of your body. If you momentarily contact a 120-V source with dry hands, the resistance of your skin is about 100 000 Ω, so the current passing through you is enough to cause a tingling sensation. However, if your hands and feet are wet, then the resistance of your body drops dramatically. As a result of the presence of salts in sweat, the resistance of your body could be as low as 100 Ω. In this case, the electric current would be painful, possibly producing muscular effects that prevent you from letting go of the wire. If these muscular effects extend to the heart, the heart muscle may remain locked in one massive contraction with fatal consequences.

Measuring Resistance

The easiest way to measure resistance is to use a multimeter. Since the dial on the meter will be set for measuring ohms, the meter can be called an **ohmmeter**. As is the case with taking any measurement with an instrument, you have to follow the proper procedure when using the multimeter as an ohmmeter:

- The dial on the meter must be set to measure resistance.
- The test leads of the meter must be correctly positioned to measure resistance.
- The power to the circuit must be switched off and there must be no other components in parallel with the component being measured.
- The meter must be connected across the component being measured.

> **ohmmeter:** an instrument that measures the resistance across two points in a circuit

Measuring Resistance

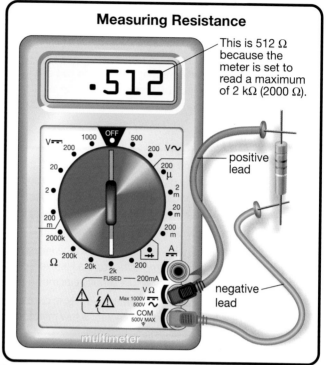

This is 512 Ω because the meter is set to read a maximum of 2 kΩ (2000 Ω).

positive lead

negative lead

Figure C1.42: Connect the meter across the component to measure resistance.

A typical ohmmeter will give a resistance value that is accurate to within about 1% of the actual value. You can ensure greater accuracy by selecting the lowest range on the ohmmeter that gives a valid reading. However, the best way to determine the value of a resistor is to collect a number of values for voltage and current and then use Ohm's law. In the next investigation you will have an opportunity to compare these two methods for determining the value of a resistor.

Investigation

Comparing Two Ways of Determining Resistance

Purpose
You will design a procedure that will provide two distinct ways of measuring the resistance of a resistor. You then will use your procedure to determine resistance values for three individual resistors.

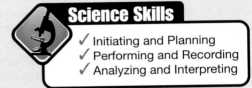
Science Skills

✓ Initiating and Planning
✓ Performing and Recording
✓ Analyzing and Interpreting

CAUTION!

- Never ground yourself while working with a live circuit. Do not touch metal pipes, electrical outlets, light fixtures, etc., that might be grounded. Be sure to keep your body insulated by keeping your hands and body dry and by wearing dry clothing and running shoes.

- Replace the fuse inside the meter with only the specified or approved equivalent fuse. Fuse replacement should only be done by the teacher or an adult lab technician.

- Use the meter only as specified in the investigation. Do not use the meter to test a wall outlet or an electric appliance. If you try to measure a voltage that exceeds the limits of the meter, you may damage the meter and expose yourself to a serious electric shock.

- Resistors can become warm—in some cases, hot enough to cause burns. Always disconnect a recently used resistor and allow it to cool for a few minutes before handling.

Materials
- digital multimeter
- 3 resistors (1000 Ω, 1500 Ω, and 2000 Ω)
- low-voltage power supply or 4 AA cells in a plastic battery pack with 3, 50-mm screws

Process
The end products for this investigation will include the following:

- a detailed diagram that clearly communicates the equipment that is to be used and clearly shows how this equipment is to be connected to the other components
- a data table and clearly communicated calculations for each of the resistors

Analysis
1. If the last coloured band on a resistor is gold, then the actual value of the resistance should be within 5% of the manufacturer's stated values. Determine whether the actual values you determined for the resistors were within this 5% guideline.

2. When evaluating data from an experiment, two key criteria are validity and reliability. Validity refers to the accuracy of the data, or how closely the data matches the actual value. Reliability refers to the consistency within the data. (Will you get the same results if the experiment is repeated?)

   a. Explain which of your two methods for determining resistance is likely to be more reliable.

   b. Explain which of your two methods for determining resistance is likely to be more valid.

Communicating the Details of Electric Circuits

Electric circuits can be found in a vast number of the devices you use every day. The manufacturers that assemble these devices and the people who repair them need a clear way to communicate how circuits are to be assembled and tested. An artist's drawing of the actual components is not practical because it would take up too much space. A more concise way to communicate the details of an electric circuit is to use a **schematic diagram**. Figure C1.43 shows a student's set-up to measure values for current and voltage for a resistor. Figure C1.44 shows the matching schematic diagram.

> **schematic diagram:** a sketch that uses symbols to detail the components of a system such as an electrical circuit

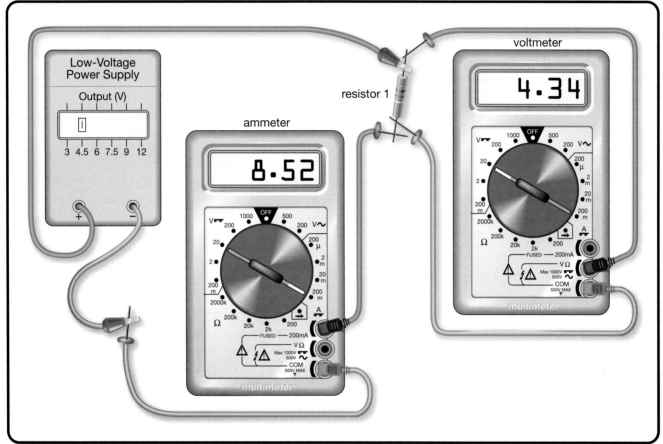

Figure C1.43: This set-up is used by a student to measure values for current and voltage of a resistor.

The schematic diagram uses symbols to represent the key components in the circuit. The schematic keeps things orderly by placing all the wires and components horizontally or vertically. Labels are used to indicate the known values in the circuit or to communicate which component a meter is measuring. The following table summarizes some of the symbols that you could use in your work with electric circuits in this lesson. A complete table of symbols is available on the handout "Symbols for Components in Schematic Diagrams" on the Science 30 Textbook CD.

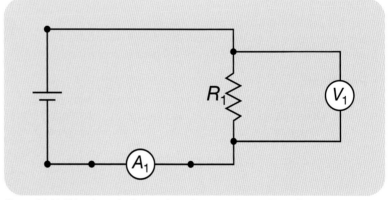

Figure C1.44: This schematic diagram shows the same circuit as Figure C1.43.

SOME SYMBOLS FOR COMPONENTS IN CIRCUIT DIAGRAMS

Component	Circuit Symbol	Function
wire	 ————————	passes current from one part of a circuit to another
wires joined		connects wires or components
switch	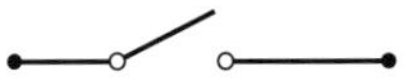	allows current to flow only when the switch is in the closed position
cell or DC power supply	1.5 V 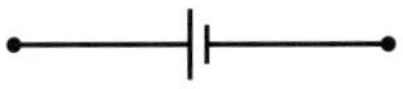	supplies electrical energy to a circuit in the form of direct current (DC) **Note:** The longer terminal is positive.
battery	6.0 V 	supplies electrical energy to a circuit in the form of direct current (DC)
resistor	 —\/\/\/—	resists the flow of electric current
lamp	 Ⓛ	converts electrical energy into light energy
voltmeter	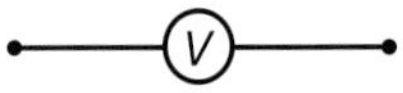 Ⓥ	measures voltage
ammeter	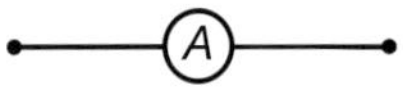 Ⓐ	measures electric current
ohmmeter	 Ⓞ	measures resistance

A great way to practise building circuits with schematic diagrams is to use the software application "Electric Circuits" on the Science 30 Textbook CD. In the next activity you will have an opportunity to explore the properties of different forms of circuits using this software.

Utilizing Technology

Cells in Series and in Parallel

Purpose

You will use software to determine the effect of adding an additional cell to an existing circuit. One circuit will involve a series connection and one will involve a parallel connection.

Science Skills

✓ Performing and Recording
✓ Analyzing and Interpreting
✓ Communication and Teamwork

Procedure

step 1: Locate "Electric Circuits" on the Science 30 Textbook CD. Open this application and read through the information in the "ShowMe" file to familiarize yourself with the software.

step 2: On the circuit board, construct the three circuits shown in Figure C1.45.

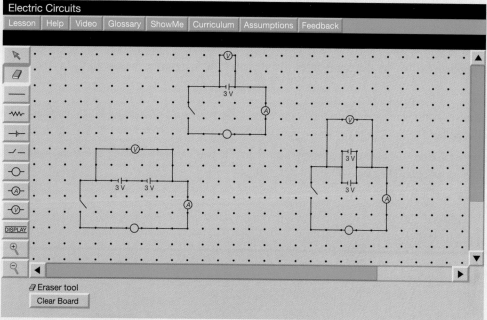

Figure C1.45

Observations

1. The circuit at the top depicts a voltage supply connected in series to a light bulb. Close the switch, record the reading on the voltmeter, and describe the brightness of the bulb.

2. The circuit at the bottom left depicts two voltage supplies connected in series, which are then connected in series to a light bulb. Close the switch, record the reading on the voltmeter, and describe the brightness of the bulb.

3. The circuit at the bottom right depicts two voltage supplies connected in parallel, which are then connected in series to a light bulb. Close the switch, record the reading on the voltmeter, and describe the brightness of the bulb.

Analysis

4. Two voltage supplies could be connected in series or in parallel. Describe an advantage of each connection.

Series and Parallel Connections of Energy Sources

Most graphing calculators use four 1.5-V cells in series to create 6.0 V to run the calculator. What is the advantage of this arrangement? As you saw with your earlier work with the motor, when cells are arranged in series, the energy output to the circuit is increased—the motor turns faster and is able to lift more with higher voltage. The total voltage for a group of cells connected in series can be summarized with the following equation.

$$V_{t_{series}} = V_1 + V_2 + \dots$$

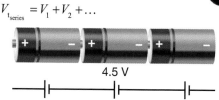

4.5 V

If connecting cells in series increases the energy available to the circuit, what is the advantage of connecting cells in parallel? The high-energy output of cells in series means that they can be drained of energy in a shorter period of time. So, it follows that when cells are connected in parallel, they tend to last much longer because the energy output is reduced. The total voltage for a group of identical cells connected in parallel can be summarized with the following equation.

$$V_{t_{parallel}} = V_1 = V_2 = V_3 = \dots$$

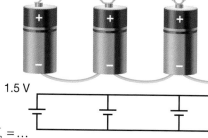

1.5 V

Example Problem 1.11

Electric service to your home is transmitted through cables that contain three wires. Two of the wires each possess voltages of 120 V, while the third wire is the neutral return wire required to complete the circuit.

a. To operate appliances that demand 120 V, describe the circuit that is required.

b. To operate appliances, like the stove and dryer, that demand 240 V, describe the circuit that is required.

Solution

a. When the transmission wires are connected to the circuit, the two wires possessing 120 V each are separated to form parallel paths. The total voltage in each path will be $V_{t_{parallel}} = V_1 = V_2 = V_3 = 120$ V.

b. When the transmission wires are connected to the circuit, the two wires possessing 120 V each are connected to form a single series path. The total voltage in this path is

$$\begin{aligned} V_{t_{series}} &= V_1 + V_2 + \ldots \\ &= 120 \text{ V} + 120 \text{ V} \\ &= 240 \text{ V} \end{aligned}$$

Practice

Laptop computers often need battery packs that have both high-energy output and long life. The solution is to combine groups of cells in combination series/parallel arrangements.

Four-Cell Combination: Series

Four-Cell Combination: Series

Four 3.6-V lithium-ion cells are connected in series to form a four-cell combination. This is then connected in parallel to another four-cell combination to form the laptop's battery pack. This configuration is called 4S2P: four cells in series to form one combination, connected in parallel to a second combination that is identical to the first.

34. If the four cells in each series combination are rated at 3.6 V, determine the total voltage of each set of four cells.

35. Use your answer to question 34 to determine the total voltage of the laptop's battery pack.

Utilizing Technology

Bulbs in Series and in Parallel

Purpose

You will use software to determine the effect of adding an additional light bulb to an existing circuit. One circuit will involve a series connection and one will involve a parallel connection.

Procedure

step 1: Locate the "Electric Circuits" software on the Science 30 Textbook CD. Open this application and read through the information in the "ShowMe" file to familiarize yourself with the software.

step 2: On the circuit board, construct the three circuits shown in figure C1.46.

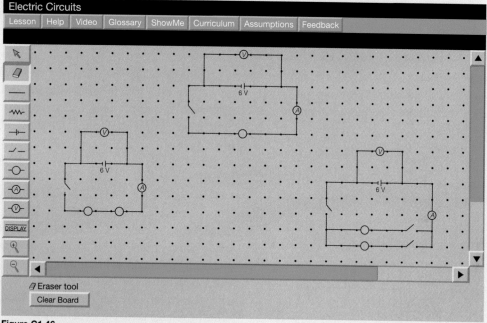

Figure C1.46

Observations

1. The circuit at the top depicts a voltage supply connected in series to a light bulb. Close the switch and record the readings on the voltmeter and the ammeter. Describe the brightness of the bulb.

2. The circuit at the bottom left depicts a voltage supply connected in series to two light bulbs. Close the switch and record the readings on the voltmeter and the ammeter. Describe the brightness of the bulbs. Open and close the switch and note the effect.

3. The circuit at the bottom right depicts a voltage supply connected in series to two light bulbs connected in parallel. Close the switches and record the readings on the voltmeter and the ammeter. Describe the brightness of the bulbs. Open and close each of the switches and note the effects.

Analysis

4. Record the readings on the ammeter and voltmeter in the top circuit.

   a. Use Ohm's law to calculate the resistance of the single bulb in that circuit.

   b. Confirm your answer by using the selection tool (the arrow in the top left corner) to click on the bulb to see the value for its resistance.

5. Record the readings on the ammeter and voltmeter in the bottom left circuit, the one with the two bulbs in series.

   a. Use Ohm's law to calculate the total resistance for the circuit.

   b. Use the selection tool to click on each bulb to see the value for each one's resistance. How do the individual resistance values compare to the total resistance for the whole circuit?

c. Use your answers to questions 5.a. and 5.b. to suggest a rule for determining the total resistance for two identical bulbs in series.

  d. Compare the reading on the ammeter in the top circuit with the reading on the ammeter in the circuit with the two bulbs in series. Suggest a reason for the differences.

6. Record the readings on the ammeter and voltmeter in the bottom right circuit, the one with the two resistors in parallel.

  a. Use Ohm's law to calculate the total resistance for the circuit.

  b. Use the selection tool to click on each bulb to see the value for each one's resistance. How do the individual resistance values compare to the total resistance for the whole circuit?

  c. Use your answers to questions 6.a. and 6.b. to suggest a rule for determining the total resistance for two identical bulbs in parallel.

  d. Compare the current readings of the ammeters in the top circuit with the circuit with the two bulbs in parallel. Suggest a reason for the differences.

7. Describe an advantage and a disadvantage of connecting two light bulbs in series and in parallel.

Equations for Calculating Total Resistance

What happens when an identical light bulb is added to a circuit operating with a single bulb? The results vary depending upon how the additional bulb is connected to the existing bulb.

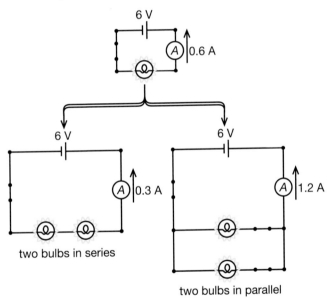

two bulbs in series

two bulbs in parallel

In the case of the series circuit, there is only one path for the moving charges to follow. If you open the switch in this circuit, or if one of the bulbs fails, the whole thing shuts down. Since the moving charges have to overcome the resistance of the first bulb and then the resistance of the second bulb, the total resistance is equal to the sum of the individual resistances.

For resistors connected in series,

$$R_{total} = R_1 + R_2 + R_3 + \dots$$

Adding the additional bulb in the parallel circuit provides an extra path for charges to follow. One outcome of this extra path is that you can open the switch to one of the bulbs without shutting off the other one. This is why parallel circuitry is so popular with household wiring—you can turn individual devices off and on independently.

Note that the additional light bulb will have the same voltage across it as the original bulb. This stems from the fact that the endpoints of the additional pathway connect to the endpoints of the original pathway. Since practically no energy is lost through the connecting wires, both bulbs have the same difference in energy across their terminals, and, therefore, have the same value of voltage across those terminals.

Perhaps the most important implication of the additional path provided by the extra bulb is the effect on electric current. Since the charges have twice as many paths to follow, twice the current is able to flow. In other words, since the current has doubled, the overall resistance must be only half as much. If a second bulb that is not identical to the first bulb is added in parallel to the circuit, the new total resistance is still lower, but it will not be exactly half as much. The following equation is helpful for determining the total resistance in these circumstances.

For resistors connected in parallel,

$$\frac{1}{R_{total}} = \frac{1}{R_1} + \frac{1}{R_2} + \frac{1}{R_3} + \dots$$

Example Problem 1.12

Strings of small, colourful lights are often used for holiday decorating and other occasions. An inexpensive string of these lights consists of 8 bulbs connected in series. The resistance of each bulb in the set is 64.0 Ω.

a. Draw a schematic diagram of this circuit.

b. If the set of lights is plugged into a 120-V outlet, determine the current that will flow through the set.

c. Use your answer to part a. to determine the current that will flow through the third bulb in the string of lights.

d. If the third bulb in the set fails, determine the effect on the other lights in the string.

Solution

a.

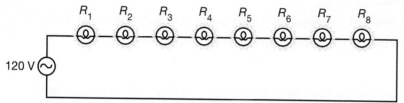

b. step 1: Determine the total resistance.

$$R_1 = R_2 = R_3 = \ldots = R_7 = R_8 = 64.0\,\Omega$$
$$R_{total} = ?$$

$$R_{total} = R_1 + R_2 + R_3 + R_4 + R_5 + R_6 + R_7 + R_8$$
$$= 8(64.0\,\Omega)$$
$$= 512\,\Omega$$

The total resistance of all eight bulbs is 512 Ω.

step 2: Determine the current.

$$R = R_{total} = 512\ \Omega$$
$$V = 120\ V$$
$$I = ?$$

$$V = IR$$
$$I = \frac{V}{R}$$
$$= \frac{120\ V}{512\ \Omega} \quad \leftarrow \Omega = V/A$$
$$= 0.234\ A$$

The current flowing through the entire set is 0.234 A.

c. In a series connection, there is only one path for the electric current. Therefore, the entire electric current flows through each component. This means that the third bulb, as well as every other bulb in the string, will have a current of 0.234 A flowing through it.

d. Since there is only one path for the electric current in a series connection, if one bulb fails, the entire current stops. Therefore, when the third bulb fails, all the other lights go out too.

A group of students is setting up for a high school dance. They work to set up some spotlights and other types of specialty lighting to help set the mood. Five spotlights are plugged into a heavy-duty power strip, each light in its own outlet. Each of the spotlights has a resistance of 96 Ω.

a. Explain why a power strip must allow parallel connections to each of the devices that plug into it.

b. Draw a schematic diagram of this circuit.

c. If the fourth spotlight has 120 V available to it, determine the voltage available to each of the other spotlights.

d. Determine the total amount of current that the power strip requires to power all five spotlights.

Solution

a. The power strip must allow parallel connections so that each of the devices that plugs into it can be turned off independently. If the power strip operated in series, all the devices would turn off as soon as one device is turned off.

b.

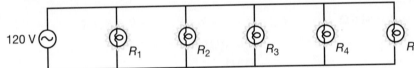

120 V ... R_1 ... R_2 ... R_3 ... R_4 ... R_5

c. Having the same voltage value is an important characteristic of devices connected in parallel. As shown in the schematic diagram, all the spotlights have the same voltage across their wires. Therefore, the potential difference available to each of the other spotlights is 120 V.

d. step 1: Determine the total resistance.

$$R_1 = R_2 = R_3 = R_4 = R_5 = 96.0 \ \Omega$$

$$R_{total} = ?$$

$$\frac{1}{R_{total}} = \frac{1}{R_1} + \frac{1}{R_2} + \frac{1}{R_3} + \frac{1}{R_4} + \frac{1}{R_5}$$

$$\frac{1}{R_{total}} = \left(\frac{1}{96 \ \Omega}\right) + \left(\frac{1}{96 \ \Omega}\right) + \left(\frac{1}{96 \ \Omega}\right) + \left(\frac{1}{96 \ \Omega}\right) + \left(\frac{1}{96 \ \Omega}\right)$$

$$\frac{1}{R_{total}} = 5\left(\frac{1}{96.0 \ \Omega}\right)$$

$$\frac{1}{R_{total}} = \frac{5}{96.0 \ \Omega}$$

$$R_{total} = 19.2 \ \Omega$$

The total resistance of the five spotlights is 19.2 Ω.

Notes: • Keep all the intermediate values in your calculator to avoid rounding errors.

• Don't forget to take the reciprocal at the end of the calculation.

• When you do take the reciprocal, use the x^{-1} key.

continued

step 2: Calculate the current.

$$R = R_{total} = 19.2\,\Omega$$
$$V = 120\ V$$
$$I = ?$$

$$V = IR$$
$$I = \frac{V}{R}$$
$$= \frac{120\ V}{19.2\,\Omega} \quad \leftarrow \ \Omega = V/A$$
$$= 6.25\ A$$

The current required by all five spotlights is 6.25 A.

These Example Problems illustrate how important it is to first categorize the circuit as being either a series connection or a parallel connection. Once this is done, you can begin to solve the problem. A typical first step is to calculate the total resistance of a number of components. Remember these ideas as you complete the Practice problems.

Practice

36. Use the following schematic diagram to answer questions 36.a. to e.

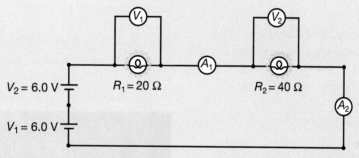

a. Determine the total voltage available to this circuit.
b. Calculate the total resistance of the two bulbs.
c. Calculate the current flowing through each of the bulbs.
d. Calculate the readings of voltmeters 1 and 2.
e. Explain what happens if one of the bulbs burns out.

37. Use the following schematic diagram to answer questions 37.a. to e.

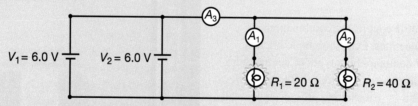

a. Determine the total voltage available to this circuit.
b. Calculate the total resistance of the two bulbs.
c. Calculate the total current flowing through the whole circuit.
d. Determine the readings of ammeters 1, 2, and 3.
e. Explain why the sum of the readings of ammeters 1 and 2 equal the reading of ammeter 3.
f. Explain what happens if one of the bulbs burn out.

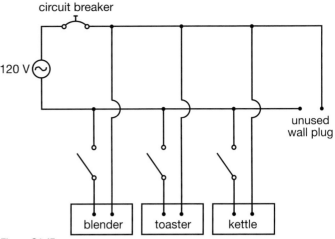

Figure C1.47

Science Skills

✓ Initiating and Planning
✓ Performing and Recording
✓ Analyzing and Interpreting

Purpose

You will determine which arrangement of three resistors will produce the maximum and minimum values of total resistance.

Materials

- 3 resistors (1000 Ω, 1500 Ω, and 2000 Ω)
- digital multimeter (used as an ohmmeter)
- test leads

Procedure, Observations, and Analysis

1. Use the multimeter to determine the actual value of each of the resistors.

2. Determine which arrangement of resistors will produce the maximum total resistance. Calculate this maximum value based upon your values from question 1.

3. Use the multimeter to verify your maximum value from the calculations in question 2. Are the values close?

4. Repeat questions 2 and 3 for the arrangement that will produce the minimum resistance.

Circuits with Both Series and Parallel Components

In reality, practical electric circuits use combinations of series and parallel connections. Even the simple kitchen circuit in Figure C1.47 combines both types of connections. The blender and the toaster oven are connected in parallel with the kettle. This ensures that shutting off one device will not shut off either of the others.

Series connections can be found with the switches that control each device. In this case, the ability of a switch to completely stop the flow of current is desirable.

This same reasoning explains the series connection of the circuit breaker to all of the other devices on the circuit. This series connection ensures that the total current for the whole circuit must flow through the breaker, allowing the breaker to monitor the current. In most household circuits, the maximum safe current is 15 A. If current values exceed safe values, there is a possibility that the household wiring inside a wall might overheat and cause a fire. By reducing the chance of electrical fires, circuit breakers play a critical role in keeping everyone in your household safe.

38. A standard 120-V AC household circuit consists of parallel connections of a number of electrical outlets, which are all in series with the circuit breaker for that circuit. Suppose the following devices are all plugged in and switched on at the same time.

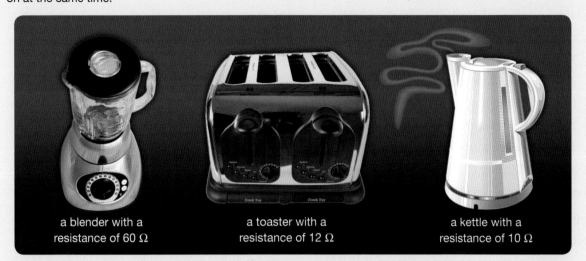

a blender with a resistance of 60 Ω   a toaster with a resistance of 12 Ω   a kettle with a resistance of 10 Ω

The circuit breaker has negligible resistance and can be treated as a special type of switch.

a. Apply Ohm's law to each device and determine the current flowing through each one.

b. Use your answer to question 38.a. to determine the total current required by the operation of all three devices.

c. Determine the total resistance of all three devices.

d. Use your answer to question 38.c. to determine the total current required by the operation of all three devices. Did you get the same value as you did in question 38.b.?

e. Use your answer to questions 38.b. and 38.d. to determine the outcome of switching on all three devices at once.

f. Each time another device is switched on in the kitchen circuit, another source of resistance is added to the circuit, but the overall total resistance of the entire circuit is reduced. Although this statement sounds contradictory, it does make sense. Use your knowledge of circuits to explain why there is no contradiction here.

1.4 Summary

A digital multimeter is a powerful tool for collecting data from simple circuits. When used as a voltmeter, a parallel connection is used to determine the voltage across a component. When used as an ohmmeter, the meter is connected across a component to determine resistance values in ohms, where $1 \, \Omega = 1 \, \text{V/A}$. When determining the electric current that flows through a component, the multimeter is connected in series.

The use of series and parallel connections extends to the circuits themselves, where the different components can be arranged in either one of these configurations or in both. When components are connected in series, the individual voltage values are added to give the total voltage and the individual resistance values are added to give the total resistance. Since there is one path in series connections, the same current flows through each component.

Parallel connections between components mean that there is more than one path for the moving charges, so the individual values of electric current in each branch add up to give the total electric current. The voltage values remain the same across each component. The effect of having more than one path available is that more current is allowed to flow, so the total resistance is lowered. The following equation is useful for determining the total resistance in a parallel circuit:

$$\frac{1}{R_{\text{total}}} = \frac{1}{R_1} + \frac{1}{R_2} + \frac{1}{R_3} + \cdots$$

Knowledge

1. State the essential components required in all electric circuits.

2. Write a mathematical expression relating voltage, current, and resistance.

3. In an electric circuit, how is the value of the current affected in the following circumstances?

    a. The voltage is doubled.

    b. The resistance in the external circuit is doubled.

4. a. State an advantage of connecting voltage sources in series.

    b. State an advantage of connecting voltage sources in parallel.

5. a. State an advantage of connecting electrical devices in series.

    b. State an advantage of connecting electrical devices in parallel.

6. Summarize the characteristics of series and parallel circuits in a table.

Applying Concepts

7. A resistor of 100 Ω is connected to a 9.00-V DC battery. Determine the current that flows through the resistor.

8. An electrical component with a resistance of 50.0 Ω is connected to an AC power supply with a voltage of 45.0 V. Determine the current that flows through the component.

9. a. Two 12.0-V DC batteries are connected to an external circuit. Determine the voltage if the two batteries are connected in series.

    b. Determine the voltage if the same two batteries are connected in parallel.

10. a. Two 50.0-Ω resistors are connected to an external circuit. Determine the total resistance if the two resistors are connected in series.

    b. Determine the total resistance if the same two resistors are connected in parallel.

11. An AC power adaptor supplies an effective voltage of 18.0 V(AC) to a 50.0-Ω and 80.0-Ω resistor connected in series. Voltmeters are connected to measure the voltage of each resistor and an ammeter measures the total current.

    a. Draw a schematic diagram of the circuit.

    b. i. Determine the total resistance of the circuit.

    ii. Determine the total current in the circuit.

    iii. Determine the voltage across the 50.0-Ω and the 80.0-Ω resistors.

    iv. What would happen to the circuit if the 50.0-Ω resistor burned out?

12. Two 1.50-V DC cells are connected in parallel. The external circuit consists of a 500-Ω and 1000-Ω resistor connected in parallel. Voltmeters are connected to measure the voltage of each resistor, and an ammeter measures the total current.

    a. Draw a schematic diagram of the circuit.

    b. i. Determine the total resistance of the circuit.

    ii. Determine the total voltage of the cells.

    iii. Determine the total current in the circuit.

    iv. Determine the voltage across the 500-Ω and 1000-Ω resistors.

    v. What would happen to the circuit if the 500-Ω resistor burned out?

13. Use the properties of series and parallel circuits to explain why voltmeters are always connected in parallel and ammeters are always connected in series.

Figure C1.48

Most people take the convenience of electrical energy for granted. When you feel like a snack in the evening, you probably don't give much thought to flipping on the kitchen light before wandering over to the refrigerator to look for something to eat. It may appear that the source of energy for these devices is the household wiring; however, you know from your work earlier in the chapter that somewhere far away from where you live, the armature of a large generator is being forced to turn rapidly on its axis at a generating station. Transmission lines, like those in Figure C1.48, ensure that the energy produced at the generating station is available for you to use in your home.

The towers on the left side of Figure C1.48 support high-voltage transmission lines that typically operate with voltage values of well over 100 000 V. The guiding principle used by the engineers who design and operate the transmission system is to keep the voltage at the highest level possible while still being safe. Why is it so important for the voltage to be kept so high in transmission lines? How is this extremely high voltage converted into the 240 V used in most circuits? Why is the entire network that distributes electrical energy an AC system? In this lesson you will have an opportunity to answer these questions.

Power

Light bulbs and many other electrical devices are rated in terms of the electrical energy they consume every second. Recall that **power** is the quantity used to describe the rate of doing work or transforming energy.

$$\underset{\text{power (watts)}}{P} = \underset{\substack{\text{work done (joules)}}}{\frac{W}{t}} = \underset{\substack{\text{energy transformed}\\ \text{(joules)}}}{\frac{E}{t}} \;\underset{\substack{\text{time interval}\\ \text{(seconds)}}}{}$$

$$\text{Units:} \quad 1\text{ W} = \frac{1\text{ J}}{\text{s}}$$

Most people are more familiar with the unit for power (the watt) than they are with the quantity itself. For example, a conventional 60-W light bulb transforms 60 J of electrical energy into thermal energy and light energy every second. Unfortunately, since most of the energy produced is thermal, these devices end up being heaters that also emit light. More efficient designs produce less thermal energy. This is reflected in the power rating: the 17-W compact fluorescent bulb shown in Figure C1.49 produces the same quantity of light energy as a conventional 60-W bulb. When it comes to lighting, the goal is to produce the required quantity of light energy while consuming the minimal quantity of electrical energy.

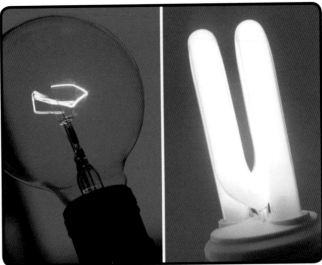

Figure C1.49: Conventional light bulbs are being replaced with more efficient designs that use less electrical energy to produce the same amount of light energy.

power: the rate of doing work or transforming energy

Example Problem 1.14

Two lamps emit the same quantity of light. One uses a 17-W compact fluorescent bulb, and the other uses a conventional 60-W bulb.

a. Calculate the electrical energy used by each bulb in 1.00 h.

b. Explain the following statement:

> Compact fluorescent bulbs initially cost more to purchase, but throughout their lifetime they are less expensive to operate than conventional bulbs.

Solution

a. 60-W Conventional Light Bulb

$P = 60$ W

$\quad = 60$ J/s

$t = 1.00 \text{ h} \times \dfrac{60 \text{ min}}{1 \text{ h}} \times \dfrac{60 \text{ s}}{1 \text{ min}}$

$\quad = 3.60 \times 10^3$ s

$E = ?$

$P = \dfrac{E}{t}$

$E = Pt$

$\quad = (60 \text{ J/s})(3.60 \times 10^3 \text{ s})$

$\quad = 2.2 \times 10^5$ J

The conventional 60-W light bulb uses 2.2×10^5 J of electrical energy in 1.0 h.

17-W Compact Fluorescent Light Bulb

$P = 17$ W

$\quad = 17$ J/s

$t = 1.00 \text{ h} \times \dfrac{60 \text{ min}}{1 \text{ h}} \times \dfrac{60 \text{ s}}{1 \text{ min}}$

$\quad = 3.60 \times 10^3$ s

$E = ?$

$P = \dfrac{E}{t}$

$E = Pt$

$\quad = (17 \text{ J/s})(3.60 \times 10^3 \text{ s})$

$\quad = 6.1 \times 10^4$ J

The 17-W bulb uses 6.1×10^4 J of electrical energy in 1.0 h.

b. The compact fluorescent bulb uses less electrical energy to produce the same quantity of light energy. Since electrical energy is purchased and paid for on a monthly bill, the total operating cost for a compact fluorescent bulb is less than that of a conventional bulb.

39. A family shopping for a new refrigerator has narrowed its search down to two possibilities. The first model is rated at 700 W, and the second is rated at 500 W.

    a. Determine the quantity of electrical energy used by each model in a day. Assume that each model runs for 6.0 h every day.

    b. The manufacturer of the 500-W model promotes their model as being "an environmentally friendly alternative." Refer to your answer to question 39.a. to explain the meaning of this statement.

Power in Electrical Systems

Someone whose hobby is car audio systems may describe the power rating of his or her speakers as 300 W. In this case, the power rating describes the maximum safe input of electrical energy required to produce sound energy. In fact, power is a quantity that is used so frequently in such a wide variety of electrical applications that special equations have been developed to describe power in terms of electric circuits, voltage, and electric current. Units provide a helpful insight into the origins of these equations:

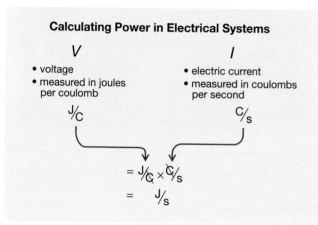

Calculating Power in Electrical Systems

V
- voltage
- measured in joules per coulomb

$\dfrac{J}{C}$

I
- electric current
- measured in coulombs per second

$\dfrac{C}{s}$

$$= \dfrac{J}{C} \times \dfrac{C}{s}$$
$$= \dfrac{J}{s}$$

Since J/s is the unit for power, the unit analysis suggests the following equation:

power (watts) ⟶ $P = VI$ ⟵ voltage (volts) / electric current (amperes)

Units: $1\ \text{W} = 1\ \text{V} \cdot \text{A}$

This equation is very useful because voltage and electric current are quantities frequently used to describe the characteristics of electric circuits. Car audio circuits are no exception, since the electrical signals sent to the speakers are also described in terms of voltage and electric current. A speaker is basically a large-scale version of the tiny earpiece of the headphones you studied earlier.

Just like headphones, a speaker is an AC device that only operates if the electric current changes directions. In this course, a simplified approach is taken that assumes the coil of the speaker acts as a constant source of resistance.

In reality, the resistance of a speaker can vary depending upon how frequently the AC signal switches directions and upon the characteristics of other components in the circuit. Example Problems 1.15 and 1.16 show how this simplified approach can be applied.

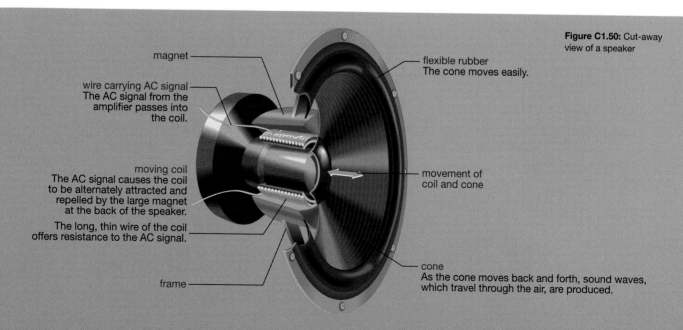

Figure C1.50: Cut-away view of a speaker

magnet

flexible rubber
The cone moves easily.

wire carrying AC signal
The AC signal from the amplifier passes into the coil.

moving coil
The AC signal causes the coil to be alternately attracted and repelled by the large magnet at the back of the speaker.

The long, thin wire of the coil offers resistance to the AC signal.

movement of coil and cone

frame

cone
As the cone moves back and forth, sound waves, which travel through the air, are produced.

Example Problem 1.15

Using a simplified approach, a speaker can be treated as a device that offers 4.0 Ω of resistance to the AC input signal, allowing only 2.00 A of current to flow. Calculate the power consumed by the speaker.

Solution

step 1: Calculate the voltage applied across the wires of the speaker.

$R = 4.0\,\Omega$ $V = IR$

$I = 2.00$ A $= (2.00\ \text{A})(4.0\,\Omega)$

$V = ?$ $= 8.0$ V

The AC voltage applied across the wires of the speaker is 8.0 V.

step 2: Calculate the power consumed by the speaker.

$V = 8.0$ V $P = VI$

$I = 2.00$ A $= (8.0\ \text{V})(2.00\ \text{A})$

$P = ?$ $= 16$ W

The power consumed by this speaker is 16 W.

Example Problem 1.16

The volume is turned up in a car with a 4.0-Ω speaker so that 4.50 A of alternating current flows to the speaker. Calculate the power consumed by this speaker.

Solution

$R = 4.0\,\Omega$ $P = I^2 R$

$I = 4.50$ A $= (4.50\ \text{A})^2 (4.0\,\Omega)$

$P = ?$ $= 81$ W

The power consumed by the speaker is 81 W.

The solution to Example Problem 1.15 required two steps because the voltage was given. Note how the first step of the solution used Ohm's law. Since there are so many cases where power needs to be calculated but voltage is unknown, another version of the power equation has been developed.

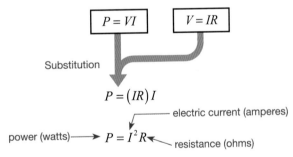

$$P = VI \qquad V = IR$$

Substitution

$$P = (IR)\,I$$

electric current (amperes)

power (watts) ⟶ $P = I^2 R$ ← resistance (ohms)

Units: $1\ \text{W} = \text{A}^2\,\Omega$

This version of the power equation is very convenient because the power can be calculated in one step in cases where the voltage is not given.

Example Problem 1.16 used the simplified approach of treating a speaker as a device that offers a constant resistance to an AC input signal. The results of these calculations give very good estimates of the power requirements of speakers. In fact, this simplified approach can also be used when determining how sets of speakers will behave when they are connected in series or in parallel.

40. Solve Example Problem 1.15 using a one-step approach. Confirm that you get the same answer using this method.

41. Solve Example Problem 1.16 using a two-step approach. Confirm that you get the same answer using this method.

Use the following information to answer questions 42 to 44.

One of the circuits in a car audio system involves a specialized speaker called a subwoofer, which is designed to produce very low-frequency sounds. This is the speaker that is responsible for the thumping bass that can often be heard some distance away from a vehicle. In Figure C1.51, the subwoofers are the four largest speakers.

Figure C1.51

Each subwoofer can be treated as a device that maintains a constant resistance of 8.0 Ω in these questions.

42. Two of the subwoofers are connected in parallel to one of the circuits in the sound system. This circuit uses a circuit breaker to ensure that the maximum current that can be drawn from the amplifier is 5.0 A.

  a. Draw a schematic diagram for the circuit involving the two subwoofers and the circuit breaker.

  b. Determine the total resistance of the two speakers in this circuit.

  c. Use your answer to question 42.b. to determine the power consumed by the two speakers if they draw the maximum current of 5.0 A.

  d. Use two different equations to verify that the sound system is supplying 20.0 V to the two speakers under these conditions.

43. Suppose the two speakers are connected in series with a circuit breaker to the same 20.0-V output of the amplifier.

  a. Draw a schematic diagram for the circuit breaker and the two speakers connected in series.

  b. Determine the total resistance of the two speakers in this circuit.

  c. Calculate the total current drawn by the speakers in this circuit.

  d. Calculate the power consumed by the two speakers in this circuit.

44. Refer to your answers to questions 42 and 43.

  a. If the goal was to produce the most sound energy from the 20-V input signal, would it be better to connect the speakers in series or in parallel?

  b. Is there a disadvantage to the type of connection that you identified in question 44.a?

Billing Consumers for Electrical Energy

As anyone who has paid an electricity bill knows, electrical energy is not free. Meters are used by utility companies to monitor the use of electrical energy, which is then used to calculate the bill that is mailed to the consumer. The traditional unit used by utility companies is the **kilowatt-hour**. As shown by the following equations, the kilowatt-hour is an energy unit derived from rearranging the equation for electric power.

> **kilowatt-hour:** the traditional unit for electrical energy used by utility companies; 1 kW·h = 3.6 MJ

$$P = \frac{E}{t}$$

$$E = Pt$$

$$\underset{\text{in kilowatt-hours}}{\text{energy measured}} = \underset{\text{in kilowatts}}{\text{power measured}} \times \underset{\text{in hours}}{\text{time measured}}$$

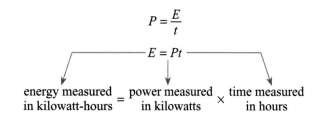

A kettle rated at 1000 W operates for a total of 60.0 min in a typical week.

a. Determine the energy consumed in kilowatt-hours.

b. Determine the energy consumed in joules.

c. State the relationship between kilowatt-hours and joules.

d. Use your answer to part c. to show an alternative method of answering part b. by using your answer to part a.

Solution

a. $P = 1000 \text{ W} \times \dfrac{1 \text{ kW}}{1000 \text{ W}}$ $\qquad P = \dfrac{E}{t}$

$\qquad = 1.000 \text{ kW}$ $\qquad\qquad E = Pt$

$\qquad t = 60.0 \text{ min} \times \dfrac{1 \text{ h}}{60 \text{ min}}$ $\qquad = (1.000 \text{ kW})(1.00 \text{ h})$

$\qquad = 1.00 \text{ h}$ $\qquad\qquad = 1.00 \text{ kW} \cdot \text{h}$

$\qquad E = ?$

The appliance consumed 1.00 kW·h of energy.

b. $P = 1000 \text{ W} \times \dfrac{1 \text{ J/s}}{1 \text{ W}}$ $\qquad P = \dfrac{E}{t}$

$\qquad = 1000 \text{ J/s}$ $\qquad\qquad E = Pt$

$\qquad t = 60.0 \text{ min} \times \dfrac{60 \text{ s}}{1 \text{ min}}$ $\qquad = (1000 \text{ J/s})(3.60 \times 10^3 \text{ s})$

$\qquad = 3.60 \times 10^3 \text{ s}$ $\qquad = 3.60 \times 10^6 \text{ J}$

$\qquad\qquad\qquad\qquad\qquad = 3.60 \text{ MJ}$

$\qquad E = ?$

The appliance consumed 3.60×10^6 J or 3.60 MJ of energy.

c. The answers to parts a. and b. indicate that 1.00 kW·h = 3.60×10^6 J = 3.6 MJ.

d. $E = 1.00 \text{ kW} \cdot \text{h} \times \dfrac{3.6 \times 10^6 \text{ J}}{1 \text{ kW} \cdot \text{h}} = 3.6 \times 10^6 \text{ J}$

Calculating the Cost of Electricity in Dollars

As Example Problem 1.17 shows, 1 kW·h is equivalent to 3.6×10^6 J or 3.6 MJ. The fact that the kilowatt-hour represents such a large quantity of energy is one of the reasons this unit is used by utility companies to bill customers. The cost of a kilowatt-hour varies, depending upon where you live and the current state of the electricity market. At the time this textbook was written, many Albertans were paying about 9.3¢/kW·h.

Example Problem 1.18

Most models of TVs and VCRs use electrical energy even when they are turned off. This stand-by power is used to run clocks in VCRs and to provide an "instant on" feature, allowing home electronics to become operational with a click of the remote control. Average values for stand-by power are about 3.0 W for a VCR and 5.0 W for a TV. Since this power is required 24 h a day, the electrical energy consumption is significant.

a. Determine the electrical energy required to supply 8.0 W of stand-by power for both a TV and a VCR during one year. Express your answer in kilowatt-hours.

b. If the price of electricity is 9.3¢/kW•h, determine the cost in dollars of providing stand-by power to the VCR and TV for 365 days (one year).

c. There are about 2.0 million TVs and VCRs that operate with stand-by power in Alberta. Use this fact to estimate the total annual cost of maintaining stand-by power for all of these devices in Alberta.

Solution

a. $P = 8.0 \text{ W} \times \dfrac{1 \text{ kW}}{1000 \text{ W}}$ $\qquad P = \dfrac{E}{t}$

$\quad = 8.0 \times 10^{-3} \text{ kW}$ $\qquad E = Pt$

$t = 365 \text{ d} \times \dfrac{24 \text{ h}}{1 \text{ d}}$ $\qquad = \left(8.0 \times 10^{-3} \text{ kW}\right)\left(8.76 \times 10^{3} \text{ h}\right)$

$\quad = 8.76 \times 10^{3} \text{ h}$ $\qquad = 70.08 \text{ kW•h}$

$\qquad\qquad\qquad\qquad\qquad = 70 \text{ kW•h}$

$E = ?$

The energy required to supply the stand-by power for one year is 70 kW•h.

b. units of energy = 70.08 kW•h $\qquad$ cost of energy = units of energy × cost per energy unit

cost per energy unit = 9.3¢/kW•h $\qquad\qquad\qquad = \left(70.08 \text{ kW•h}\right)\left(\$0.093/\text{kW•h}\right)$

$\qquad\qquad\qquad = \$0.093/\text{kW•h}$ $\qquad\qquad\qquad = \$6.52$

cost of energy = ?

The annual cost of maintaining the stand-by power for the combination of a VCR and a TV is $6.52.

c. $\dfrac{\text{number of TVs and}}{\text{VCRs in Alberta}} = 2.0$ million $\qquad \begin{matrix}\text{annual cost for all} \\ \text{TVs and VCRs} \\ \text{in Alberta}\end{matrix} = \begin{matrix}\text{number of} \\ \text{TVs and VCRs} \\ \text{in Alberta}\end{matrix} \times \begin{matrix}\text{annual cost} \\ \text{for 1 TV} \\ \text{and 1 VCR}\end{matrix}$

$\dfrac{\text{annual cost for}}{\text{1 TV and 1 VCR}} = \$6.52$ $\qquad\qquad\qquad\qquad = \left(2.0 \text{ million}\right)\left(\$6.52\right)$

$\qquad\qquad\qquad\qquad\qquad = \$13$ million

$\dfrac{\text{annual cost for all TVs}}{\text{and VCRs in Alberta}} = ?$

The annual cost to provide stand-by power for all the TVs and VCRs in Alberta is about $13 million.

45. Compile a list of all the devices in your home that use stand-by power. To determine whether a device uses stand-by power, the following criteria may be helpful:

    • It uses a stand-alone power supply, like an AC adaptor.
    • It has a remote control.
    • It has a soft-touch keypad.
    • It charges the battery of a portable device, like a cordless phone.
    • It is warm to the touch even when it is turned off.
    • It does not have an "off" switch.
    • It has a digital clock display.

46. After listing all the devices in her home that use stand-by power, Mikaila determines that the total stand-by power consumed by the appliances in her household is 87 W.

    a. Determine the total energy (in kW·h) required to supply all the appliances in this household with stand-by power for 365 days (one year).

    b. If the price of electricity is 9.3¢/kW·h, determine the annual cost (in dollars) of the electrical energy required to supply the stand-by power for this household.

    c. Describe how the use of stand-by power impacts the environment.

Calculating Some of the Environmental Costs of Electricity

Figure C1.52: The Genesee generating station near Edmonton uses the combustion of pulverized coal to produce electricity.

In Alberta, about 75% of the electricity generated is produced at generating stations that burn coal. The energy released from the combustion of the coal is used to produce high-pressure steam that drives a turbine connected to the armature of a large generator.

In the traditional, coal-fired generating stations currently in operation today, the coal is first pulverized into a fine powder before it is burned to produce steam. As you learned in a previous unit, the products of this combustion reaction include carbon dioxide (CO_2); sulfur oxides (SO_x); nitrogen oxides (NO_x); particulate matter; and trace amounts of other compounds, including mercury.

Figure C1.53: This generating station in Florida looks more like a refinery because the coal is first converted into synthetic gas, or syngas. The syngas is cleaned before it is burned.

New technologies are being used to reduce the environmental impact of burning coal to produce electricity. Experimental, low-emission generating stations first convert the coal into a hydrocarbon vapour called synthetic gas, or syngas for short. The syngas is then stripped of impurities before it is burned to produce the steam that drives the turbine, which is connected to the armature of the generator. As the following table demonstrates, new technologies are helping to reduce some of the harmful effects of coal as a source of energy.

COMPARING COAL-COMBUSTION TECHNOLOGIES

Type of Emission	Mass Released Generating Electrical Energy (g/kW·h)	
	Traditional Generating Station	Experimental, Low-Emission Generating Station†
$CO_2(g)$	about 1.0×10^3	less than 8.0×10^2
$SO_x(g)$	less than 1.9*	less than 0.2
$NO_x(g)$	less than 1.4*	less than 0.05
particulate matter	less than 0.14*	less than 0.03

* Maximum value allowed under Alberta Emission Standards (2001)
† Data from experimental, low-emission generating stations

The table "Comparing Coal-Combustion Technologies" is a rich source of information that answers some questions and suggests some new ones. Note that the new coal-combustion technologies dramatically reduce the emissions of sulfur oxides, nitrogen oxides, and particulate matter; but the reductions in carbon dioxide are much more modest. Although it is possible to use scrubbers and other technologies to remove impurities from the coal, the one thing that cannot be removed is the energy-rich hydrocarbon compounds that are the essential component of coal as a fuel. Since coal is the starting point in both systems, the ability to reduce carbon dioxide emissions has its limitations. Given the connections between carbon dioxide emissions and global climate change, some people are hesitant to embrace new coal-combustion technologies.

The next table shows data for when natural gas is burned in a gas turbine coupled to the armature of a generator. The hot exhaust gas is used to produce steam that can also produce electricity using a steam turbine connected to the armature of a generator.

NATURAL GAS-COMBUSTION TECHNOLOGY

Type of Emission	Mass Released Generating Electrical Energy (g/kW·h)*
$CO_2(g)$	about 4.0×10^2
$SO_x(g)$	less than 0.003
$NO_x(g)$	less than 0.01
particulate matter	less than 0.02
* Data from natural gas combined-cycle generating stations	

Figure C1.54: An electrical engineer supervises operations at a generating station.

One way to significantly reduce the amount of carbon dioxide emissions from combustion reactions is to start with a different fuel. When natural gas is used as fuel for generating electricity, the amount of carbon dioxide released is about 400 g/kW·h, which is about half of the best values produced by the most advanced coal-combustion technologies. Since natural gas has already been cleaned of sulfur, and special burners can reduce the emission of nitrogen oxides, many people regard the existing natural gas-fired generating stations as being a better choice for the environment than the leading-edge, coal-fired options.

These tables provide only a glimpse of some of the environmental consequences of using fossil fuels to generate electricity. Although it is certainly possible to dig deeper into the technical data supporting the use of one technology over another, it is also important to step back and keep the big picture in mind by considering people's use of electrical energy.

Figure C1.55: It has been estimated that about 80% of the energy consumed by a typical microwave oven in its lifetime is used for its clock and stand-by power.

Is it really necessary for so many appliances to have electronic displays and clocks that use electrical energy on a continual basis? Although newer standards are reducing the energy consumed by products that use stand-by power, these efforts are offset by an increasing number of products, like dishwashers, washers, and dryers, that are starting to utilize electronic displays and, therefore, require stand-by power. Unfortunately, many observers of these trends suspect that the stand-by power consumed by each household will continue to increase.

Use the following information to answer questions 47, 48, and 49.

An Alberta family used about 1.05×10^4 kW•h of electrical energy last year. This use of energy has a significant effect on the family budget because they pay 8.8¢/kW•h.

47. Assume that the electric utility company generates electricity using a traditional coal-fired generating station, where the coal is pulverized into a powder and then burned to produce steam to drive a generator.

   a. Use the tables "Comparing Coal-Combustion Technologies" and "Natural Gas-Combustion Technology" to estimate the mass (in kilograms) of the annual emissions of $CO_2(g)$, $SO_x(g)$, $NO_x(g)$, and particulate matter that are a consequence of this family's electricity use.

   b. Calculate the annual cost (in dollars) of electrical energy for this family.

48. Careful inspection of the electrical devices reveals that a total of 85 W of power is consumed to maintain stand-by power in this family's home.

   a. Determine the electrical energy (in kilowatt-hours) consumed on an annual basis to maintain the stand-by power in the electrical devices used by this family.

   b. Determine the percentage of this family's annual electric utility bill and the percentage of the corresponding annual emissions into the environment that can be traced to the consumption of stand-by power.

49. List some of the strategies this family could use to reduce the consumption of electrical energy and the corresponding emissions into the environment.

Transmitting Electrical Energy

Consumers are not the only people interested in reducing the wasteful use of electrical energy. Electric utility companies have designed their transmission and distribution systems to minimize energy losses. Every kilowatt-hour that is lost in the transmission process from the generating station to your home represents a loss in profit as well as a step backward in the efforts of the utility company to meet environmental regulations. The main source of power loss in the electrical distribution system is the heat produced by the electric current passing through many kilometres of conducting cables. The following equation identifies the key factors affecting these power losses.

power lost in the cables due to heating effects (watts) ——↘   resistance of kilometres ↙—— of cable (ohms)

$$P = I^2 R$$

↑
current passing through the cables (amperes)

Once the resistance of the cables has been made as low as possible, the only way to reduce power losses is to keep the current to a minimum.

Note that the value of the electric current is squared in the equation $P = I^2R$. This means that any reductions in the electric current will dramatically reduce power losses due to heating within the cables. The engineers who

design electric power-distribution systems put this strategy into action by increasing the voltage within the transmission system. The thinking behind this approach is illustrated in Example Problems 1.19 and 1.20.

A 100-km length of transmission cable has a resistance of 5.0 Ω. This cable transmits 500 kW of power from the generator to a small town.

a. Determine the electric current required to transmit the 500 kW of power if the voltage used within the system is 5000 V.

b. Use your answer to part a. to calculate the power lost due to heating effects through the 100 km of conducting cable.

c. Use your answer to part b. to determine the percentage of the transmitted power that was lost due to heating effects in this arrangement.

Solution

a. $P = 500 \ \cancel{kW} \times \dfrac{1000 \ W}{1 \ \cancel{kW}}$ $P = IV$

$\quad = 5.00 \times 10^5 \ W$ $I = \dfrac{P}{V}$

$V = 5000 \ V$ $\quad = \dfrac{5.00 \times 10^5 \ W}{5000 \ V}$

$I = ?$ $\quad = 100 \ A$

The electric current required is 100 A.

b. $I = 100 \ A$ $P = I^2 R$

$R = 5.0 \ \Omega$ $\quad = (100 \ A)^2 (5.0 \ \Omega)$

$P = ?$ $\quad = 5.0 \times 10^4 \ W$

The power lost due to heating effects within the cable is 5.0×10^4 W.

c. transmitted power $= 5.00 \times 10^5$ W

power lost to heating $= 5.0 \times 10^4$ W

% of power lost $= ?$

$\%\text{ of power lost} = \dfrac{\text{power lost to heating}}{\text{transmitted power}} \times 100\%$

$\quad = \dfrac{5.0 \times 10^4 \ W}{5.00 \times 10^5 \ W} \times 100\%$

$\quad = 10\%$

In this system, 10% of the available power was lost due to heating effects within the transmission cables.

Repeat the analysis of Example Problem 1.19 by increasing the voltage within the system to 50 000 V.

Solution

a. $P = 500 \ \cancel{kW} \times \dfrac{1000 \ W}{1 \ \cancel{kW}}$ $P = IV$

$\quad = 5.00 \times 10^5 \ W$ $I = \dfrac{P}{V}$

$V = 50 \ 000 \ V$ $\quad = \dfrac{5.00 \times 10^5 \ W}{50 \ 000 \ V}$

$I = ?$ $\quad = 10.0 \ A$

The electric current required is 10.0 A.

b. $I = 10.0 \ A$ $P = I^2 R$

$R = 5.0 \ \Omega$ $\quad = (10.0 \ A)^2 (5.0 \ \Omega)$

$P = ?$ $\quad = 5.0 \times 10^2 \ W$

The power lost due to heating effects within the cable is 5.0×10^2 W.

c. transmitted power $= 5.00 \times 10^5$ W

power lost to heating $= 5.0 \times 10^2$ W

% of power lost $= ?$

$\%\text{ of power lost} = \dfrac{\text{power lost to heating}}{\text{transmitted power}} \times 100\%$

$\quad = \dfrac{5.0 \times 10^2 \ W}{5.00 \times 10^5 \ W} \times 100\%$

$\quad = 0.10\%$

In this system, 0.10% of the available power was lost due to heating effects within the transmission cables.

Transforming Voltages

As the calculations in Example Problems 1.19 and 1.20 demonstrate, less power is lost to heating effects within the conducting cables if the transmission system minimizes the electric current by using high voltages. Depending upon the amount of power that is being transmitted, the voltages used on the main conducting cables can be as high as 500 kV. Although these ultra-high voltage values are ideal for transmitting electrical energy, they are many times higher than the 240 V or 120 V typically used in homes. Since nearly every home is fed electrical energy from the main transmission system, it is natural to wonder how the ultra-high transmission voltages are transformed into the much lower values used in homes.

The transmission voltages are reduced by a number of devices called **transformers**. As the name suggests, a transformer transforms the voltage value of one circuit into a different value to be used by another circuit. Each of the large cylindrical devices on the power pole in the photograph is called a step-down transformer because it reduces the voltage on the primary circuit (in this case about 4 kV) to a lower value that will enter homes—typically 240 V, which is then split into the 120 V used by most household circuits.

transformer: a device that transforms the AC voltage of one circuit into a different AC voltage for another circuit using separate coils of wire wound around a common iron core

This transformer increases the voltage from the 20 kV produced at the generating station to the ultra-high voltages (500 kV or 230 kV) used for the transmission of electrical energy. Since the voltage is increasing, this device is referred to as a step-up transformer.

Key Components of a Transformer

The essential design of a transformer involves two coils of insulated wire, each wrapped around a common core of laminated iron. The **primary coil** receives the input voltage from some external source, which causes a current to flow. The primary current and the primary voltage remain within the primary coil because the wire of this circuit is insulated. Although the **secondary coil** is a separate circuit that does not contact the primary circuit, the secondary current and the secondary voltage of this coil are a result of the electric current in the primary coil. How is the primary coil able to influence the charges within the secondary coil if they are separate circuits with no electrical connection between the two? You will have an opportunity to discover the answer to this question in the next investigation.

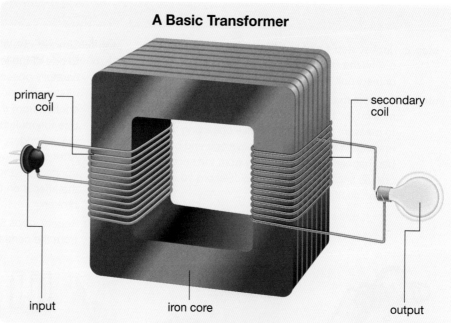

A Basic Transformer

primary coil

secondary coil

input

iron core

output

primary coil: the coil to which the input voltage is applied in a transformer

secondary coil: the coil that supplies the output voltage of a transformer

Investigation

Exploring the Transformer

Purpose
You will build a simple transformer and observe its operation.

 CAUTION!

This investigation involves briefly passing a current through the coil that you build. The coil will become warm and remain that way for a few seconds after the current has passed. If the coil is left connected for more than a few seconds, it will become uncomfortably warm and will unnecessarily drain the batteries. Allow the current to pass through the coil for only a few seconds at a time.

Materials
- 4 AA cells in a plastic battery pack with leads
- digital multimeter
- cardboard cylinder, about 4 cm in diameter and 10 cm in length (empty toilet-tissue roll)
- 2, 10-m pieces of 26- or 28-gauge enamelled magnet wire
- 4 test leads with alligator clips at each end
- strong bar magnet
- iron rod from a ring stand
- small knife
- adhesive tape

 Science Skills

✓ Performing and Recording
✓ Analyzing and Interpreting

Procedure and Observations

step 1: Wrap 10 m of enamelled magnet wire around the cardboard cylinder to make a small coil. Leave about 10 cm of wire free from each end to act as contacts. Use adhesive tape to hold the contacts and the coils in place. Use a small knife to carefully scrape the enamel coating from the last 5 cm of each contact, as shown in Figure C1.56.

Figure C1.56

step 2: Repeat step 1 and build a second coil. Label one coil as the secondary coil and the other as the primary coil.

step 3: Connect the secondary coil to the digital multimeter. Set up the multimeter so it is able to measure DC millivolts. While observing the reading on the multimeter, move one end of the bar magnet toward and away from the secondary coil, as shown in Figure C1.57. Record your observations.

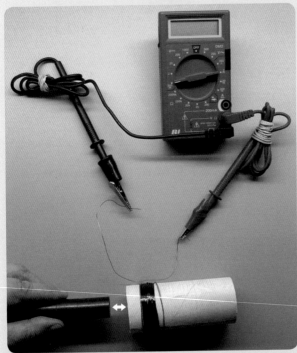

Figure C1.57

step 4: Use the equipment described in step 3 to determine which circumstances produce the largest output on the multimeter and which circumstances produce no output on the multimeter. Record your observations.

step 5: Set up the apparatus as shown in Figure C1.58.

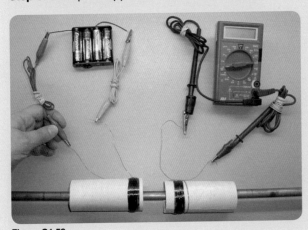

Figure C1.58

step 6: Connect one of the leads from the primary coil to one of the leads of the battery pack. While carefully observing the display on the digital multimeter, momentarily connect the other contact from the primary coil to the battery pack. Use the multimeter to observe the effects on the secondary coil when contact is first made. After only a few seconds of contact, break the connection and use the multimeter to observe the effects on the secondary coil when contact is broken.

step 7: Repeat steps 5 and 6 with the iron rod removed from the centres of the two coils.

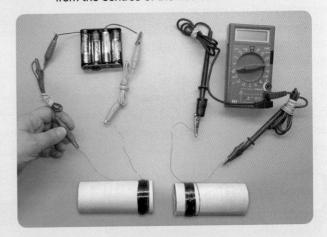

Analysis

1. Review your observations from step 3, when you moved the magnet in and out of the secondary coil.

   a. Was the secondary coil acting as a motor or a generator?

   b. Although the magnet did not touch the secondary coil, a current was induced in the secondary coil. Explain how this effect was able to occur.

2. Review your observations from step 4, when you determined which circumstances produced the maximum and minimum effect on the secondary coil. Summarize your findings.

3. Review your observations from step 6, when you made intermittent contact with the battery pack and the primary coil while using the multimeter to observe the effects on the secondary coil. Although the primary coil did not touch the secondary coil, there was an effect on the secondary coil. Explain how this effect was able to occur.

4. Review your observations from step 7. Suggest a reason why it is important for a transformer to have an iron core.

Describing the Operation of a Transformer

In the "Exploring the Transformer" investigation, you observed that the secondary coil is affected by the primary coil only if current within the primary coil is changing. If a switch connecting the primary coil to a battery pack is suddenly closed, an increasing magnetic field is produced within the secondary coil.

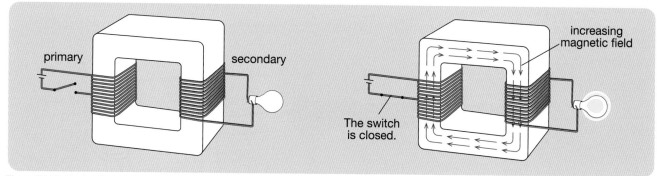

Figure C1.59: Closing the switch causes the current in the primary coil to increase. The magnetic field increases through the secondary coil. A current is induced to flow in the secondary coil.

It is the changing magnetic field within the secondary coil that is central to this process. As long as the magnetic field is changing, a current will be induced in the secondary coil. Since decreasing the magnetic field is also a change, opening the switch can cause a current to be induced in the secondary coil.

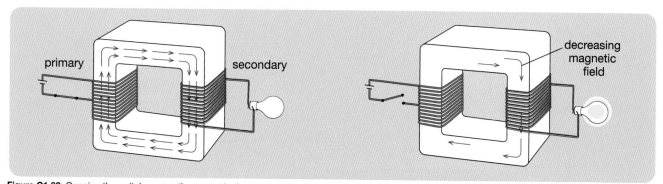

Figure C1.60: Opening the switch causes the current in the primary coil to decrease. The magnetic field decreases within the secondary coil. A current is induced to flow in the secondary coil.

Instead of opening and closing a switch that connects to a DC source, like a battery pack, a more effective way to change the magnetic field is to connect the primary coil to a source of alternating current. In this scheme, the current within the primary coil is continually changing, so the magnetic field is continually changing. The end result is that the induced current in the secondary coil is continually changing in the form of an AC output.

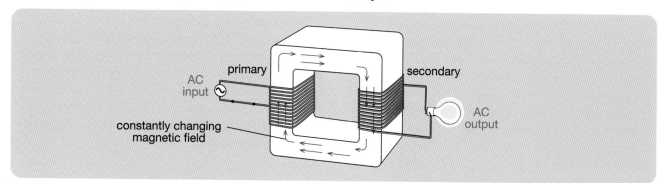

Figure C1.61: A source of alternating current (AC) connected to the primary coil ensures that the magnetic field is constantly changing within the secondary coil. An alternating current (AC) is maintained in the secondary coil.

Stepping Up or Stepping Down Voltage

A transformer is an AC device capable of transforming a voltage value from the primary circuit into another voltage value in the secondary circuit.

Early experiments with transformers revealed that the number of loops or turns of wire on the secondary coil compared to the number of loops of wire on the primary coil determined whether the voltage was stepped up or stepped down.

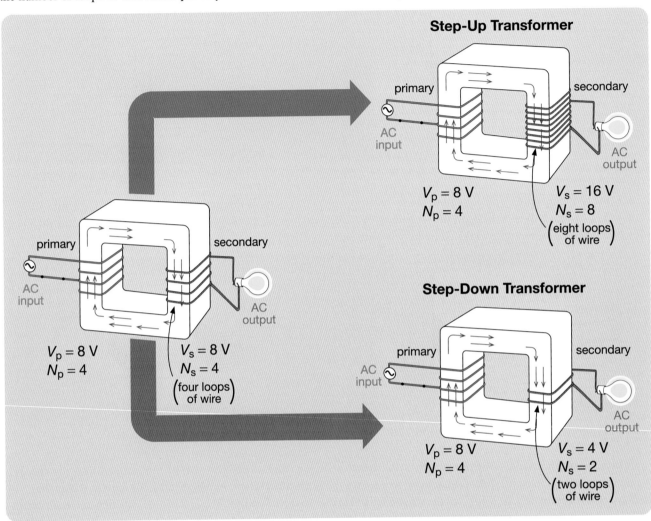

Step-Up Transformer

primary | secondary | AC input | AC output

$V_p = 8$ V
$N_p = 4$

$V_s = 16$ V
$N_s = 8$
(eight loops of wire)

Step-Down Transformer

primary | secondary | AC input | AC output

$V_p = 8$ V
$N_p = 4$

$V_s = 4$ V
$N_s = 2$
(two loops of wire)

primary | secondary | AC input | AC output

$V_p = 8$ V
$N_p = 4$

$V_s = 8$ V
$N_s = 4$
(four loops of wire)

Figure C1.62

In Figure C1.62 the step-up transformer has twice the number of loops of wire on its secondary coil compared to the primary coil. Experiments have shown that if the secondary coil has double the number of loops as the primary coil, the output voltage of the secondary coil is double that of the primary coil. The same reasoning applies to the step-down transformer: if there are half the number of loops on the secondary coil as on the primary coil, the output voltage of the secondary coil is half the value of the primary coil. These ratios can be summarized by the following equation:

This description is incomplete because it is important to remember that energy is conserved. Voltage values cannot be stepped up or stepped down without some other variable responding to rebalance the output energy with the input energy. Transformers can be designed so that energy losses are minimized. Ideally, the input energy equals the output energy; therefore, the power into the primary coil equals the power out of the secondary coil.

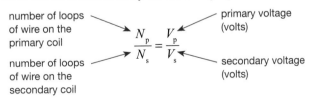

number of loops of wire on the primary coil → N_p ← primary voltage (volts)

number of loops of wire on the secondary coil → N_s $= \dfrac{N_p}{N_s} = \dfrac{V_p}{V_s}$ ← secondary voltage (volts)

As the following equations indicate, the current within the primary and secondary coils is the variable that counteracts changes to the voltage values to ensure that energy is conserved.

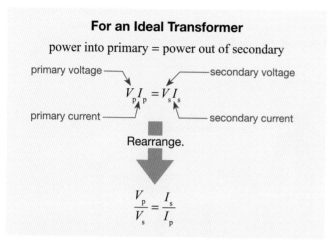

For an Ideal Transformer

power into primary = power out of secondary

primary voltage ⟶   ⟵ secondary voltage

$$V_p I_p = V_s I_s$$

primary current ⟶   ⟵ secondary current

Rearrange.

$$\frac{V_p}{V_s} = \frac{I_s}{I_p}$$

The earlier work with step-up and step-down transformers relates the primary and secondary voltages to the number of turns on each coil.

number of loops of wire on primary coil ⟶

$$\frac{N_p}{N_s} = \frac{V_p}{V_s}$$

⟵ number of loops of wire on secondary coil

These equations can be combined.

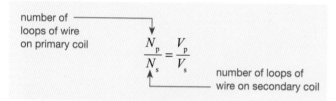

$$\frac{N_p}{N_s} = \frac{V_p}{V_s} = \frac{I_s}{I_p}$$ This is the equation for the ideal transformer.

This equation describes an ideal transformer with no energy losses. In reality, transformers lose a small fraction of the input energy in the form of heat; however, these energy losses are so small that this equation can be used to describe most commercially available transformers.

DANGER
KEEP OUT
28,000 VOLTS
TRANSFORMER

A large neon sign is powered by a high-voltage power supply. The power supply takes a 240-V input and then uses a transformer to increase the voltage to 12 000 V to operate the sign.

a. Does the power supply use a step-up or step-down transformer?

b. If the transformer has 125 turns of wire on the primary coil, determine the number of coils on the secondary coil.

c. The power supply requires 25.0 A of input current. Determine the output current that powers the sign.

Solution

a. Since the input or primary voltage is 240 V and the output or secondary voltage is 12 000 V, this is a step-up transformer.

b. $V_p = 240$ V

$V_s = 12\ 000$ V

$N_p = 125$

$N_s = ?$

$$\frac{N_p}{N_s} = \frac{V_p}{V_s}$$

$$N_s = \frac{N_p V_s}{V_p}$$

$$= \frac{(125)(12\ 000\ \text{V})}{240\ \text{V}}$$

$$= 6.25 \times 10^3$$

The secondary coil of the transformer has 6.25×10^3 turns of wire.

c. $V_p = 240$ V

$V_s = 12\ 000$ V

$I_p = 25.0$ A

$I_s = ?$

$$\frac{V_p}{V_s} = \frac{I_s}{I_p}$$

$$I_s = \frac{V_p I_p}{V_s}$$

$$= \frac{(240\ \text{V})(25.0\ \text{A})}{12\ 000\ \text{V}}$$

$$= 0.500\ \text{A}$$

The output current to power the sign is 0.500 A.

Use the following information to answer questions 50 and 51.

Transformers play a vital role in the distribution and transmission of electrical energy. In the following diagram, transformers can be seen playing a role at the generating station, at the power substation, and on the power poles.

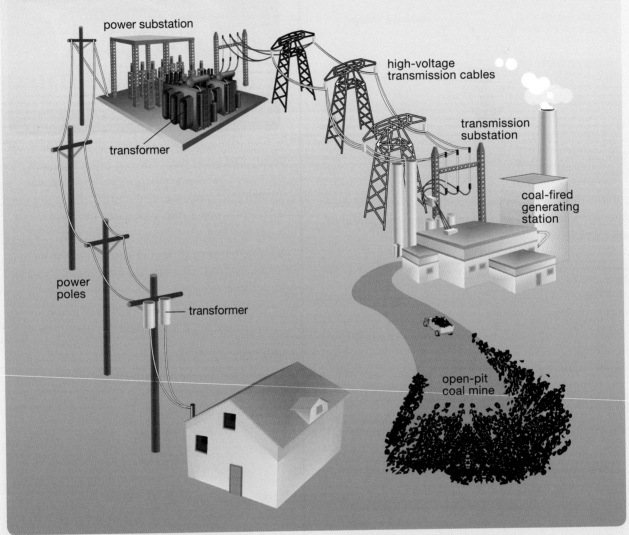

50. The transformer on a power pole takes an input voltage of 4.00 kV and then delivers 240 V to a home.

   a. Is this device a step-up or step-down transformer?

   b. If there are 180 turns of wire on the secondary coil of this transformer, determine the number of turns of wire on the primary coil.

   c. If the maximum current supplied to the home is 100 A, determine the current supplied to the transformer.

51. The generator at the coal-fired generating station supplies the station's transformer with 20.0 kV. The transformer then boosts this voltage value to 230 kV for transmission.

   a. Is this device a step-up or step-down transformer?

   b. Most of the customers of the utility company only require 240 V or 120 V to run the appliances in their households. Explain why the utility company boosts the 20.0 kV from the generator to even higher values.

   c. If the power transmitted is 1.2 MW, calculate the current flowing through the transmission cables.

   d. Use the transformer equation to determine the current the generator is supplying to the transformer at the generating station.

   e. Check your answer to question 51.d. using a different equation.

Power is a quantity that describes the rate of doing work or using energy in joules per seconds or watts. Power was used throughout this lesson to describe the rate at which electrical energy is used in light bulbs, speakers, and a variety of household appliances. The kilowatt-hour is the unit traditionally used by electric utility companies to bill their customers.

The next time you use a kitchen appliance to make waffles, toast bread, or beat an egg, ask yourself this question: "Why is this appliance designed to operate on alternating current?" The answer has everything to do with reducing power losses during transmission and the central role played by transformers.

To reduce power losses in the transmission of electrical energy from the generating station to your home, it is essential that the current in the conducting cables be kept low by keeping the voltage high. However, a high transmission voltage means that there must be some way to reduce the voltage before it enters the homes of consumers. Transformers can reduce and increase voltages very effectively, with minimal energy losses, but transformers are AC devices. Since the entire distribution and transmission system depends upon the use of transformers, the system is based on alternating current.

1.5 Questions

Knowledge

1. Explain why it is misleading to call the bill from a utility company a "power bill."

2. Identify which coil in a step-up transformer has more turns of wire.

Applying Concepts

3. Explain why it is necessary to use alternating current with transformers.

4. Calculate the power dissipated by a toaster with a resistance of 14.0 Ω when it is plugged into a 120-V source.

5. A household clock rated at 5.0 W is operated for 365 days. Calculate the total electrical energy cost if the charge for electrical energy is 8.7¢/kW•h.

6. An ideal transformer has 100 turns of wire in the primary coil and 1000 turns of wire in the secondary coil. If the voltage and current in the primary coil is 120 V and 10.0 A, respectively, determine

   a. the voltage and current in the secondary

   b. the power in the primary and the secondary

7. Explain why it is advantageous to transmit power over large distances at high voltages.

Obtain the handout "Generating Electricity with Fossil Fuels" from the Science 30 Textbook CD. Use the information on this handout to answer question 8.

8. A family just purchased a new refrigerator that consumes 450 kW•h of electrical energy every year. The previous refrigerator was an old, inefficient model that consumed 605 kW•h of electrical energy every year.

   a. If the cost of electrical energy is 8.5¢/kW•h, how much money will this family save on their electric bill each year by using their new refrigerator?

   b. The utility company that provides electrical energy to this family uses a traditional coal-burning facility that pulverizes the coal into a fine powder before burning it to produce steam to drive the turbines. Calculate by how much the family will have reduced their annual emissions of $CO_2(g)$, $SO_x(g)$, $NO_x(g)$, and particulate matter by switching to the newer refrigerator.

   c. Consider your answers to questions 8.a. and 8.b. Which reduction do you think is the most significant?

Chapter 1 Summary

In Chapter 1 you saw how fields surround you and are an integral part of many of the technologies you use every day. Gravitational fields enable Earth to exert forces on objects without physically touching them. Earth's gravitational field keeps satellites in orbit, ensures that raindrops and snowflakes fall to the ground, and ensures that any ball you throw will always return to the surface of the planet. Electric fields enable lightning bolts to travel across the sky and ensure that electrons flow though the wires and circuits of every electrical device you have ever used. In nature, magnetic fields help to shield the surface of Earth from the harmful effects of the solar wind, and sometimes provide a path for these same particles to produce the spectacular displays called the northern lights. Magnetic fields also play a central role in a wide variety of devices, like motors, generators, headphones, microphones, speakers, and transformers.

The influence of electric and magnetic fields does not end here. In Chapter 2 you will see how these two fields can combine to produce the electromagnetic waves responsible for TV signals, microwave cooking, X-ray imaging, and even visible light. Stars emit electromagnetic waves. This is what enables the Sun to sustain life on Earth and provides scientists with valuable information about distant parts of the universe.

Summarize Your Learning

In this chapter you have learned a number of new terms, concepts, equations, and techniques for problem solving. You will have a much easier time recalling and applying the information you have learned if you take some time to organize it into some sort of pattern. Now that you have come to the end of this chapter, this is an appropriate time to focus on the patterns within the things you have learned. Since the pattern has to be in a form that is meaningful to you, you have some options about how you can create this summary. Each of the following options is described in detail in "Summarize Your Learning Activities" in the Reference section.

Option 1: Draw a concept map or a web diagram.	Option 2: Create a point-form summary.	Option 3: Write a story using key terms and concepts.	Option 4: Create a colourful poster.	Option 5: Build a model.	Option 6: Write a script for a skit (a mock news report).

Knowledge

1. In this chapter you investigated three kinds of fields: gravitational fields, electric fields, and magnetic fields. Copy and complete the following table in your notes to summarize the key features of each kind of field.

Type of Field	General Description of Source(s)	General Description of Test Bodies	Equation That Describes Strength of Field	Example of How Field Assists You in a Task or Activity
gravitational field				
electric field				
magnetic field				

2. Refer to your answer to question 1 as you answer questions 2.a. and 2.b.

   a. Compare and contrast gravitational fields with electric fields.

   b. Compare and contrast electric fields with magnetic fields.

3. The concept of a field is a fundamental idea that has been referred to throughout Chapter 1. Distinguish between the following pairs of terms that all relate to the concept of a field.

   a. force and field

   b. field lines and field strength

   c. source of field and test body

4. Obtain the handout "Sketching Fields" from the Science 30 Textbook CD. Follow the instructions on this handout and add the required information.

5. Identify the common source for all magnetic fields.

6. Sketch a simple diagram of a DC electric motor. Label all the key parts.

7. Sketch a simple diagram of an AC generator. Label all the key parts.

8. Explain the differences between the output of a DC generator and the output of an AC generator. Use voltage-versus-time graphs to aid in your explanation.

9. With the aid of diagrams, describe how each of the following instruments is properly connected for taking measurements.

   a. voltmeter

   b. ammeter

   c. ohmmeter

10. Explain the meaning of *kilowatt-hour*. Provide an example of how this unit is used.

11. Transformers play a critical role in the transmission and distribution of electricity.

    a. Sketch a simple diagram that shows the basic parts of a transformer.

    b. With the aid of diagrams, illustrate how a step-up transformer differs from a step-down transformer.

12. Explain why electrical energy is distributed through transmission cables with very high voltage and why this system is designed to run with alternating current.

Applying Concepts

13. A car is parked with its engine off, but the car's owner forgot to turn off the headlights. The car's battery does 6000 J of work to move 500 C of charge from one contact of the headlight bulb to the other.

    a. Calculate the voltage between the two contacts of the headlight.

    b. Determine the energy emitted as heat and light by the bulb of the headlight.

14. In Roman mythology Mars (the god of war) had two attendants, Phobos (fear) and Deimos (panic). This is the origin of the names for the two moons of the planet Mars. Phobos has a mass of 1.08×10^{16} kg and an average radius of 1.35×10^{4} m, while Deimos has a mass of 1.8×10^{15} kg and an average radius of 7.5×10^{3} m.

    a. Calculate the gravitational field strength at the surface of each moon.

    b. Calculate the force of gravity that would act on an astronaut with a total mass of 107 kg on the surface of each moon.

    c. Explain how the same astronaut can experience a different force of gravity on each moon even though the astronaut's mass is the same.

    d. Sketch a diagram of each moon to illustrate the pattern of the gravitational field lines around each moon.

15. A van de Graaff generator is a machine that is able to put large quantities of charge on the metal globe on its top surface. During the winter months, when the air inside buildings is very dry, the globe on top of a van de Graaff generator can hold significant quantities of charge. For this question, consider that charge to be $+5.5 \times 10^{-6}$ C.

    a. Calculate the number of electrons that were moved to produce this charge, and determine whether these electrons were added or removed from the large metal globe.

    b. Calculate the strength of the electric field at the following distances from the centre of the large metal globe.

       i. 40 cm

       ii. 80 cm

       iii. 120 cm

       iv. 160 cm

    c. A speck of dust with a charge of -2.5×10^{-12} C moves into each of the positions described in question 15.b. Calculate the magnitude and direction of the electric force on the dust speck in each location.

    d. Explain how the same speck of dust can experience different amounts of electric force in each location.

    e. Use your answers from question 15.b. to produce a graph of electric field strength versus distance from the centre of the large van de Graaff generator globe. Add the best-fit line.

    f. Explain the reason for the shape of the resulting best-fit line.

    g. Sketch a diagram to show the large van de Graaff generator globe, using arrows to represent the electric field vectors at each of the locations described in question 15.b.

16. Repeat the analysis outlined in all the parts of question 15 if the globe on the van de Graaff generator had a charge of -5.5×10^{-6} C.

17. A car speaker is connected to an AC circuit within the amplifier that supplies the speaker with 20.0 V. Consider the speaker to have a constant resistance of 4.0 Ω for all parts of this question.

a. Calculate the electric current that flows through the speaker.

b. Use your answer to question 17.a. to determine the power rating of this speaker.

c. Use your answers to questions 17.a. and 17.b. to determine the electrical energy that is supplied to the speaker during 10.0 min of operation. Answer in joules.

18. Repeat the analysis outlined in the steps of question 17 using a speaker with a resistance of 8.0 Ω. Use your analysis to determine which speaker would sound louder.

Use the following information to answer questions 19 to 21.

A student uses the following equipment to complete a Science 30 lab activity:

- 3 resistors (500 Ω, 1000 Ω, and 1500 Ω)
- 6.0-V battery pack
- several leads for connecting the components of circuits
- digital multimeter capable of measuring volts, amperes, and ohms

These materials can be used to build either a series circuit or a parallel circuit.

19. The first task is to build a circuit that will incorporate all three resistors and use the minimum amount of electrical energy from the battery pack.

a. Sketch a schematic diagram of this circuit. Be sure to include how the meter would be used to measure the current through all three resistors and the voltage across each of the three resistors.

b. Using the data provided, calculate the total resistance for the resistors in your circuit.

c. Use your answer to question 19.b. to calculate the current that would flow through all three resistors.

d. Use your answer to question 19.b. to calculate the electrical energy that would be used by this circuit if it were allowed to operate for 10.0 min.

20. Repeat the analysis outlined in the parts of question 19 for a circuit that will incorporate all three resistors and will use the maximum amount of energy from the battery pack.

21. Refer to your answers to questions 19 and 20. Determine whether it was the series circuit or the parallel circuit that used the maximum amount of energy.

Use the following information to answer questions 22 to 25.

The Second Price Tag

When most people purchase a major appliance, the main consideration is the cost to buy the appliance, which is printed on the price tag. Another consideration is the cost to operate the appliance over its lifetime. This cost could be called the second price tag because, after the initial purchase, this cost will be paid month after month on the electric bill. Although more energy-efficient appliances may have a slightly higher purchasing cost, this is balanced against their lower operating costs.

Environmental Considerations

Another set of considerations is the impact the use of an appliance will have on the environment. In Alberta, most electricity is generated by burning coal or other fossil fuels to drive a turbine that turns the shaft of a generator. This means that every kilowatt-hour of electricity has an environmental consequence in terms of the emissions of $CO_2(g)$, $NO_x(g)$, $SO_x(g)$, and particulate matter.

Comparison Shopping

The following data was collected for two 22-cubic-foot refrigerators with top-mounted freezers.

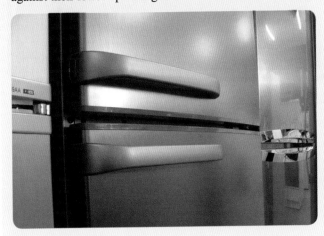

Refrigerator	Model A	Model B
Cost to Purchase	$1699.99	$1200
Annual Energy Consumption	435 kW•h	545 kW•h
Life Expectancy of Refrigerator	17 years	17 years
Lifetime Operating Costs		
Environmental Considerations		

22. Use 9.3¢/kW•h to calculate the following costs.

  a. the lifetime operating costs for Model A

  b. the lifetime operating costs for Model B

23. Obtain the handout "Generating Electricity with Fossil Fuels" to calculate the mass of $CO_2(g)$, $SO_x(g)$, $NO_x(g)$, and particulate matter emitted for Model A if the electricity is generated using a traditional coal-fired generating station that uses pulverized coal.

24. Repeat the analysis outlined in question 23 for Model B.

25. In this set of questions you have examined three criteria to be considered when buying a major appliance: the cost to purchase, the lifetime operating costs, and some environmental considerations.

  a. How do you think most consumers rank these three criteria?

  b. How do you think these three criteria should be ranked in the minds of consumers?

  c. If you were purchasing a new refrigerator, would you buy Model A or Model B?

26. The doorbell of a home requires 10.0 V to operate. A transformer is used to connect the doorbell to a 120-V circuit within the home. The doorbell transformer has 500 turns on the primary coil and supplies the doorbell with 900 mA of current.

  a. Determine whether the transformer features a step-up or step-down design.

  b. Calculate the number of turns on the secondary coil.

  c. Calculate the current that is drawn from the 120-V household circuit to operate the doorbell.

Use the following information to answer questions 27 to 32.

Obtain the handout "An Energy-Conversion Device" from the Science 30 Textbook CD. Use the information on this handout to answer the next six questions.

27. Identify the proper name for the device shown in Part 1 of the handout.

28. Describe the rotation of the loop in detail from step 1 through to step 4 in Part 1 of the handout. Be sure to explain the direction of motion of the highlighted section of the loop in each step.

29. Refer to the diagram for Modification 1 in Part 2 of the handout. Carefully compare this diagram with step 1 in Part 1, and explain how this modification will affect the motion of the loop.

30. Refer to the diagram for Modification 2 in Part 2 of the handout. Carefully compare this diagram with step 1 in Part 1, and explain how this modification will affect the motion of the loop.

31. Refer to the diagram for Modification 3 in Part 2 of the handout. Carefully compare this diagram with step 1 in Part 1, and explain how this modification will affect the motion of the loop.

32. Refer to the diagram for Modification 4 in Part 2 of the handout. Carefully compare this diagram with step 1 in Part 1, and explain how this modification will affect the motion of the loop.

Use the following information to answer questions 33 to 35.

The diagram shows two devices that transform an input of mechanical energy into an output of electrical energy. Note that the output displayed on the voltmeter changes as the loop is forced to rotate between the two stationary magnets.

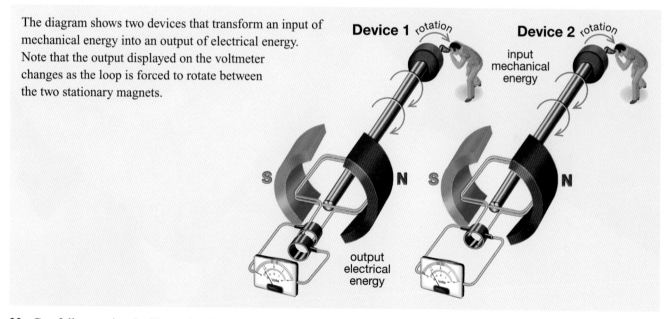

33. Carefully examine the illustration for Device 1.

   a. Identify the proper name for this device.

   b. Sketch a graph of voltage versus time to describe the output from this device.

   c. The number of rotations the loop is forced to make every minute can be increased. Sketch a graph of voltage versus time to show the output from the device under these circumstances.

34. Carefully examine the illustration for Device 2.

   a. Identify the proper name for this device.

   b. Sketch a graph of voltage versus time to describe the output from this device.

   c. The number of rotations the loop is forced to make every minute can be increased. Sketch a graph of voltage versus time to show the output from the device under these circumstances.

35. The stationary magnets on either side of the rotating loops play an essential role in the operation of each of these devices. Without these magnets, no electrical energy would be produced if the loops were forced to rotate; yet, these stationary magnets do not even touch the loops. Explain how the stationary magnets are able to exert forces and produce an electric current within the loop even though there is no physical contact.

Chapter **2** The Electromagnetic Spectrum

In 1987 there were just 100 000 cellphones in Canada. By 2001, there were over 9.5 million. Some experts estimate that by the year 2010 there will be over 2.2 billion cellphone users worldwide. Teenagers make up the fastest growing segment of the market in Canada. Recent statistics indicate that a typical Canadian teenager with a cellphone sends or receives more than nine text messages and makes at least three phone calls a day.

Many people are surprised to learn that a cellphone is actually a transmitter and receiver of radio waves. Radio waves are used in communications and broadcasting and in microwave ovens to heat food. Radio waves emitted by objects in space are collected by astronomers using very large radio telescopes. These radio waves provide valuable information about solar flares, sun spots, and the surface temperatures of planets.

How are the radio waves sent and received by cellphones different from the radio waves emitted from distant stars and planets? How are they the same? Why are the telescopes used to detect radio waves so much larger than the telescopes used to detect light waves? How do light waves compare to radio waves?

In this chapter you will have an opportunity to answer these questions as you explore the properties of radio waves, light, and the rest of the electromagnetic spectrum.

Try This Activity

Exploring Coded Signals

Background Information

Remote controls can be used to send commands to a large number of consumer electronics, such as televisions, VCRs, and DVD players. Nearly all remote controls use an invisible wave to send coded signals to the machine being controlled. When the waves containing the coded signal strike a photovoltaic cell, energy in the wave is transformed into electrical energy. If the photovoltaic cell is connected to a set of headphones, you can hear what the signal sounds like.

Purpose

In Part A you will compare the coded signals produced by different types of remote controls. In Part B you will explore some of the properties of the waves that carry these coded signals.

Part A: Listening to the Coded Signal

Materials

- photovoltaic cell with two leads
- 2 test leads with alligator clips at each end
- pair of sensitive headphones (the type you might use with a portable music player)
- at least two different remote controls, preferably with different brand names
- "Properties of the Waves Emitted by Remote Controls" handout

Procedure and Observations

step 1: Use the two test leads to connect the photovoltaic cells to the headphones, as shown in Figure C2.1.

Figure C2.1

step 2: Test the detector you built in step 1 by bringing it close to a strong light source and covering and uncovering the surface of the photovoltaic cell with your hand. You should be able to hear a wavering sound that corresponds to light intermittently hitting the surface.

step 3: Aim one of the remote controls at the photovoltaic cell. Press one of the keys and note the sound that is created as the coded signal strikes the photovoltaic cell. Test the other keys to see if you can hear differences in the sounds that relate to the corresponding signals. Record your observations.

step 4: Repeat step 3 for at least one other remote control that has a different brand name. Record your observations.

Part B: Properties of the Waves Emitted by Remote Controls

Procedure and Observations

step 1: Obtain the handout "Properties of the Waves Emitted by Remote Controls" from the Science 30 Textbook CD.

step 2: Follow the instructions on this handout, and record your observations.

Analysis

1. Suggest a reason why one brand of remote control is often unable to operate another brand of television.

2. Sketch a simple flowchart to show the energy transformations that occur from the batteries in the remote control to the sound you heard in your headphones.

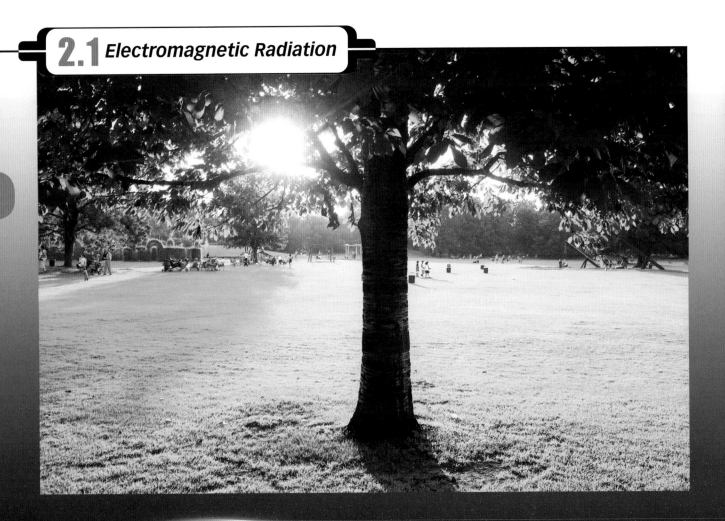

Imagine
walking between some
shade trees early on a warm summer
morning. Although the air is still cool, the
effect of the sunlight is noticeable the instant
you pass from a shaded spot to an area bathed in
sunlight. Upon leaving the shadows, your eyes might
automatically squint in response to the dramatic increase
in the brightness of the light. Your skin would also detect
a change as the Sun's rays create a warming sensation on
exposed surfaces. If the day happened to be one with
record-breaking high temperatures, the black asphalt
pavement on roadways would absorb and then re-emit
energy from the Sun for hours into the evening, long
after the sun has set. Your eyes would not be able
to detect this re-emitted radiant heat, but
the thermal receptors in the skin on
your fingertips could.

You have learned in previous courses that energy travels from the Sun to Earth through the near-perfect vacuum of space in the form of **radiation**. Recall that the radiation from the Sun is vitally important since it provides the essential input energy for virtually every food web and warms Earth so that the planet can be habitable. In Chapter 1 you learned about solar wind—radiation from the Sun in the form of particles with mass like electrons and protons.

radiation: energy emitted in the form of particles or waves

FORMS OF RADIATION FROM THE SUN

Type of Radiation	solar-wind particles	electromagnetic radiation
How Energy Is Transmitted	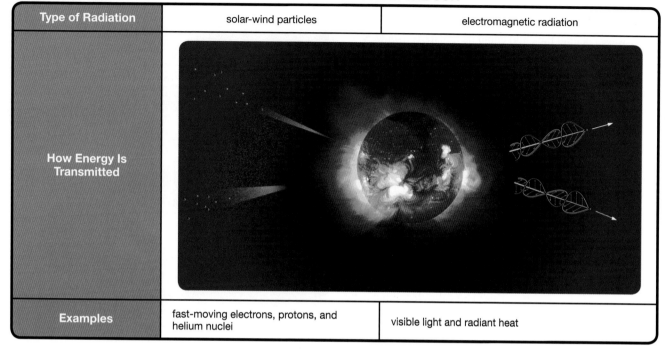	
Examples	fast-moving electrons, protons, and helium nuclei	visible light and radiant heat

The type of radiation that you can see with your eyes and sense as radiant heat with your skin does not involve particles with mass; instead, it is transmitted in the form of **electromagnetic radiation**, or **EMR**. Electromagnetic radiation consists of a changing electric field and a changing magnetic field travelling at right angles to one another. As you learned in Chapter 1, electric fields are produced by charged objects, whereas the source of all magnetic fields is moving charges. Electromagnetic radiation originates from accelerating charges.

In this lesson you will have an opportunity to survey the many forms of electromagnetic radiation. You may be surprised at how many everyday devices utilize electromagnetic technologies.

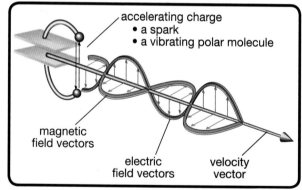

Figure C2.2: Electromagnetic radiation

electromagnetic radiation (EMR): a wave that consists of a changing electric field and a changing magnetic field travelling at right angles to one another

Practice

Use the table "Forms of Radiation from the Sun" to answer questions 1 and 2.

1. A straight line drawn from the centre to the perimeter of a circle is called a radius. Suggest an explanation for the origins of the word *radiation*.

2. In Chapter 1 you learned that in addition to solar wind, astronauts need to be protected from cosmic rays. Cosmic rays are large, positively charged particles emitted from stars in distant parts of the galaxy.

   a. Explain whether or not cosmic rays can be classified as a type of electromagnetic radiation.

   b. Describe evidence from your own experiences that supports the idea that distant stars emit electromagnetic radiation that travels to Earth.

Transmitting Energy Through Vibrations

Carefully examine Figure C2.3. The idea that waves transmit energy from one place to another through vibrations is demonstrated in the photograph.

The child's splashes disturb the surface of the water. As the water's surface returns to equilibrium, vibrations are set up in the form of ripples. The ripples transmit energy away from the child along the water's surface. In a similar way, the larger waves behind the child could be transferring energy from a boat far offshore.

Above the water, the child's voice disturbs the molecules in the air and causes a pattern of vibrations to carry sound waves away from the child through the air. As the sound energy reaches the ears of other people on the beach, they might turn in the direction of the source.

In the background of the photo, electromagnetic radiation from the setting Sun warms everyone on the beach and provides the last hours of daylight. These waves are different from the sound waves and the water waves because, in this case, the wave energy is not transmitted by vibrating matter.

When it comes to electromagnetic radiation, it's electric and magnetic fields that are doing the vibrating. You know from your work in Chapter 1 that these fields are invisible and are not a form of matter. This is how the electromagnetic radiation is able to travel through the vacuum of space to Earth. If electromagnetic radiation required matter to carry the vibrations, the energy from the Sun would be unable to reach Earth. Since electric and magnetic fields can exist in matter as well as in a vacuum, the electromagnetic radiation is able to travel through the gases of Earth's atmosphere to the shore in the photograph.

Figure C2.3

Practice

Use the following information to answer questions 3 and 4.

As electric current passes through the filament of an incandescent light bulb, the resistance of the tungsten filament causes it to heat up and emit light. Nearly all the air has been removed from the bulb so that the extreme temperature of the filament will not cause the filament to burn. This type of light source is considered to be inefficient because only 10% of the electrical energy produces light energy. The other 90% of the input energy produces waste heat.

3. Identify ways in which your body could detect the electromagnetic radiation emitted by the light bulb.
4. Explain how electromagnetic radiation is able to travel from the filament to the surrounding glass if the air inside the bulb is almost completely removed.

Electromagnetic Radiation Transfers Energy

Background Information

Some devices, like small calculators and garden lights, can be powered by a photovoltaic cell, which converts light energy into electrical energy. This technology can be used to build a detector that indicates the intensity of electromagnetic radiation.

Purpose

You will assemble and use a simple detector to explore the electromagnetic radiation emitted from an overhead projector.

Materials

- overhead projector set up with an equilateral prism by your teacher
- photovoltaic cell with two leads
- 2 test leads with alligator clips at each end
- digital multimeter
- "Electromagnetic Energy to Electrical Energy" handout

Procedure and Observations

step 1: Set up the digital multimeter to measure millivolts.

step 2: Connect one end of each test lead to the photovoltaic cell. Connect the other ends of each test lead to the digital multimeter, as shown in Figure C2.4.

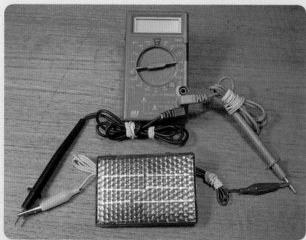

Figure C2.4

step 3: It is important to test the detector to ensure it is working. Bring the open face of the photovoltaic cell close to a light source and note how the display on the multimeter changes. Record your observations.

step 4: Obtain the handout "Electromagnetic Energy to Electrical Energy" from the Science 30 Textbook CD. You will record your results for the remaining steps on this handout.

Science Skills

✓ Performing and Recording
✓ Analyzing and Interpreting

step 5: Your teacher will turn on the projector with the prism and then turn off the lights in the room. You should see the white light from the projector being separated into all the colours of the rainbow on the screen.

step 6: Set the multimeter on its most sensitive setting. Place the photovoltaic cell in the violet region of the spectrum. Slowly move it toward the red end as you note the readings for each colour on the multimeter. Continue to move the photovoltaic cell beyond the red area until the values displayed on the multimeter reach a low value that no longer changes. Measure how far you were able to move into the dark area, away from the red region, to reach this point. Record the multimeter readings and your position on the handout.

step 7: Place the photovoltaic cell in the violet region of the spectrum and move it toward the area of darkness. Note the multimeter readings. Continue to move the apparatus until the signal reaches a low value that no longer changes. Measure how far you were able to move into the dark area to reach this point. Record the multimeter readings and your position on the handout.

Analysis

1. Describe how the multimeter readings changed as you moved the photovoltaic cell closer to a bright light source.

Refer to your observations on the handout as you answer the following questions.

2. Describe how the multimeter readings changed as you moved your detector
   a. through each colour of the spectrum
   b. into the dark region that borders the red region
   c. into the dark region that borders the violet region

3. The simple detector you built transforms electromagnetic energy into electrical energy. Use this fact to interpret your results from question 2 by describing how the intensity (strength) of the electromagnetic radiation changed in each case.

4. Your eyes are able to detect the electromagnetic radiation that produces all the colours of the rainbow. Describe the evidence from this investigation that suggests that your eyes are unable to detect all the electromagnetic radiation emitted by the projector.

Describing Electromagnetic Radiation

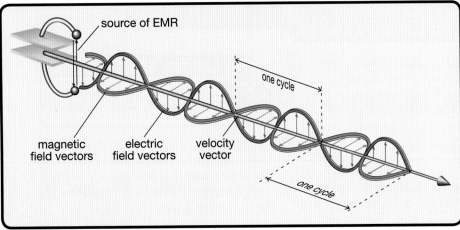

transverse wave: a wave in which the vibrations are perpendicular to the direction the wave is travelling

cycle: one complete vibration of a wave

wavelength: the distance from a point on one wave to the corresponding point on the next wave; the length of one cycle

Figure C2.5: EMR is a transverse wave. The magnetic field vectors are at right angles to the velocity vector. The electric field vectors are at right angles to the velocity vector.

Electromagnetic radiation can be described using the same terminology that you applied to other types of waves in previous courses. Electromagnetic radiation is a **transverse wave** because the direction of the vibrations is at right angles to the wave's direction of travel. Just like other transverse waves, electromagnetic radiation has crests and troughs. One **cycle** of the wave contains one crest and one trough of either the electric field vibration or the magnetic field vibration. A wave train is a series of many cycles and forms a repeating pattern of vibrations. The notion of a cycle is also important because it is central to two of the most important measurements used to describe a wave—wavelength and frequency.

Wavelength

The distance required for one complete cycle is a key characteristic of the wave. The length of one cycle is called the **wavelength**. In other words, wavelength is the distance from a point on one wave to the corresponding point on the next wave. The symbol for wavelength is the Greek letter *lamda, λ*.

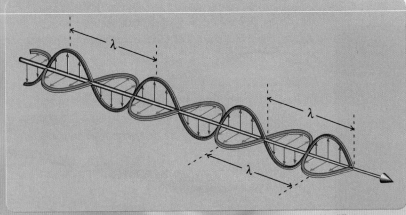

Figure C2.6: The wavelength, λ, of electromagnetic radiation can be measured in different ways.

Example Problem 2.1

Determine the wavelength of this electromagnetic radiation.

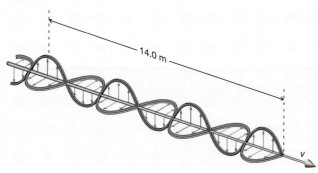

14.0 m

Solution

step 1: Determine the number of wavelengths in the space.

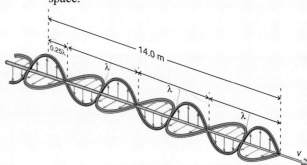

0.25λ   14.0 m   λ   λ   λ

There are 3.25 wavelengths in the space.

step 2: Calculate the wavelength of the EMR.

$$3.25 \, \lambda = 14.0 \text{ m}$$

$$1 \, \lambda = \frac{14.0 \text{ m}}{3.25}$$

$$= 4.31 \text{ m}$$

The wavelength of this EMR is 4.31 m.

Practice

5. Determine the wavelength of the following examples of electromagnetic radiation.

a.

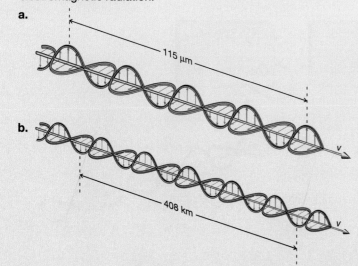

115 μm

b.

408 km

Frequency

Electromagnetic radiation can also be described in terms of how frequently a cycle passes a stationary point. This is known as the **frequency** of the wave. The symbol for frequency is f. If three cycles pass a point in one second, the frequency is said to be three cycles per second. To keep the communication more concise, "cycles per second" is simply called **hertz (Hz)**, in honour of Heinrich Hertz, who discovered radio waves. So, a frequency of three cycles per second is simply written as $f = 3$ Hz. If five cycles pass a point in a second, then the frequency is described as five cycles per second, or $f = 5$ Hz.

▶ **frequency:** the number of cycles per second

▶ **hertz (Hz):** the unit for frequency

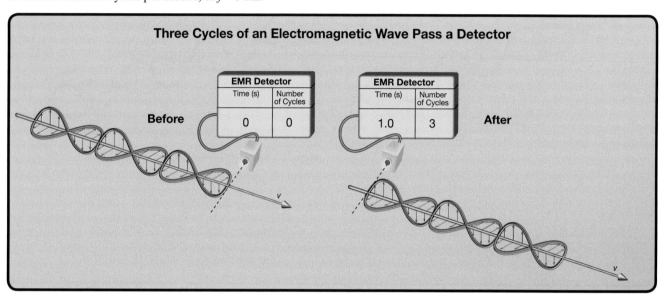

Three Cycles of an Electromagnetic Wave Pass a Detector

Example Problem 2.2

The following diagram shows an illustration of an electromagnetic radiation passing a detector. Use this information to determine the frequency of the EMR.

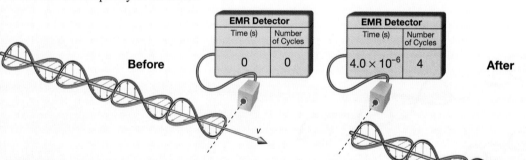

Solution

number of cycles passing detector = 4

time for the cycles to pass $= 4.0 \times 10^{-6}$ s

$f = ?$

$$f = \frac{\text{number of cycles passing detector}}{\text{time for the cycles to pass}}$$

$$= \frac{4}{4.0 \times 10^{-6} \text{ s}}$$

$$= 1.0 \times 10^{6} \text{ Hz}$$

$$= 1.0 \text{ MHz}$$

The frequency of the EMR is 1.0 MHz.

Alternative Solution

If four cycles pass in 4.0×10^{-6} s, then one cycle passes in 1.0×10^{-6} s. That means, for every second, one million cycles pass. This gives a frequency of one million cycles per second, or 1.0 MHz.

6. Determine the frequency of the following examples of electromagnetic radiation.

   a. In 1.00 ms, 740 radio waves pass the antenna of a radio.

   b. In 1.00 μs, 2450 microwaves pass through a point on a piece of cheese in a microwave oven.

Universal Wave Equation

The measurements of wavelength and frequency not only describe key characteristics of waves, they also provide a very convenient way to calculate the speed of the wave.

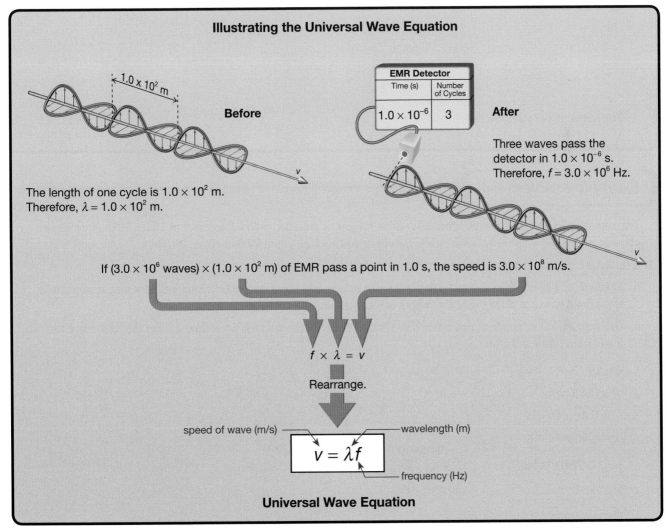

Illustrating the Universal Wave Equation

The length of one cycle is 1.0×10^2 m.
Therefore, $\lambda = 1.0 \times 10^2$ m.

EMR Detector

Time (s)	Number of Cycles
1.0×10^{-6}	3

Three waves pass the detector in 1.0×10^{-6} s.
Therefore, $f = 3.0 \times 10^6$ Hz.

If $(3.0 \times 10^6$ waves$) \times (1.0 \times 10^2$ m$)$ of EMR pass a point in 1.0 s, the speed is 3.0×10^8 m/s.

$$f \times \lambda = v$$

Rearrange.

speed of wave (m/s) ——— ——— wavelength (m)

$$v = \lambda f$$

——— frequency (Hz)

Universal Wave Equation

The equation $v = \lambda f$ is called the universal wave equation because it applies universally to all types of waves. When it comes to electromagnetic radiation, there is a very wide range of wavelength and frequency values, but the speed of all these waves when travelling through a vacuum is always the same, 3.00×10^8 m/s (the speed of light). This particular speed value has a special significance in science; so, it is given its own symbol, c. That's why the universal wave equation is often written as $c = \lambda f$ when it involves electromagnetic radiation. The speed of light is not always mentioned in problems involving electromagnetic radiation. It is important to remember the value of c or to be able to find it in the Science Data Booklet or some other resource.

Example Problem 2.3

An excited atom in a neon sign emits electromagnetic radiation with a wavelength of 6.4×10^{-7} m.

a. Calculate the frequency of the electromagnetic radiation.

b. If the neon sign was located 25.0 m from an observer, how long would it take the light from the sign to reach the observer?

Solution

a. $\lambda = 6.4 \times 10^{-7}$ m

$v = c = 3.00 \times 10^8$ m/s

$f = ?$

$c = \lambda f$

$f = \dfrac{c}{\lambda}$

$= \dfrac{3.00 \times 10^8 \text{ m/s}}{6.4 \times 10^{-7} \text{ m}}$

$= 4.7 \times 10^{14}$ 1/s

$= 4.7 \times 10^{14}$ Hz

The frequency of the EMR is 4.7×10^{14} Hz.

b. $\Delta d = 25.0$ m

$v = c = 3.00 \times 10^8$ m/s

$\Delta t = ?$

$v = \dfrac{\Delta d}{\Delta t}$

$\Delta t = \dfrac{\Delta d}{c}$

$= \dfrac{25.0 \text{ m}}{3.00 \times 10^8 \text{ m/s}}$

$= 8.33 \times 10^{-8}$ s

The light would take 8.33×10^{-8} s to travel from the sign to the observer.

Example Problem 2.4

The antenna of a FM radio station broadcasts electromagnetic radiation with a frequency of 104.5 MHz. A driver in a car is receiving these FM radio waves while travelling down a highway at 90.0 km/h, or 25.0 m/s.

a. Calculate the wavelength of the electromagnetic radiation.

b. Some of the FM radio waves can leave Earth's atmosphere and travel into space. Calculate how long it would take these radio waves to reach the Moon, which is located about 3.84×10^8 m from Earth.

c. Use your answer to part b. to determine how far the car would travel in the same time it takes the radio wave to travel from Earth to the Moon.

Solution

a. $f = 104.5$ MHz

$= 104.5 \times 10^6$ Hz

$= 104.5 \times 10^6$ 1/s

$v = c = 3.00 \times 10^8$ m/s

$\lambda = ?$

$c = \lambda f$

$\lambda = \dfrac{f}{c}$

$= \dfrac{104.5 \times 10^6 \text{ 1/s}}{3.00 \times 10^8 \text{ m/s}}$

$= 0.348$ m

The wavelength of the EMR is 0.348 m.

b. $\Delta d = 3.84 \times 10^8$ m

$v = c = 3.00 \times 10^8$ m/s

$\Delta t = ?$

$v = \dfrac{\Delta d}{\Delta t}$

$\Delta t = \dfrac{\Delta d}{v}$

$= \dfrac{3.84 \times 10^8 \text{ m}}{3.00 \times 10^8 \text{ m/s}}$

$= 1.28$ s

The FM radio wave would take 1.28 s to travel from Earth to the Moon.

c. $\Delta t = 1.28$ s

$v = 25.0$ m/s

$\Delta d = ?$

$v = \dfrac{\Delta d}{\Delta t}$

$\Delta d = v \Delta t$

$= (25.0 \text{ m/s})(1.28 \text{ s})$

$= 32.0$ m

The car would travel 32.0 m in the same time that it takes the radio wave to travel from Earth to the Moon.

7. An AM radio station broadcasts on a frequency of 960 kHz.
   a. Calculate the wavelength of this electromagnetic radiation.
   b. If a city block is about 100 m long, approximately how many city blocks would it take to contain one wavelength of this electromagnetic radiation?

8. Digital cellphones operate by sending and receiving electromagnetic radiation with a wavelength of about 16.5 cm.
   a. Determine the frequency of the electromagnetic radiation emitted by a digital cellphone.
   b. Determine your height in metres; then calculate how many wavelengths from a digital cellphone could fit in the space between your feet and the top of your head.

The Electromagnetic Spectrum

The complete range of all electromagnetic radiation is called the **electromagnetic spectrum**. The types of waves are usually organized according to wavelength and frequency.

> **electromagnetic spectrum:** the wide band of different types of electromagnetic radiation ranging from radio waves to gamma rays

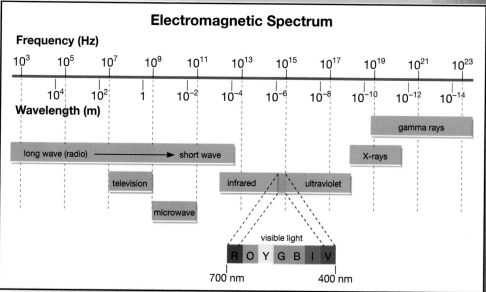

Figure C2.7: The electromagnetic spectrum

Note that some of the individual bands of electromagnetic radiation overlap one another. This is because the same type of electromagnetic radiation can be used to accomplish a number of very different tasks. As an example, waves with a frequency between 10^9 and 10^{11} Hz can be used for both communication (classified as radio waves) and for radar (classified as microwaves). The best way to understand how the individual bands on this chart relate to one another is to look at three key characteristics:

- the nature of the source for each band
- the energy transmitted by each band
- the effects of each band on living tissue

Radio Waves

Radio waves have the lowest frequency of all types of electromagnetic radiation because they are produced by the low-frequency vibrations of electrons within electric circuits. The ability of these waves to travel through the atmosphere makes them ideally suited for communication. However, the inability of radio waves to penetrate metal objects means that an external **antenna** is often required.

Figure C2.8: The antenna on this tower broadcasts radio waves into the surrounding countryside.

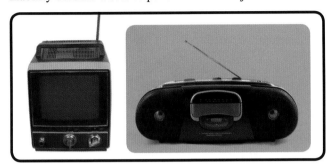

> **radio wave:** a type of electromagnetic radiation with a frequency less than 3000 GHz; used primarily for communications
>
> **antenna:** a transmitter or receiver of electromagnetic energy
>
> **extremely low frequency (ELF):** electromagnetic radiation with a frequency between 3 and 300 Hz; emitted from power distribution cables
>
> **magnetic resonance imaging (MRI):** a method of obtaining internal images of objects, especially living organisms, by using radio waves and strong magnetic fields

When a radio wave passes the antenna of a receiver, the vibrating electric fields within the wave cause electrons within the antenna to vibrate as well. The circuitry attached to the antenna decodes this electric signal, providing the user with the radio or TV broadcast. Since many radio waves can be received by the same antenna, the circuitry must allow users to select the particular frequency used by the station they wish to listen to or watch.

The effects of radio waves on living tissue vary, depending upon the specific frequency or wavelength. Radio waves with the lowest frequency are called **extremely low frequency** waves, or **ELF** for short. These radio waves are emitted from the 60 Hz of AC current found in household wiring and from power lines. It is unclear whether these waves have any effect on human health.

Radio waves with a wavelength of about 4 m are used with strong magnetic fields in **magnetic resonance imaging** (**MRI**) machines to produce detailed images of the inside of the human body. When these radio waves are directed at a specific body part, the nuclei of the hydrogen atoms in that body part give off energy, which is used by a computer to create an image. These particular radio waves are chosen for this purpose because they appear to have no harmful effects on the body. This lack of effects is thought to be due to the generally low energy content of these waves.

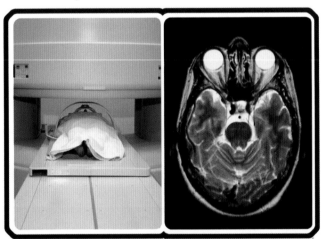

Figure C2.9: A magnetic resonance imaging, or MRI, machine uses radio waves to produce images of internal body parts.

Practice

9. Identify which part of a radio wave causes electrons in a car's antenna to vibrate.

10. In Chapter 1 you learned that metal objects can shield both electric and magnetic fields.
    a. Explain why a car's antenna must be located outside the car or built into the windshield.
    b. Explain why a car's radio is momentarily unable to receive a signal when the car travels under a highway overpass.

11. Many people enjoy speculating about the possibility of intelligent life inhabiting planets that orbit stars other than the Sun. It has been estimated that the first television shows broadcast in the mid-1900s would take about 50 years to reach all of the planets orbiting the nearest 400 stars to Earth. Estimate how far a radio wave containing a TV signal could travel in 50 years.

Microwaves

Although **microwaves** overlap with very short wavelength radio waves, they are usually classified as a distinct category because they generally transmit more energy than radio waves. To produce the desired high-frequency radiation of microwaves, high-frequency circuits are used. These circuits require special vacuum tubes to create microwaves.

> **microwaves:** a type of electromagnetic radiation with a frequency between 1 GHz and 100 GHz; used for radar, satellite communications, and cooking food

The tube in Figure C2.10 is from a microwave oven. It is specially designed to produce electromagnetic radiation with a frequency of 2450 MHz. This frequency is best for causing water molecules to increase their molecular motion and to start rotating within the changing electric field of the microwaves. The result is that the rotating water molecules increase the molecular motion of other molecules in the food, causing a temperature increase.

Figure C2.10

Similar heating effects also occur when microwaves interact with fat or sugar molecules, but the fastest cooking occurs when the food has a high water content.

Figure C2.11: Whole eggs can explode when heated in a microwave oven. This is due to the buildup of steam within the egg's shell.

Since living tissue contains a high percentage of water molecules, the effects of microwaves on living tissue can be hazardous, particularly to those tissues that form the lens of the eye. There is evidence that prolonged exposure to microwaves leads to cataracts later in life.

Higher-frequency microwaves (ones that are not absorbed by water molecules) are used in telecommunications because they are particularly effective at penetrating through rain, snow, haze, and smoke. This makes microwaves ideally suited for radar applications and satellite communications.

? DID YOU KNOW?

The global positioning system (GPS) is a system of Earth-orbiting satellites that can provide information about the exact location of anyone with a GPS receiver. Each satellite transmits microwave signals that are modulated by timed pulses. When pulses are received from four or more other satellites, an inexpensive GPS receiver can determine positions on Earth with an accuracy of ±5 m.

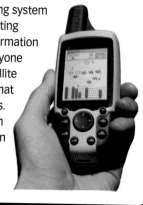

Practice

12. If microwave ovens use electromagnetic radiation with a frequency of 2450 MHz, calculate the wavelength of the microwaves.

13. Explain the following statement.

    When reheating a plate of food in a microwave oven, it is important not to leave a metal fork on the plate. The metal fork will act as an antenna for the microwaves in the oven, resulting in dangerous sparking.

Infrared Radiation

When sunlight passes through a prism, it is separated into all the colours of the rainbow. If thermometers with blackened bulbs are placed in the coloured region of the spectrum, the temperature increases relative to a control thermometer that is shielded from the prism. These temperature increases indicate that visible light transfers energy. If a thermometer is placed in the dark area beside the red region, it shows an increase in temperature as well. Even though there is no visible light in this area, the thermometer indicates that energy is being transmitted. When this experiment was first done in 1800, the conclusion was that an invisible form of light was separated from the sunlight by the prism. Today, this light is called **infrared light** or **infrared radiation**. The word *infra* is Latin for "below." As the name suggests, infrared light has a frequency just below red.

There is a range of electromagnetic radiation that is classified as infrared. The temperature-sensitive nerve endings in your skin can detect infrared waves. So, when you feel the warmth of a campfire, you are sensing infrared radiation. The remote controls you use with TVs and DVD players also use infrared radiation. Your skin is not able to detect the heating effects of the infrared waves produced by a remote control; but, as indicated in the "Exploring Coded Signals" activity, these waves can still transfer energy.

> **infrared light or infrared radiation:** a type of electromagnetic radiation, with a frequency between 3.0×10^{11} Hz and 4.3×10^{14} Hz, that increases the vibrations between molecules, resulting in heating effects

Infrared radiation is emitted by the vibration or rotation of the molecules within a material; so, objects that are warm or hot tend to emit energy in the infrared part of the electromagnetic spectrum. It is advantageous for humans and most other animals to be able to sense infrared radiation—objects that emit infrared radiation tend to be hot and may represent a burn hazard.

Practice

14. In addition to being able to detect infrared radiation, humans are also sources of infrared radiation. Most people emit a band of infrared radiation with a peak wavelength of about 10 μm.
    a. Explain the mechanism that allows the human body to emit this radiation.
    b. Calculate the frequency of this radiation.

15. Sunlight pours in through a window as two friends watch a football game on television. A hot bowl of popcorn sits between them as they use the remote control to switch between games on different channels.
    a. Identify the sources of infrared radiation.
    b. If the TV is operated by an infrared remote control, how does the circuitry within the TV distinguish between the signal from the remote control and the infrared radiation generated by other objects in the room?

Using Infrared Radiation for Communication

Handheld computers (PDAs) are a popular way for working people to stay in touch with their e-mail accounts, scheduling software, and customer-account information when they are away from the office. These devices are able to send and receive signals with other devices, such as printers, laptop computers, cellphones, digital cameras, and other handheld computers.

Since most of the radio-wave frequencies are already heavily used, many of these devices communicate using an encoded infrared signal. This form of communication is often called **beaming**. In the next investigation you will have an opportunity to explore some of the characteristics of this technology by building a simple infrared transmitter and receiver.

> **beaming:** the communication of data between wireless devices using a beam of infrared light

Investigation

Building and Testing an Infrared Transmitter and Receiver

Purpose
You will build and test a simple infrared transmitter and receiver.

Science Skills
✓ Performing and Recording
✓ Analyzing and Interpreting

Materials
- portable music system with a headphone jack (e.g., CD player or MP3 player)
- set of sensitive headphones for the portable music system
- 7 test leads with alligator clips at each end
- 7 small elastic bands to shorten the test leads
- 1 AA cell in a holder with leads
- photovoltaic cell with leads
- infrared LED (light-emitting diode) with peak wavelength of 940 nm
- 0.22-μF capacitor (50 WVDC max)
- audio cable with 3.5 mm ($\frac{1}{8}$-inch) stereo plugs at each end (must be less than 2 m long)
- infrared remote control
- 6 sheets of facial tissue
- "Building an Infrared Transmitter and Receiver" handout

Procedure and Observations

Part A: Building the Infrared Transmitter and Receiver
Obtain the handout "Building an Infrared Transmitter and Receiver" from the Science 30 Textbook CD. Follow the instructions in this handout to build the transmitter and receiver.

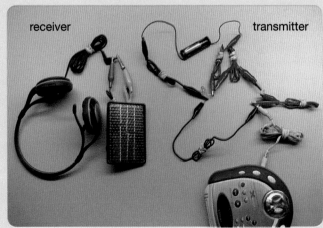

receiver   transmitter

Part B: Testing the Infrared Transmitter and Receiver

Procedure and Observations

step 1: Determine how the equipment should be arranged to produce the strongest signal between the transmitter and the receiver. Record your results.

step 2: While listening through the headphones, slowly pull the photovoltaic cell away from the LED to determine the maximum distance that the receiver is able to receive a useable signal from the transmitter. Record your results.

step 3: Determine how many sheets of facial tissue are required to absorb the infrared energy from the transmitter when the photovoltaic cell is located 8.0 cm from the LED.

Analysis

1. Suppose the transmitter and receiver you built in this investigation were the prototype for a new model of wireless communication technology. Use the results of this experiment to write a concise summary that describes some of the strengths and weaknesses of your infrared transmitter and receiver as a communication technology.

2. Use the Internet as a tool to gather information about the strengths and weaknesses of commercially available infrared communication technologies.

Visible Light

In the entire electromagnetic spectrum, the colours red through violet make up a very thin slice called the **visible spectrum**. Many students use the name "**Roy G Biv**" as a memory device to help them remember the order of all the colours in the visible spectrum: red, orange, yellow, green, blue, indigo, and violet. Individuals have different abilities to see colours. For most people, the limits of vision extend from radiation with a wavelength of about 700 nm at the red end to about 400 nm at the violet end.

In general, visible light is emitted by objects that are hot: the filament of a light bulb, the flame of a candle, or the surface of the Sun. In all cases, the temperature is high enough to cause electrons to jump within the overlapping energy levels of closely packed atoms or molecules.

Just over 100 years ago, at the beginning of the twentieth century, Albert Einstein proposed a radical adjustment to the idea that visible light was an electromagnetic wave. Einstein proposed that although light had a wavelength and a frequency, it was not emitted in long trains of connected waves. Instead, it was emitted in bundles of energy called **photons**. A photon can behave like a particle in that it can collide and interact with an individual atom, but it has no mass because it is a tiny packet of electromagnetic energy. The energy of an individual photon depends upon the frequency of the radiation—the higher the frequency, the greater the energy of the photon. In the visible spectrum, red photons have the least amount of energy, while violet photons have the most.

visible spectrum: the complete range of all colours of light that can be seen by the human eye: red, orange, yellow, green, blue, indigo, and violet; frequencies range from 4.3×10^{14} Hz to 7.5×10^{14} Hz

photon: a small bundle of electromagnetic energy

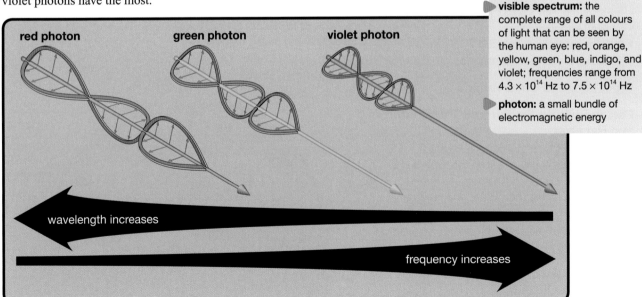

Photosynthesis

One of the best illustrations of the photon model of light is photosynthesis. The input energy for this process is visible light energy from the Sun. Within the cells on the leaf of a green plant, a specialized structure called a chloroplast contains the pigment molecules called chlorophyl. The pigment molecules act like antennae—discs spread out in horizontal patterns to absorb as much energy from the incoming photons as possible.

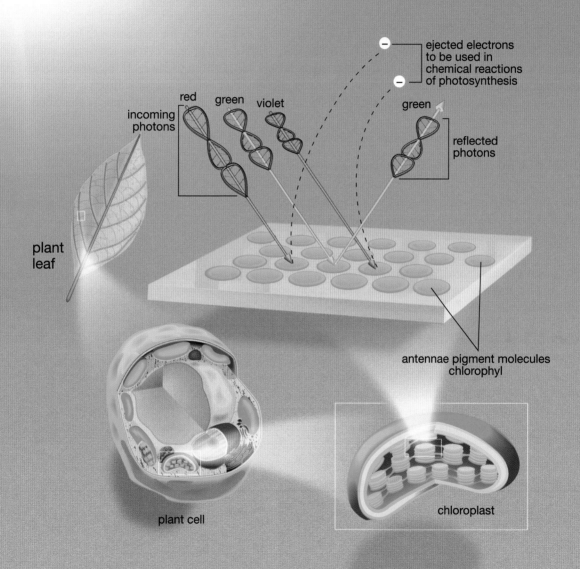

ejected electrons to be used in chemical reactions of photosynthesis

red   green   violet

incoming photons

green

reflected photons

plant leaf

antennae pigment molecules chlorophyl

plant cell

chloroplast

Note that the chlorophyl molecules absorb the energy in the photons of red and violet light—using this energy to eject electrons. These electrons are then picked up by other molecules that participate in the chemical reactions of photosynthesis.

The photons of green light are not absorbed because they do not have the exact amount of energy needed to eject electrons in the chlorophyl molecules. You could say that the chlorophyl "antennae" are not "tuned" to this particular frequency of electromagnetic radiation. Since green-light photons are not absorbed, the energy is reflected. This is why a plant leaf looks green under white light: the light from the red and violet ends of the visible spectrum has been absorbed, leaving only the light from the middle of the visible spectrum—green—to be reflected to your eyes.

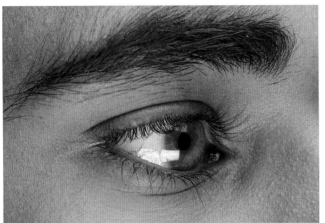

Photosynthesis is just one example of how photons of visible light interact with living tissue. The reactions that occur as photons strike the retina are similar. In both cases, the energy of the photons is sufficient to cause an electron to be ejected from a specialized receptor molecule, but the energy is not so great that irreversible chemical changes occur. As you will see later in this lesson, if photons with more energy than visible light strike these cells, permanent damage can occur.

Although Einstein's photon model for light applies to the whole electromagnetic spectrum, the effects have practical applications only for radiation with frequencies close to visible light or higher. At the radio-wave end of the spectrum, continuous wave effects dominate—radio-wave photons would be very difficult to detect. At the gamma-ray end of the spectrum, the particle-like behaviour of photons is most significant, while continuous wave effects are difficult to detect. Visible light is positioned in the middle of the spectrum, so it is ideal for demonstrating the unique blend of both continuous wave and photon characteristics.

Practice

16. Identify the types of sources that produce visible light.
17. Compare and contrast a photon of red light with a photon of violet light.
18. Why do the leaves of most plants look green?
19. Use the words *photon*, *antenna*, and *chlorophyl* to explain why green plants tend to turn their leaves toward a light source.

Ultraviolet Radiation

The Latin word for "beyond" is *ultra*, so it shouldn't be surprising that the radiation that has a frequency just beyond violet is called **ultraviolet light**, **ultraviolet radiation**, or just **UV**. Ultraviolet photons are emitted from sources that are very hot—hotter than the sources for visible light. Some people refer to an ultraviolet light source as a "black light," but the word *black* means the absence of light, so this is not really an accurate description. The best way to think of ultraviolet light is in terms of photons. Since ultraviolet photons have a higher frequency than those in the visible spectrum, they have more energy.

> **ultraviolet light, ultraviolet radiation, or UV:** a type of electromagnetic radiation that is emitted by very hot objects; frequencies range from 7.5×10^{14} Hz to 1×10^{18} Hz

Figure C2.12: This lamp emits both visible light and ultraviolet radiation.

Figure C2.13: Good-quality goggles used for snowboarding and skiing have special coatings to absorb ultraviolet radiation.

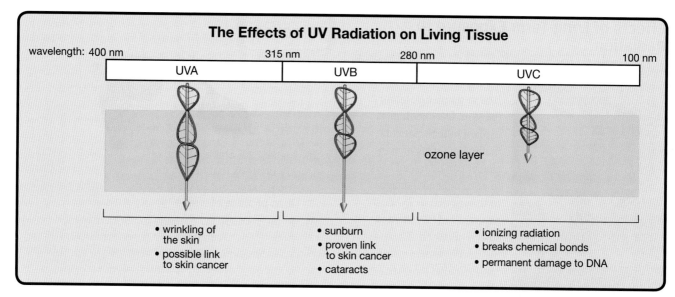

The Effects of UV Radiation on Living Tissue

wavelength: 400 nm   315 nm   280 nm   100 nm

UVA	UVB	UVC

ozone layer

- wrinkling of the skin
- possible link to skin cancer

- sunburn
- proven link to skin cancer
- cataracts

- ionizing radiation
- breaks chemical bonds
- permanent damage to DNA

In terms of wavelength, the ultraviolet band spans from 400 nm down to 100 nm. This band can be divided further into UVA, UVB, and UVC. You will likely run across these terms on product labels when shopping for sunglasses or goggles for outdoor activities. It's important to ensure that the sunglasses or goggles you buy will stop 100% of the UVA and UVB radiation from entering your eyes. High-energy photons can do permanent damage to living tissues. UVC photons are even more hazardous, but Earth's ozone layer absorbs most of the UVC radiation before it reaches Earth's surface.

Photons of UVC radiation have so much energy that they eject electrons from atoms, ionizing the atoms and leading to the formation of free radicals. As you learned in Unit B, free radicals are highly reactive particles that accelerate the decomposition of organic compounds. This is why UVC is classified as a type of **ionizing radiation**. When a UVC photon collides with a molecule of DNA, the ionization triggers the formation of free radicals, which causes one of the DNA strands to break.

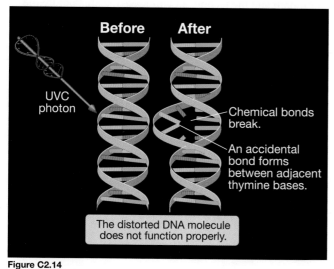

Figure C2.14

As shown in Figure C2.14, a UVC photon can break chemical bonds and cause an accidental bond to be formed between adjacent bases. The DNA molecule becomes distorted and is no longer able to replicate properly. If this kind of event happens in several places along the DNA of a bacterium, the micro-organism is no longer able to replicate its DNA. It dies or will be unable to reproduce. This is the basis of technologies that use ultraviolet radiation to sterilize medical and laboratory tools.

Figure C2.15: Most schools use cabinets like this to sterilize safety goggles with UVC light. As a safety mechanism, the bulb that is the source of the radiation turns on only when the door is closed.

> **ionizing radiation:** high-energy radiation capable of ionizing the material through which it passes, leading to the formation of free radicals

Effects of Long-Term Exposure to Radiation

Figure C2.16: Long-term exposure to UV light causes the skin to wrinkle, sag, and become leathery.

Many years of exposure to UV light from the Sun can lead to premature aging of the skin. Dermatologists explain to their patients that many forms of skin cancer can be traced back to accumulated damage to tissues that have been exposed to UV radiation since childhood. The medical evidence clearly indicates that long-term exposure to low doses of UV radiation can have negative effects on health. Researchers are currently investigating other areas of the electromagnetic spectrum to explore the connections between long-term exposure to low doses of radiation and illness.

Science Links

Many scientists suspect that skin cancers caused by exposure to UV light could become more of a problem in the future because a key component of the atmosphere that protects people from this radiation is being depleted. Most of the UV photons emitted by the Sun are absorbed by ozone in the stratosphere. As described in Unit B, human activities release compounds, such as CFCs, that reduce the concentration of ozone in the stratosphere.

X-rays: high-energy electromagnetic radiation with a frequency between 10^{18} and 10^{21} Hz; can be produced when fast-moving electrons strike a metal target

Practice

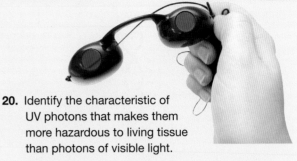

20. Identify the characteristic of UV photons that makes them more hazardous to living tissue than photons of visible light.

21. To help reduce UV damage to the skin, many people apply sunblock or a sunscreen before spending time in the sun. These lotions contain compounds that are specially designed to absorb different types of ultraviolet radiation:

    • UVA absorbers—titanium dioxide, zinc oxide, and avobenzone
    • UVB absorbers—homosalate, octyl salicylate, and octyl methoxycinnamate

    a. Describe the health benefits of a sunblock that has homosalate as an ingredient.

    b. Describe the health benefits of a sunblock that has zinc oxide as an ingredient.

    c. If the most hazardous type of ultraviolet radiation is UVC, explain why there isn't an ingredient in sunscreen to block UVC rays.

X-rays

Annual dental checkups typically begin with diagnostic **X-rays** of your teeth. The patient in Figure C2.17 is wearing a lead apron and is temporarily holding the film in place while the X-ray machine is brought into position. Once everything is in place, the patient will remove her finger from her mouth and the technician will leave the area before the machine is switched on, emitting a momentary stream of X-rays. After the procedure is over, the lead apron is removed and the patient can then meet with the dentist, who carefully examines the images.

Figure C2.17

X-ray radiation can produce images of the insides of teeth or other body parts due to the fact that X-rays can penetrate some body tissues. The X-rays cause photographic film to be exposed by causing a chemical reaction to change the film from white to grey or black. The more dense tissues—like teeth, bones, and dental fillings—absorb more X-ray photons, so the film behind those areas appears white or lighter. Less dense tissues—like skin, fat, muscle, and blood vessels—appear darker on the film because more X-rays are able to pass through. A tooth that has a cavity or a crack allows more X-rays to pass through, so these features form darker areas on the image.

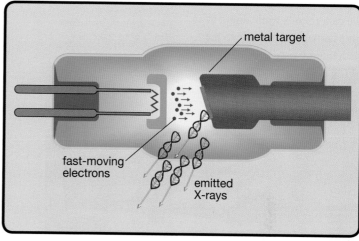

X-rays are produced using a high-voltage tube. The high voltage is used to give electrons high speeds so that they collide with a metal target, producing X-rays. The X-rays that leave the tube can travel from the tube through the air and then enter living tissue. When an X-ray photon collides with a molecule in a cell, a valence electron is knocked out of the molecule. Due to the high energy of the X-ray photon, the ejected electron leaves with a large quantity of kinetic energy, allowing it to ionize hundreds or thousands of other molecules in the area of the initial collision. Clearly, X-rays are a powerful form of ionizing radiation. When DNA is ionized by this kind of interaction, it is possible for both strands of the double helix to break. A double-strand break is much more difficult to repair than a single-strand break. If a fragment of DNA is lost during the repair process, the results can include mutations, chromosome aberrations, or the death of the cell. Given the effects of ionizing radiation on living tissue, you can see why it is so important to minimize your exposure to X-rays.

GUIDELINES FOR MINIMIZING EXPOSURE TO SOURCES OF IONIZING RADIATION

For the Safety of the Patient	For the Safety of the Technician
• Use the minimum photon energy to accomplish the task. • Use shielding to protect tissues not involved in the procedure, especially tissues with rapidly dividing cells. • Avoid exposing unborn children and infants to X-ray radiation.	• Reduce time spent near the source. • Increase distance from the source. • Use shielding between the source and the technician.

ALARA: As Low As Is Reasonably Achievable

Long-term exposure to low doses of ultraviolet light can create health problems later in life. The same can likely be said for long-term exposure to low doses of X-rays or any other form of ionizing radiation. The person or the body organ that is repeatedly exposed to low doses of radiation may survive, but the cells can become damaged. This damage can lead to cancer and other negative effects years after the initial exposure. Since current scientific evidence indicates that any radiation dose, no matter how small, may result in some negative effects on human health, it is best to keep the exposure to ionizing radiation as low as is reasonably achievable, or ALARA for short.

Rapidly dividing cells, like those that produce blood cells in bone marrow, are particularly vulnerable to the effects of ionizing radiation because these cells spend a large percentage of their time in the process of DNA replication. Recall from Unit A that the processes that run cell division involve the replication of DNA and the lining up of chromosomes before cell division. These processes inadvertently increase the chances for genetic damage by presenting a large target to the radiation for an increased period of time. Unborn children are especially sensitive to ionizing radiation because their cells are dividing at a high rate and are developing into different kinds of tissue.

Since rapidly dividing cells are the ones most susceptible to damage from ionizing radiation, it makes sense that X-rays can also be used to kill cancer cells. When a focused beam of radiation is used to shrink or eliminate cancerous tumours, the process is called **radiation therapy**. The goal of this cancer treatment is to kill the cancer cells while doing as little damage as possible to the surrounding tissue.

> **radiation therapy:** the medical use of ionizing radiation to treat disease, especially forms of cancer

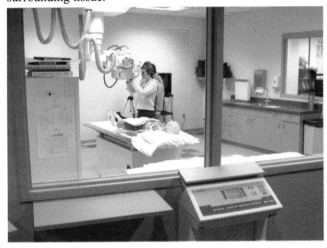

Gamma Radiation

One of the leading ways to treat a brain tumour is to target the tumour with beams of very high-energy photons emitted from the nuclei of **radioactive** materials. The material used in this machine is cobalt-60, a radioactive isotope produced in nuclear reactors. The special name for photons emitted from radioactive sources, like cobalt-60, is **gamma radiation**. Gamma photons have the highest frequency of all types of electromagnetic radiation. It follows, then, that gamma photons also have the highest energy and the greatest penetrating power. Gamma radiation overlaps X-rays in the electromagnetic spectrum. They both produce ionizing radiation and they have an exceptional ability to penetrate matter. The only real differences stem from the fact that gamma photons originate from the nuclei of radioactive materials and can have even higher frequencies than X-rays.

> **radioactive:** a term used to describe substances that spontaneously emit radiation from unstable nuclei

> **gamma radiation:** the highest energy form of electromagnetic radiation with frequencies above 10^{19} Hz; emitted from the nuclei of radioactive materials

Use the information below to answer questions 22 to 25.

Figure C2.18 shows a patient's X-ray after reconstructive surgery to repair a broken jaw. The same kind of panoramic X-ray is taken during orthodontic work.

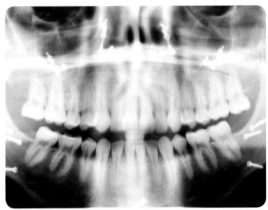

Figure C2.18

22. Explain why the tiny screws appear white in the image.

23. Closely examine the teeth on the lower left of Figure C2.18. Describe the evidence that supports the idea that these teeth have soft tissue, like nerves and blood vessels, inside them.

24. An X-ray machine produces photons with a frequency of 7.1×10^{18} Hz. Calculate the wavelength of these X-ray photons.

25. A woman slipped and fell on the ice while curling. She thinks that she may have injured her hip. Explain why it is important for the doctor to ask the woman if there is a possibility that she might be pregnant before recommending an X-ray be taken.

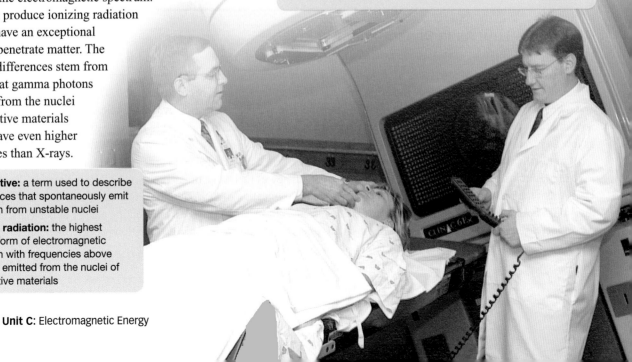

Minimizing Exposure to Radiation

Purpose
You will use a questionnaire and other resources as you work with other students to develop strategies to minimize your exposure to radiation.

Science Skills
✓ Initiating and Planning
✓ Performing and Recording
✓ Communication and Teamwork

Part A: Ionizing Radiation

Background Information
Each day you are exposed to a number of different types of ionizing radiation. Some of the sources of radiation are unavoidable, while other sources could be classified as voluntary because they are due to decisions you have made about how you live your life. In this activity you will work with other students to identify strategies that will help keep your exposure to ionizing radiation as low as is reasonably achievable.

Procedure and Analysis
step 1: Obtain the handout "Questionnaire: Estimating Your Annual Dose of Ionizing Radiation" from the Science 30 Textbook CD. Complete this questionnaire, and add up the totals for each section as well as the grand total from all sources.

step 2: Compare your results from step 1 with the results of your classmates. Use the questionnaire to identify the sources that account for the differences in the results between individual students. Suggest strategies that could be used to minimize the exposure to radiation for students with higher scores.

Part B: Non-Ionizing Radiation—Radio Waves

Background Information
Since the 1990s there has been a dramatic increase in the amount of radiation in the form of radio waves that comes in contact with human tissue. Although there are many technologies that have contributed to this increase, the most significant is the growing popularity of handheld cellphones. Many people would argue that since radio waves are not a form of ionizing radiation, the health risks associated with the use of this technology are minimal. Others disagree, indicating that the high use of this technology could present a situation similar to the exposure to solar UV, where long-term exposure to low doses of radiation creates health problems, including cancer, many years after the initial exposure. Since so many people use cellphones, it is important to learn whether this source of radiation presents a health hazard—and to reassure the users of this technology if it does not.

Procedure and Analysis
1. Estimate the number of minutes you spend using a handheld cellphone every month. You may need to consult the monthly statement from your service provider. Compare your results with those of other students, and determine the average number of minutes of monthly cellphone use for your group. Use the average value for your group to estimate the total length of time that cellphones would be used in one year and in one lifetime.

2. Refer to the table "Guidelines for Minimizing Exposure to Sources of Ionizing Radiation" that was presented earlier in this lesson. Using the guidelines presented on this table, work with other students to develop a list of strategies that could be used to reduce the exposure to the radio waves produced by a cellphone. Identify the strengths and weaknesses of each strategy.

3. Work with members of your group to develop a list of specific questions that researchers should consider when designing experiments to investigate the possible connections between cellphone use and human health.

4. Perform an Internet search to determine some of the specific questions that researchers are currently investigating on the topic of cellphone use and human health. Compare the results with the list of questions you developed in question 3.

The electromagnetic spectrum includes a wide variety of electromagnetic radiation. When listed from lowest frequency to highest frequency, the spectrum includes radio waves, microwaves, infrared radiation, visible light, ultraviolet radiation, X-rays, and gamma rays. Visible light is the form of radiation that people are most familiar with because it includes all the colours that can be detected by the human eye: red, orange, yellow, green, blue, indigo, and violet. Visible light is uniquely positioned in the electromagnetic spectrum because it is able to demonstrate the wave characteristics of the radio-wave end of the spectrum and the photon characteristics of the gamma-ray end of the spectrum. Gamma rays, X-rays, and UVC are all classified as ionizing radiations because each of them can break chemical bonds, which triggers the production of free radicals.

2.1 Questions

Knowledge

1. Obtain the handout "Summarizing the Characteristics of the Electromagnetic Spectrum" from the Science 30 Textbook CD. Complete the table by adding rows for each type of electromagnetic radiation and by adding concise descriptions under each category. Note that you may have to continue the table on additional pieces of paper.

Applying Concepts

2. The X-rays used by a dentist to produce images of a patient's teeth have a frequency of 7.2×10^{18} Hz.

   a. Calculate the wavelength of these dental X-rays.

   b. Hydrogen is the smallest atom. When a hydrogen atom is unexcited, the orbit of the electron is about 5.29×10^{-11} m from the nucleus. Compare the wavelength of the dental X-ray to the radius of the electron's orbit for an unexcited hydrogen atom.

3. A GPS satellite emits two microwave signals: one with a wavelength of 19.0 cm and the other with a wavelength of about 24.4 cm. Calculate the frequency of each of these signals.

4. The door of a microwave oven includes a window made from a metal mesh screen attached to glass. Explain why the metal screen is a critical part of the design.

5. Explain why the specialized light bulbs used for growing plants indoors tend to have a reddish-purple colour.

6. Explain why people who use tanning beds should wear protective goggles.

7. An X-ray technician may deal with dozens of patients requiring X-rays every day. Explain why it is important for the technician to operate the X-ray machine from behind a shielded wall.

Use the following information to answer questions 8 and 9.

Ultrasound is the preferred imaging technology for checking the development of an unborn child. This technology produces images that can be displayed on a computer monitor.

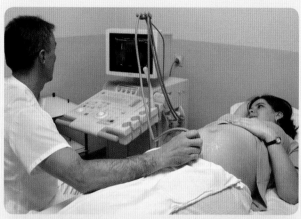

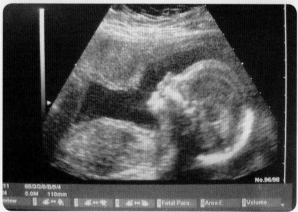

8. Carefully examine the photo of an ultrasound technician scanning the pregnant woman's abdomen with ultrasound. List details from the photo that support the idea that ultrasound is **not** a form of ionizing radiation.

9. Explain why X-rays are not used to monitor the development of unborn children.

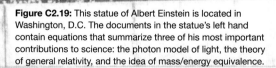

Figure C2.19: This statue of Albert Einstein is located in Washington, D.C. The documents in the statue's left hand contain equations that summarize three of his most important contributions to science: the photon model of light, the theory of general relativity, and the idea of mass/energy equivalence.

Figure C2.20

For thousands of years, humans have been living north of the Arctic Circle. To thrive in this beautiful but sometimes harsh environment, the First Peoples need a detailed knowledge of the interconnections among a number of complex systems: ecosystems, weather patterns, seasonal variations in climate, and other interactions between the terrestrial and marine environments. For example, successful hunting depends upon a knowledge of the seasonal variations in sea ice and how these changes affect the behavioural patterns of marine mammals, like whales, seals, and walruses.

As you learned in Units A and B, the traditional ecological knowledge of the Inuit has been acquired over thousands of years through their direct contact with the environment. This is a dynamic approach to developing new understandings of human interactions with the environment. This view of the world focuses on the inseparable relationships among land, resources, and culture. Since the environment includes the effects of objects that are beyond Earth, human interaction with this part of the environment also plays a role in traditional ecological knowledge.

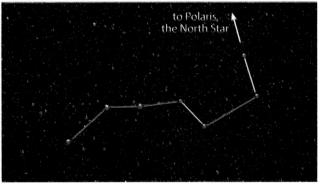

to Polaris,
the North Star

Figure C2.21: The Big Dipper constellation

The group of stars in Figure C2.21 is perhaps the most familiar to people living in the northern hemisphere. Some cultures call this **constellation** the Big Dipper. Others recognize it as a small part of a larger constellation called the Great Bear. For the Inuit living in the Arctic, this constellation represents a caribou. This constellation is important because it can be used to locate the North Star—a valuable reference point when navigating at night, especially on moving sea ice.

> **constellation:** a group of stars perceived as being in the shape of a figure or a design

Given that the arctic environment consists of vast tracts of nearly featureless territory and that the Sun is continually below the horizon for many weeks of the arctic winter, survival depends upon an efficient and reliable system of being able to find your way. Traditional navigation techniques involve using a number of different indicators from the environment, including stars, wind patterns shown by the subtle shapes of snowdrifts, and rock cairns called inuksuk.

Figure C2.22: Inuit Elders explain that inuksuks are stone monuments that guide the people on the land and serve to mark special places, many of them sacred.

An important aspect of Inuit traditional ecological knowledge is that it is practical: new technologies are often integrated into the existing knowledge base and culture. This happened over 100 years ago, with the adoption of firearms, and again about 40 years ago, with the introduction of snowmobiles to Inuit communities. Recently, GPS (global positioning system) technology has been adapted as a new tool to supplement the traditional methods of navigation.

Inuit Elders stress the importance of not relying too heavily on this new technology. The extreme cold of the arctic environment can cause the batteries that power the GPS receivers to fail and can leave the display screens inoperable. Becoming lost on the tundra or on the frozen surface of the Arctic Ocean can truly be a matter of life and death! That's why the Elders recommend the hunters continue to practise the traditional navigation techniques, with GPS technology only being used to assist in certain circumstances. Being able to navigate by the stars is still an important survival skill for the Inuit who obtain traditional sources of food through hunting.

In addition to navigation, for thousands of years the relative positions of the stars in the night sky have provided the Inuit with a reliable way to mark the passing of time. Given the scarcity of light during the arctic winter, it is important to be able to predict the hours of daylight available for any given day so that activities can be planned. The position of the Big Dipper relative to the North Star is used as a clock to determine time. The positions of other constellations on the horizon are used, along with other environmental clues, as a calendar to track the passing of the seasons and the periodic changes in animal migration patterns.

Using EMR from Beyond Earth

Electromagnetic radiation from objects in outer space has played an essential role in human existence for a long time. Today, people are still gathering information from stars in an effort to better understand the universe and to improve daily life. In this lesson you will see how the characteristics of the electromagnetic spectrum have been applied to these studies and to the science of **astronomy**.

astronomy: the science of objects and phenomena that originate outside Earth's atmosphere

Practice

26. Consider the idea of utilizing electromagnetic radiation from beyond Earth.

   a. How does Figure C2.20 on page 436 relate to this idea?

   b. Describe some of the ways you use electromagnetic radiation from beyond Earth.

27. A technology used to solve one problem can often be the source of a new set of unintended problems.

   a. Explain how the introduction of CFCs as a refrigerant illustrates this idea.

   b. Explain how this idea could apply if the next generation of Inuit hunters did not learn the traditional navigation techniques and came to rely exclusively on GPS technology.

   c. Interconnectedness is a key characteristic of traditional ecological knowledge. Explain how this characteristic is helpful for reducing some of the negative impacts associated with the introduction of new technologies.

The Nearest Star

Which star is closest to Earth? Would you have to use an Internet search engine to answer this question, or would you think "outside the box" and come up with the answer of the Sun.

The heat and light that is so essential to life on Earth is the result of nuclear reactions deep within the Sun's interior. Within the Sun's core, the temperature is estimated to be about 15 000 000°C, and the pressure is thought to be millions of times higher than the atmospheric pressure on Earth. Under these circumstances, molecules are torn apart into atoms, and electrons are stripped from atoms, leaving the positively charged nuclei. A series of collisions between hydrogen nuclei results in the formation of a helium nucleus and the release of gamma photons. This reaction is called **nuclear fusion**.

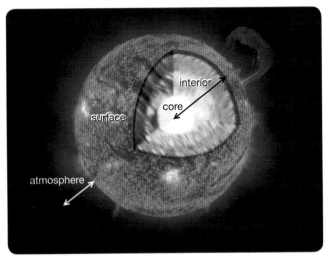

Figure C2.23

> **nuclear fusion:** a process in which two smaller nuclei join to form a larger nucleus, releasing energy

Science Links

Just as chemical reactions are described with chemical equations, nuclear reactions are described with nuclear equations. You'll learn more about nuclear reactions and the equations used to describe them in Unit D.

$$^{2}_{1}H + ^{2}_{1}H \rightarrow ^{3}_{2}He + ^{1}_{0}n$$

EMR Emitted by the Sun

As a gamma photon is released from a fusion reaction and travels outward from the Sun's core, a countless number of interactions occur between the photon and the charged particles that make up the Sun's interior. In each interaction, the energy of the photon is absorbed and then re-emitted. However, since the charged particles are given kinetic energy in these interactions, the re-emitted photon emerges with less energy than the incoming photon. After an innumerable number of collisions, the photons that eventually reach the Sun's surface no longer have the energy of gamma photons.

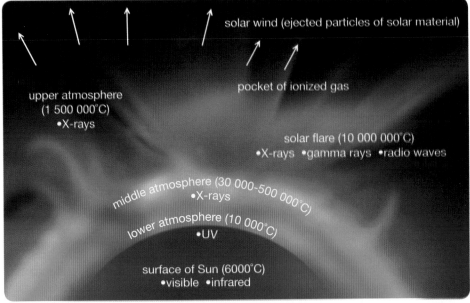

Figure C2.24

The electromagnetic radiation from the Sun's surface consists of visible and infrared photons. This is consistent with the behaviour of objects that have the same temperature as the surface of the Sun, about 6000°C. For reasons that are not entirely understood, the temperature of the Sun's atmosphere increases with height above the surface of the Sun. As shown in Figure C2.24, as the temperature in a region of the Sun's atmosphere increases, the energy of the emitted radiation also increases. This is why the photons with the most energy, X-rays and gamma rays, are emitted from the hottest region of the Sun's atmosphere in a solar flare. A solar flare is a very powerful eruption in the Sun's atmosphere that is triggered by the sudden realignment of intense magnetic field lines emerging from the surface of the Sun. Even though radio waves have the lowest energy content of all EMR, they are produced by solar flares as well. The fluctuations of these huge regions of intense magnetic field lines accelerate charged particles in the vicinity, causing these particles to emit radio waves.

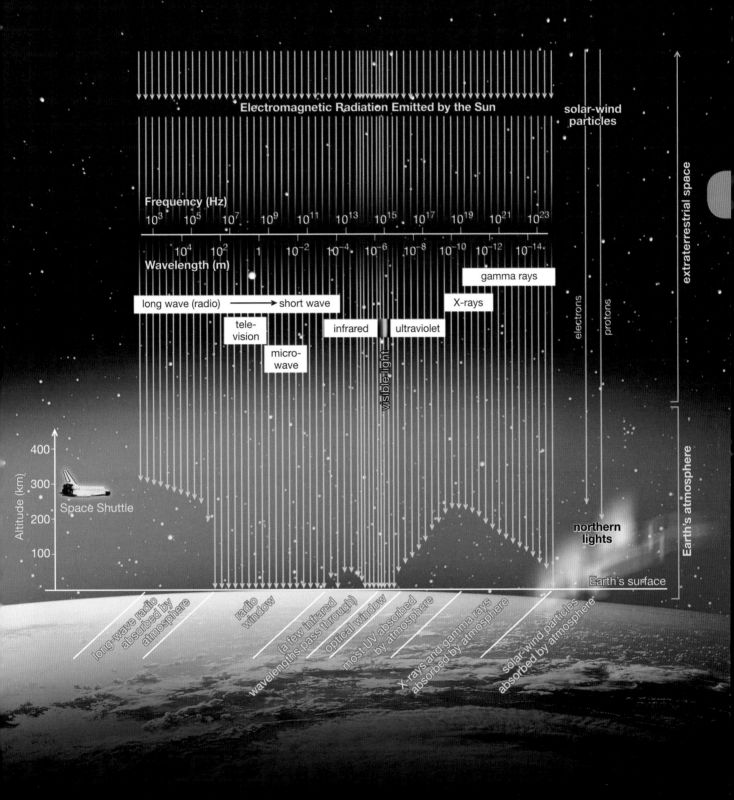

The Sun emits radiation across the whole electromagnetic spectrum—from radio waves to gamma rays; however, only a fraction of this radiation is able to reach the surface of Earth. The atmosphere provides a window for only short-wavelength radio waves and the wavelengths of EMR close to the visible spectrum (short-wavelength infrared, visible light, UVA, and UVB).

As you learned earlier in the course, molecules of oxygen and ozone absorb the energy of the more energetic UVC photons. These are not the only molecules in the atmosphere that can absorb EMR. Recall from previous courses that molecules of water vapour, methane, and carbon dioxide are able to absorb infrared radiation. This causes the kinetic energy of these molecules to increase, adding to a general heating of the atmosphere that is often called the "greenhouse effect."

The X-rays and gamma rays from the Sun tend to be absorbed by collisions with individual atoms. These collisions ionize the atoms and liberate electrons. The electrons then act to absorb the energy of the long-wavelength radio waves.

28. Trace the path of energy that is released at the Sun's core to the type of EMR that is released from the surface of the Sun.

29. Refer to Figure C2.24, which shows the details of the Sun's surface and atmosphere.

   a. Identify a region of the Sun that emits UV photons.

   b. Identify a region of the Sun that emits X-ray photons.

   c. Explain the characteristic of each region of the Sun that determines the type of EMR emitted.

30. Astronomers and other scientists use detectors and other scientific instruments for studying the EMR emitted by the Sun.

   a. Explain why there are limits to the EMR that can be studied if the detectors are placed on the surface of Earth.

   b. Suggest alternative locations for some of the EMR detectors that would expand the EMR that can be studied.

Exploring the Properties of Visible Light

Figure C2.25: Sunlight is bent as it travels through ice crystals, creating the illusion that the Sun has two bright companions, called "sundogs."

Although daytime during the arctic winter is short, it would be a mistake to assume that winter days in the north are dreary. Since the Sun stays close to the horizon in the winter, the conditions are ideal for an interesting atmospheric phenomenon called sundogs. In Figure C2.25, a pair of bright patches of light can be observed on each side of the Sun. Because these patches of light "sit obediently" on each side of the Sun and often appear to have "tails of light" that stream away from the Sun, they are called sundogs. Sundogs are caused by the **refraction**, or bending, of light from the Sun as the rays travel through ice crystals in the atmosphere. Sundogs are a common occurrence in Alberta as well, also because the Sun spends a great deal of time near the horizon during the winter months.

> **refraction:** a bending in the direction of a wave that occurs when the wave changes speed
>
> **reflection:** a return of a wave from a boundary
>
> **polarization:** confining a wave to vibrate in one direction
>
> **diffraction:** the bending of a wave as it passes by obstacles or by the edges of an opening

The low position of the Sun in the sky, combined with the abundance of snow, accounts for the tremendous amount of **reflection** that can occur on a winter's day. People who enjoy outdoor winter activities can protect their eyes from the glare by wearing sunglasses. The most effective type of sunglasses deal with the annoying glare by taking advantage of the fact that **polarization** occurs as light reflects from horizontal surfaces. Manufacturers refer to this feature on sunglasses by advertising that the lenses are polarized.

Figure C2.26: Polarized lenses in sunglasses help to absorb the light energy reflected from horizontal surfaces.

In the next investigation you will have an opportunity to learn more about reflection, refraction, and polarization—as well as another property of light called **diffraction**. The diffraction that occurs as light rays pass through the pupil of the eye helps explain why people have a difficult time distinguishing the visual details of objects that are far away.

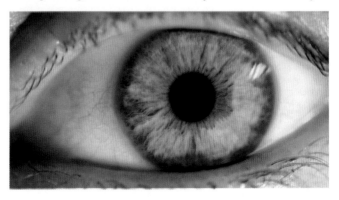

Observing the Properties of Visible Light

Purpose

You will use data tables and labelled diagrams to gather data and record observations related to the reflection, refraction, diffraction, and polarization of visible light.

Science Skills

✓ Initiating and Planning
✓ Performing and Recording
✓ Analyzing and Interpreting

CAUTION!

In parts of this investigation, you have the option of using a ray box or a laser pointer to produce rays of light. If you are using a laser pointer, it is important to employ all the recommended safety precautions to avoid having light from this source travel directly to your eyes.

Mandatory Safety Precautions for Working with Laser Light

- Never aim a laser at a person's eye.
- Avoid having the unprotected eye along or near the beam axis.
  - If you are working at a table, this means keeping the laser light parallel to the table's surface so that your eyes are well above the work surface.
  - Anticipate the path the laser light will take and arrange the apparatus so that the beam will not inadvertently be directed near the eyes of other students. One useful strategy is to work around the perimeter of the room, with the laser light directed toward the outside wall. This arrangement also ensures that your eyes are facing away from other groups.
- Keep the room well-lit so pupils remain small, reducing the "window" available for the entry of laser light.
- Avoid having the laser produce light for extended periods of time. Once the apparatus is in place, most measurements or observations can be made in a matter of seconds, and then the laser can be switched off.

Materials

The materials for each part of this investigation are listed on the handouts.

Procedure, Observations, and Analysis

step 1: Obtain each of the following handouts from the Science 30 Textbook CD:

- "Investigating Refraction"
- "Investigating Polarization"
- "Investigating Diffraction"
- "Investigating Reflection"

step 2: For each handout, complete the procedure, collect the data, and record your observations according to the instructions provided.

Astronomers Apply the Properties of Visible Light

With the exception of some moon rocks retrieved during the Apollo missions, astronomers are not able to physically touch the objects they are studying. Distant planets, stars, comets, and clouds of interstellar dust are too far away to retrieve samples. Fortunately, the electromagnetic radiation that is emitted or reflected from objects in space provides a rich source of information. Thousands of years ago, the first astronomers used their eyes to observe the visible light emitted by objects in the heavens. Astronomers' ability to observe the heavens was significantly improved with the invention of the telescope about 400 years ago.

Galileo's Refracting Telescope

Even though these devices were simple by today's standards, Galileo was able to observe the craters of the Moon, the four moons of Jupiter, and the rings of Saturn. The simple telescope he used consisted of a convex lens at one end and a concave lens at the other.

It is remarkable that Galileo was able to make such detailed observations with such a primitive instrument. One problem was the quality of the glass used to make the lenses. Other problems were related to the fact that his design forced the light to enter the telescope through a relatively small opening. The small opening produced two problems. The first problem was that very little light was able to enter the instrument. This meant that faint sources would have looked quite dim to Galileo and would have been difficult to see. The second problem was that sources that were close together would have been difficult to distinguish due to the effects of diffraction.

Diffraction occurs when light passes through a tiny opening. This can be demonstrated if laser light passes through a tiny opening and then travels to a distant screen. Instead of the laser light forming an exact image of the tiny hole, it spreads out, producing a pattern of concentric circles called a **diffraction pattern**.

Two sources that are close together will each produce a diffraction pattern when the light from these sources passes through narrow openings. If the opening is large enough, the objects may look a little fuzzy, but on the screen two distinct images are formed. If the opening is too small, the amount of diffraction can increase to the point where the diffraction patterns overlap, making it difficult to determine if there are two sources or just one.

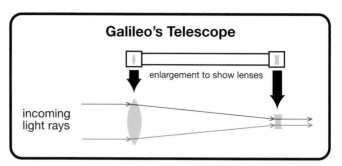

Galileo's Telescope

enlargement to show lenses

incoming light rays

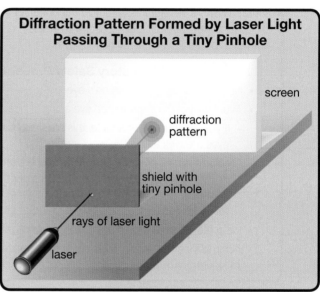

Diffraction Pattern Formed by Laser Light Passing Through a Tiny Pinhole

screen

diffraction pattern

shield with tiny pinhole

rays of laser light

laser

▶ **diffraction pattern:** a pattern produced by waves that have undergone diffraction

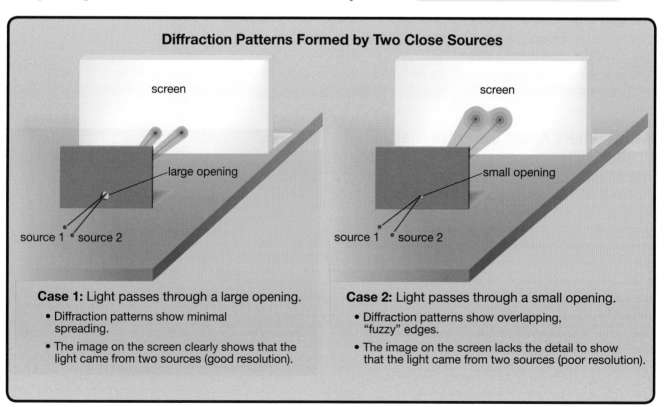

Diffraction Patterns Formed by Two Close Sources

screen

large opening

source 1 • source 2

screen

small opening

source 1 • source 2

Case 1: Light passes through a large opening.
- Diffraction patterns show minimal spreading.
- The image on the screen clearly shows that the light came from two sources (good resolution).

Case 2: Light passes through a small opening.
- Diffraction patterns show overlapping, "fuzzy" edges.
- The image on the screen lacks the detail to show that the light came from two sources (poor resolution).

Astronomers describe the ability of a telescope to distinguish the fine details of an object or collection of objects as the **resolution** of the telescope. Diffraction means that telescopes capable of resolving the details of finely spaced objects must have large openings to reduce the effects of overlapping diffraction patterns. Although it was understood at the time that a telescope with a wider opening would be desirable, the properties of glass imposed limits on the size of the lenses that could be used. The force of gravity acting on a large mass of glass made mounting the glass very difficult, and eventually pulled the glass out of shape—reducing the effectiveness of the lens to form a crisp image. Larger telescopes would require a new technology.

▶ **resolution:** the amount of small detail visible in an image; low resolution means only large features can be seen, while high resolution means that small details can be seen

Newton's Reflecting Telescope

While Galileo's telescope was designed using lenses based upon the principles of refraction, Isaac Newton improved the magnifying ability of the telescope with a new design that featured a curved mirror that utilized the principles of reflection.

The reflecting telescope has a number of advantages over refracting telescopes:

- A lens can have the same effect as a prism, causing white light to separate into its component colours. This can distort images observed through a refracting telescope, causing some objects to appear to be surrounded by a rainbow. Mirrors do not have this disadvantage.

- Reflecting telescopes can be made with very large openings. Since the light does not pass through the mirror, but bounces off its top surface, a very large curved mirror can be supported from underneath so that it maintains its ideal shape.

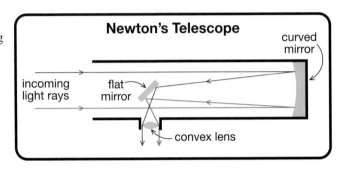

Modern Reflecting Telescopes

The Canada-France-Hawaii Telescope, or CFHT for short, is one of the world's largest reflecting telescopes, using a mirror that is 3.6 m in diameter. This telescope is located on top of a dormant volcano in Hawaii because the atmosphere above this high-altitude site is clear, dry, and stable most nights of the year.

Astronomers who study distant stars with this telescope not only consider the brightness and colour of the light they collect, they also use special instruments to measure the polarization of the starlight. Research in this area indicates that the degree to which the starlight is polarized is an indicator of the state of interstellar magnetic fields at the point of origin. Evidence also suggests that starlight can become polarized as it passes through clouds of interstellar dust. Research into the polarization of starlight provides information about stars and the space surrounding them that could not be obtained any other way.

Figure C2.27: Canada-France-Hawaii Telescope

31. Figure C2.28 shows a telescope that was designed by Johann Kepler.

   a. Is Kepler's telescope a refracting telescope or a reflecting telescope?

   b. Carefully compare the light rays in this telescope to the light rays in Galileo's telescope. Determine a disadvantage of Kepler's design.

32. Explain the following statement:

   The eyes of an eagle have unusually large pupils, which allow the eagle to see the small details in distant objects.

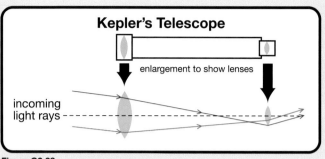

Kepler's Telescope

enlargement to show lenses

incoming light rays

Figure C2.28

False-Colour Images

Figure C2.29: This photograph was taken with an infrared camera.

Although humans can detect infrared radiation with nerve endings in their skin, it is not possible to detect this radiation with their eyes because the specialized cells located on the retina only respond to the visible spectrum. However, special detectors can transform the patterns made by infrared photons into electrical signals. The electrical signals can then be used to produce a visual image that can be detected by the eyes. The image in Figure C2.29 was made using this process. The white and yellow areas correspond to the places emitting the most infrared radiation, while the darker blue and black areas indicate the places emitting the least infrared radiation. An image like this is called a **false-colour image** because the colours do not correspond to what a person would normally see with his or her eyes. As you'll see in the next activity, false-colour images can be used to make observations of radiation that is normally invisible.

> **false-colour image:** an image that depicts an object in colours that differ from how a person would see the same object using only his or her eyes; often used to produce images using EMR outside of the visible spectrum

Try This Activity

Seeing the Invisible

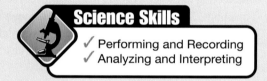

Science Skills

✓ Performing and Recording
✓ Analyzing and Interpreting

Purpose

You will observe false-colour images using a digital camera and an infrared remote control.

Materials

- digital camera
- infrared remote control

Procedure and Observations

step 1: Point the infrared remote control at your eyes and observe the lens at the end of the remote control as you press several buttons. Record your observations.

step 2: Repeat step 1, but this time view the lens at the end of the remote control using the screen of a digital camera that has been turned on. Record your observations.

Analysis

1. Produce a simple flowchart to summarize the energy transformations that occur from the infrared photons entering the lens of the digital camera to the visible light photons leaving the camera's screen.

2. Refer to your answer to question 1 to explain why it is misleading to say that a person can "see" infrared radiation with a digital camera.

Multiwavelength Astronomy

Another advantage of reflecting telescopes is that there is no large lens to absorb some of the incoming infrared and ultraviolet radiation. This means that reflecting telescopes can be used to gather infrared and ultraviolet radiation as well. The Canada-France-Hawaii Telescope is used to observe the infrared radiation emitted from objects in space on nights when moonlight makes it unfavourable for observations of the visible spectrum. The only place better for infrared astronomy than the high-altitude observatories on Earth is in orbit, high above the distortion and filtering that occurs as the radiation passes through the atmosphere.

The *Hubble Space Telescope*, or HST for short, is able to gather infrared and ultraviolet radiation, in addition to visible light, from its orbit about 600 km above Earth. Although huge clouds of interstellar gas and dust can obscure part of the visible universe, these clouds are transparent to infrared radiation. Since most of the radiation emitted by interstellar matter, planets, comets, and asteroids is in the infrared region of the electromagnetic spectrum, infrared radiation supplies astronomers with information they could not get any other way. In fact, each type of electromagnetic radiation provides astronomers with unique information. This is the reason why astronomers will often study an object using many different types of EMR, an approach known as **multiwavelength astronomy**. Since there is such a range in the wavelengths of EMR, the types of telescopes used at the low- and high-energy ends of the electromagnetic spectrum are quite different.

Figure C2.30: The *Hubble Space Telescope* collects visible light, infrared radiation, and ultraviolet radiation.

Recall that radio waves are the EMR with the largest wavelength and the lowest energy content; so, if astronomers are going to gather this radiation, it requires an enormous dish to reflect the waves to a detector. The fact that radio waves have a very long wavelength means that diffraction can create significant difficulties with resolution if two sources of radio waves are very close together. The solution in these cases is to make the effective size of the opening of a telescope even larger by collecting data from a group of radio telescopes that are linked together. One arrangement that addresses this problem is called a **very large array**. This array simultaneously collects data from a number of individual radio telescopes, which is then processed by computers to produce a single image.

Figure C2.31: This radio telescope uses a 43-m dish to collect radio-wave data.

> **multiwavelength astronomy:** the study of objects in space using the principle that these objects reveal different aspects of their behaviour through the many wavelengths of EMR they emit

> **very large array:** a group of radio telescopes distributed over many kilometres along the arms of a Y-shaped track

Figure C2.32: This very large array in New Mexico consists of 27 individual radio telescopes. Each arm of the array, consisting of nine telescopes, can be up to 20 km long.

You will recall from your work earlier in this chapter that types of radiation from the middle of the electromagnetic spectrum are unique in that they can effectively demonstrate both wave characteristics and photon characteristics. This is why visible light can be refracted as a wave as it enters the lenses of a digital camera, and then the light can interact with individual atoms as its photons collide with the camera's sensor. For high-energy radiation, like X-rays and gamma rays, the photon properties tend to dominate, while the wave properties are more difficult to observe. This creates design challenges for astronomers gathering X-ray and gamma radiation.

The *Chandra* X-ray telescope cannot use a large curved mirror at the end opposite the opening because the penetrating ability of the X-rays would cause the radiation to pass through the mirror instead of bouncing off its surface. Mirrors are still used, but in this case they are arranged along the inside of the body tube of the telescope. X-rays will only reflect if the direction of the radiation is almost parallel to the surface of the specially designed mirror. *Chandra* is a good example of how astronomers have to take into account the properties of the radiation that they want to collect when they design their instruments. As Figure C2.34 indicates, the wave properties of reflection, refraction, and diffraction are more difficult to observe at the high-energy end of the electromagnetic spectrum.

Despite these differences, there are characteristics astronomers can measure from all regions of the electromagnetic spectrum: energy content, wavelength, frequency, degree of polarization, and speed.

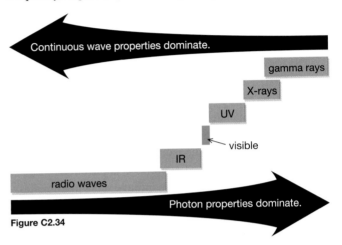

Figure C2.34

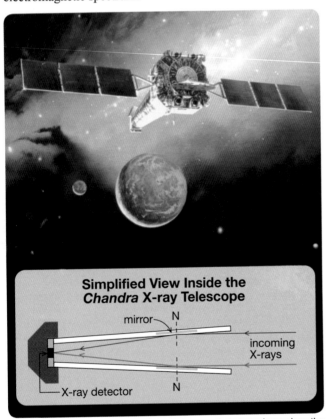

Figure C2.33: *Chandra* is a space-based telescope that uses mirrors along the inside of the body tube to focus incoming X-ray radiation.

Utilizing Technology

Tracking Space-Based Telescopes and Other Satellites

Science Skills

✓ Performing and Recording
✓ Analyzing and Interpreting

Purpose
You will use computer software available from a NASA website to compare the orbits of space-based telescopes and other satellites.

Procedure
Obtain the handout "Tracking Space-Based Telescopes and Other Satellites" from the Science 30 Textbook CD. Follow the instructions on the handout to find the Internet site and then collect the data from this site.

Analysis
Concisely explain how Earth is able to exert gravitational force on a fast-moving satellite so that it maintains an orbit around the planet.

33. Explain why astronomical observatories for infrared radiation are sometimes located in specially outfitted aircraft that can fly at high altitudes.

34. Explain why radio telescopes are so large.

Analyzing Starlight

Given the challenges of gathering EMR with telescopes, astronomers take great care to thoroughly analyze the radiation data they collect. One technique is to use a prism to separate the radiation into its component wavelengths. This can also be done with a **diffraction grating**. A diffraction grating is a piece of glass or plastic with thousands of tightly spaced parallel lines etched on its surface.

> **diffraction grating:** a piece of glass or plastic with thousands of tightly spaced lines etched on its surface; used to produce spectra

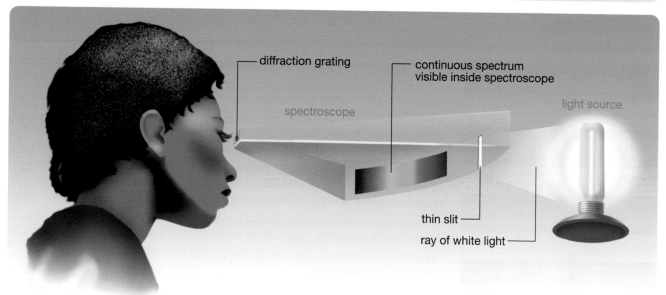

If the source of the EMR is a dense material heated to about 6000°C, most of the radiation emitted is from the visible spectrum. Since the resulting rainbow of colour is continuous, with one colour blending into another, this spectrum is called a **continuous spectrum**. This is what would be observed if it were possible to send a probe carrying a prism or a diffraction grating to the surface of the Sun. This kind of spectrum is not observed by probes that are beyond the Sun's atmosphere because the gases in the cooler parts of the Sun's outer atmosphere absorb certain wavelengths of light. Each wavelength that is absorbed corresponds to a dark line on the rainbow of colours.

> **continuous spectrum:** a spectrum having no distinct lines that is distributed over an unbroken band of wavelengths

Since each dark line corresponds to a wavelength of radiation that has been absorbed, this is called a **dark-line spectrum** or an **absorption spectrum**. The atoms of a particular element in a low-pressure gas will only absorb certain wavelengths, creating a dark-line spectrum that is unique to that gas. This is a very useful property for astronomers because the dark-line spectrum acts like a fingerprint, allowing astronomers to identify the presence of certain atoms in the atmosphere of the Sun based on the patterns of dark lines.

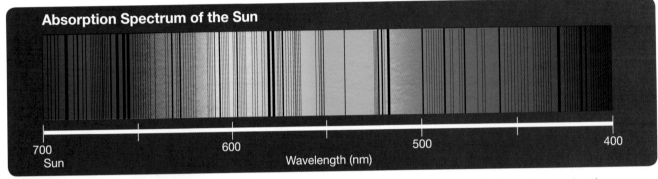

Absorption Spectrum of the Sun

Wavelength (nm)

700 Sun   600   500   400

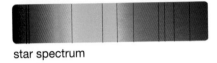

star spectrum

hydrogen

helium

calcium

magnesium

bright-line spectrum of hydrogen

dark-line spectrum of hydrogen

This fingerprinting idea can be taken one step further when an electric current is forced to pass through a low-pressure gas. In this case, the same wavelengths that the gas absorbs when light passes through it are emitted when the atoms of the gas are excited to higher energy levels. This spectrum of a few separated wavelengths is called an **emission spectrum** or a **bright-line spectrum**.

Both emission and absorption **spectra** are normally analyzed with a diffraction grating mounted on a device that enables an observer to determine the wavelength of each emitted line. Such a device is called a **spectrometer**, since it allows precise measurements of the absorbed wavelengths in a spectrum to be made.

Since only certain wavelengths are emitted, this pattern is called an emission spectrum or a bright-line spectrum. In the next investigation you will have an opportunity to use a spectroscope to observe and record the emission spectra for a number of different gases.

Science Links: Thickness of the Ozone Layer

Ultraviolet light from the Sun can be reflected from Earth back into space. Spectrometers on satellites use this reflected UV radiation to produce an absorption spectrum. This data is then analyzed to determine the thickness of the ozone layer. The connections among ultraviolet light, the thickness of the ozone layer, and the release of CFCs into the atmosphere was explored in Unit B.

> **absorption spectrum or dark-line spectrum:** a spectrum that has a pattern of dark lines due to the light passing through an absorbing medium; can be used to identify a material

> **emission spectrum or bright-line spectrum:** a spectrum that has a pattern of separate bright lines that is emitted from an excited gas under low pressure; can be used to identify a material

> **spectra:** plural form of *spectrum*

> **spectrometer:** an optical instrument that is used to measure the wavelengths of light

Investigation

Observing Spectra

Purpose

You will use a spectroscope to record the patterns of wavelengths emitted by excited atoms in a gas-discharge tube and by the wavelengths emitted by the hot filament of a light bulb.

Materials

- handheld spectroscope
- high-voltage power supply that can run gas-discharge tubes
- gas-discharge tubes for different gases (hydrogen, helium, mercury, and neon)
- showcase light bulb mounted in a lamp with a dimmer switch
- standard fluorescent tube light source (often used as ceiling lighting for classrooms and kitchens)
- coloured pens or pencils
- "Observing Continuous and Emission Spectra" handout

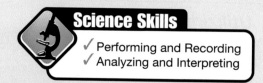

Science Skills

✓ Performing and Recording
✓ Analyzing and Interpreting

 CAUTION!

- The gas-discharge tubes can become hot after running for a few minutes. Switch off the power and let the bulb cool before handling.
- The high-voltage power supply represents a significant shock hazard. Be sure it is switched off when changing bulbs.

Part A: Observing a Continuous Spectrum

Procedure and Observations

step 1: Switch on the showcase bulb and adjust the dimmer switch so the bulb is bright. Observe the spectrum produced by the bulb by looking through the spectroscope. Note the relative brightness of each of the colours seen through the spectroscope. Use coloured pens or pencils to record your results.

step 2: Use the dimmer switch to gradually reduce the bulb's brightness. Note the changes in the relative brightness of each of the colours seen through the spectroscope. Record your results.

Analysis

1. Describe the differences between the spectra produced by the bulb on maximum brightness and the bulb on a dim setting.

Part B: Observing Emission Spectra

Procedure and Observations

step 1: Obtain the handout "Observing Continuous and Emission Spectra" from the Science 30 Textbook CD.

step 2: Connect the gas-discharge tube containing neon gas to the power supply. Switch on the power supply and dim the lights in the room. Observe the light from the tube through the spectroscope. Use coloured pens or pencils to record your results on the handout. Switch off the power supply.

step 3: Repeat step 2 for mercury, helium, and hydrogen. In each case, record your results on the handout.

Analysis

2. The unaided eye sees each of the gas-discharge tubes as producing one colour of light, while the spectroscope reveals a number of separate bright lines. Speculate on how the human eye arrives at one colour from all the colours produced by a gas-discharge tube.

Part C: Applications

Procedure and Observations

Using a spectroscope, observe the light produced by a standard fluorescent tube light source. Note the wavelengths of the bright lines produced in the middle of the spectrum. Record your results.

Analysis

3. Use your data from Part B to determine the type of excited gas inside a standard fluorescent tube.

Chapter 2: The Electromagnetic Spectrum **449**

How Astronomers Analyze Spectra

One way starlight can be analyzed is to determine the chemical composition of the clouds of cool gases found in a star's outer atmosphere. In the next activity you will have an opportunity to see how this is done as you review what you learned about spectra.

Utilizing Technology

Spectral Analysis

Science Skills

✓ Performing and Recording
✓ Analyzing and Interpreting

Purpose
You will use the applet called "Spectral Analysis" to learn how astronomers analyze starlight to determine the chemical composition of stars.

Procedure
step 1: Locate the applet "Spectral Analysis" on the Science 30 Textbook CD.
step 2: Follow the instructions on the application to complete this activity.

Doppler Shift

Think back to the last time you were passed by an emergency vehicle with its siren wailing. Recall the change in pitch that occurred as the siren approached you and then as it passed by. Figure C2.35 compares an observer's experience with sound waves emitted from a stationary source with the sound waves emitted from a moving source. If the source is moving towards the observer, the incoming waves get bunched together, resulting in an apparent higher-frequency wave than what is experienced from a stationary source. If the source is moving away from the observer, the incoming waves get spaced farther apart, resulting in an apparent lower-frequency wave than experienced from a stationary source. This shift in the frequency of a wave due to relative motion between the observer and the source is called the **Doppler effect**.

> **Doppler effect:** a change in the observed frequency of a wave due to motion between the source and the observer
>
> **blue shift:** an increase in frequency due to a source of EMR moving toward an observer, due to the Doppler effect
>
> **red shift:** a decrease in frequency due to a source of EMR moving away from an observer, due to the Doppler effect

This same effect can occur with the electromagnetic radiation emitted by stars as they move relative to observers on Earth. In the case of EMR, a shift to higher frequencies is called a **blue shift** and occurs when stars are moving toward an observer. A **red shift** in EMR occurs when a star is moving away from an observer. In the next activity you will have an opportunity to learn more about how astronomers use the Doppler effect to determine the motion of distant stars relative to Earth.

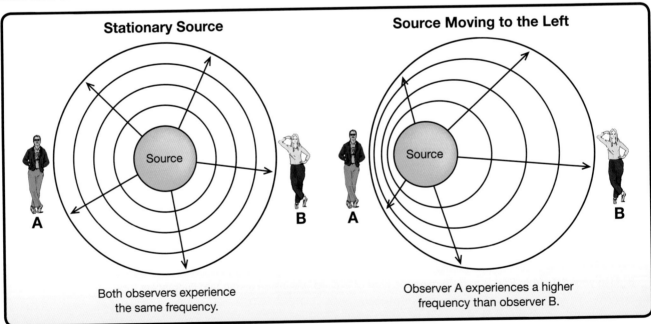

Figure C2.35

Purpose

You will use the applet "Red Shift" to learn how astronomers apply the Doppler effect to starlight to determine the motion of stars relative to Earth.

Science Skills

✓ Performing and Recording
✓ Analyzing and Interpreting

Procedure

step 1: Locate the applet "Red Shift" on the Science 30 Textbook CD.

step 2: Follow the instructions on the application to complete this acitivity.

Practice

35. Explain the differences between an emission spectrum, an absorption spectrum, and a continuous spectrum.

36. Every remote galaxy in the universe has red-shifted light. Explain how this evidence supports the idea that the universe is expanding.

Classification of Stars

In an earlier investigation, you analyzed the spectra produced by a light bulb in a lamp with a dimmer switch. Using more sophisticated equipment, researchers have conducted similar experiments by measuring the temperature of the object emitting the light and then carefully recording the spectra produced. The patterns from these investigations give astronomers a powerful tool because they can work backward by using the spectra to determine the surface temperature of stars. Although there will be dark lines in these spectra, if the brightness of the emitted light is plotted against wavelength, interesting patterns emerge.

If the peak of the continuous spectrum occurs with wavelengths slightly longer than red light (in the infrared region), the star likely has a surface temperature of about 2900°C. This is why a star like Betelgeuse appears red to the unaided eye. As the peak of the emitted light shifts to shorter wavelengths and increases to greater brightness, the surface temperature of the star increases. Notice that very hot stars, like Rigel, have their peak in the ultraviolet region of the electromagnetic spectrum. Although your eye would interpret this as a bluish-white colour, most of the emitted radiation is in the ultraviolet region. Note that the connection between temperature and emitted radiation is consistent with your earlier work with the surface of the Sun.

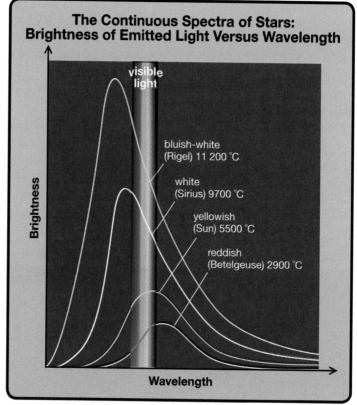

The Continuous Spectra of Stars: Brightness of Emitted Light Versus Wavelength

visible light

bluish-white (Rigel) 11 200 °C

white (Sirius) 9700 °C

yellowish (Sun) 5500 °C

reddish (Betelgeuse) 2900 °C

Brightness

Wavelength

Evolution of Stars

Given the variation in the colour and brightness of the light emitted by stars, it is natural to wonder why these variations occur. Current theories explain the spectra of a particular star in terms of the star's mass and its stage in stellar evolution. Although all stars form in regions rich in hydrogen gas and dust, the stages of evolution depend on the original mass of the star.

Evolution of Low-Mass Stars

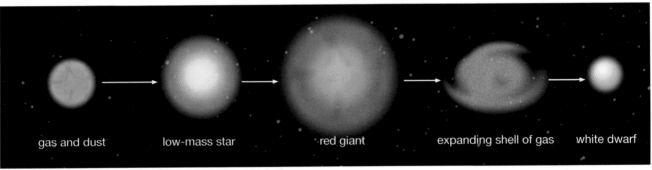

gas and dust   low-mass star   red giant   expanding shell of gas   white dwarf

Figure C2.36: The mass of a low-mass star is between 0.1 and 1.4 solar masses.

red giant: a star of great size and age that has a relatively low surface temperature

nebula: an interstellar cloud of gas and dust

white dwarf: a compact star found as the last stage in the evolution of low-mass stars

supernova: a stellar explosion that produces a very bright cloud of ionized gas that remains a very bright object in the sky for weeks or months

neutron star: a super-dense star consisting mainly of neutrons formed as the last stage in the stellar evolution of intermediate-mass stars

pulsar: a rotating neutron star that emits radiation in regular pulses

Small stars are those stars that have a mass less than 1.4 times the mass of the Sun. These stars begin when gravitational attraction causes gas and dust to collect. Once the core temperature of the gathering mass reaches about 10 000 000°C, nuclear fusion reactions begin and the star is born. The Sun is an example of a low-mass star. Astronomers suspect that the Sun's hydrogen fuel will be exhausted in about 5 billion years. According to this theory, the core will collapse while the outer layers expand, transforming the Sun into a **red giant**. Betelgeuse is an example of a star in this stage of its evolution. In the final stages of evolution, the core temperature rises and the outer layers are thrown off as an expanding shell of gas called a **nebula**. All that remains of the original star is its core, which has exhausted its nuclear fuel. A star in this stage is called a **white dwarf** because it is a small source of dim white light.

If the mass of the starting matter is between 1.4 and 8 times the Sun's mass, the process of stellar evolution happens more quickly. Astronomers suspect that the additional mass means that a supergiant with a core temperature of about 3 000 000 000°C will form. They think that the next steps result in the core imploding, followed by a rebound explosion called a **supernova**. Most of the stellar material is hurled into space, leaving behind a super-dense object called a **neutron star**. A neutron star is thought to spin very rapidly on its axis, emitting radio waves. In some cases, neutron stars emit radio waves as pulses, which is why this kind of source is called a **pulsar**. A pulsar in the Crab Nebula is thought to be the remains of a supernova explosion that was visible from Earth in the year 1054.

Evolution of Intermediate-Mass Stars

gas and dust   intermediate-mass star   supergiant star   supernova   neutron star

Figure C2.37: The mass of an intermediate-mass star is between 1.4 and 8 solar masses.

If the mass of the star is greater than 8 solar masses, when the core of the supergiant implodes, the result is not a supernova. Instead, the core continues to collapse, becoming more and more dense. Eventually the gravitational field of this incredibly dense matter is so great that not even light can escape. The result is called a **black hole** because no electromagnetic radiation is emitted while this object consumes surrounding matter.

> **black hole:** an area in space with a gravitational field so strong that neither matter nor EMR can escape; formed as the last stage in the evolution of high-mass stars

Evolution of High-Mass Stars

gas and dust   high-mass star   supergiant star   star collapses   dense black hole

Figure C2.38: The mass of a high-mass star is greater than 8 solar masses.

Practice

37. Suppose two new stars are discovered. One star appears to emit light that is slightly less yellow and more white than the light emitted by the Sun. The other star appears to emit light that is more orange than the light emitted by the Sun. Use this information to compare the temperature of each star to the Sun.

38. The final object that a star becomes in stellar evolution is either a white dwarf, a neutron star, or a black hole. Identify the feature of a star that determines what its endpoint will be in stellar evolution.

39. Explain why it is impossible to view a black hole through a telescope.

Utilizing Technology

Risks and Benefits of Deep-Space Probes

Background Information

Unpiloted spacecraft that collect data from the planets and other objects that lie beyond the orbit of Mars are called "deep-space probes" because the distances from Earth to these objects are so large. The *Cassini-Huygens* probe that was sent to Saturn certainly meets this criteria because Saturn is about twice as far from the Sun as is Jupiter and nearly ten times farther from the Sun than Earth is.

Science Skills
✓ Initiating and Planning
✓ Performing and Recording
✓ Analyzing and Interpreting
✓ Communication and Teamwork

Purpose

You will use the Internet as a research tool to assess the risks and benefits of the *Cassini-Huygens* deep-space probe that was sent to Saturn.

Research Procedure

Use the information from NASA, the European Space Agency, the Italian Space Agency, and other websites to help answer the following questions.

1. The *Cassini-Huygens* deep-space probe was not launched from Earth on a direct path to Saturn. Instead, its path involved looping around the Sun twice using a technique called "gravity assist" before moving toward the outer parts of the solar system.

   a. Explain what is meant by "gravity assist" and why this was necessary for the *Cassini-Huygens* deep-space probe.

   b. Use a diagram to describe the path taken by the *Cassini-Huygens* deep-space probe on its way from Earth to Saturn.

2. On June 30, 2004, the *Cassini-Huygens* deep-space probe entered Saturn's orbit and began to collect data that was transmitted back to Earth. Use a table to describe some of the instruments onboard *Cassini* that were used to collect data using EMR. Record the research focus for each instrument as well as the wavelengths detected and the region of the electromagnetic spectrum that was sampled.

3. In January 2005, the *Huygens* probe separated from *Cassini*. The *Huygens* probe then dropped into the atmosphere of Titan, one of Saturn's moons, and collected data as it descended and as it sat on the surface.

   a. Explain why scientists were so interested to collect data from Titan.

   b. Describe some of the findings from this research.

4. None of the instruments onboard the *Cassini-Huygens* deep-space probe could collect data or send data back to Earth without a source of electrical energy. This energy was provided by three radioscopic thermoelectric generators, or RTGs for short, which convert heat from the natural radioactive decay of plutonium dioxide into electricity. The mass of $PuO_2(s)$ on board *Cassini-Huygens* is about 33 kg.

   a. Explain why photovoltaic cells would not be a practical way to generate electrical energy for the *Cassini-Huygens* deep-space probe.

   b. Plutonium dioxide is highly toxic, since it is a potent source of ionizing radiation. Even a few grains of $PuO_2(s)$ dust lodged in the lungs can cause cancer.

      i. Explain why some of the residents living close to the launch site for the *Cassini-Huygens* deep-space probe wanted the launch of this probe cancelled.

      ii. Explain why some environmentalists in several countries protested the gravity-assist flyby of the *Cassini-Huygens* deep-space probe.

Analyzing the Issue

5. a. Analyze the results of your research by concisely organizing your findings in a table, with "Risks" at the top of one column and "Benefits" at the top of the other.

   b. Review the lists of risks and benefits from the point of view of the stakeholders. How would residents living close to the launch site, environmentalists in other countries, and scientists who were going to use the data from *Cassini-Huygens* each react to the entries on your lists?

Taking a Stand and Defending Your Position

6. Do the benefits of a deep-space probe, like *Cassini-Huygens*, outweigh the risks? Take a clear position on this issue by writing a few concise paragraphs. Your position should be supported by the body of research and should indicate that you have considered the question from more than one viewpoint.

Evaluation

7. It is very helpful at this stage to share your findings with others. How do their points of view differ from yours? Are the arguments made to support these views consistent with the information you researched? Did other students find additional information that was unknown to you? How has your position changed since you started? If you had to make this decision again, what would you have done differently?

2.2 Summary

Some people say that astronomy is the oldest science because humans have been looking into the sky for many thousands of years. In the beginning, the light from stars was used to help with navigation, to tell time, and to predict the seasons. Now, starlight is also used to determine the chemical composition of stars, the motion of stars relative to Earth, and the temperature on the surface of stars.

In addition to visible light, other forms of EMR are emitted by objects beyond Earth. The fact that each type of radiation can provide unique information about the source is the basis for multiwavelength astronomy.

Knowledge

1. Obtain the handout "Summarizing Multiwavelength Astronomy" from the Science 30 Textbook CD. Complete this handout by adding the necessary information to each column.

Applying Concepts

Obtain the handout "Reference Absorption Spectra" from the Science 30 Textbook CD. Use the information on this handout to answer questions 2 and 3.

2. Often a spectrum will contain the lines of more than one excited gas. Identify the two gases that produced the following spectrum.

3. Describe the effect on the pattern of spectral lines observed on Earth if a star is moving away from Earth and if a star is moving toward Earth.

Use the following information to answer questions 4, 5, and 6.

Historical records indicate that in the year 1054 an object that glowed as brightly as a full moon appeared in the sky. Archaeological evidence suggests that the ancient Pueblo People (also known as the Anasazi), who lived in what is now Arizona, recorded the appearance of a new star in the sky.

Figure C2.39: Archaeologists suspect the star-like image to the left of the crescent moon is the supernova. The image of the hand is thought to indicate that this site is sacred.

The accounts recorded by people living in Japan and China pinpoint the location of this very bright new object near the constellation Taurus. This same location in the sky is currently the location of a glowing cloud of interstellar gas and dust known as the Crab Nebula.

The current interpretation of all this data is that the Crab Nebula is the remains of a supernova explosion that was observed by people on Earth over 900 years ago.

The Crab Nebula emits EMR from all regions of the electromagnetic spectrum. Figure C2.40 shows images that were produced using visible radiation (VIS), ultraviolet radiation that is near the visible spectrum or near ultraviolet (NUV), ultraviolet radiation that is far from the visible spectrum or far ultraviolet (FUV), and X-ray radiation. Not shown is the data from the radio spectrum, which indicates the presence of a pulsar—a rotating neutron star at the centre of the nebula.

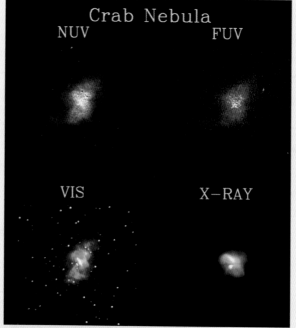

Figure C2.40: Images of the Crab Nebula produced from emitted EMR

4. Describe the stages of evolution for the star that produced the Crab Nebula.

5. Explain why astronomers have collected data for the Crab Nebula using so many different types of EMR.

6. Archaeological evidence suggests that the Anasazi People had an agricultural economy that was centred on corn, beans, and other crops.

   a. Suggest reasons why astronomical observations would have been important to the Anasazi People.

   b. Suggest a reason why the Anasazi People decided to leave a record of this astronomical event.

Chapter 2 Summary

In this chapter you have surveyed each region of the electromagnetic spectrum, from radio waves with wavelengths that can be kilometres long to gamma rays with wavelengths smaller than atoms. The differences in wavelength, frequency, and energy among the different types of electromagnetic radiation account for the variety of interactions that are possible with matter. Examples include visible light being used by a dandelion in photosynthesis and microwaves being beamed from satellites in orbit to satellite dishes on Earth's surface. Clearly, EMR plays a key role in living systems and in the growing number of high-tech devices that are used in daily life.

People have utilized the visible radiation from stars in the form of constellations for thousands of years. Inuit people use this EMR for navigation, for telling time, and for predicting changes in the seasons. Modern astronomers have developed technologies that allow them to use radiation from across the whole electromagnetic spectrum as they study stars and other objects beyond Earth.

Summarize Your Learning

In Chapter 2 you learned a number of new terms, processes, and theories. Many of the concepts are related, and you will have an easier time recalling them if they are organized into patterns.

Since the patterns have to be meaningful to you, there are some options about how you can create this summary. Each of the following options is described in "Summarize Your Learning Activities" in the Reference Section. Choose one of these options to create a summary of the key concepts and important terms in Chapter 2.

Option 1: Draw a concept map or a web diagram.	Option 2: Create a point-form summary.	Option 3: Write a story using key terms and concepts.	Option 4: Create a colourful poster.	Option 5: Build a model.	Option 6: Write a script for a skit (a mock news report).

Chapter 2 Review Questions

Knowledge

1. In Chapter 2 you saw how each region of the electromagnetic spectrum is applied to technologies on Earth and to the study of astronomy. In many cases, the penetrating ability of the radiation plays a significant role in how the radiation is used. Copy and complete the following table to summarize what you have learned.

APPLICATIONS OF ELECTROMAGNETIC RADIATION

Type of EMR	Range of Frequencies	Applications on Earth That Illustrate Penetrating Ability		Applications in Astronomy That Illustrate Penetrating Ability
radio waves				
microwaves				
infrared radiation				
visible light				
UV radiation				
X-rays				
gamma rays				

2. Some forms of EMR are classified as ionizing radiation.

   a. Explain the meaning of this term.

   b. Describe the effects ionizing radiation has on living tissue.

   c. Describe strategies you can use to reduce your exposure to ionizing radiation.

3. One way to analyze EMR is to pass the radiation through a prism or a diffraction grating. This causes the radiation to separate into its component wavelengths, producing a spectrum. Depending upon the source, three types of spectra can be observed. For each of the following types of spectra, describe a possible source and indicate how this information could be used by astronomers.

   a. continuous spectrum

   b. absorption spectrum (dark-line spectrum)

   c. emission spectrum (bright-line spectrum)

4. Sketch a series of diagrams to show the main steps in the evolution of stars like the Sun.

5. A black hole is one of the most intriguing regions of space studied by astronomers.

   a. Describe some of the characteristics of a black hole.

   b. Describe how a black hole is formed.

Applying Concepts

6. In astronomy, the unit that is often used to describe distances between Earth and stars other than the Sun is the light-year. For example, Alpha Centauri (after the Sun, the closest star to Earth that can be seen with the naked eye) is 4.3 light-years from Earth.

   a. Determine how many metres there are in one light-year.

   b. Use your answer to question 6.a. to determine the distance (in metres) from Alpha Centauri to Earth.

   c. Explain the following statement:

   > If you were to see Alpha Centauri on a clear night, you would not be seeing the way this star looks now. You would be seeing the way it looked 4.3 years ago.

   d. Sirius is the brightest star in the night sky and is located 8.3×10^{16} m from Earth. When you look at Sirius in the night sky, how far back in time are you actually seeing it?

7. A truck driver uses a citizen's band, or CB, radio to communicate with other truckers. If the broadcast frequency is 27.965 MHz, calculate the wavelength of the radio wave.

8. Figure C2.41 shows the wavelengths of light that are absorbed by pigments in the chloroplasts of plants.

   a. Identify the wavelengths of light that are strongly absorbed by all three pigments.

   b. Identify the wavelengths of light that are not strongly absorbed by these three pigments.

   c. If you looked at a plant leaf that contained these three pigments, what would be the colour of the leaf? Explain your answer.

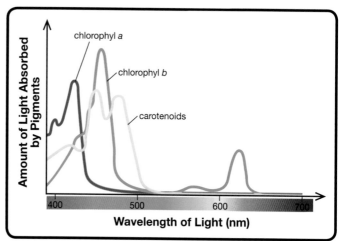

Figure C2.41

9. The world's largest airborne astronomical observatory is NASA's Stratospheric Observatory for Infrared Astronomy, or SOFIA for short. In Figure C2.42, the black square near the tail shows where the open cavity for the telescope is located.

Figure C2.42

   a. Explain why it is necessary to go more than 10 km above Earth's surface to make observations in the infrared and microwave regions of the electromagnetic spectrum.

   b. What specific astronomical phenomena is SOFIA designed to study? You can answer this question by using the Internet as a research tool to find out the key objectives on NASA's SOFIA website. To find the website, enter the following keywords into your Internet seach engine: *NASA + SOFIA*.

Use the following information to answer questions 10 to 13.

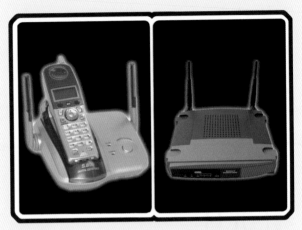

There has been a dramatic increase in the number of devices in homes and workplaces that utilize radio waves to make connections between devices. These devices are very convenient because they eliminate the need for cables to carry signals. This is why they are sometimes called "wireless radio" technologies. Two of the most common wireless radio technologies are cordless telephones and wireless routers that enable more than one computer to access the Internet using a single modem.

When a new technology is introduced to solve one problem, a new set of unintended problems is often created.

10. The fact that you can listen to a portable radio inside most buildings illustrates an important property of radio waves—the ability to penetrate walls made of wood, cement, and glass.

   a. Explain why this property of radio waves is essential to the design of wireless devices.

   b. Explain how this property of radio waves can create security issues when wireless devices are used to communicate sensitive information, such as credit card numbers or passwords for bank cards.

   c. Explain why businesses that use wireless communication systems reduce the power of their transmitters to the minimum level necessary to run all the devices within the building.

11. The owner's manual for a wireless router includes the following recommendations for the location of the router:

   • Place the wireless router in a central location within a home or business, away from outside walls.
   • Avoid placing the wireless router near large metal objects, like filing cabinets.

   Use your knowledge of the behaviour of radio waves to explain each of these recommendations.

12. Many brands of cordless telephones use a frequency of 2.4 GHz. This same frequency is also utilized by manufacturers of wireless routers.

   a. Explain what the phrase "a frequency of 2.4 GHz" means in terms of the interaction of a radio wave with an antenna.

   b. Calculate the wavelength of the radiation associated with this signal.

   c. Explain the difficulties that could occur if a person was using a cordless phone while using their computer's wireless router.

   d. Suggest some solutions to this problem.

13. Since the number of wireless radio devices is continuing to increase, alternative technologies are being developed. Wireless infrared systems use a beam of infrared radiation to send a signal from one device to another. You utilize a system that transmits infrared signals every time you use a remote control to operate a TV or VCR. Use your experiences with remote controls to outline some of the possible advantages and disadvantages of a wireless infrared communication system.

14. In addition to making astronomical observations, telescopes can also be used for observing objects on Earth. A mounted set of binoculars at Lake Louise gives tourists a magnified view of the glacier at the far end of the lake.

   Use Figure C2.43 to determine whether the design of this device is closer to being a reflecting telescope or a refracting telescope.

Figure C2.43: Lake Louise, Alberta

15. X-rays produced in a diagnostic imaging machine have a wavelength of 8.8 nm. Determine the frequency of this radiation.

Use the following information to answer questions 16 and 17.

This diamondback rattlesnake has a pair of infrared receptors on its head, between its eye and its nostril.

eye —
infrared —
receptor

To utilize these receptors, the snake moves its head back and forth until the radiation detected by the receptor on the left is equal to the radiation detected by the receptor on the right. When this occurs, the prey emitting the infrared radiation is straight ahead of the snake. This system can guide the snake as it hunts in dark conditions.

16. Diamondbacks are most sensitive to infrared radiation with a wavelength of 10 μm.

   a. Calculate the frequency of this radiation.

   b. Speculate why snakes have evolved to be sensitive to this frequency of infrared radiation.

17. Draw a diagram to show how a mouse that is straight ahead of a diamondback's head would send equal amounts of infrared radiation to each sensor. Draw another diagram to show how a mouse that is off-centre would send more radiation to one sensor than the other.

Use the following information to answer question 18.

In Chapter 2 you learned of the hazards to living tissue caused by exposure to ionizing radiation. You also learned that health-care professionals go to great efforts to keep the exposure to themselves and their patients as low as reasonably achievable, or ALARA for short.

18. Safety procedures are used to ensure the safety of patients and the technicians who operate X-ray machines. Describe the procedures that are based on ALARA to minimize the risks to patients and to the health-care professionals operating the equipment.

Obtain the handout "Reference Absorption Spectra" from the Science 30 Textbook CD. Use the information on this handout to help answer questions 19 and 20.

19. Identify the excited gases that produced the following spectra.

   a.
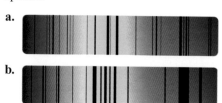

   b.

20. Often a spectrum will contain the lines of more than one excited gas. Identify the two gases that produced each of the following spectra.

   a.
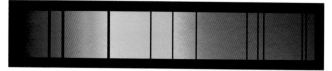

   b.

21. The following spectrum was produced by a source that was stationary in relation to the observer.

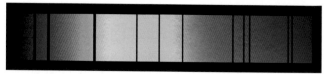

The next spectra were produced by sources that were moving with respect to the observer. In each case, determine whether

- the spectrum is an example of red shift or blue shift
- the source of the spectrum is moving toward the observer or away from the observer

   a.

   b.

22. Refer to the spectra shown in questions 21.a. and 21.b. Determine which of these two spectra was produced by the faster-moving source. Explain your reasoning.

Unit C Conclusion

When you began this unit, you were asked to think about the connections between natural phenomena, like the northern lights, and a number of technologies that utilize electromagnetic energy. The key concepts that ran through all of these topics were electric fields and magnetic fields. Motors, generators, and transformers are all technologies based upon the properties of electric and magnetic fields. When these two fields interact, the result is an electromagnetic wave that can be organized into the regions of the electromagnetic spectrum. Long-wavelength radio waves, incredibly tiny X-rays, and the full rainbow of colours within the visible spectrum are all examples of electromagnetic waves.

Throughout the unit you also considered these topics from the point of view of personal health. Whether it's avoiding regions of intense electric field lines under a thundercloud or reducing your exposure to ionizing radiation, the effects of electromagnetic energy require careful consideration. In Unit D you will extend these ideas from the health of an individual to the health of the whole planet.

Career Profile

Biomedical Flight Controller

Tara (Williams) Volpe, a descendant of the Mohawk People, studied Biology at the University of Montreal. Upon graduation, Tara searched for career opportunities in fields that interested her and would utilize her skills. While travelling in Russia, she was fortunate enough to meet NASA employees working in Moscow supporting the *MIR Space Station*. When she inquired about career opportunities in the Manned Space Flight Program, they led her in the right direction.

Tara was hired as a Biomedical Flight Controller at the Johnson Space Centre in Houston, Texas. After several years of training, she worked in Mission Control as a member of the flight control team for the *International Space Station* (ISS). During missions, Tara advised the ISS crew on the operation, maintenance, and repair of the extensive Crew Health-Care System, which includes medical, fitness, and environmental analysis equipment. In addition, she ensured a safe and healthy environment onboard the space station by monitoring the temperature, pressure, and atmospheric gas composition.

Tara is currently working with a team of doctors, engineers, scientists, and astronauts to develop the medical requirements necessary to safely return a human crew to the Moon, and eventually to travel to Mars. With missions lasting up to two-and-a-half years, they need to consider long-term exposure to weightlessness, increased radiation, and, of course, how much food to pack.

Tara loves her job with NASA and advises other Aboriginal students to set their career goals high and reach for the stars.

Unit C Review Questions

1. The following table summarizes the important quantities studied in this chapter. Copy and complete the table in your notebook.

Name	Symbol	Most Common Unit	Equations
gravitational field			
electric field			
magnetic field			
voltage			
current			
resistance			
power			
wavelength			
frequency			
wave speed			
speed of EMR in a vacuum			

2. Define each of the following terms. In each case, include a simple diagram to illustrate the key points in your definition.

   a. field

   b. test body

   c. alternating current

   d. transformer

   e. electromagnetic radiation

   f. reflection

   g. refraction

   h. diffraction

   i. polarization

   j. photon

3. A car's block heater is rated at 1000 W and is plugged in for 12.0 h every night during each of the 31 days in January.

   a. Calculate the electrical energy consumed by the block heater in both joules and kilowatt-hours.

   b. If the cost of electricity is 9.4¢/kW•h, calculate the cost to operate the car's block heater for all of January.

4. Repeat question 3, only this time assume that the car's owner uses a timer that allows the block heater to turn on for only 3.00 h every day.

5. Refer to your work in questions 3 and 4. Beyond saving money, describe some of the other benefits of using a timer for the car's block heater.

6. A radio station broadcasts to its listeners on a wave with a wavelength of 405.4 m. Calculate the frequency of this broadcast.

7. The human eye is most sensitive to yellow-green light that has a frequency of 5.5×10^{14} Hz.

   a. Calculate the wavelength of this light.

   b. Suggest a reason why some fire engines and other emergency vehicles are often painted a yellow-green colour.

8. The following graphic shows the spectrum of the Sun.

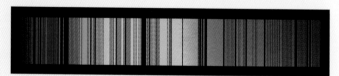

   a. Identify this spectrum as a continuous spectrum, an emission spectrum, or an absorption spectrum.

   b. Concisely explain why there are dark lines on this spectrum.

9. Obtain the handout "Reference Absorption Spectra" from the Science 30 Textbook CD. Use the information on this handout to help identify the excited gas that produced the following spectrum.

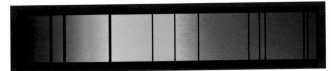

10. The following spectrum was produced by a source that was stationary in relation to the observer.

The next spectra were produced by sources that were moving with respect to the observer. In each case, determine whether

- the spectrum is an example of red shift or blue shift
- the source of the spectrum is moving toward the observer or away from the observer

a.

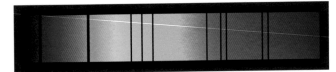

b.

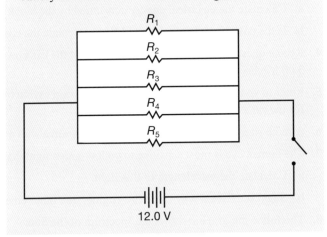

11. Refer to the spectra shown in questions 10.a. and 10.b. Determine which of these two spectra was produced by the faster-moving source. Explain your reasoning.

Use the following information to answer questions 12 and 13.

This circuit shows the connections between two resistors, a switch, and a battery. Note that in addition to labelling the components, each of the contact points in the circuit has been labelled for the purposes of these questions.

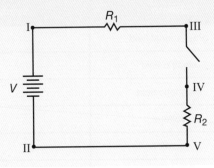

12. Describe how you would use other equipment to measure the following values.

a. the voltage across the battery

b. the current through resistor R_1

c. the resistance of resistor R_2

13. Calculate the electric current flowing through R_2 given the following values: $V = 6.00$ V, $R_1 = 510$ Ω, and $R_2 = 1000$ Ω.

Use the following information to answer questions 14 and 15.

The rear-window defroster of a car consists of five heating wires that each have a resistance of 32 Ω. The wires are connected to a switch and to the 12.0-V car battery as shown in the schematic diagram.

14. Calculate the equivalent resistance of the five heating wires.

15. Use your answer to question 14 to calculate the current that would flow through the closed switch.

Use the following information to answer questions 16 to 19.

A student went online shopping for a new pair of goggles to be used for snowboarding and downhill skiing. There were many brands to choose from, with a variety of models within each product line. Although the various websites provided photographs, one manufacturer supplied technical data describing the ability of each pair of goggles to transmit various wavelengths of EMR.

Note that the visible spectrum extends from 400 nm to 700 nm.

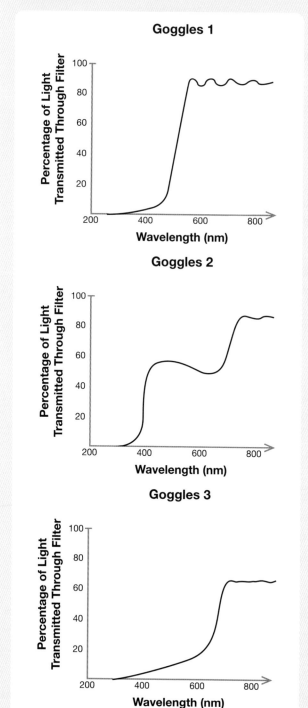

Goggles 1

Goggles 2

Goggles 3

16. Compare the ability of each pair of goggles to transmit ultraviolet radiation.

17. Compare the ability of each pair of goggles to transmit infrared radiation.

18. When the full spectrum of solar radiation is analyzed, it is found that more protons with a wavelength of 500 nm arrive at Earth's surface than any other wavelength. Compare the ability of the three pairs of goggles to absorb the energy of the 500-nm photons.

19. Determine which pair of goggles would have the greatest darkening effect on incoming light.

Use the following information to answer questions 20 to 22.

This device transforms an input of mechanical energy into an output of electrical energy.

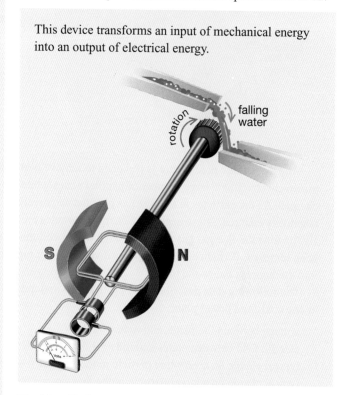

20. Identify the proper name for this device.

21. Sketch a voltage-versus-time graph to show the output from this device.

22. Repeat question 21 to show how the output would change if the number of rotations per minute was decreased.

Use the following information to answer questions 23 to 27.

Electricity generating stations that burn pulverized coal as a fuel often have particulate matter, such as bits of uncombusted coal, in the exhaust gas that leaves the furnace. This exhaust gas is called flue gas, and the particulate matter in flue gas can be a significant source of air pollution if it is not removed before entering the environment.

The Electrostatic Precipitator

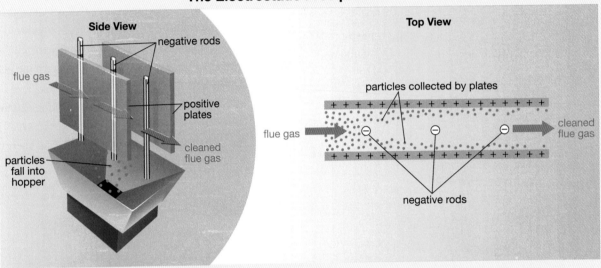

An electrostatic precipitator is designed to remove particulate matter from flue gas. This technology works by positively charging a large number of parallel plates while the metal rods hanging between the plates are negatively charged. As the particles in the flue gas pass the negatively charged rods, the particles pick up negative ions and become negatively charged. These negatively charged particles are then attracted to the positive plates where they are collected. By the time the flue gas has passed through a long column of rods and plates, over 99% of the particulate matter has been removed. Periodically the large positive plates are rapped with automated hammers, causing the particles to drop into the hoppers below the plates.

The following data describes the negative rods and the positive plates for the electrostatic precipitator at one coal-fired power plant:

voltage between the plates and rods = 72.0 kV
electric field between plates and rods = 1.28×10^5 N/C
typical charge on a very tiny particle in the flue gas = -1.6×10^{-18} C
typical charge on a larger particle in the flue gas = -3.2×10^{-15} C

23. Draw a simple diagram showing the shape of the electric field lines between the negatively charged rods and the positively charged plates.

24. Calculate typical values for the electric force on a very tiny particle and on a larger particle in the flue gas.

25. Concisely explain how the negatively charged rods and positively charged plates are able to exert forces on the moving charged particles in the flue gas even though the particles are not touching the rods or the plates.

26. The electric force values that you calculated in question 24 were quite small. Explain how such small forces are able to produce the desired effects.

27. The electrostatic precipitator is designed to address one of the environmental concerns about burning coal to produce electricity—the release of particulate matter. However, there are other environmental concerns that this technology does not address.

   a. List at least two other environmental concerns related to the burning of coal to produce electricity.

   b. Describe possible technological fixes for the issues you identified in question 27.a.

   c. Many people argue that it is important to think more broadly than simply using one technology to solve the problems created by another technology. Identify some alternative, broad-based strategies that address the environmental concerns related to using coal as a fuel to generate electricity.

Use the following information to answer questions 28 to 30.

The voltage needed by the negatively charged rods and the positively charged plates in an electrostatic precipitator is supplied by a transformer. The transformer takes an input voltage of 480 V on its primary coil and increases it to 72.0 kV on its secondary coil.

28. Determine whether this is a step-up transformer or a step-down transformer.

29. If there are 80 coils on the primary coil of the transformer, calculate the number of coils on the secondary coil.

30. Would you expect the current in the secondary coil to be larger or smaller than the current in the primary coil? Explain.

Use the following information to answer questions 31 to 38.

The *Hubble Space Telescope* has a mass of 11 600 kg and it orbits Earth at an altitude of 600 km. Earth has a mass of 5.98×10^{24} kg and a radius of 6.37×10^6 m. The EMR collected by the telescope is analyzed by a spectrometer that has three sensors capable of detecting EMR in the following ranges.

Type of Sensor	Wavelengths of EMR Detected (nm)
cesium iodide detector	115 to 170
cesium telluride detector	165 to 310
charge-coupled device	305 to 1000

Note that the visible spectrum extends from 400 nm to 700 nm.

31. Calculate the strength of the gravitational field of Earth at the location occupied by the *Hubble Space Telescope*.

32. Use your answer to question 31 to calculate the force of gravity that Earth exerts on the *Hubble Space Telescope* at its location in orbit.

33. Compare your answer to question 32 to the force of gravity that Earth exerts on the *Hubble Space Telescope* if it is located on Earth's surface.

34. Use the concept of gravitational field to explain the difference between your answers to questions 32 and 33.

35. Identify the type of sensor on *Hubble's* spectrometer that detects the most EMR with the most energy.

36. Identify the sensor or sensors that are capable of detecting the following types of EMR.

    a. infrared radiation   **b.** visible light   **c.** ultraviolet radiation

37. Explain why these sensors would not be as effective if they were placed on ground-based telescopes on Earth's surface.

38. At the time this textbook was published, NASA was planning a mission to upgrade the *Hubble Space Telescope* in May 2008. The preliminary planning called for a crew of seven to travel on Space Shuttle *Discovery* to deliver nearly 10 tonnes of replacement parts and upgrades. The estimated cost of the mission is US$900 million.

    a. In general terms, list some of the benefits of space-based research.

    b. In your opinion, do the benefits of space-based research justify the costs? Support your answer by referring to the items you listed in question 38.a.

Unit D Energy and the Environment

There are many kinds of farms in Alberta, and each one relies on solar energy in some way. Unlike most farms, this wind farm near Pincher Creek does not involve photosynthesis or the food chain. The turbines mounted on the tall towers are used to harvest wind—the kinetic energy of the atmosphere—and transform it into electrical energy. What role does solar energy play in this operation? Why is Pincher Creek ideally situated for this kind of development?

Radiation from the Sun causes Earth's surface to heat unevenly, resulting in surface winds. The rotation of the planet causes these winds to blow from the western parts of Canada toward the eastern parts. Although the Rocky Mountains form a barrier to the prevailing westerly winds, gaps in the mountains can create natural wind corridors. At Crowsnest Pass, the energy from the prevailing winds is funnelled toward Pincher Creek, making this area an ideal location for wind farms.

Compared to other methods of generating electrical energy, wind turbines are relatively quick and inexpensive to set up and appear to have a negligible impact on the environment. As you have learned in previous units, the same cannot be said for other methods of generating electrical energy. People around the world seem to have an increasing need for energy; and yet, evidence is mounting that the biosphere cannot sustain activities that produce energy at the expense of the environment. In this unit you will examine methods used to produce energy and consider how they can be used to balance the need for human progress with environmental stewardship.

What You Will Cover

Chapter 1: Dreams of Limitless Energy

Chapter 2: Dreams of a Sustainable Future

Chapter 1 Dreams of Limitless Energy

When was the last time you felt the urge to go out with a friend and grab a snack? For some Canadians, this means hopping in the car and heading to a fast-food restaurant. Burgers, fries, and soft drinks are among the most popular choices on the drive-through menu. One issue associated with eating fast food is that its high-calorie content may upset an individual's daily balance between energy intake and energy output.

You may be surprised to know that other things, not only the food, make going to the drive-through an energy-consuming activity. The food industry is dependent upon petroleum used to grow, process, and ship the food to the restaurant. Petroleum is also used during the production of all the food wrappers and containers that are later thrown away. And don't forget the petroleum used to run the vehicle that takes you to the drive-through window.

In this chapter you will analyze patterns of energy consumption in the modern world. You will explore the inner workings of some technologies that transform energy from natural sources into forms available for everyday use. You will then focus on fossil fuels as a major source of energy for generating electricity and fueling automobiles. Finally, you will consider the use of nuclear energy as a possible alternative to the combustion of fossil fuels.

Try This Activity

Electric Hand Dryer Versus Paper Towel

Restaurants may have washrooms equipped with an electric hand dryer or paper towels for drying your hands. If you managed a restaurant and wanted to be conscious of energy use, which method of drying hands would you make available for employees and customers?

Purpose

You will identify and consider the advantages and disadvantages of two methods used for drying hands.

Procedure

Obtain the "Hand-Drying Methods" handout from the Science 30 Textbook CD. For each criteria listed in the table, determine whether the hand-drying method is an advantage or a disadvantage. You may do this individually or as a group.

Science Skills

✓ Analyzing and Interpreting

All employees must wash their hands before returning to work.

Analysis

1. Identify which hand-drying method is preferred based on the table you completed in the handout.

2. Use the information in the following table to evaluate each method for drying hands based on cost. Based on this information, which method is preferred?

Description	Energy per Use (kJ)	Cost per 1000 Uses
non-recycled paper towel	743	$23
recycled paper towel	460	$23
standard electric dryer	222	$1.47
low-temperature, high-wind dryer	76	$0.50

3. Was the preferred method identified in question 1 different from the one identified in question 2? If so, consider all factors and state the preferred method for drying hands.

4. Explain why paper towels use so much more energy than electric hand dryers.

5. Use the list of perspectives on page 590 to identify the perspectives represented by each aspect listed in the Criteria column of the table in the handout.

6. In this situation, the environmental and economic perspectives are in agreement. The more environmentally friendly choice is also more economical. Give an example of an issue where the environmental and economic perspectives clash.

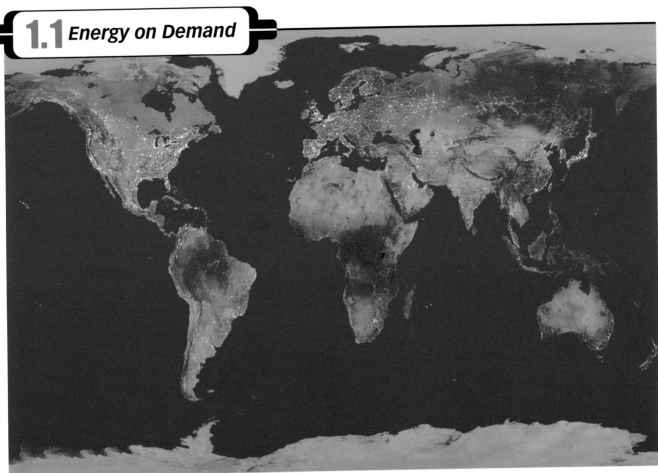

Figure D1.1: A composite of many satellite images shows light from cities across Earth that is visible from space.

Earth viewed at night from space shows a beautiful snapshot of energy use across the globe. Clusters of glowing cities dot the continents, revealing a planet transformed by human activity—activity that requires energy. Notice that some areas of the globe are not as bright as others. Is there a correlation between how bright an area appears in this photograph and energy use? How is a country's energy use affected by its level of development, economy, and climate? Imagine how this picture would change if developing countries were able to achieve the standard of living of developed countries.

Energy—The Currency of the Universe

For anything to happen around you or even in your own body, **energy** is required. When you lift a grocery bag and place it on the kitchen counter, you expend energy in your muscles to do that work. Some of the chemical potential energy stored in your muscles is transformed into an increase in the gravitational potential energy of the bag and its contents. When somebody drives a car, the engine uses energy stored in the gasoline to do work. Some of the

> **energy:** the capacity to do work

chemical potential energy stored in the molecules of gasoline is converted into the car's kinetic energy. When you turn on the lights in your home, electrical energy is used to do work, resulting in the release of radiant energy in the form of visible light and other forms of electromagnetic radiation. Even as you read this paragraph, the cells in your brain are working. They are using the energy stored in glucose molecules to carry out the functions of comprehending and establishing memories. All of this work takes energy. Every action has its energy price. Refer to the "Some Common Expressions for Energy" table for examples of units used to express energy.

?〉DID YOU KNOW?

Food is a source of chemical potential energy. On average, 38.9 MJ are contained within 1 kg of fat compared to 17.2 MJ in 1 kg of carbohydrate and 31.5 MJ in 1 kg of gasoline.

SOME COMMON EXPRESSIONS FOR ENERGY

Unit		Symbol	Definition	Joules Equivalent	Example of Energy Involved
joule		J	energy needed to apply a force of 1 N over a distance of 1 m	1 J	Drawing a 25-cm line with a pencil on paper requires about 1 J of energy.
		TJ	terajoule	1×10^{12} J	This is equal to the energy stored in 24 tonnes of oil.
		PJ	petajoule	1×10^{15} J	This is equal to the energy stored in 24 000 tonnes of oil.
		EJ	exajoule	1×10^{18} J	This is equal to the energy stored in 24 million tonnes of oil.
calorie		cal	energy needed to raise the temperature of 1 g of water 1°C	4.19 J	A foraging hummingbird consumes about 15 cal of energy per second.
food calorie		Cal or kcal	energy needed to raise the temperature of 1 kg of water 1°C	4190 J	A human walking 33 steps consumes an average of 1 Cal.
British thermal unit		BTU	energy needed to raise the temperature of 1 pound of water by 1°F	1054 J	A typical barbecue has an energy output of 8 BTU for each second it operates.
kilowatt-hour		kW•h	equal to the work done by one kilowatt acting for one hour	3 600 000 J	This is equal to the work done during 5 h of vigorous cycling.

In the next activity you will explore the trends in world energy use, world population, and **per capita** energy use since 1850. These trends provide important background information for you to refer to throughout this unit.

per capita: for each person

Utilizing Technology

Trends in Energy Use

Purpose

You will use a spreadsheet to perform calculations and analyze data of world energy use.

Science Skills

✓ Analyzing and Interpreting

Procedure

step 1: Open the "World Energy Use" spreadsheet from the Science 30 Textbook CD.

step 2: Complete the fourth column of the spreadsheet, Per Capita Energy Use.

step 3: Graph the following:

- the world energy use from 1850 to 2000
- the world population from 1850 to 2000
- the per capita energy use from 1850 to 2000

Analysis

1. Consider the graph of world energy use from 1850 to 2000.

   a. Describe the trend in world energy use.

   b. Based on the trend, extrapolate your graph to the year 2050.

   c. Explain why you extrapolated your graph the way you did. List the factors you considered.

   d. How certain are you that your projection of energy use from the present to the year 2050 is reasonable?

2. Consider the graph of world population from 1850 to 2000.

   a. Describe the trend in world population.

   b. Compare and contrast the trends on the graphs of world energy use and world population.

3. Consider the graph of per capita energy use from 1850 to 2000.

   a. Describe the trend shown in this graph.

   b. Identify when differences to the general trend occur. Suggest a reason for differences to the general trend.

   c. List some factors that influence per capita energy use.

4. Explain how the size of the world population affects on energy use.

A Canadian Way of Life

It may not surprise you that the average Canadian enjoys a lifestyle that consumes large quantities of energy. Some of this energy use is necessary to meet basic needs, such as heating homes, providing food, and travelling to and from school or work. A great deal of energy is used to support a quality of life that extends beyond basic needs.

In the early to mid 1990s, new automobile sales shifted significantly from cars to light-duty trucks (e.g., sport-utility vehicles or SUVs).

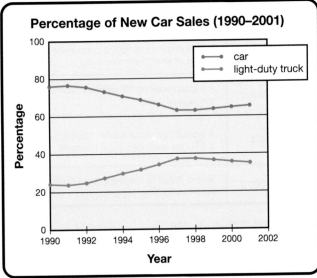

Figure D1.2

Consumers responded strongly to a general perception that driving an SUV brought with it versatility and status. However, these light-duty trucks are less fuel efficient than cars. Between 1990 and 2002, the shift in consumer preference toward SUVs resulted in an increase in energy used for passenger travel. Perception appears to strongly motivate automotive buyers. Even though smaller, more fuel-efficient vehicles are available, Canadians tend to choose heavier, more-powerful automobiles. Many people buying new vehicles are not deterred by the higher energy requirements. It is estimated that an additional $370 per year is spent on fuel for the average SUV. This value will increase as the price of fuel increases.

Practice

Use Figure D1.2 to answer questions 1 to 3.

1. Calculate the change in light-duty-truck sales from 1990 to 1997.

2. Identify reasons used to justify the purchase of light-duty trucks and other larger vehicles.

3. Suggest reasons for the trend in light-duty-truck sales shown after 1997.

Gross Domestic Product (GDP)

The reasons you provided in the answer to Practice question 2 demonstrate some of the attitudes and needs Canadians have regarding their vehicles. These attitudes and needs are, in part, reasons for Canada's large per capita energy use. How does Canada's energy use compare to other countries?

One indicator of a country's economic activity is **gross domestic product (GDP)**. Gross domestic product is measured in billions or trillions of US dollars so that comparisons can be made among countries. As an example, Canada's GDP in 2002 was US$753 billion and Kenya's was US$10 billion. Both countries have similar population sizes, but the total value of all the goods and services produced by Canada is over 75 times greater than that of Kenya. This may not be surprising given that the Kenyan economy is largely agricultural, consisting of major exports of tea and coffee. The Canadian economy, by comparison, includes a great deal of industry—exports of finished products (e.g., motor vehicles, wood products, petroleum products, and telecommunications equipment) and raw materials (e.g., metals and lumber).

Figure D1.3: Farmers' market in Kenya

Industry and the development of natural resources contribute largely to Canada's GDP; but they also use a great deal of energy. A measure of a country's GDP relative to its energy use is called **energy intensity**. Energy intensity is calculated by dividing the energy used by a country in one year by the GDP. Countries with a greater proportion of service and high-tech industries tend to have low energy intensities.

> **gross domestic product (GDP):** the total market value of all goods and services produced by the country in one year; often considered as an indication of a country's economic output

> **energy intensity:** the ratio of energy input (in joules) to economic output (in US$); commonly expressed in terajoules (TJ) per billions of US$ of GDP

DID YOU KNOW?

It takes the energy equivalent of two barrels of oil to produce three barrels of petroleum from oil sand.

Practice

4. Use the following table to calculate the energy intensities for Kenya, Sweden, and Canada.

Country	Energy Use (EJ)	GDP (trillions of US$)
Kenya	0.200	0.010
Sweden	2.22	0.300
Canada	13.80	0.753

5. Compare the energy intensities calculated in question 4. Do these values correspond with the tendency for countries with high-tech economies to have lower energy intensities?

6. Predict the change to Kenya's energy intensity if farmers introduced techniques that increased crop productivity.

7. Suggest reasons why Canada—a developed country—has a high energy intensity.

You will have an opportunity to explore the many factors that affect international energy use in the next activity.

DID YOU KNOW?

On average, developed countries use 7 to 8 times more energy than that of developing countries.

Utilizing Technology

Comparing Energy Use—Canada and Other Countries

Science Skills

✓ Performing and Recording
✓ Analyzing and Interpreting

Purpose

You will use a spreadsheet to compare the energy used by different countries.

Background Information

A variety of factors, like climate and size of the economy, influence the quantity of energy used by a country.

Pre-Lab Questions

1. List some behaviours of people who live in colder climates. Hypothesize how these behaviours would affect a country's total energy use.

2. State aspects that determine the size of a country's economy.

3. Explain why gross domestic product (GDP) is used to measure the size of a country's economy.

Part A: Energy Use by Country

Procedure

step 1: Open the "Comparing Energy Use" spreadsheet on the Science 30 Textbook CD. Click on the tab labelled "Part A." You should see the "Part A: Energy Use by Country (2002)" table.

step 2: Construct a bar graph showing the total energy use by each country in 2002.

step 3: Construct a bar graph showing the per capita energy use in each country in 2002.

Analysis

4. Consider the graph showing the total energy use by each country in 2002.

   a. Of the countries on your graph, which had the greatest total energy use in 2002?

   b. Which country had the lowest total energy use in 2002?

   c. In 2002, the United States used 2.3 times more energy than China, despite the fact that China's population was 5.5 times larger than the United States's. Provide a reason for this difference.

5. Consider the graph showing the per capita energy use for each country in 2002.

   a. Of the countries on your graph, which had the greatest per capita energy use in 2002?

   b. State possible reasons for Canada having a higher per capita energy use than the United States.

   c. State one advantage of having data describing per capita energy use in addition to total energy use when comparing energy use by countries.

Part B: Effect of Climate on Energy Use

Procedure

step 1: In the "Comparing Energy Use" spreadsheet, select the tab labelled "Part B." You should see the "Part B: Effect of Climate on Energy Use (2002)" table.

step 2: Construct a graph showing the per capita energy use on the vertical axis and average annual temperature of each country's capital city on the horizontal axis.

step 3: Add a linear line of best fit to your graph by selecting "Add Trend line" in the Chart menu. **Note:** This menu only appears when you click on the graph.

Analysis

6. Describe the general relationship between per capita energy use and average annual temperature of a country's capital city.

7. State a generalization about the level of economic development of the countries positioned above and below the line of best fit.

8. Berlin has the same average annual temperature as Ottawa, yet Germany's per capita energy use is less than half that of Canada's. Suggest reasons for the difference in per capita energy use between these two countries.

9. Identify two limitations of any conclusions made from studying this data.

Part C: Effect of Size of Economy on Energy Use

Procedure

step 1: In the "Comparing Energy Use" spreadsheet, select the tab labelled "Part C." You should see the "Part C: Effect of Size of Economy on Energy Use (2002)" table.

step 2: Construct a graph showing each country's GDP (in trillions of US$) on the horizontal axis and the total energy use on the vertical axis.

step 3: Draw a linear line of best fit on your graph.

step 4: Calculate each country's energy intensity (in EJ/trillion of US$), filling in the appropriate column in the table.

step 5: Construct a bar graph showing each country's energy intensity (in EJ/trillion of US$).

Analysis

10. Describe the general relationship between total energy use and GDP.

11. State a generalization about the level of economic development of the countries positioned above and below the line of best fit on your graph.

12. Identify which country has the highest energy intensity. Provide a possible explanation as to why this country's value is the highest.

13. Compare the energy intensity of Canada to those of the United States and Japan. Suggest reasons for the differences in energy intensity between these three countries.

Factors Affecting Energy Use

Climate

As you found in the last activity, there is a relationship between climate and energy use. People who live in cooler climates, like Canada and Russia, use energy to heat their homes. However, people who live in warmer countries, like Australia, use energy to cool their homes. In fact, the most important aspect of climate that influences energy use is extremes in temperature. For example, in Canada in 2002, a cooler than usual winter and warmer than usual summer caused a 47.9-PJ increase in the amount of energy used to heat and cool homes. For comparison purposes, one petajoule (PJ) is approximately the quantity of energy needed to meet the needs of a town of 3800 people for one year.

Figure D1.4: Factors including colder weather and reduced daylight during winter influence energy use in Canada.

Activity

The term *activity* refers to how much work is being done. For many industries, activity can be measured in terms of tonnes of steel manufactured or number of cars produced. In other parts of Canada, activity has to be measured using other criteria. The financial industry is an important part of Canada's economy, and its activity is measured by dollars made from investments. Activity in the transportation sector is measured by how many kilometres are travelled. Regardless of how you measure activity within an economy, energy is required to maintain it.

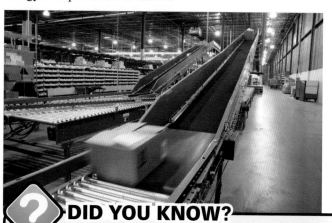

Earlier, you learned that the total economic value of a country's industrial activity is measured as gross domestic product (GDP). Countries that enjoy a high standard of living tend to have thriving economies and large GDPs. In Part C of the "Comparing Energy Use—Canada and Other Countries" activity, you saw that the United States has the world's largest GDP. It should not surprise you to recall that the United States, which has the highest economic activity, also has the largest total energy use. Since Canada has a much smaller economy than the US, it has a smaller GDP in addition to a lower total energy use.

Population

Regardless of other measures of a country's economy, per capita energy use is a valuable measure of a country's level of prosperity. The goal of many developing countries is to industrialize and improve the standard of living for its citizens. As you have seen, in order to meet these goals, developing countries will also become larger users of energy and of natural resources (e.g., coal, oil, and natural gas) that can be combusted to supply energy. Recall that increasing the standard of living often requires an increase in the energy use per capita. Many developing countries have large populations, drastically increasing the energy required to meet these goals. Improvement to the standard of living may not only cause total energy use to rise drastically; it may also adversely affect the environment if the consequences are not considered.

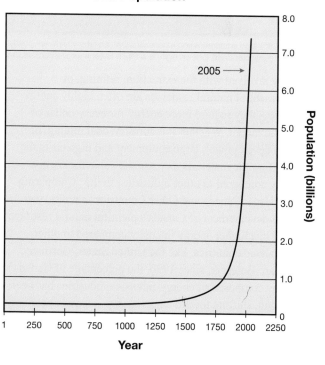

? DID YOU KNOW?

Service-sector industries that are less energy intensive include communications, banking, insurance, real estate, education, and health care. Also included are the manufacturing of computers, electronics, and machinery.

Energy Intensity

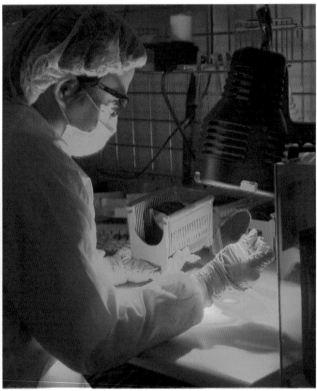

Figure D1.5: Large equipment and extensive pipelines (shown left) are costly parts of the process to produce petroleum from oil sand. Manufacturing silicone wafers for computer chips (shown right) is a much lower energy-intensive process.

Industry involved with the extraction, refining, or development of natural resources are often highly energy intensive—they require more energy for every dollar of economic output. Whether it is forestry, coal mining, or oil sand development, large equipment and high costs for transporting the materials increase the value for energy intensity compared to other industries. In the "Comparing Energy Use—Canada and Other Countries" activity, you saw that development of Canada's plentiful natural resources resulted in a higher energy intensity compared to other industrialized countries, like the United States, Germany, and Japan. However, since 1990, the percentage of Canada's economy composed of energy-intensive industries has been decreasing, shifting toward a less energy-intensive economy.

?DID YOU KNOW?
Tires for the trucks used to haul oil sand cost about $50 000 each.

> ### Practice
>
> 8. The energy intensities of Canada and Germany in 2002 were 18 and 6 (in EJ/trillion US$ of GDP), respectively. Use the Internet to identify and compare Canada's and Germany's major exports. Explain how the differences among exports support the different energy intensities of these two countries.

Energy Efficiency

Figure D1.6: The Energy Star symbol identifies the most energy-efficient appliances available.

Every time energy is used, some of it is transformed. The proportion transformed into a desired form is called **useful output energy**. Do you recall a demonstration in Unit C where the energies of different forms of electromagnetic radiation emitted by a light bulb were measured? In this demonstration, electrical energy was the **input energy** to the light bulb and visible light was considered the useful output energy of this energy conversion. In the demonstration a large amount of non-visible radiation was detected, including infrared (often called thermal energy). The **energy efficiency** of a light bulb is determined by the proportion of input energy that is converted into visible light and not into other forms of energy. For all devices that convert energy, some energy is always lost as thermal energy. Energy efficiency is often represented as a percentage of input energy that has been transformed into useful output energy.

> **useful output energy:** the desired energy form resulting from a process involving a transformation of energy

> **input energy:** the form of energy entering into a process involving a transformation of energy

> **energy efficiency:** the percentage of input energy that has been transformed into useful output energy

$$\text{energy efficiency} = \frac{\text{useful output energy}}{\text{input energy}} \times 100\%$$

The types of input and output energies vary with the device. Refer to the "Input and Output Energy for Some Energy-Converting Devices" table.

INPUT AND OUTPUT ENERGY FOR SOME ENERGY-CONVERTING DEVICES

Device	Input Energy	Useful Output Energy	Waste Energy
light bulb	electrical	visible light	non-visible EMR, such as infrared (heat)
car engine	chemical potential (gasoline)	kinetic	thermal
oven	electrical	thermal energy transferred to food	thermal energy not transferred to food
television	electrical	visible light	non-visible EMR, thermal

Practice

9. Calculate the energy efficiency of a water heater that uses 200 J of energy to increase the thermal energy of water 55 J.

10. If an automobile engine is 20% efficient, calculate the useful output energy from 1 kg of gasoline containing 44.5 MJ of chemical potential energy.

Figure D1.7: The 60-W incandescent light bulb (left) and the 17-W compact fluorescent light bulb (right) produce the same quantity of useful output energy but with greatly different efficiencies. Legislation in Canada will ban the sale of incandescent light bulbs by 2012.

When selecting a replacement bulb for the lamp beside your desk, you may have considered the power rating of the bulbs you had to choose from. Although a 60-W light bulb is not as bright as a 100-W light bulb—the bulb with the higher energy requirement—both devices have similar efficiencies. If you had the chance to consider using a compact fluorescent bulb, you may have noticed that it has a considerably lower power rating (17 W); and it provides the equivalent amount of light as a 60-W incandescent bulb. The drastic reduction in input energy to produce the same quantity of useful output energy is the result of increased efficiency of compact fluorescent lights compared with incandescent bulbs.

Practice

11. Using power ratings, determine the percentage of the total power required by a compact fluorescent bulb versus the total power required by an incandescent light bulb that provides similar output energy.

12. Improvements to energy efficiency from 1990–2003 were estimated to be 883 PJ. If the estimated energy requirement of a small town is 47.9 PJ, calculate the energy saved in terms of the number of additional towns that could have their energy needs met due to improvements in efficiency.

Science Links

Compact fluorescent lights contain trace amounts of mercury. If improperly disposed of, mercury may collect in landfills. Despite this risk, the increased efficiency of compact fluorescent lights could result in an overall reduction in mercury released into the environment from the combustion of coal. Unit B provides further information regarding the effects of mercury and other heavy metals within ecosystems and the effects of other by-products from the combustion of coal.

The use of more efficient electrical devices and other technologies, including the replacement of incandescent lights with compact fluorescent lights, is an important way to offset the increasing need for energy. For example, since 1990, the use of computers in Canadian workplaces has increased 73%, but the energy used by these devices as a whole only increased by 50%. The energy savings of 23% was the result of improvements in the energy efficiency of computers during this time. Improvements in efficiency can also occur in large industry. In fact, between 1990 and 2002, energy use in Canada's mining industry decreased by 12%. This was mostly due to improvements that made processes more energy efficient.

Figure D1.8: A worker operates a remote-control scoop tram at the Rabbit Lake mine in northern Saskatchewan.

? DID YOU KNOW?

The Athabasca Basin in northern Saskatchewan is home to the world's richest, high-grade uranium mines. Although there are some open-pit facilities, the most productive operations use deep shafts to provide access to the uranium ore found hundreds of metres below the surface. The person shown in Figure D1.8 is working approximately 400 m underground.

Alberta's Energy-Based Economy

Within Canada, Alberta is known for its development of non-renewable energy resources of coal, petroleum, and natural gas. Alberta, however, also produces energy through renewable resources, like wind and hydro. The role of the energy industry is vital to Alberta's economy. Fossil fuels make up over half of the province's exports. In addition, **royalties** paid to the Alberta government by energy companies that extract and process natural resources account for about one-third of the province's total revenue. Also, nearly one in six workers in Alberta is employed, either directly or indirectly, by the energy sector.

> **royalty:** money paid to the government that is a share of the profits made from the development of a natural resource

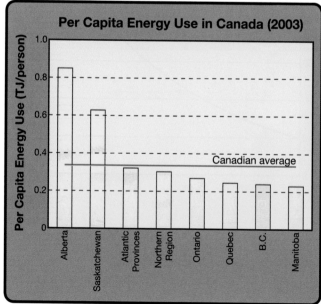

Figure D1.9: Many refineries are located near Edmonton and Fort Saskatchewan and are involved in processing petroleum or its components.

Although Alberta has an abundance of energy resources, the processes used to extract and process coal, natural gas, and petroleum are very energy intensive. Figure D1.10 shows the 2003 per capita energy use in Canada. Notice that Alberta's per capita energy use is two-and-a-half times greater than the national average.

Per Capita Energy Use in Canada (2003)

Canadian average

Figure D1.10

1.1 Summary

Energy use is on the rise globally due to exponential population growth and increasing development. Canada is a major contributor to global energy production and energy use, and it is one of the developed world's largest per capita energy users. Factors that affect energy use by countries include climate, size of economy, economic diversity, level of technology, and efficiency in the conversion of energy.

1.1 Questions

Knowledge

1. Identify considerations, apart from energy use, that influence decisions about the purchase of products.

2. Describe the trend of the world's energy use from 1850 to the present.

3. Define *per capita* and *gross domestic product* (*GDP*).

4. State an example of how a change in consumer preference led to an increase in the quantity of energy used by Canadians for transporting both people and products.

5. List five factors that affect energy use. Provide definitions for each factor.

6. Describe the relationship between the size of a country's economy (as measured by GDP) and its total energy use.

Applying Concepts

7. The United States is Canada's largest trading partner and shares many similarities in terms of lifestyle and culture.

   a. Compare the total energy consumption of Canada to that of the United States.

   b. Compare the per capita energy use of Canada to that of the United States.

   c. Provide reasons for the differences between the per capita energy use of these two countries.

Use the following information to answer questions 8 and 9.

This table summarizes the average Canadian's energy use for various activities as a percentage of total daily energy use.

Household Item	End-Use of Energy (% of total daily energy use)
furnace/air conditioner	45
water heater	11
washer and dryer	10
lighting	7
refrigerator	6
TV, VCR, DVD	2
computer	2
dishwasher	2
other	15

8. For each household item listed in the table, suggest one action that would reduce personal energy use.

9. Describe how you would develop an experiment or a study to determine the effect of making the changes suggested in question 8. State any data or information you would need to complete this experiment or study.

Use the following information to answer questions 10 to 12.

A yearly increase of 2% in GDP is considered to be an indicator of a healthy economy. The graph given shows an economy growing at a constant rate of 2% per year for 100 years.

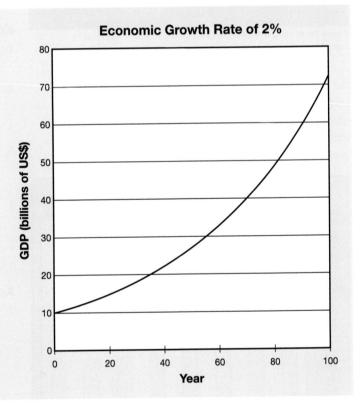

Economic Growth Rate of 2%

10. Describe the pattern of change in GDP over the time shown on the graph.

11. Discuss the implications that this type of economic growth would have in terms of total energy use.

12. Identify an important strategy for reducing energy use that would counteract an increasing energy demand.

It is a hot, dry summer afternoon deep in a northern forest. It has been weeks without rain when, finally, a thunderstorm rolls in. Lightning strikes the dry grass, igniting a wildfire that eventually engulfs several hundred hectares of forest. The flames are evidence of a violent release of energy.

In previous science courses you learned that **chemical potential energy** is stored in plant material. The original source for almost all energy, including the energy stored in plant material, is the Sun. Nuclear reactions occurring within the Sun's core produce energy that is emitted into space as electromagnetic radiation. A tiny fraction of the **radiant energy** from the Sun strikes Earth, allowing some of it to be absorbed by the complex molecule called chlorophyl, which drives a glucose-making process called photosynthesis. Once the glucose is made, much of it is used to power the plant's growth and reproduction. The remaining glucose within the plant is transformed into other compounds, most notably cellulose—the main component of wood.

All over the world, humans have long harnessed the chemical potential energy of wood for cooking and warmth. The light and heat from wood fires enabled First Peoples to inhabit colder regions of the planet, like the forests of northern Alberta. Heat from fires brings about changes in food as it is cooked, helping make some foods possible to eat and thereby increasing the supply of available food. The vital importance of wood and the ability to release its energy is evident in many stories from Canada's First Nations that describe how fire came to be controlled and used over the past 10 000 years.

Figure D1.11: This diorama—created from stories passed down by elders—at the Royal Alberta Museum shows how First Nations people traditionally dried and smoked fish in the boreal forest of northern Alberta hundreds of years ago.

> **chemical potential energy:** the energy present within the chemical bonds of a substance
> **radiant energy:** the energy of electromagnetic waves

In developing countries, like Kenya, wood is still the least expensive and most accessible form of energy. Wood is the standard fuel for cooking. Most of the wood fuel consists of dead trees and fallen branches collected from fields or from roadsides. Collecting the fuel wood is exhausting work that can consume hours of every day. Since the wood is often burned in an open pit or in a poor-quality stove, incomplete combustion occurs, releasing CO(g), polycyclic aromatic hydrocarbons (PAHs), particulate matter, and other pollutants into the cooking area.

Figure D1.12: A woman in Kenya stands outside her hut beside a pile of firewood.

It has been suggested that health and quality of life could improve in developing countries if charcoal were used for cooking instead of firewood. Charcoal is a fuel produced from wood that used to be commonly used in North American barbecues before gas-fueled models became popular. Although charcoal is a more energy-rich fuel than wood, the process to make charcoal produces many harmful emissions.

? DID YOU KNOW?

Charcoal is made during the combustion of wood when extra care is taken to reduce oxygen. In many early societies, charcoal was an important fuel and was made by skilled workers.

Science Links

Substances contained within smoke from combustion can cause asthma, respiratory problems, and even cancer. More information about the health effects of substances within smoke appears in Units A and B.

Practice

13. Studies indicate that approximately 1.6 million people worldwide die prematurely from respiratory diseases caused by the pollution from inefficient wood-burning fires. Refer to your work in previous units to describe the health concerns related to the release of CO(g), polycyclic aromatic hydrocarbons (PAHs), and particulate matter into the environment.

From Wood to Coal

Although wood has been used as a fuel by humans since the beginning of recorded history, it has drawbacks. Wood is bulky, for example, which makes it hard to store and transport. Since charcoal is a more compact, cleaner fuel, it represents an improvement. As populations grow and countries industrialize, new fuels may have to be found in order to meet energy demands.

Figure D1.13: A worker stokes the furnace of a steam locomotive with coal.

Coal, a carbon-rich mineral found in Earth's crust, had been used by ancient societies—in particular the Greeks, Romans, and Chinese—but only for minor applications. In the mid-1800s, coal became the preferred fuel in England. Because of its abundant supply and energy richness, coal provided a dependable energy source for industrial processes and transportation, fuelling the Industrial Revolution.

? DID YOU KNOW?

Small pieces of coal can be found along the banks of many rivers in Alberta.

Figure D1.14 shows that coal quickly replaced wood as the dominant energy source after the start of the Industrial Revolution. It is this plentiful and powerful fuel that first inspired humans to dream of a world with limitless energy—a dream where coal-powered machines, such as the steam engine, would lead to lives of leisure and prosperity. Today, coal continues to be an important source of energy across the world. Albertans rely on coal to provide many of their basic needs and wants, since coal is used to generate about 70% of Alberta's electricity.

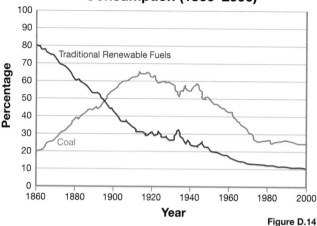

Percentage of World Total Energy Consumption (1860–2000)

Figure D.14

Practice

Use Figure D1.14 to answer questions 14 and 15.

14. The two fuels shown are coal and traditional renewable fuels. Identify materials that could be classified as traditional renewable fuels.

15. Determine the total percentage of energy consumption provided from coal and traditional renewable fuels in 1950. Account for the value calculated. What other energy sources could be accounting for the difference?

Making Coal

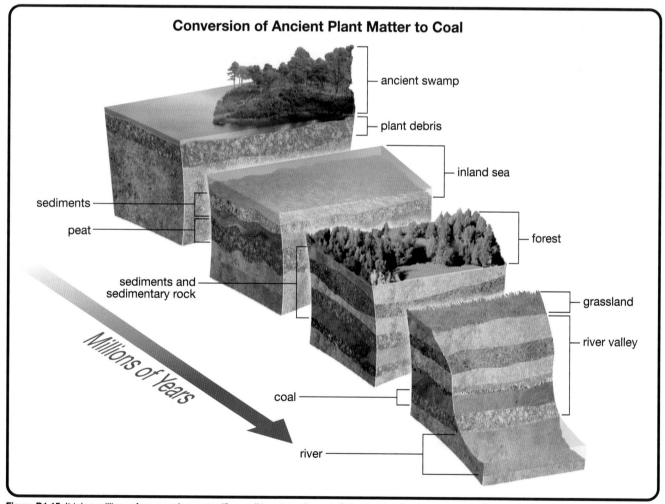

Conversion of Ancient Plant Matter to Coal

- ancient swamp
- plant debris
- inland sea
- forest
- grassland
- river valley
- sediments
- peat
- sediments and sedimentary rock
- coal
- river

Millions of Years

Figure D1.15: It takes millions of years and very specific conditions to make coal. Only a tiny fraction of one percent of the solar energy striking the ecosystem is eventually stored in the chemical bonds of coal.

Specific conditions are required to make coal. In tropical, swampy areas—where moisture and sunlight are abundant—thick layers of plant debris collect in the swamp over time. This layer, called peat, begins to decompose while submerged under water (in conditions without much oxygen). As more layers of plant debris and other sediments accumulate, the peat is compressed, beginning the process of its transformation into coal. The transformation of peat into coal requires millions of years and the pressure of many more layers of sediment. Since coal is derived from the remains of prehistoric life, coal is referred to as a **fossil fuel**.

> **fossil fuel:** a hydrocarbon deposit (e.g., petroleum, coal, and natural gas) derived from plants and animals that lived millions of years ago that is used for fuel

Figure D1.16: Structures of plant parts are often visible on the surface of coal. Parts of a plant's stem are visible as vertical lines in this photograph.

More recent geological events—such as the retreat of the glacial ice sheets that once covered Alberta—removed some of the top layers of sediment that helped compress the coal. The massive runoff from the continental glaciers carved deep river valleys in the Alberta landscape. Events like this exposed coal seams close to the surface, making them accessible for mining.

Lots of Coal

Figure D1.17: A tipple, like this one seen at an abandoned coal mine near Drumheller, Alberta, is used to clean, screen, size, and load coal into rail cars.

Figure D1.18: Many of the coal mines currently in operation in Alberta are open-pit mines, where the topsoil is removed to allow the coal to be loaded into large trucks.

Coal has been mined in Alberta since the early 1900s. Towns like Drumheller, Bellevue, Hillcrest, and Frank have museums where you can view the original buildings and equipment used. Today, coal mining is still a vibrant industry in Alberta and around the world.

In Alberta, surface mining is primarily used to extract coal. Surface mining involves the removal of layers of earth above the coal deposit. The coal seam lying beneath appears like a black carpet and is removed using large mechanical shovels and trucks. Although the cost of machinery to conduct surface mining is high, coal is a relatively inexpensive fuel to obtain using surface-mining techniques. Coal reserves in Alberta that are accessible using surface-mining techniques are estimated to be 620 billion tonnes.

?DID YOU KNOW?

When exposed to oxygen, coal begins to decompose, releasing heat. Coal stored outside power plants must be covered with dirt to prevent spontaneous combustion.

In Alberta, areas where coal and other natural resources have been extracted must undergo **reclamation**. Provincial regulations require mining companies to restore land to a condition similar to what existed prior to mining. Areas that have undergone surface mining in Alberta have been restored to make farmland or to blend with the neighbouring natural habitat.

> **reclamation:** restoring an area to its original form or some other usable form

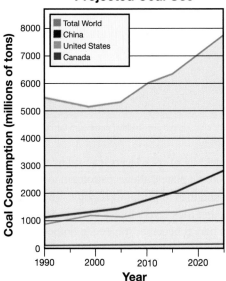

Figure D1.19: Reclamation of the Egg Lake Mine, near Legal, has restored the local ecosystem.

Coal Use on the Rise Around the World

Coal use has increased worldwide and is projected to increase dramatically in the near future. For emerging countries with extensive coal reserves, like China, the availability of coal and the ease by which it can be turned into energy are contributing to the increased use of this energy source. Even in more developed countries, the relatively low cost of coal mining makes it an economical energy source.

DID YOU KNOW?

Coal is the largest commodity carried by Canadian railways.

Practice

16. Peat forms at an average rate of 5.0×10^{-4} m/a (metres per year). It takes 10 m of peat to make 1 m of coal.

   a. Calculate the time it took to produce the peat required to make a 5-m thick layer of coal. (**Hint:** Think of this question as a speed problem, $v = \frac{d}{t}$.)

   b. Does your answer to question 16.a. account for the total time it would take to make the 5-m thick coal layer? Explain.

   c. According to the evidence and the answers to the previous questions, should coal be classified as a renewable or non-renewable resource?

17. Energy density—the energy available per kilogram of combusted fuel—is often used to compare fuels. The following table compares the energy density of bituminous coal (the type found in Alberta), wood, and charcoal.

ENERGY DENSITIES OF SOME FUELS

Fuel	Energy Density (MJ/kg)
coal (bituminous)	23.9
wood	13.5
charcoal	29.0

   a. Identify the fuel with the highest energy density.

   b. State reasons why the use of charcoal as a fuel is restricted.

   c. Explain the benefit of comparing fuels based on energy density.

   d. Is it possible to determine the energy density of liquid fuels?

Petroleum—Today's Dominant Fuel

In the 1950s, due mostly to the impact of the automobile on society, **petroleum** became the world's primary fuel. In the 10 years following World War I (1918 to 1928), the number of automobiles in the United States and Canada increased by a factor of 4. By the beginning of World War II, most families in Canada and the United States owned a car or truck. Today, petroleum is by far the world's top energy source. Petroleum is a mixture of hydrocarbons—each a rich energy source but suited for different purposes. One of the early uses for petroleum was to make kerosene for lamps.

> **petroleum:** liquid hydrocarbons formed over millions of years from the remains of ancient microscopic marine organisms

?→DID YOU KNOW?

Gasoline, the mixture of hydrocarbons consisting of seven to ten carbon-atom chains, is one of the by-products of making kerosene. In the mid-1800s there was no use for gasoline, so it was discarded.

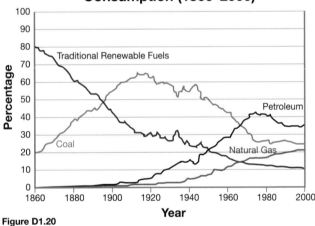

Percentage of World Total Energy Consumption (1860–2000)

Figure D1.20

Practice

18. Use Figure D1.20 to answer questions 18.a. to 18.d.

    a. In the year 2000, identify the two fuels, other than coal, used the most.

    b. Describe the trend in the use of coal from 1860 to 1920.

    c. Identify the fuels that began to replace coal as an energy source from 1920 to 1950. Suggest reasons why coal was replaced.

    d. Describe the trend in energy supplied by coal from 1975 to 2000. Suggest a reason for this trend.

Figure D1.21: In the 1950s, parked cars lined Edmonton's Jasper Avenue, signifying society's reliance on the automobile and the importance of petroleum.

Making Petroleum

Petroleum, like coal, requires special conditions and a great deal of time to form. The shallow tropical seas that existed 360 million years ago over what we now call Alberta contained coral reefs that covered many hundreds of square kilometres. Photosynthetic plants within the reef ecosystem trapped and stored solar energy. Over millions of years, the pressure from hundreds of metres of sediments that covered these reefs, and just the right amount of heat, converted the molecules containing carbon from these organisms into petroleum.

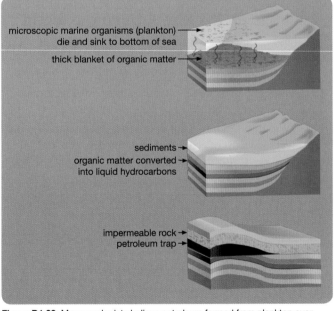

Figure D1.22: Many geologists believe petroleum formed from plankton over millions of years.

The buckling of rock layers, caused by movement of Earth's tectonic plates, allows petroleum to seep from within the rocks and then to form larger pools. The movement of water through rock layers forces the less dense petroleum upward, where it becomes trapped in dome-shaped formations that contain today's petroleum reservoirs. Since the discovery of petroleum near Leduc in 1947, Alberta has enjoyed a lucrative industry to extract and process petroleum.

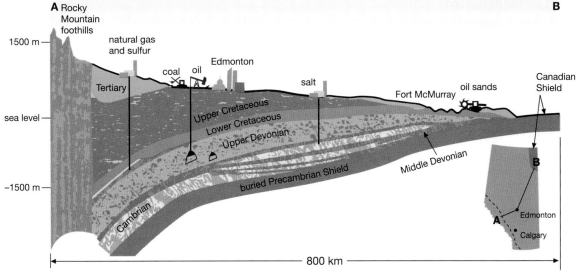

Figure D1.23: A cross section of Alberta shows major rock layers and some of the mineral resources they contain.

Enhanced Oil-Recovery Process

Over half of the petroleum within a deposit is difficult to remove. Enhanced oil-recovery techniques involve the pumping of water, chemicals, or gases into the rock layers that surround a petroleum reservoir to force petroleum into the well for extraction.

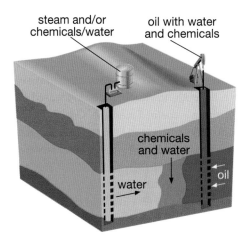

Practice

19. A great deal of concern exists over the use of water from lakes and rivers for enhanced oil recovery. Use the Internet to prepare a list of some of the concerns expressed over the use of water for enhanced oil recovery.

The Athabasca Oil Sands

Alberta's Athabasca oil sands may be one of the world's largest petroleum reserves; however, the petroleum is relatively difficult to extract. Rather than being deposited in a trap, as with conventional petroleum reservoirs, the petroleum in oil sand is stuck to individual grains of sand.

The production of petroleum from oil sand is an expensive endeavor. Oil sand can be removed using surface mining techniques similar to those used in open-pit coal mines. Approximately two tonnes of earth is removed to produce one barrel of petroleum. After extraction, the oil sand is washed with water and solvents. Two main products from washing include bitumen (a black tar) and tailings (a wet, sandy mixture). Thermal energy is required to break the hydrocarbon molecules in bitumen into smaller molecules suitable for use in products like diesel fuel. Additional production costs include reclamation of the land, cleaning of the tailings from the mine, and the treatment of water use in the oil sand extraction process.

Figure D1.24: The Athabasca oil sands span 77 000 km² of land and contain up to 18% petroleum.

? DID YOU KNOW?

In 2006, the average cost to produce petroleum from oil sand was just over $27 per barrel.

Natural Gas (Methane)

Natural gas is a mixture of hydrocarbons primarily composed of methane and, to a lesser extent, ethane, propane, and butane. Natural gas forms in much the same way as crude petroleum. The key factor that determines whether the ancient organic material will become natural gas instead of petroleum is temperature—natural gas requires more heat as it forms. Natural gas is often extracted by drilling deep underground. It is then transported by networks of pipes to individual buildings, like homes and schools. It is natural gas that most likely fuels a home's furnace and water heater and, possibly, kitchen stove; it likely fuels any Bunsen burner that may be in a school's science laboratory. Natural gas is the primary fuel used for heating in industrial processes, like processing bitumen from oil sands. It is also used as an essential ingredient for thousands of industrial and consumer products.

Coalbed Methane and Methane Hydrate

Concern about the limited supply of conventional hydrocarbon resources has created interest in new sources of hydrocarbons, namely methane. As you learned earlier, methane, $CH_4(g)$, is the major component of natural gas. Although methane is the smallest hydrocarbon molecule, it has a very high energy density—over three times that of wood. Given its energy richness and the ease by which it can be used, reserves of methane are highly sought after.

Recently, attention has been focused on a new source of methane—coalbed methane. Coal, being a porous material, often contains water. During the processes that make coal, methane is also produced and becomes trapped within the layers of coal, dissolving into the water within the coal bed. Dissolved methane can be removed from the coal bed by pumping the water within the coal formation to the surface. As the water nears the surface, the reduction in pressure causes the methane to vapourize and separate from the water. Unlike enhanced oil recovery, water is not needed to collect coalbed methane; but the water collected by this process tends to contain high concentrations of dissolved minerals, making it unsuitable for irrigation or other uses.

The development of coalbed methane projects in Alberta is connected to water issues. There are concerns that if you draw water from coalbeds, there will be an impact on water wells used by farmers. Also, the fate of water drawn from a coal bed is not certain. Simple solutions like pumping it back underground where it could contaminate other water sources may not be suitable.

Methane can also be found within ice as methane hydrate. In deeper, high pressure regions of Earth's oceans, where water temperatures are near freezing, methane leaks from geological sediments and becomes trapped within ice.

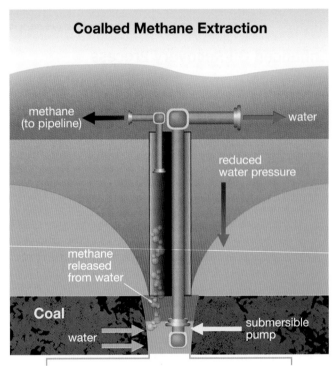

Coalbed Methane Extraction

methane (to pipeline)

water

reduced water pressure

methane released from water

Coal

water

submersible pump

water within coal containing dissolved methane

Figure D1.25: Methane hydrate (right) is methane frozen within water. The methane molecule (above) is surrounded by water molecules to form methane hydrate.

Fossil Fuels—Non-Renewable Resources

Coal, petroleum, and natural gas are all fossil fuels. As the name implies, they are extremely old and take a very long time to form. Fossil fuels are **non-renewable**. This means that once the world's supplies of coal, petroleum, and natural gas are consumed, they cannot be replaced. Fossil fuels are often called **hydrocarbons** because they contain mostly hydrogen and carbon.

Many scientists believe that over half of the world's petroleum supplies have already been used up; but, as shown in Figure D1.26, the world's petroleum production is increasing. Estimates of how long coal, petroleum, and natural gas reserves will last vary significantly. Differences between estimates are often due to the research methods selected to collect data or the interpretation of the data.

Whenever you hear information or conclusions from a study, you must consider the source of the information and any possible **bias**. Research—since it is an activity conducted by humans—needs to be evaluated for any potential bias. For example, a team of researchers sponsored by a large multinational oil company could have a different set of biases than a team sponsored by an environmental organization.

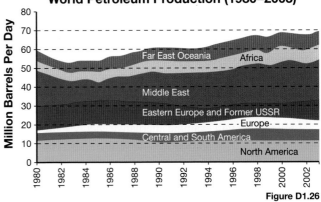

World Petroleum Production (1980–2003)

Figure D1.26

> **non-renewable:** can only be used once within the scope of human timescales

> **hydrocarbon:** an organic compound containing only carbon and hydrogen atoms

> **bias:** a preference for one particular point of view that interferes with neutral or objective decision making

Utilizing Technology

How Long Will Fossil Fuels Last?

Background Information
Information or opinions must be considered for any possible bias. In this activity you will consider the bias of sources as you collect estimates regarding the length of time that the world's supplies of fossil fuels will last.

Purpose
You will find three estimates of how long each type of fossil fuel will last, and you will evaluate the resources from which the information is obtained.

Procedure
step 1: Obtain the document "Researching the Future of Fossil Fuels" from the Science 30 Textbook CD.

step 2: Use the Internet to complete the "Estimates of How Long Conventional Fossil Fuels Will Last" table on page 1 of the handout.

step 3: Use the Internet to complete the "Newly Developed Sources of Fossil Fuel Energy" table on page 2 of the handout.

Science Skills
✓ Performing and Recording
✓ Analyzing and Interpreting

Analysis
1. In step 2, you likely found that predictions concerning the availability of fossil fuels in the years to come varied. This indicates that there is some uncertainty surrounding this issue. Should this uncertainty prevent industry, governments, and consumers from investing time and money in research into alternatives to fossil fuels?

2. Identify at least one action you think should be taken by each of the following groups to address the likelihood of the world's petroleum and natural gas supplies running out in the next several decades.
   - citizens
   - government
   - industry

3. Suppose new sources of hydrocarbon fuels, such as coalbed methane and methane hydrate, could meet the world's energy demand for several centuries. Suggest reasons why efforts should still be made to find alternative fuels.

1.2 Summary

Fossil fuels—such as coal, petroleum, and natural gas—are important energy sources. All fossil fuels are finite and non-renewable. Given the present rates of consumption, estimates suggest that supplies of petroleum and natural gas will likely be depleted within decades. Estimates for coal suggest it will be depleted within centuries. In the lessons that follow, you will examine alternative energy sources to fossil fuels and the contributions these alternative energy sources can make toward meeting projected energy demands.

1.2 Questions

Knowledge

1. List the three main fossil fuels used today. Of these fuels, identify which is consumed globally at the highest rate.

2. Identify the energy source used to generate most of Alberta's electricity.

3. Describe how burning fossil fuels results in the release of solar energy.

4. Define the following terms.

   a. fossil fuel
   b. solar energy
   c. hydrocarbon
   d. non-renewable
   e. chemical potential energy

5. Identify the world's main energy source prior to the widespread use of coal in the 1800s.

Applying Concepts

6. Determine whether the energy stored in fossil fuels is best classified as kinetic energy or chemical potential energy. Explain your reasoning.

7. Imagine that fossil fuels are no longer available and there is no replacement available. List the activities in your life that would no longer be possible or would have to change.

Use the following information to answer questions 8 to 10.

Many countries, like Japan and the United States, rely heavily on petroleum imports, which can be threatened by political instability. This was the case in 1973 when the members of OPEC (Organization of the Petroleum Exporting Countries) would not export petroleum to the United States. This embargo on the shipment of petroleum had many effects on the United States's economy. At the height of the crisis, gasoline prices quadrupled. This massive petroleum shortage motivated the automobile industry to develop more fuel-efficient engines.

8. As petroleum and natural gas become more difficult to extract in the coming decades, describe the likely effect on the price of gasoline.

9. Identify the main areas of the economy that would be affected by a shortage of petroleum and natural gas.

10. Explain why a shortage of petroleum might lead to new developments in automotive technology.

Which device—the snowmobile or the camera phone—is powered by fossil fuels? The snowmobile's internal combustion engine runs on gasoline, a petroleum product. As you learned in the previous lesson, petroleum is a valuable fossil fuel. But what is the energy source for a camera phone? These phones run on rechargeable batteries that must be periodically plugged into a wall outlet for recharging. The number of devices like camera phones that run on rechargeable batteries demonstrates the importance of electricity in society. In Alberta, coal—a fossil fuel—is used to generate over 75% of the electricity. So, like almost every other device that runs on rechargeable batteries in Alberta, the camera phone is also powered by a fossil fuel.

Are you surprised that both of these devices are fossil-fueled? Most people in Alberta don't make the connection between electricity and fossil fuels. As you covered in Lesson 1.2, fossil fuels are non-renewable. Even though supplies of fossil fuels are being depleted, you have learned that the rate at which they are being used as an energy source is actually increasing. In this lesson you will investigate what makes fossil fuels so energy-rich, how the energy content of fuels is determined, and how the energy from fossil fuels is released and converted into other forms of energy.

? DID YOU KNOW?

In 2006, over 2000 tonnes of rechargeable batteries were discarded in Canada. Rechargeable batteries can contain metals like nickel, cadmium, aluminium, and cobalt, all of which can be toxic to organisms within the environment. Many areas have programs to promote the proper disposal of rechargeable and non-rechargeable batteries to help prevent metals from leaching into water and soil.

Energy Released in Combustion Reactions

Releasing the stored energy in gasoline or coal involves **combustion**. Recall that combustion is a type of chemical reaction that requires oxygen and, in the case of hydrocarbons, yields carbon dioxide and water vapour. During a combustion reaction, the chemical bonds within the fuel are broken and new chemical bonds are formed. The process of breaking and forming chemical bonds results in a change of chemical potential energy. Hydrocarbons are considered to be energy-rich molecules. The chemical potential energy of a hydrocarbon is the sum of the potential energy stored in all of the bonds in the molecule.

> **combustion:** a chemical reaction that occurs in the presence of oxygen and results in the release of energy

Combustion of Octane

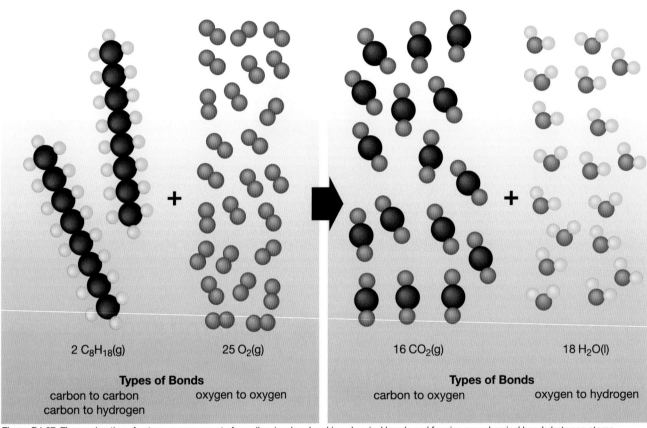

| 2 C_8H_{18}(g) | 25 O_2(g) | 16 CO_2(g) | 18 H_2O(l) |

Types of Bonds

carbon to carbon   oxygen to oxygen   carbon to oxygen   oxygen to hydrogen
carbon to hydrogen

Figure D1.27: The combustion of octane, a component of gasoline, involves breaking chemical bonds and forming new chemical bonds between atoms.

The release of energy that occurs as a result of a combustion reaction can take many forms. Radiant energy in the form of infrared and visible light photons is emitted from the flame produced by the reaction. During a combustion reaction, the kinetic energy of the molecules involved also changes. The products of a combustion reaction are at a higher **temperature** than the reactant molecules. Recall that the collision between molecules with different kinetic energies results in a transfer of energy from warmer to cooler objects—this is often called a transfer of **heat**. The following illustration shows the energy changes that occur during the operation of a snowmobile engine:

Combustion in a Typical Snowmobile Engine

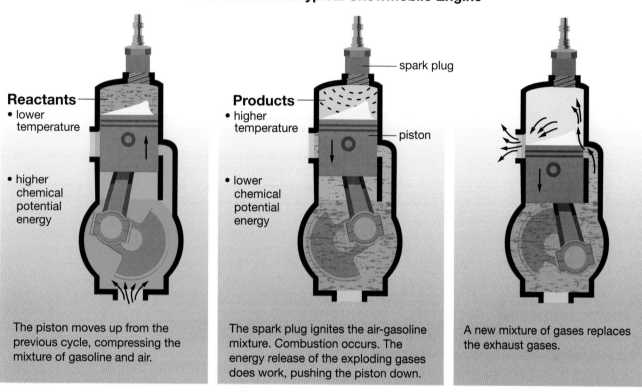

Reactants
- lower temperature
- higher chemical potential energy

The piston moves up from the previous cycle, compressing the mixture of gasoline and air.

Products
- higher temperature
- lower chemical potential energy

spark plug

piston

The spark plug ignites the air-gasoline mixture. Combustion occurs. The energy release of the exploding gases does work, pushing the piston down.

A new mixture of gases replaces the exhaust gases.

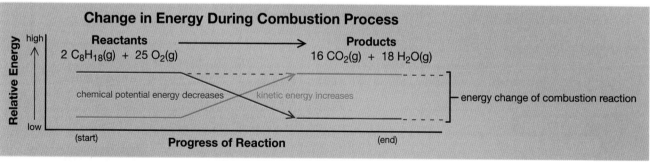

Change in Energy During Combustion Process

Reactants
$2 C_8H_{18}(g) + 25 O_2(g)$

Products
$16 CO_2(g) + 18 H_2O(g)$

Relative Energy — high / low

chemical potential energy decreases

kinetic energy increases

energy change of combustion reaction

(start) **Progress of Reaction** (end)

It is important to remember that not all of the energy released by the combustion of a fossil fuel does useful work on the moving parts of the engine. The radiant energy from the spark does not contribute to the useful work of pushing the piston down, nor does the energy that transfers to the non-moving parts of the engine. Earlier, you learned that energy efficiency is defined as the proportion of input energy that is converted into useful output energy.

Practice

20. Identify the forms of the input energy and output energy associated with the operation of a snowmobile engine.

21. Rewrite the formula for energy efficiency to reflect the forms of energy involved in operating a combustion engine like one found in a snowmobile.

Heat of Combustion

The rearrangement of atoms that occurs during a chemical reaction results in a change of potential energy. When the chemical reaction involves combustion, the product molecules store less chemical potential energy in their bonds relative to the bonds between the atoms of the reactant molecules. The difference in the potential energies of the reactants and products corresponds to the energy released during the combustion reaction. Figure D1.28, an energy diagram, summarizes the energy change that occurs during a combustion reaction.

The symbol $\Delta_c H°$, the **heat of combustion**, is used to represent the quantity of energy released during the combustion reaction. As shown in Figure D1.28, the molecules in the products have a lower potential energy than the molecules in the reactants. This means a release of energy in this combustion reaction occurred. Chemical changes that involve a release of energy are called **exothermic changes**. As you will see later, an exothermic energy change can be represented using a negative sign to signify that energy is released by the process to the surroundings.

In Lesson 1.2 you compared the energy densities of wood, charcoal, and coal. The energy densities you compared express the heat of combustion for each of these fuels per gram of fuel combusted. In the next investigation you will have an opportunity to perform an experiment to determine the heats of combustion and energy densities of some fuels.

Energy Diagram for the Combustion of Octane, C_8H_{18}(l)

Potential Energy / Progress of Reaction

$2\ C_8H_{18}$(l) $+ 25\ O_2$(g) reactants

$16\ CO_2$(g) $+ 18\ H_2O$(g) products

energy change (released)

Figure D1.28

> **heat of combustion ($\Delta_c H°$):** the amount of heat released when a substance undergoes combustion

> **exothermic change:** a chemical change that involves a release of energy, usually in the form of heat, to the surroundings

Investigation

Determining Heat of Combustion

Purpose

You will determine and compare the amount of heat released by the combustion of three different fuels.

Science Skills

✓ Performing and Recording
✓ Analyzing and Interpreting

Experimental Design

During the experiment you will measure the mass of each fuel required to raise the temperature of 20.0 mL of water 20.0°C. The data you collect will be used to calculate an experimental value for the heat of combustion of each fuel tested.

CAUTION!

Because you will be working with open flames in this investigation, ensure that you and your partners take the following precautions:

- Wear safety goggles.
- Avoid wearing loose clothing.
- Tie back long hair.
- Keep your workspace clear of combustible materials.
- Be aware of the procedures for safely dealing with fire in the laboratory.

Materials

- graduated cylinder
- electronic balance
- test tube clamp
- matches
- test tube rack
- thermometer
- candle holder
- ethanol burner
- 3, 25 mm by 200 mm test tubes
- 60 mL of distilled water at room temperature
- thermometer clamp
- 100% paraffin wax candle
- eyedropper
- laboratory stand
- butane lighter
- "Determining Heat of Combustion" handout from the Science 30 Textbook CD

Procedure

step 1: Use a graduated cylinder to fill each of the three test tubes with 20.0 mL of distilled water. Once you have filled the test tubes, place them in a test tube rack for later.

step 2: Use the electronic balance to measure the initial masses of each of the following: ethanol burner with ethanol inside, butane lighter, and candle plus candle holder. Record these values in the data table given in the handout.

step 3: Assemble the apparatus as shown in the handout. The bulb of the thermometer should not be touching the bottom or walls of the test tube. Measure the initial temperature of the water in the first test tube, and record it in the data table.

step 4: Determine the desired final temperature by adding 20.0°C to the initial temperature, and record it in the data table.

step 5: Ignite the ethanol burner, and quickly place it under the test tube so that the upper tip of the flame just touches the bottom of the test tube. Carefully monitor the rising temperature of the water. Once it reaches the final desired temperature, quickly remove the ethanol burner and extinguish the flame.

step 6: Replace the first test tube with another test tube from the test tube rack, and repeat steps 4 and 5 with the butane lighter.

step 7: Replace the test tube with the last test tube in the rack, and repeat steps 4 and 5 to test the paraffin (candle) wax.

step 8: Use the electronic balance to measure the final masses of each of the following: the alcohol burner containing the ethanol, the lighter containing the butane, and the candle. Record these values in the data table given in the handout.

step 9: Disassemble and clean the apparatus, and return all materials to their appropriate places. Make sure your work area is also clean.

Analysis

1. Complete the table in the Analysis part of the "Determining the Heat of Combustion" handout.

2. Identify the manipulated and responding variables in this experiment.

3. List three variables that were controlled during this experiment. Describe the actions you took to maintain consistency between trials.

4. Since the energy change for each trial was identical, use the mass of fuel combusted to rank the three fuels from most energetic to least energetic.

5. Use the calculated values for heat of combustion from your table to rank the fuels from highest heat of combustion per mole to the lowest.

6. Describe the relationship between the molar mass of the molecule tested and the heat of combustion per mole of each fuel tested.

7. Compare the rankings listed in your answers to questions 4 and 5. Account for any differences between the two answers.

8. Identify one major flaw in the design of this experiment. Hypothesize how this flaw may have affected your results.

9. Suggest improvements to the apparatus that might minimize the flaw indicated in question 8. If possible, include a diagram of your improvements to the apparatus used in the experiment.

Calorimetry—Measuring Energy Changes

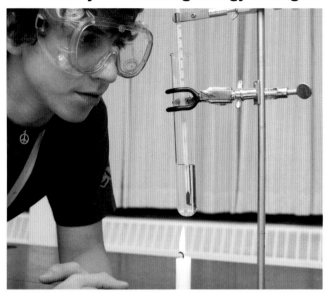

A **calorimeter**, like the one you constructed and used in the "Determining Heat of Combustion" investigation, is a device that measures the energy transferred to the water due to the combustion of a substance. Using a calorimeter yields an experimental value for the heat of combustion. Energy from the combustion reaction is transferred to the contents of the calorimeter and is observed as a temperature change to the water within the calorimeter.

▶ **calorimeter:** a device that measures energy changes

In the "Determining Heat of Combustion" investigation, you were probably able to indicate more than one flaw, most likely involving the probable loss of energy. Energy radiating away from the water cannot be measured using a calorimeter. Energy losses that occur with crude calorimeters decrease the accuracy of experimental values. Scientists performing experiments use more advanced calorimeters that are better able to ensure that the energy released by the reaction is mostly, if not completely, transferred to the water. This ensures that more accurate changes in temperature are measured. In a bomb calorimeter, the combustion reaction occurs within a sealed chamber (bomb) submerged in the water. The water is contained in an outer double-walled container—similar to that of a Thermos bottle—designed to reduce the transfer of energy to the surroundings. These modifications to the basic design of a calorimeter minimize energy loss to the surroundings and improve the accuracy throughout the experiment.

? DID YOU KNOW?

At one time, the values for energy in food were determined using a calorimeter. Now, values for energy are calculated using the mass of fat, carbohydrates, and protein within the food and the heat of combustion values for each gram of fat, carbohydrates, and protein.

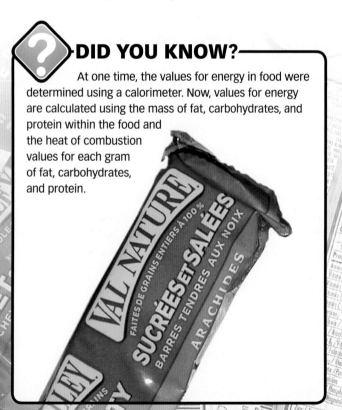

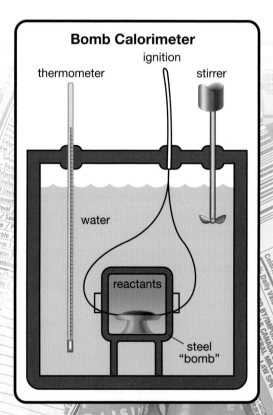

Bomb Calorimeter

Theoretical Heat of Combustion—Hess's Law

When determining heat of combustion, another approach is to consider the energy involved in the formation of the products and the reactants within a chemical system. Although it is impossible to exactly know the potential energy of any substance, the energy associated with a substance's formation—its **standard heats of formation**—can be used to estimate its chemical potential energy. As you have seen, the difference between the chemical potential energies of the products and the chemical potential energies of the reactants is equal to the energy change for the reaction.

The standard heat of formation for an element, when not part of a compound, is defined as zero. Each compound is given a standard heat of formation that is equal to the energy change that occurs during the chemical reaction in which the compound is formed. Giving elements an arbitrary value of zero allows for comparisons to be made among compounds and for an estimation of the potential energy of a compound (higher or lower than its respective elements). Using the standard heats of formation for all the substances involved in a reaction allows for a comparison of the potential energy of the products relative to the reactants. This is summarized in the formula for energy change of reaction, $\Delta_r H°$.

> **standard heat of formation ($\Delta_f H°$):** the energy change for a chemical reaction that involves the formation of a compound from its elements determined at standard conditions

$$\Delta_r H° = \sum n\Delta_f H° \text{ products} - \sum n\Delta_f H° \text{ reactants}$$

where $\Delta_r H°$ = energy change of reaction (kJ)

$\sum$ = the sum of

n = amount (number of moles) represented by coefficient from balanced chemical equation

$\Delta_f H°$ = standard heat of formation

If the reaction is a combustion reaction, $\Delta_r H° = \Delta_c H°$. This means that the heat of combustion, $\Delta_c H°$, is equal to the difference between the sum of the heats of formation of the products and the sum of the heats of formation of the reactants for that equation. Example Problem 1.1 shows how this formula can be applied to predicting the energy change for a chemical reaction.

Example Problem 1.1

The balanced chemical equation for the combustion of methane is as follows.

$$CH_4(g) + 2\ O_2(g) \rightarrow CO_2(g) + 2\ H_2O(g)$$

Use standard heats of formation to calculate the energy change for the combustion for methane, the main component of natural gas.

Solution

$$\Delta_c H° = \sum n\Delta_f H° \text{ products} - \sum n\Delta_f H° \text{ reactants}$$

Organize the information in a table.

Substance	Products		Reactants	
	$CO_2(g)$	$H_2O(g)$	$CH_4(g)$	$O_2(g)$
Coefficient	1 mol	2 mol	1 mol	2 mol
$\Delta_f H°$	−393.5 kJ/mol	−241.8 kJ/mol	−74.6 kJ/mol	0

$$\Delta_c H° = \sum n\Delta_f H° \text{ products} - \sum n\Delta_f H° \text{ reactants}$$

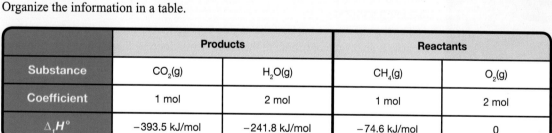

$$= (-393.5\ \text{kJ} - 483.6\ \text{kJ}) - (-74.6\ \text{kJ} + 0)$$
$$= -802.5\ \text{kJ}$$

The energy change is -802.5 kJ.

22. The following balanced chemical equations are for the combustion reactions for each of the fuels tested in the "Determining Heat of Combustion" investigation. Calculate the heats of combustion for each reaction.

  a. $C_2H_5OH(l) + 3 O_2(g) \rightarrow 2 CO_2(g) + 3 H_2O(g)$

  b. $2 C_4H_{10}(g) + 13 O_2(g) \rightarrow 8 CO_2(g) + 10 H_2O(g)$

  c. $2 C_{36}H_{74}(s) + 109 O_2(g) \rightarrow 72 CO_2(g) + 74 H_2O(g)$

  Note: Assume the heat of formation for paraffin wax, $C_{36}H_{74}(s)$, is -1862.6 kJ/mol.

23. Express the heats of combustion in question 22 as energy changes per mole of fuel combusted. State a reason why energy changes are often expressed per mole of reactant.

DID YOU KNOW?

The formula $\Delta_r H° = \sum n\Delta_f H°$ products $- \sum n\Delta_f H°$ reactants can also be used to predict the energy change for any chemical reaction, as long as standard heats of formation for the products and reactants are provided. This formula is one way to state Hess's Law, named after Germain Henri Hess—a Swiss chemist who, in 1840, published his work with energy changes in chemical reactions. Hess's Law states that the energy change for a process is the same whether it occurs in one step or many steps. Energy diagrams are another way to summarize Hess's contribution to a greater understanding of energy changes in chemical reactions.

Machines—Always Leaking Energy

Think back to the first time you ever checked a machine's oil level. Checking fluid levels has become a standard part of most driver-training classes. At some point in the instructions of how to locate and read the oil level on the dipstick, instructors will also warn you that the engine will still be hot, even though it is not running. As with any engine that runs by burning fuel, the combustion of the fuel results in energy being transferred to the engine parts.

It's important to remember that all the energy transferred to the engine is an important component of the total energy output of the engine. The total output energy of the engine is always equal to the total input energy of the engine. In other words, energy can neither be created or destroyed. In previous courses you may have referred to this as the law of conservation of energy. It is also called the **first law of thermodynamics**.

The flow of heat to parts of the engine is classified as non-useful output energy because it does not contribute to the useful work done by the engine. The engine is designed to exert a force on the moving parts that give the vehicle kinetic energy. Whenever energy does work, some of it is wasted. Some of it is lost to the surroundings in the form of heat. In the "Determining Heat of Combustion" investigation, you probably realized that not all of the thermal energy released by the combustion reaction is transferred to the water. Some thermal energy escaped to the room at large. Even if you tried to capture 100% of that escaping energy, as is attempted with bomb calorimeters, you will never fully succeed. A tiny fraction of the energy always escapes. So, inevitably, when people harness energy to do work, some energy passes to the environment as waste heat. The **second law of thermodynamics** states that 100% efficiency is impossible. All people can do when designing machines is to try and minimize waste heat.

▶ **first law of thermodynamics:** a law stating that energy cannot be created or destroyed

Energy is always conserved.

▶ **second law of thermodynamics:** a law stating that when energy is transferred or changed from one form into another, some of the energy is always transferred to the surroundings (usually as waste heat)

Example Problem 1.2

During a trip, a car uses 2.35×10^7 kJ of chemical potential energy supplied by combustion of gasoline. The car's engine is able to transform 4.73×10^6 kJ of that chemical potential energy into useful work.

a. Calculate the efficiency of the car.

b. Use the first law of thermodynamics to determine the percentage of the car's input energy that is transformed into non-useful forms of output energy.

c. List some of the non-useful forms of energy produced by the car's engine.

d. Explain why the non-useful forms of output energy can never be completely eliminated.

Solution

a. useful output energy $= 4.73 \times 10^6$ kJ

input energy $= 2.35 \times 10^7$ kJ

energy efficiency $= ?$

$$\text{energy efficiency} = \frac{\text{useful output energy}}{\text{input energy}} \times 100\%$$
$$= \frac{4.73 \times 10^6 \text{ kJ}}{2.35 \times 10^7 \text{ kJ}} \times 100\%$$
$$= 20.1\%$$

The energy efficiency of the car is 20.1%.

b. According to the first law of thermodynamics, energy is conserved; therefore, the total energy output equals the total energy input. Since 20.1% of the output energy does useful work, that means $100\% - 20.1\% = 79.9\%$ of the input energy is transformed into non-useful forms of energy.

c. The non-useful forms of energy include the thermal energy that passes as waste heat to the environment, the radiant energy produced during combustion, and the sound energy produced by the car's engine.

d. According to the second law of thermodynamics, it is impossible for a machine designed to do useful work to be 100% efficient because some energy is always lost in the transfer.

DID YOU KNOW?

Energy loss is at its greatest when objects are hot because the greater the temperature difference, the greater the rate of heat loss to the cooler surroundings.

Investigation

Calculating the Efficiency of a Calorimeter

Science Skills

✓ Analyzing and Interpreting

Purpose

In this investigation you will use the results from the "Determining Heat of Combustion" investigation and the heats of combustion calculated in Practice question 23 to calculate the energy efficiency of the calorimeter.

Pre-Lab Question

1. For a calorimeter, define *useful output energy* and *input energy*. Describe how useful output energy is measured.

Procedure

step 1: Record the following table into your notebook.

Fuel	ethanol	butane	paraffin wax
Useful Output Energy (kJ/mol)			
Input Energy (kJ/mol)			
Energy Efficiency of Calorimeter (%)			

step 2: Insert your results from the "Determining Heat of Combustion" investigation into the first row of the table.

step 3: Insert your answers to Practice question 23 into the second row of the table.

Analysis

2. Calculate the energy efficiencies of the calorimeter. Record these values in the third row of the table.

3. Calculate an average efficiency of the calorimeter.

4. List possible reasons why the energy efficiency of the calorimeter was less than 100%.

5. State the precision (number of decimal places) of the balance used in the "Determining Heat of Combustion" investigation. Describe the effect the precision of the masses measured has on the values calculated for the efficiency of your calorimeter.

Coal-Fired Generating Stations

Coal is used to produce more than 70% of Alberta's electricity. Because of the increased price for petroleum, coal's popularity has increased as a source of energy to meet ever-increasing energy needs. A coal-fired generating station operates by burning coal, converting its chemical potential energy into electricity.

The process of transforming the energy within coal requires that it first be crushed into a fine dust and blown into a combustion chamber, where it ignites. The energy released by the combusting coal is then absorbed by water contained within a network of tubes surrounding the combustion chamber. The combustion chamber and water lines form the boiler, allowing the water in the lines to be converted into high-pressure steam. The force generated by the expansion of the high-pressure steam causes the turbine to spin. The axle of the turbine is connected to a generator, which is composed of a conductive wire spinning within a magnetic field. As you saw in Unit C, a generator induces an electrical current in the conducting wire—thus producing electricity. The following flowchart summarizes how the energy is transformed during the conversion of coal into electricity by the generating station.

Coal-Fired Generating Station

stack

steam line

turbine

generator

coal supply

switchyard

conveyor belt

river or reservoir

boiler

condenser

cooling water

Figure D1.29: Energy conversions in a coal-fired generating station

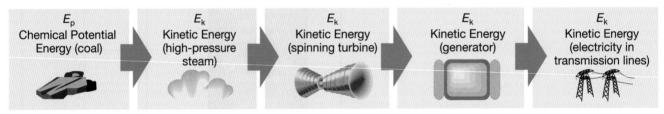

| E_p Chemical Potential Energy (coal) | E_k Kinetic Energy (high-pressure steam) | E_k Kinetic Energy (spinning turbine) | E_k Kinetic Energy (generator) | E_k Kinetic Energy (electricity in transmission lines) |

Practice

24. Electricity can be produced using natural gas—a fossil fuel—in place of coal. Use the Internet to research natural gas-fired electricity generation. Identify similarities and differences between coal-fired electricity generation and natural gas-fired generation in terms of processes used to produce electricity and the energy transformations involved.

25. Modifications to the processes in a coal-fired power plant are listed in the following table. Explain how each modification could improve the energy efficiency of the plant.

Modification	Description
I	evaporating water normally found within coal prior to combustion
II	allowing the steam to pass more than once across turbine blades

Science Links

Older coal-fired generating stations are only about 33% efficient. Experimental, low-emission generating stations may improve energy efficiency to 45% or higher. More information about the processes involved in low-emission coal-fired power plants appears in Units B and C.

Fossil fuel combustion reactions provide the energy for many of the technological devices you use daily, like vehicles, electrical appliances, and electronic devices. The energy released by a combustion reaction can be measured experimentally or by using standard heats of formation. All energy conversions are less than 100% efficient. This is due to some of the energy being transferred to the environment as heat.

1.3 Questions

Knowledge

1. Identify the energy source used to generate the majority of Alberta's electricity.

2. Name the type of energy present within fossil fuels.

3. Identify the type of chemical reaction used to release the energy stored in fossil fuels.

4. Write the formula used to calculate energy change for a combustion reaction using standard heats of formation. Identify each variable in the formula.

5. Define *heat of combustion* and *standard heat of formation*.

Applying Concepts

6. Explain how the combustion of a hydrocarbon causes a change in potential energy.

7. Describe the result of a change in potential energy during a chemical reaction.

8. Draw an energy diagram for an exothermic process indicating the position of the reactants, products, and net energy change.

9. A natural gas-fired generating station uses 2.5 MJ of heat from the combustion of methane.

   a. Calculate the station's energy efficiency if 1.3 MJ of electrical energy is generated.

   b. Compare this to the typical efficiency of a coal-fired generating station.

10. For thousands of years, the Inuit traditionally relied upon animal power for transportation. In the 1970s, gasoline-powered snowmobiles replaced dogsleds as the primary mode of transportation for Inuit in the Arctic during the winter months.

   a. Write the balanced combustion reaction for octane, $C_8H_{18}(l)$, the main component of gasoline.

   b. Use standard heats of formation to calculate the heat of combustion for octane.

11. For millennia, Inuit people have burned seal and whale blubber as sources of heat and light. Design an experiment that could compare the heat of combustion of seal blubber with that of whale blubber. Your design should include a problem statement; manipulated, responding, and controlled variables; a diagram of the apparatus you will use; and a data table showing the information you wish to measure and record.

Figure D1.30: Pickering, Ontario, is home to one of the world's largest nuclear power facilities.

On the shore of Lake Ontario, just east of Toronto, Pickering Nuclear Power Stations A and B produce enough electricity to power a city of about 2 million people. Each domed building, of which there are eight, contains a **CANDU** nuclear reactor. Each building has thick concrete walls to contain the gamma radiation emitted during the nuclear reaction that provides the energy to generate electricity. The cylindrical building with the flat roof in Figure D1.30 is part of the plant's safety system. It contains low-pressure air that can capture any radioactive gases that might escape from the reactors.

How, exactly, does the energy produced by nuclear reactions generate electrical energy? Is the nuclear reaction that takes place within the reactor buildings the same as the nuclear reactions that occur within the Sun's core? In addition to gamma radiation, are any other types of radiation produced? How does the process of generating electricity from nuclear reactions compare to the processes that occur in a coal-fired power plant? In this lesson you will have an opportunity to answer these questions as you incorporate what you have already learned about energy transformations and electricity production with information about nuclear reactions.

> ▶ **CANDU:** Canadian Deuterium Uranium Reactor; a nuclear reactor technology developed in Canada and now operating in Canada and six other countries

Describing the Nucleus

Every atom has a nucleus composed of **protons** and **neutrons**. The number of protons determines an element's identity. The number of protons is called the **atomic number**. For example, all beryllium atoms have 4 protons. Although all atoms of the same element must have the same number of protons, they can vary in mass due to differences in the number of neutrons they possess. For example, the most common type of beryllium is called beryllium-9. Since the nucleus of beryllium-9 has 4 protons and 5 neutrons, it has a **mass number** of 9. Since protons and neutron make up the nucleus, they are often referred to as **nucleons**; therefore, the beryllium-9 nucleus has a total of 9 nucleons. The nucleus of beryllium-9 can be concisely described using **nuclear notation** as follows.

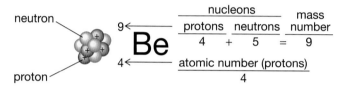

Other forms of the beryllium atom, like beryllium-10, have a different number of nucleons (mass number) but the same atomic number. Beryllium-9 and beryllium-10 are **isotopes**. As you learn more about nuclear reactions, it will be important to differentiate between the isotopes of various elements.

? DID YOU KNOW?

Beryllium-10 is formed in the upper atmosphere when cosmic rays collide with oxygen or nitrogen atoms.

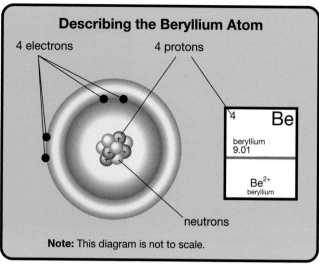

Describing the Beryllium Atom

Note: This diagram is not to scale.

Figure D1.31: A beryllium atom is made up of protons, neutrons, and electrons. Here is one such representation.

▶ **proton:** a component of an atomic nucleus with a mass of 1 atomic mass unit and a charge of 1+

▶ **neutron:** a component of an atomic nucleus with a mass of 1 atomic mass unit and no net charge

▶ **atomic number:** the number of protons in the nucleus of an atom; determines the identity of an element

▶ **mass number:** the total number of protons and neutrons in an atom; frequently written after the name of an element to identify a specific isotope

▶ **nucleon:** the name applied to protons and neutrons (the parts of an atom's nucleus)

▶ **nuclear notation:** representation of an atom, $_Z^A X$, that lists the chemical symbol for the element (X), its atomic number (Z), and its mass number (A)

▶ **isotope:** a particular variety of an element as defined by its atomic mass

Practice

26. Complete the following table.

Isotope	Atomic Number	Mass Number	Number of ...		
			Protons	Neutrons	Nucleons
hydrogen-2 (deuterium)					
carbon-13					

27. The masses of a proton, neutron, and an electron are as follows:
   - proton: $1.007\ 28 \times 10^{-3}$ kg/mol
   - neutron: $1.008\ 66 \times 10^{-3}$ kg/mol
   - electron: 5.49×10^{-7} kg/mol

   a. How many times larger are protons than electrons?

   b. It is customary to delete the mass of electrons when calculating the atomic mass. Use your answers to question 27.a. to justify this practice.

28. Using nuclear notation, express the following isotopes.

   a. uranium-235   **b.** uranium-238   **c.** polonium-210   **d.** polonium-218

Alpha Radiation

If a nucleus is comprised of protons and neutrons, a good question to ask is what keeps it together? After all, shouldn't the positive charge of such tightly packed protons repel one another? Recall from Unit C that the force between two charges increases exponentially in response to a reduction in their distance. Therefore, to keep a nucleus together, the forces at work within it must be greater than the force of repulsion between protons.

A Stable Nucleus—Balanced Forces in $^9_4$Be

$\vec{F}_{electrical}$: a force of repulsion acting between protons

$\vec{F}_{strong\ nuclear}$: an attractive force acting between neighbouring protons and neutrons

---

A **strong nuclear force** is a force that attracts protons to neutrons, neutrons to neutrons, and even protons to protons. Although this force attracts all these particles to one another, it only acts between particles that are close enough to touch each other. The electrical force generated by repelling particles acts over any distance. Larger nuclei—those containing more protons—require neutrons to "dilute" the repulsive forces within the nucleus. In addition to spreading out the repulsive electrical force, neutrons increase the strong nuclear force by acting like glue to hold nucleons together. The **radioactive decay** demonstrated by unstable isotopes demonstrates the role of neutrons in balancing the forces within the nucleus.

Beryllium-8 is an unstable isotope when compared to beryllium-9. The difference of one neutron reduces the strong nuclear force relative to the force caused by the repulsion between protons. The instability caused by the imbalance between forces within the nucleus causes the beryllium-8 atom to break apart into two **alpha particles**. Alpha particles are nuclei composed of two protons and two neutrons, having a net charge of 2+. The alpha particles have the same composition as the nucleus of a helium atom and are often written as $^4_2$He. The release of alpha particles during nuclear decay is called **alpha radiation**. For beryllium-8, its radioactive decay is unusual in that both products happen to be alpha particles. In most situations, only one product of the decay is an alpha particle.

An Unstable Nucleus—Unbalanced Forces in $^8_4$Be

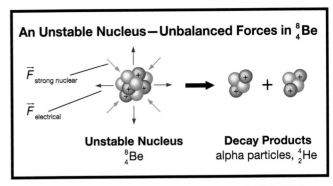

$\vec{F}_{strong\ nuclear}$

$\vec{F}_{electrical}$

Unstable Nucleus	Decay Products
$^8_4$Be	alpha particles, $^4_2$He

---

strong nuclear force: an attractive force between nuclear particles that acts over short distances

radioactive decay: a spontaneous change in which an unstable nucleus emits radiation

alpha particle: a positively charged particle consisting of two neutrons and two protons, which is a helium nucleus

alpha radiation: a stream of alpha particles emitted from unstable nuclei; one of the three principal types of nuclear radiation

The process of radioactive decay can be represented using a nuclear equation. When balancing a nuclear equation, the number of nucleons is conserved. Example Problem 1.3 shows how to balance a nuclear equation.

Example Problem 1.3

Many smoke detectors contain the isotope americium-241. Alpha particles emitted during the decay of americium-241 ionize molecules in the air, allowing an electric current to flow between two plates in the smoke detector. During a fire, smoke particles that come between these two plates interfere with the current, setting off the detector's alarm.

a. State the name of the process that produces an alpha particle.

b. Write a balanced nuclear equation describing the decay of americium-241 that results in an alpha particle and another product.

Solution

a. The process that releases an alpha particle is called alpha radiation.

b. Write the nuclear equation. Let $_{Z}^{A}X$ represent the unknown product.

Reactant   **Products**

$$_{95}^{241}\text{Am} \ \rightarrow \ _{2}^{4}\text{He} \ + \ _{Z}^{A}X$$

alpha   unknown
particle   product

step 1: In a table, list the mass numbers (total nucleons) and the atomic numbers of the reactant side and the products side of the nuclear equation.

	Reactant	Products
Mass Number	241	$4 + A$
Atomic Number	95	$2 + Z$

step 2: Determine the mass number and the atomic number of the unknown product. **Note:** The reactant side and the products side must have the same total.

$$241 = 4 + A \qquad 95 = 2 + Z$$
$$A = 237 \qquad Z = 93$$

The mass number and atomic number of the other product are 237 and 93, respectively.

step 3: Identify the other product, and write its nuclear notation.

atomic number 93 = neptunium, Np

Therefore, $_{Z}^{A}X = _{93}^{237}\text{Np}$.

step 4: Write the balanced nuclear equation.

$$_{95}^{241}\text{Am} \rightarrow _{2}^{4}\text{He} + _{93}^{237}\text{Np}$$

29. Write the balanced nuclear equation showing the alpha decay for each isotope given.
    a. beryllium-8
    b. uranium-232
    c. polonium-210

30. Each of the following atoms is a product of an alpha-decay reaction. Write a balanced nuclear equation for each.
    a. uranium-235
    b. plutonium-236

31. Radium-226 is an unstable isotope that decays to radon-222.
    a. Write the balanced nuclear equation for this process.
    b. Identify the type of radiation produced by the decay of radium-226.

Beta Radiation

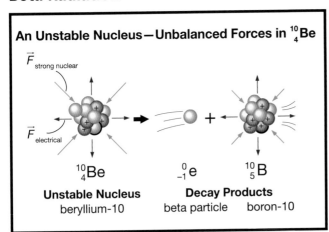

An Unstable Nucleus—Unbalanced Forces in $^{10}_{4}Be$

$\vec{F}_{\text{strong nuclear}}$

$\vec{F}_{\text{electrical}}$

$^{10}_{4}Be$ $^{0}_{-1}e$ $^{10}_{5}B$

Unstable Nucleus	Decay Products	
beryllium-10	beta particle	boron-10

Figure D1.32

You have seen that an imbalance between the strong nuclear force and the electrical force within a nucleus results in an unstable nucleus. The instability within the nucleus of beryllium-10 leads to the emission of a **beta particle**—an electron. A beta particle is represented by the symbol $^{0}_{-1}e$.

A stream of negatively charged beta particles is called **beta radiation**. Even though a beta particle is an electron, the term *beta particle* is used to indicate that each particle originates from the nucleus and not from the orbiting electrons that participate in chemical bonding.

> **beta particle:** a high-speed electron emitted from an unstable nucleus; the result of the change of a neutron to a proton during a nuclear reaction

> **beta radiation:** a stream of beta particles emitted from unstable nuclei; one of three principle types of nuclear radiation

Reactant   Products

$$^{1}_{0}n \rightarrow \; ^{0}_{-1}e + \; ^{1}_{1}p$$
neutron   beta particle   proton

	Reactant	Products
Mass Number	1	0 + 1
Atomic Number	0	−1 + 1

Note: The reactant and products sides of the equation balance.

Beta particles are ejected from the nucleus when a neutron is converted into a proton. During **beta decay**, the number of nucleons comprising a nucleus does not change, but the atomic number does. The 1− charge of a beta particle is balanced by the conversion of a neutron into a proton, as demonstrated in the nuclear equation for the decay of beryllium-10 (Figure D1.32).

> **beta decay:** a spontaneous change in which an unstable nucleus emits beta radiation

Beryllium-10 Decay

$$^{10}_{4}Be \rightarrow \; ^{0}_{-1}e + \; ^{10}_{5}B$$

	Reactant	Products
Mass Number	10	0 + 10
Atomic Number	4	−1 + 5

Note: The reactant and products sides of the equation balance.

Since beta decay causes the conversion of one neutron into a proton, beryllium-10 nuclei are converted into boron-10 nuclei. The boron nucleus has one more proton (5) than the beryllium nucleus (4).

Carbon-14 is a radioactive isotope that emits beta radiation. Carbon-14 is found in the atmosphere and eventually finds its way into living systems. Once a plant or animal dies, the amount of carbon-14 remaining in the tissue can be used to estimate the number of years that have passed since the organism's time of death. This is done by using the half-life of carbon-14. To get a clearer picture of human history, archaeologists use carbon-14 dating to estimate the age of ancient remains, like teeth or bone fragments.

Use this information to write a balanced nuclear equation for the beta decay of carbon-14.

Solution

step 1: List the reactant and the products.

> **reactant:** $^{14}_{6}C$
>
> **products:** $^{0}_{-1}e$ and $^{A}_{Z}X$

step 2: In a table, list the mass numbers (total nucleons) and the atomic numbers of the reactant and the products.

	Reactant	Products
Mass Number	14	$0 + A$
Atomic Number	6	$-1 + Z$

step 3: Determine the mass number and the atomic number of the other product.

> $14 = 0 + a$ $\quad 6 = -1 + Z$
>
> $A = 14$ $\qquad z = 7$

The mass number and atomic number of the unknown product are 14 and 7, respectively.

step 4: Identify the unknown product, and write its nuclear notation.

> atomic number 7 = nitrogen, N
>
> Therefore, $^{A}_{Z}X = ^{14}_{7}N$.

step 5: Write the balanced nuclear equation.

> $^{14}_{6}C \rightarrow ^{0}_{-1}e + ^{14}_{7}N$

Practice

32. Each isotope listed undergoes beta decay. Write a balanced nuclear equation showing the change that occurs.

   a. krypton-87

   b. silicon-32

33. Each isotope listed is a product of beta decay. Use a balanced nuclear equation to determine the identity of the isotope that underwent nuclear change.

   a. gallium-71

   b. nickel-60

Gamma Radiation

Unlike alpha and beta radiation, gamma radiation is not comprised of a stream of charged particles. As you learned in Unit C, gamma radiation consists of a stream of gamma photons—the most energetic form of electromagnetic radiation.

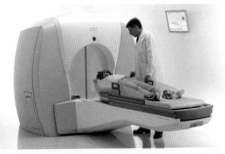

A Gamma (γ) Photon

no mass ⟶ $_0^0\gamma$
no charge ⟶

magnetic field vectors

electric field vectors

velocity vector

Because a photon is a bundle of electromagnetic energy—consisting of electric and magnetic fields—photons have no mass or charge. The symbol for a gamma photon, $_0^0\gamma$, concisely communicates this information.

Gamma radiation is usually emitted as an additional product of alpha or beta decay, but it can be emitted on its own. In Unit C, when you were comparing forms of electromagnetic radiation, you discovered that gamma rays have even more energy than X-rays. As a result, gamma rays are very damaging when they are absorbed by biological molecules. This is why gamma radiation is frequently used in cancer therapy to kill cancerous cells.

Example Problem 1.5

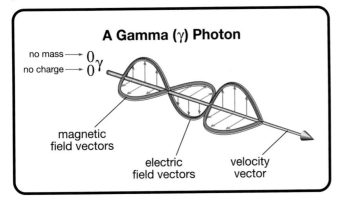

Cobalt-60 is a source of gamma radiation that is frequently used to treat patients with cancer. Machines used in modern cancer therapy, like the one in the photograph, can focus narrow beams of gamma radiation from over 200 cobalt-60 sources to destroy cancer cells deep within the patient.

Write a balanced nuclear equation to describe the emission of beta and gamma radiation from a cobalt-60 source.

Solution

$$_{27}^{60}\text{Co} \rightarrow {}_0^0\gamma + {}_{-1}^0\text{e} + {}_Z^A X$$

	Reactant	Products
Mass Number	60	0 + 0 + a
Atomic Number	27	0 + −1 + z

Determine the mass number and the atomic number of the unknown product.

$$60 = 0 + 0 + A \qquad 27 = 0 + -1 + Z$$
$$A = 60 \qquad\qquad Z = 28$$

The product with an atomic number of 28 is nickel. Therefore, $_Z^A X = {}_{28}^{60}\text{Ni}$.

Thus, the balanced nuclear equation is

$$_{27}^{60}\text{Co} \rightarrow {}_0^0\gamma + {}_{-1}^0\text{e} + {}_{28}^{60}\text{Ni}.$$

Shielding Nuclear Radiation

Radioactive materials are used in a number of specialized medical procedures. These materials are transported and stored in shielded containers that absorb the emitted particles or photons and ensure that radiation does not pass into the environment. Would the shielding requirements be different if the radioactive isotope in the vial were a source of alpha radiation or beta radiation? Why is shielding so important when working with these materials?

In Units B and C you discovered that high-energy radiation is capable of ionizing the material through which it passes, leading to the formation of free radicals. Ionizing radiation is harmful to living tissue—particularly to DNA, which is especially vulnerable to the damage caused by free radicals. This is why it is important to ensure that exposure to ionizing radiation is kept ALARA (as low as reasonably achievable).

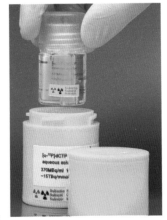

Figure D1.33: Radioactive materials are stored and transported in specially shielded containers.

Alpha, beta, and gamma radiation are all classified as ionizing radiation because they are each capable of ionizing the material they penetrate. As you have seen in this lesson, each of these types of nuclear radiation has remarkably different properties. As a result, the type of material that is an effective shield for one type of radiation may not necessarily be effective for another. So, different types of shielding materials can be used for transporting isotopes or in the design of a nuclear reactor.

The effectiveness of a shielding material can be determined by placing it between a source of a particular radiation and a device that can detect the radiation, like a **Geiger counter**. The output of a Geiger counter displays the number of charged particles and/or photons that have entered the device. In the next activity you will have an opportunity to use an animated version of this kind of set-up.

▶ **Geiger counter:** a device that detects and measures the intensity of ionizing radiation

Figure D1.34: A Geiger counter

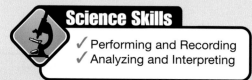

Practice

34. Antimony-126, a beta particle, and a gamma photon are the three products of a nuclear reaction. Identify the isotope that undergoes a nuclear reaction to form these products.

35. Polonium-218 emits an alpha particle and a gamma photon. Identify the other product of the decay of polonium-218.

Utilizing Technology

Shielding Radiation

Science Skills
✓ Performing and Recording
✓ Analyzing and Interpreting

Purpose
You will use the applet "The Alpha, Beta, and Gamma of Radiation" from the Science 30 Textbook CD to determine which types of materials are capable of shielding alpha, beta, and gamma radiation.

Background
Before starting, familiarize yourself with the features of the applet. Select an isotope, select different barriers (shielding materials), and adjust the position of the Geiger counter. In the first part of the procedure, you will measure the radiation emitted by natural sources, often referred to as background radiation. You will then complete measurements of the radiation emitted from different isotopes as it travels through air and through other barriers.

Procedure
Obtain the "Shielding Radiation" handout from the Science 30 Textbook CD.

step 1: Set the Geiger counter 10 mm to the right of the shielding material.

step 2: Measure the background radiation. To do this, select "No isotope" for the isotope and "Air" for the barrier; then click on "Start Count." **Note:** The applet is set to collect data over five seconds.

step 3: Record the total radiation count from the Geiger counter in the appropriate place on the handout. Repeat this step two more times.

step 4: Repeat steps 2 and 3 with uranium-238, strontium-90, and cobalt-60 as the isotope. Record your results in the appropriate places.

step 5: Repeat steps 1 to 3 using paper, aluminium, and lead as the barrier. Record your results in the appropriate place.

1. Complete the data tables in the handout.

Analysis

2. Rank the barriers tested from greatest to least shielding ability for each type of radiation.

3. Use the applet to collect data that allows you to write a balanced nuclear equation describing the decay reaction for each isotope. Explain how you used the data from the applet to write these equations.

Shielding with Solid Materials

The results from the "Shielding Radiation" activity demonstrate that the type of radiation emitted by a source must be considered before you can select an appropriate shielding material. Shielding involves using a material that absorbs the radiation emitted by an isotope. The size of the alpha particle makes it one of the easiest forms of radiation to absorb by sheilding, whereas the considerably smaller beta particle has the ability to penetrate denser substances, like those that were tested. Gamma sources are the most difficult to shield. They require thick walls of lead or, in the case of CANDU nuclear reactors, several metres of concrete. As you can see, shielding is an important technique in the safe use of radiation for many technologies.

Science Links

Shielding protects life on Earth from the harmful effects of ionizing radiation from space. You discovered in Unit C that Earth's protective shield consists of two parts: Earth's magnetic field and the molecules, like ozone, that make up Earth's atmosphere.

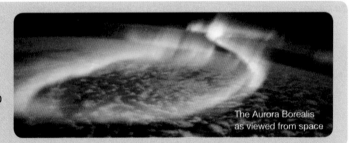

The Aurora Borealis as viewed from space

Nuclear Fission

Earlier you learned that radioactive decay involves atoms spontaneously changing from one element into another, and that a nuclear change is accompanied by a release of energy in the form of radiation. Radiation emitted during alpha and beta decay can possess sufficient energy to harm living tissue, but not enough energy to be used for large-scale energy production. Currently, the only application for the energy released by these processes is providing electricity and heat for deep-space probes. Using nuclear energy for the large-scale generation of electricity requires a different process.

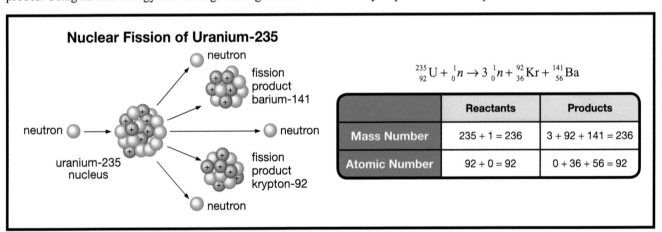

Nuclear Fission of Uranium-235

neutron

fission product barium-141

neutron

neutron

uranium-235 nucleus

neutron

fission product krypton-92

neutron

$$^{235}_{92}U + ^{1}_{0}n \rightarrow 3\,^{1}_{0}n + ^{92}_{36}Kr + ^{141}_{56}Ba$$

	Reactants	Products
Mass Number	$235 + 1 = 236$	$3 + 92 + 141 = 236$
Atomic Number	$92 + 0 = 92$	$0 + 36 + 56 = 92$

Figure D1.35

The nuclear reaction used to release energy in CANDU reactors, like those at Pickering Nuclear Power Stations A and B, is **nuclear fission**. Nuclear fission involves splitting atoms. It was used in the first atomic bombs and is still used today to generate electricity for millions of homes, businesses, and industries in Canada and throughout the world. A fission reaction occurs when a large nucleus, such as uranium-235, is struck by a neutron and breaks into two smaller nuclei, called fission products. As shown in Figure D1.35, the fission of uranium-235 also yields three neutrons and high-energy gamma radiation which is not shown. View the "Nuclear Fission" applet, from the Science 30 Textbook CD, to see an animation of a fission reaction.

nuclear fission: a nuclear reaction in which a large nucleus splits into smaller nuclei or particles with the simultaneous release of energy

The kinetic energies of the neutrons and fission products add up to a lot of energy—much more than is released by a chemical reaction. In a nuclear reactor, this energy is transferred as heat to water surrounding the nuclear fuel.

Practice

36. The fission of uranium-235 can produce many different products. The following equations show one product of the fission of uranium-235. Use a balanced nuclear reaction to determine the unknown product, $_{Z}^{A}X$, in each reaction.

a. $_{92}^{235}U + _{0}^{1}n \rightarrow 3\,_{0}^{1}n + _{Z}^{A}X + _{53}^{137}I$

b. $_{92}^{235}U + _{0}^{1}n \rightarrow 3\,_{0}^{1}n + _{Z}^{A}X + _{35}^{90}Br$

Electricity from Nuclear Fission—CANDU

Products of a fission reaction have large quantities of kinetic energy. If this energy can cause water to boil and become high-pressure steam, it can spin turbines, which can spin generators, which can generate electricity. Sound familiar? It should. This is very similar to the design of a conventional coal-fired power plant. A nuclear power plant enables the release of **intranuclear potential energy**, allowing it to be transformed into useful electricity. Nuclear power plants are similar to fossil fuel power plants in that they are both thermal sources of electricity. The best way to get an overview of how all this works is to take a quick tour of a generating station powered by a CANDU reactor.

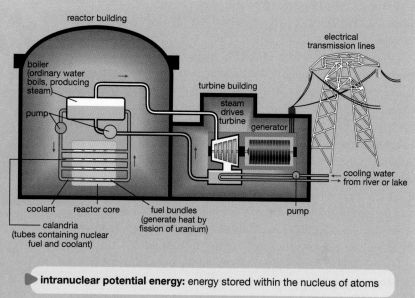

▶ **intranuclear potential energy:** energy stored within the nucleus of atoms

Figure D1.36: Cross section of a CANDU power plant

Utilizing Technology

Reactor Operation

Reactor Operation

Watch the video "Reactor Operation" from the Science 30 Textbook CD. Use the information from the video to answer the Analysis questions.

Science Skills

✓ Performing and Recording

Analysis

1. Prepare a table with three columns, and use the following headings: Similar Components, Similar Processes, and Unique Processes. In the first column, list the similar components found in coal-fired and nuclear power plants. In the second column, list the similar processes used in coal-fired and nuclear power plants. In the third column, list the processes that are unique to nuclear power plants.

2. Identify two functions of heavy water in a CANDU nuclear reactor.

3. Explain "Defence in Depth."

4. Justify the practices used to train nuclear-plant operators, including a careful selection of experienced individuals and participation in intensive training programs.

37. Refer to the cross section of a CANDU nuclear power plant (Figure D1.36) and to the cross section of a coal-fired power plant (Figure D1.29 on page 500). Compare these two methods of producing electricity by considering the following:
   - energy source
   - form of energy in energy source
   - reaction used to release energy from the energy source
   - list of energy transformations for water during the process
   - method of converting kinetic energy into electrical energy

Controlling the Fission Reaction

Controlling the release of energy from the energy source is an important aspect of plant operation and design. In a coal-fired generating station, the release of energy can be controlled by adjusting the amount of pulverized coal that is fed into the furnace.

The energy released by a CANDU reactor is determined by the mass of uranium-235 that undergoes fission. As shown in Figure D1.35 on page 510, the fission of uranium-235 requires a supply of neutrons. Uranium-235 used in the CANDU process is in the form of uranium dioxide pellets assembled into cylindrical fuel bundles. Within the reactor, sections of the fuel bundles are exposed, allowing them to undergo fission. How does exposing a section of a fuel rod allow for the control of a fission reaction? Recall that the key to a fission reaction is neutrons. Controlling the neutrons that strike the U-235 regulates the mass of isotope that reacts and, therefore, the quantity of energy released by the reactor.

One means of controlling neutrons within the reactor involves the use of **heavy water**. The higher density of heavy water acts to slow neutrons to a speed that is ideal for colliding with U-235 nuclei, initiating its fission. Heavy water is often referred to as a **moderator** when used to control the speed of neutrons in a nuclear reactor.

Figure D1.37: Fuel bundles are used to generate electricity in CANDU reactors.

heavy water: water composed of two atoms of the heavier isotopes of hydrogen and one atom of oxygen

moderator: a substance of low molecular mass capable of reducing the speed of neutrons during the operation of a nuclear reactor

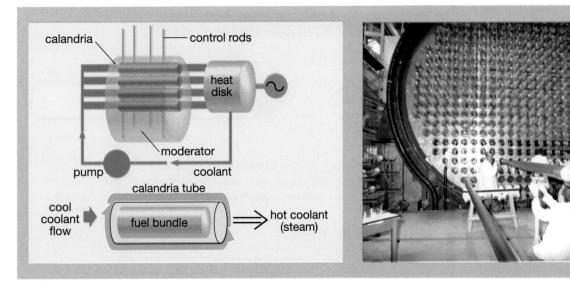

Figure D1.38: The core of a nuclear reactor is a calandria, composed of many long tubes in which the fuel rods are placed. The tubes containing the fuel rods are each surrounded by larger tubes containing coolant (heavy water). Thermal energy from the fission reaction in the fuel is transferred to the heavy water, converting the water into steam.

A second method of controlling neutrons and the energy output of the reactor is the use of control rods. Lowering the control rods further into the core of the reactor allows for greater absorption of neutrons, thereby decreasing the number of fission reactions that occur and reducing the energy output of the reactor.

The emergency-shutdown systems of a CANDU reactor are also based on controlling the neutrons that initiate fission reactions. The first emergency-shutdown system involves quickly inserting neutron-absorbing control rods into the reactor to immediately stop the reaction. The second involves the injection of neutron-absorbing liquid into the moderator.

You may have noticed that all of the safety and control mechanisms mentioned for a CANDU reactor involve mechanisms to control neutrons. Previously, you discovered that the fission reaction of uranium-235 is initiated by a collision with a neutron. This collision then releases three neutrons as products. The proper control of neutrons produced by each fission reaction prevents an uncontrolled **chain reaction,** whereby an exponential increase in the number of fission reactions that occur results in an exponential release in energy.

A rapid energy release could occur due to poor control of fission reactions in the reactor or to poor control of the transfer of energy from the reactor. This could result in extensive damage, often called **nuclear meltdown**.

DID YOU KNOW?

Cobalt-60 is an isotope created when cobalt-59 is used within adjuster rods of some CANDU reactors. Cobalt-60 undergoes beta decay and releases gamma radiation, making it useful for cancer radiotherapy and for sterilizing medical instruments.

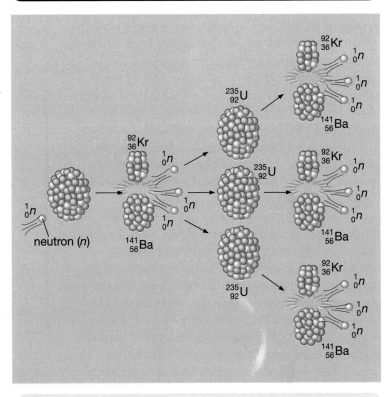

▶ **chain reaction:** a nuclear reaction that perpetuates itself; the release of neutrons during nuclear fission that initiates the fission of other atoms

▶ **nuclear meltdown:** the result of improper control of a nuclear reaction within a reactor; the increase in the temperature of the core of a nuclear reactor, resulting in damage and increasing the risk of releasing radioactive substances into the environment

Reactor meltdowns, like the one that occurred on April 25, 1986, in Chernobyl, Ukraine, can result in the release of radioactive materials into the environment. Although the CANDU reactor is designed in such a way that a meltdown is extremely unlikely, the Chernobyl incident was such a frightening event that many people are still nervous about embracing nuclear power.

DID YOU KNOW?

Since 1991, children from the Ukraine and Belarus who were born with low-functioning immune systems—believed to be the result of the incident in Chernobyl—have been coming to Canada for a break from the exposure of radiation in their environment. These visits have allowed the children to strengthen their immune systems and, thus, increase their ability to fight simple infections like colds.

Mass-Energy Equivalence—$E = mc^2$

A pellet of uranium used in nuclear power plants has a mass of about 7 g; but it can release the same quantity of energy as 3.5 barrels (556.5 L) of oil, 480 000 L of natural gas, or 807 kg of coal. How can such a small pellet of uranium be an enormous source of energy?

The answer can be traced back to the work of Albert Einstein, who in the early 1900s published articles describing a theory of general relativity (pertaining to gravity) and a special theory of relativity (describing the motion of particles approaching the speed of light). One of the predictions of the special theory was that mass could be converted into energy and energy could be converted into mass. In other words, mass and energy are interchangeable. Previously you have always balanced reactions with respect to the law of conservation of mass, focusing on either the number of nucleons or the number of moles of each type of atom involved. Einstein's theory redefined people's understanding of the nature of matter and energy.

In Einstein's theory, mass is not just the sum of its constituent parts; it is also the sum of the kinetic, potential, and mass energy. Energy is now considered to be the only commodity in the universe that cannot be created or destroyed. Any difference between the masses of the products and the reactants of a process must be the result of mass having been converted into energy. Einstein was able to describe the relationship between the change in mass and its conversion to energy by using his famous equation, $E = mc^2$.

It is more descriptive to express Einstein's equation as $\Delta E = \Delta mc^2$, where

ΔE = change in energy

Δm = change in mass
    = mass of products − mass of reactants

c = speed of light $\left(3.00 \times 10^8 \text{ m/s}\right)$

Because the square of the speed of light is an enormous number, a small change in mass corresponds to a very large energy change. You can see how this equation is used in Example Problem 1.6.

Example Problem 1.6

In the fission of 1 mol of beryllium-8, the mass of the products is determined to be 2.29×10^{-5} kg less than the mass of the reactants. Calculate the change in energy that corresponds with this change in mass. Identify whether this reaction is exothermic or endothermic.

Solution

$\Delta m = 2.29 \times 10^{-5}$ kg

$c = 3.00 \times 10^8$ m/s

$\Delta E = ?$

$\Delta E = \Delta mc^2$

$\quad = \left(2.29 \times 10^{-5} \text{ kg}\right)\left(3.00 \times 10^8 \text{ m/s}\right)^2$

$\quad = 2.06 \times 10^{12} \text{ kg} \cdot \text{m}^2/\text{s}^2$

$\quad = 2.06 \times 10^{12}$ J

The energy change for 1 mol of beryllium-8 is 2.06×10^{12} J. Since the mass of the products is **less** than the mass of the reactants, the missing mass must have converted into energy. Therefore, the reaction is exothermic.

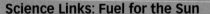

Science Links: Fuel for the Sun

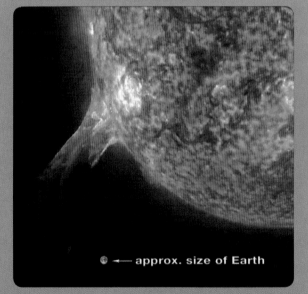

© ⟵ approx. size of Earth

The radiation that the Sun pours into space originates from nuclear reactions deep within its core. Every second, approximately 3.8×10^{26} J of energy is emitted from the Sun's surface. Using the equation $E = mc^2$, this means that the Sun must be converting about 4.2×10^9 kg of mass into energy every second. Although this seems like a very large value, this loss of mass is actually quite small compared to the total mass of the Sun, which is about 2×10^{30} kg.

The electromagnetic radiation emitted from stars can be analyzed by astronomers to provide valuable information about the composition and temperature of these distant suns. This work is described in Unit C.

Earlier, you learned that beta decay involves the conversion of a neutron into a proton and a beta particle: $^{1}_{0}n \rightarrow ^{0}_{-1}e + ^{1}_{1}p$. Use the "Masses of Subatomic Particles and Radiation" table from the Science Data Booklet to calculate the change in mass between the products and the reactants. Identify whether this reaction is exothermic or endothermic.

Solution

$$^{1}_{0}n \rightarrow ^{0}_{-1}e + ^{1}_{1}p$$

Determine the mass of the reactant and the mass of the products.

$$m_{reactant} = 1.008\ 66 \times 10^{-3}\ kg$$

$$m_{products} = m_{beta} + m_{proton}$$
$$= (1\ mol)(0.000\ 549 \times 10^{-3}\ kg/mol)$$
$$+ (1\ mol)(1.007\ 28 \times 10^{-3}\ kg/mol)$$
$$= 1.007\ 829 \times 10^{-3}\ kg$$

Determine the change in mass.

$$\Delta m = m_{reactant} - m_{products}$$
$$= 1.008\ 66 \times 10^{-3}\ kg - 1.007\ 829 \times 10^{-3}\ kg$$
$$= 0.000\ 831 \times 10^{-3}\ kg$$
$$= 8.31 \times 10^{-7}\ kg$$

The change in mass is 8.31×10^{-7} kg when 1 mol of neutrons is converted. Since the mass of the products is less than the mass of the reactant, this reaction is exothermic.

The fission of uranium-235 that occurs in a CANDU reactor involves the following reaction.

$$^{235}_{92}U + ^{1}_{0}n \rightarrow 3\ ^{1}_{0}n + ^{141}_{56}Ba + ^{92}_{36}Kr$$

Calculate the change in mass between the reactants and the products for this reaction and the corresponding energy change.

Solution

$$^{235}_{92}U + ^{1}_{0}n \rightarrow 3\ ^{1}_{0}n + ^{92}_{36}Kr + ^{141}_{56}Ba$$

Determine the mass of the reactants.

$$m_{reactants} = m_{U} + m_{n}$$
$$= (1\ mol)(235.043\ 92 \times 10^{-3}\ kg/mol)$$
$$+ (1\ mol)(1.008\ 66 \times 10^{-3}\ kg/mol)$$
$$= 236.052\ 58 \times 10^{-3}\ kg$$

Determine the mass of the products. Recall that three neutrons are produced during each fission reaction.

$$m_{products} = 3m_{n} + m_{Ba} + m_{Kr}$$
$$= (3\ mol)(1.008\ 66 \times 10^{-3}\ kg/mol)$$
$$+ (1\ mol)(91.926\ 11 \times 10^{-3}\ kg/mol)$$
$$+ (1\ mol)(140.914\ 41 \times 10^{-3}\ kg/mol)$$
$$= 235.866\ 50 \times 10^{-3}\ kg$$

Determine the change in mass.

$$\Delta m = m_{reactants} - m_{products}$$
$$= 236.052\ 58 \times 10^{-3}\ kg - 235.866\ 50 \times 10^{-3}\ kg$$
$$= 0.186\ 08 \times 10^{-3}\ kg$$
$$= 1.8608 \times 10^{-4}\ kg$$

The change in mass is 1.8608×10^{-4} kg.

Now, determine the energy change.

$$\Delta E = \Delta mc^2$$
$$= (1.8608 \times 10^{-4}\ kg)(3.00 \times 10^{8}\ m/s)^2$$
$$= 1.67 \times 10^{13}\ kg \cdot m^2/s^2$$
$$= 1.67 \times 10^{13}\ J$$

The energy change for 1 mol of uranium-235 is 1.67×10^{13} J.

Vast Amounts of Energy from a Tiny Fraction of Total Mass

When completing Example Problems 1.7 and 1.8, you calculated the change in mass of a nuclear process using more accurate masses for subatomic particles and nuclides. The mass difference for nuclear reactions is often very small—often a fraction of a gram. Recall that only the unaccounted mass (Δm) is converted into energy. Einstein's theory states that when mass "disappears," it must be converted into some form of energy. In the operation of a nuclear reactor, the energy released during the fission of uranium is converted into heat and, eventually, into electricity.

Practice

38. Calculate the change in mass and corresponding energy change per mole of uranium-235 in the nuclear reactions given. Use masses given in the Science Data Booklet and those provided in the following table.

Nuclide	Mass (10^{-3} kg/mol)
bromine-91, $^{91}_{35}$Br	90.916 27
lanthanum-142, $^{142}_{57}$La	141.899 71
strontium-94, $^{94}_{38}$Sr	93.915 29
xenon-140, $^{140}_{54}$Xe	139.918 43

   a. $^{1}_{0}n + ^{235}_{92}U \rightarrow 2\,^{1}_{0}n + ^{94}_{38}Sr + ^{140}_{54}Xe$

   b. $^{1}_{0}n + ^{235}_{92}U \rightarrow 3\,^{1}_{0}n + ^{91}_{35}Br + ^{142}_{57}La$

39. Calculate the change in mass that would correspond to a release of 2.0×10^{14} J of energy.

Concerns About Nuclear Waste

You learned in this lesson that the small change in mass that occurs to the uranium-235 within a CANDU reactor can be used to meet the energy demands of huge numbers of people. In 2003, the 17 operating nuclear power plants in Canada produced almost 62 000 spent fuel bundles. For comparison, the space these bundles would occupy is less than the size of two classrooms within a school. You also learned that the spent fuel contains the products of fission reactions, which may emit ionizing radiation for many years. How is spent nuclear fuel dealt with? What concerns do people have about nuclear waste?

In Canada, spent fuel from reactors still contains a small amount of unreacted uranium-235 and is first stored under water in the nuclear power plant. The water in the deep pools absorbs thermal energy released by the fission of the remaining isotope and acts as a shield, preventing the release of radiation. After a few years in the pools, spent fuel bundles are moved into concrete canisters and stored above ground. Currently, there is no long-term storage facility for spent nuclear fuel in Canada. Such a facility, when developed, would have to ensure that the containers of waste remain intact and isolated. Current plans suggest that a long-term storage facility could be developed deep within the granite rock formation of the Canadian Shield. A major concern about the development of a long-term storage facility for nuclear waste is the possibility of accidentally releasing radioactive substances during transport.

? DID YOU KNOW?

Some military submarines operate using uranium fission reactions as a power source. Because of the large quantity of energy contained within nuclear fuels, like uranium, a nuclear submarine can operate for ten years without refuelling. Some icebreaker ships and aircraft carriers are also nuclear powered. The main disadvantage of nuclear-powered vessels is the risk of reactor damage or meltdown. Unless contained, the reactor damage or meltdown could expose the crew and the environment to ionizing radiation and radioactive isotopes. Once decommissioned, nuclear vessels must also be properly dismantled. This involves the removal and long-term storage of radioactive components. The estimated cost of a submarine is $30 million.

Nuclear Fusion

Thus far, you have studied alpha, beta, and gamma decay and nuclear fission. The final type of nuclear reaction to consider is **nuclear fusion**. In one sense, nuclear fusion is the opposite of nuclear fission: *fusion* means "to bring together," whereas *fission* means "to break apart."

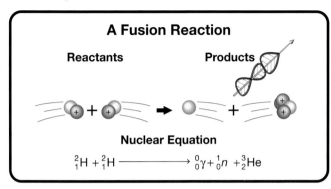

A Fusion Reaction

Reactants   **Products**

Nuclear Equation

$$_1^2H + _1^2H \longrightarrow _0^0\gamma + _0^1n + _2^3He$$

> **nuclear fusion:** a process in which two smaller nuclei join to form a larger nucleus, with the simultaneous release of energy

> **deuterium:** a heavy isotope of hydrogen with one proton and one neutron in the nucleus

Figure D1.40: Nuclear fusion is the source of the Sun's energy.

In a fusion reaction, a heavy isotope of hydrogen called **deuterium**, nuclides collide at high speed to form a product, helium-3, that has a larger nucleus than either of the reactants. Recall from Unit C that hydrogen fusion reactions occur deep within the Sun, where extremely high temperatures and pressures exist. Also recall that the fusion of hydrogen within the Sun emits radiation that is the primary energy source for photosynthesis—the process that provides food either directly or indirectly for all organisms on Earth.

? DID YOU KNOW?

All elements are born in stars. Fusion reactions within stars produce larger elements from hydrogen. The largest atom made by fusion within the Sun is iron, which has 26 protons. Larger elements—like gold, platinum, and uranium—are formed in supernovas (exploding stars). Supernovas leave behind gas and dust that serve as raw materials for making new planets.

Practice

40. For each fusion reaction given, complete the equation and identify the unknown product, $_Z^AX$.

   a. $_1^2H + _1^3H \rightarrow _0^1n + _Z^AX$ b. $_7^{14}N + _1^1H \rightarrow _0^0\gamma + _Z^AX$

41. Calculate the energy change for each reaction in question 40. Determine whether the fusion reaction results in a release of energy. Support your answer.

Solar Fusion Reactions

hydrogen to deuterium: $_1^1H + _1^1H \rightarrow _{+1}^0e + _1^2H$

Note: The symbol, $_{+1}^0e$, represents a positron—an elementary particle with the same mass as an electron, but with a positive charge.

deuterium to helium-3: $_1^2H + _1^1H \rightarrow _0^0\gamma + _2^3He$

helium-3 to helium-4: $_2^3He + _2^3He \rightarrow 2\,_1^1H + _2^4He$

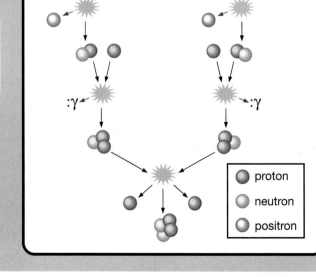

- proton
- neutron
- positron

Figure D1.41

The series of fusion reactions shown in Figure D1.41 identifies the conversion of some of hydrogen—which makes up over 70% of the Sun's mass—into helium. Fusion reactions like those occurring within the Sun's core are considered to be possible energy-releasing reactions for reactors in power plants on Earth.

From the Science 30 Textbook CD, view the "Nuclear Fusion" applet to see a simulation of the conditions that must be created within a fusion reactor. In the "Is Fusion the Energy Source of the Future" activity, you will investigate the state of fusion research and the potential for energy from fusion to meet world energy demands.

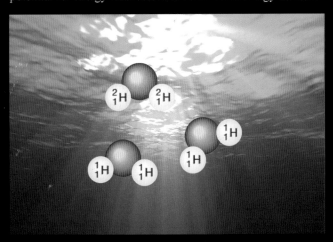

It might surprise you to know that the deuterium necessary for fusion reactions is plentiful in seawater. Deuterium and other isotopes to be considered for use in fusion reactions are considered inexhaustible, making fusion a **renewable energy** source. Energy production that relies on the combustion of fossil fuels or nuclear fission is considered to be **non-renewable energy**. In the next chapter you will learn more about technologies to develop renewable energy sources.

> **renewable energy:** energy derived from continuously available sources that can be replenished in a short period of time

> **non-renewable energy:** energy derived from sources that will become depleted because they are not able to be replenished in a short period of time

Utilizing Technology

Is Fusion the Energy Source of the Future?

Science Skills

✓ Performing and Recording
✓ Analyzing and Interpreting

Purpose

You will investigate the current state of fusion research and the development of electricity generation from fusion reactions.

Procedure

Use the Internet, library, or other sources to research this issue. You may work on your own or within in a small group. Use the focus questions as a guide to develop an information package, brochure, model, or brief presentation to identify the status of the development of systems that use fusion power.

Focus Questions

1. What is nuclear fusion? Identify the reactants used in fusion reactions currently being studied.

2. Describe the conditions necessary for fusion to occur. Describe the challenges in attempting to create a fusion reactor that can sustain these conditions.

3. Describe the status of current efforts to produce a reactor that can sustain a fusion reaction.

4. Identify advantages and disadvantages of fusion power as an energy source.

1.4 Summary

Radiation refers to the energy released during nuclear reactions. Ionizing radiation released by nuclear reactions takes three main forms: alpha, beta, and gamma. The energy provided by nuclear fission reactions is currently used to generate electricity in many countries, helping to meet the world's energy needs. Fission and other nuclear reactions result in some mass being converted into energy. The amount of energy associated with a reaction can be calculated using the equation $\Delta E = \Delta mc^2$. Nuclear fusion may, some day, join fission as a process for meeting the world's energy needs.

1.4 Questions

Knowledge

1. For the nucleus $^{92}_{36}\text{Kr}$, identify the

    a. atomic number   b. charge   c. mass number   d. number of nucleons

2. Define the following terms.

    a. radioactive decay   b. nuclear fission   c. nuclear fusion

3. List the similarities and differences between a coal-fired power plant and a nuclear power plant.

4. Describe how the fission chain reaction is controlled in a CANDU nuclear reactor.

5. Identify and explain one risk and one benefit associated with the use of nuclear fission reactions for generating electricity.

Applying Concepts

6. Balance each reaction and identify the unknown product, $^A_Z X$. For each reaction, state the type of nuclear change shown.

    a. $^{14}_{6}\text{C} \rightarrow \,^{0}_{-1}e + \,^A_Z X$ b. $^{241}_{95}\text{Am} \rightarrow \,^A_Z X + \,^{237}_{93}\text{Np}$ c. $^{3}_{1}\text{H} + \,^{2}_{1}\text{H} \rightarrow \,^{1}_{0}n + \,^A_Z X$ d. $^A_Z X + \,^{1}_{0}n \rightarrow 3\,^{1}_{0}n + \,^{107}_{44}\text{Ru} + \,^{130}_{50}\text{Sn}$

    e. $^{90}_{38}\text{Sr} \rightarrow \,^A_Z X + \,^{90}_{39}\text{Y}$ f. $^{226}_{88}\text{Ra} \rightarrow \,^A_Z X + \,^{222}_{86}\text{Rn}$ g. $^{129}_{53}\text{I} \rightarrow \,^{0}_{0}\gamma + \,^A_Z X + \,^{129}_{54}\text{Xe}$

7. Is nuclear energy from the fission of uranium a renewable or non-renewable energy source? Provide a reason for your answer.

8. A possible reaction for fusion power involves a fusion between helium-3 and deuterium nuclei. The products of the reaction are helium-4 and a proton.

    a. Present the process described as a balanced nuclear equation.

    b. Calculate the change in mass and the corresponding energy change for the fusion between helium-3 and deuterium nuclei.

9. The following table shows the amount of energy released by physical, chemical, and nuclear changes. Identify the type of change for each, and determine how many times greater the energy release is compared to condensing water vapour.

Change	Energy Released (kJ/mol)	Type of Change (physical, chemical, or nuclear)	How Many Times Greater Than Condensing Water Vapour
condensing water vapour $H_2O(g) \rightarrow H_2O(l) + \text{energy}$	40.7		
combusting methane (a component of natural gas) $CH_4(g) + 2\,O_2(g) \rightarrow CO_2(g) + 2\,H_2O(g) + \text{energy}$	802		
fission of uranium-235 $^{1}_{0}n + \,^{235}_{92}\text{U} \rightarrow 3\,^{1}_{0}n + \,^{92}_{36}\text{Kr} + \,^{141}_{56}\text{Ba}$	1.67×10^{10}		
fusion of deuterium and tritium $^{2}_{1}\text{H} + \,^{3}_{1}\text{H} \rightarrow \,^{1}_{0}n + \,^{4}_{2}\text{He}$	1.82×10^9		

Since the Industrial Revolution, new technologies, changes in lifestyle, and human population growth have caused an exponential increase in energy use. The world's demand for energy is largely met by the combustion of fossil fuels, like coal and oil. As part of the effort to supplement fossil fuel energy, nuclear technologies have also been used. In the next chapter you will examine renewable resources, how they have helped meet world energy demands, and how likely they will take on an increasing role in the future.

Summarize Your Learning

In this chapter you learned a number of new terms, concepts, and techniques for problem solving. You will have a much easier time recalling and applying the information you have learned if you take some time to organize it into some sort of pattern. Now that you have come to the end of the chapter, this is an appropriate time to focus on the patterns within the things you have learned.

Since the patterns have to be meaningful to you, there are some options about how you can create this summary. Each of the following options is described in "Summarize Your Learning Activities" of the Reference Section. Choose one of these options to create a summary of the key concepts and important terms in Chapter 1.

Option 1: Draw a concept map or a web diagram.	Option 2: Create a point-form summary.	Option 3: Write a story using key terms and concepts.	Option 4: Create a colourful poster.	Option 5: Build a model.	Option 6: Write a script for a skit (a mock news report).

Chapter 1 Review Questions

Knowledge

1. Define *energy*. Then list and define the types of energy studied in Chapter 1.

2. Describe the general trend in world energy use between 1850 and 2000. Provide a reason for the trend.

3. Compare total energy use and per capita energy use between developing countries and developed countries.

4. Provide reasons why Canada's per capita energy use is higher than that of the United States.

5. Define *energy efficiency*. Identify examples that promote improved energy efficiency. Explain how improvements to energy efficiency would affect total energy use in Canada.

6. Describe the relationship between a country's gross domestic product (GDP) and its total energy use.

7. How does per capita energy use in Alberta compare to other Canadian provinces? Account for any differences.

8. Predict the effect that a rapid industrialization of developing countries will have on the world's total energy use during the next few decades.

9. List the non-renewable energy sources described in Chapter 1.

10. State the main fuel used by First Nations communities before the arrival of Europeans.

11. For each energy source given, state how it is formed and how it is used.

    a. coal   **b.** petroleum   **c.** natural gas

12. Which fossil fuel, listed in question 11, is currently the world's top energy source?

13. Explain why extracting petroleum from oil sand is much more energy intensive than conventional drilling.

14. List some applications of hydrocarbons other than as energy sources.

15. Explain why energy conversions can never be 100% efficient.

16. Describe the energy transformations that occur in a coal-fired power plant during the production of electricity.

17. Define each term given, and provide a technological application.

    a. radioactive decay   **b.** nuclear fission   **c.** nuclear fusion

18. Compare nuclear fission with nuclear fusion.

19. List the series of energy transformations that occur within a generating station that uses a CANDU nuclear reactor.

20. Identify technical difficulties associated with developing fusion power.

Applying Concepts

21. List the factors you would need to consider in order to estimate the energy required to manufacture a paper coffee cup and lid.

22. Refer to Figure D1.42. Describe the trends for predicted changes to population and electricity demand in China. Provide an explanation for the prediction for electricity demand in light of the predicted population change.

23. Describe the sequence of energy conversions for energy radiated by the Sun that becomes energy used to heat up leftover chili in your microwave oven.

24. Use the Internet to research the following questions.

    a. Describe how hybrid automobiles work differently than conventional gas-powered automobiles.

    b. Compare the fuel economy of hybrid automobiles with conventional gas-powered automobiles.

    c. Provide a reason why individuals would be motivated to purchase hybrid cars.

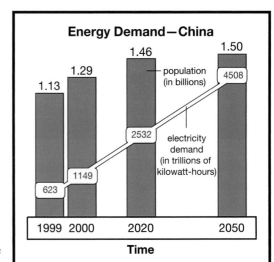

Figure D1.42

25. Use standard heats of formation and the balanced combustion equations to calculate the energy change per mole for the combustion of the fuel listed.

    a. ethane, $C_2H_6(g)$ (a component of natural gas)

    $C_2H_6(g) + 3.5\ O_2(g) \rightarrow 2\ CO_2(g) + 3\ H_2O(g)$

    b. propane, $C_3H_8(g)$ (a common barbecue fuel)

    $C_3H_8(g) + 5\ O_2(g) \rightarrow 3\ CO_2(g) + 4\ H_2O(g)$

26. Draw an energy diagram for the combustion of propane that demonstrates the products have a lower chemical potential energy than the reactants and shows the energy released during the reaction.

27. Use your answer from question 25.b. to calculate the efficiency of a barbecue that produces 795 kJ of useful output energy for cooking when it burns 1 mol of propane.

28. Calculate the chemical potential energy necessary for a power plant to generate 1.6×10^9 J if it is 44% efficient.

29. Radium was discovered in the early 1900s and was at one time used in many consumer products because of its luminescence. The use of radium in consumer products stopped when it became known that it produces ionizing radiation. Write a balanced nuclear equation for the alpha decay of radium-226.

30. The deuterium-deuterium fuel cycle proposed for nuclear fusion is as follows:

    $^2_1H + {}^2_1H \rightarrow {}^1_0n + {}^3_2He$

    Calculate the energy change of this reaction per mole of helium-3.

Chapter 2 Dreams of a Sustainable Future

Can you spot the sources of renewable energy in this photograph? You most likely identified the wind turbines that punctuate the skyline; but through careful observation, you may have also identified that the entire upper surface of the car is covered with photovoltaic cells. This futuristic car is an experimental race vehicle that runs entirely on solar energy. The lessons learned from experimental vehicles like this may, some day, help engineers to come up with alternatives to the conventional automobiles that rely on fossil fuels. A much less obvious form of renewable energy in this photo is the crop of corn in the background. Corn can be used to make ethanol—a renewable fuel. Ethanol can be used to supplement or possibly even replace petroleum.

With so many hungry people in the world, is it wise to turn a potential food into fuel? Are there other questions surrounding the widespread use of wind turbines, photovoltaic cells, biomass, or other renewable energy technologies? What kinds of questions need to be asked before you can decide which technologies are suitable choices for meeting current and future energy demands?

In this chapter you will have an opportunity to investigate many sources of renewable energy that are alternatives to the use of non-renewable fuels. This knowledge will offer you more than just a way to look to the future; it will also provide you with a valuable opportunity to summarize many key concepts from the entire course.

Try This Activity

Process Maps

Background Information

Earth is a closed system. This means that matter must be continuously cycled. The water cycle and the carbon cycle, which you studied in previous courses, are examples of biogeochemical cycles for matter. Energy, in most cases from the Sun, is important to the cycling of matter.

Science Skills

✓ Performing and Recording
✓ Analyzing and Interpreting

Purpose

In this activity you will prepare process maps depicting the energy and matter changes for photosynthesis, combustion of fossil fuels, and nuclear fission.

Procedure

Obtain three copies of the handout "Process Map" from the Science 30 Textbook CD.

step 1: On the first copy of the handout, write "Photosynthesis" in the box in the centre.

step 2: In the upper-left quadrant of the diagram (Energy Input), identify the energy inputs for photosynthesis. You may use a list or arrows to indicate flow or changes that occur.

step 3: Repeat step 2 for the other quadrants: Energy Output, Matter Input, and Matter Output.

step 4: Repeat these steps for the combustion of fossil fuels and for nuclear fission.

Analysis

1. On your process maps, identify matter outputs or energy outputs that may harm the biosphere.

2. Identify any process that is able to use the energy output as an energy input. (Can energy be recycled?)

3. Can the matter output from any of the processes be transformed back into a matter input? (Can matter be recycled?) If so, compare the rates for the processes. (Can the matter be replenished as quickly as it is being used?)

4. Recall the definition for renewable energy. Identify the processes that are renewable. Identify which processes could be used to meet energy needs in the short term and over the long term. Give reasons for your answers.

Figure D2.1: A mountain meadow in Banff National Park

What kind of impact could humans have on an established ecosystem like the one shown in Figure D2.1? A mountain meadow does not require people to input raw materials or to remove wastes because matter is cycled in biogeochemical cycles. Artificial lights are not required because green plants are able to transform the energy in the Sun's photons into chemical potential energy through photosynthesis. Photosynthesis provides a way for energy to be passed on to other organisms through the food chain. Since an ecosystem is capable of maintaining itself indefinitely, it is said to be **sustainable**. Barring disruption, as long as the Sun shines and matter continues to be cycled, an ecosystem like this one continues to exist.

sustainable: capable of being maintained at length without interruption, weakening, or loss of essential characteristics (such as matter and energy)

An established ecosystem stands in stark contrast to most of the current systems set up to maintain the towns and cities most people live in. In a city, matter is not cycled. This is evident in the armies of transport trucks that bring goods into the city and in the legions of garbage trucks depositing waste daily at the local landfill.

As far as energy is concerned, fossil fuels may not be dependable energy sources for future generations if society continues to consume them at the current rate. Because of the current usage patterns for materials and energy, the vast majority of human settlements in industrialized countries are described as being **non-sustainable**. These systems have the potential to break down because the supply of raw materials and the non-renewable sources of energy will eventually become exhausted.

Does it make sense to be so dependent upon resources that will one day run out? Is it appropriate for the current human population to deplete the supply of limited resources, leaving a long list of environmental problems for future generations? Should continued development of non-sustainable human systems be questioned? What are the long-term consequences of abusing Earth's life-support system?

You may hear people asking questions like these when discussing the growth of cities or the expansion of industry within your local area. These questions indicate a growing concern among people and a willingness to consider new approaches to development. Approaches that consider meeting human needs today while balancing the long-term implications, including possible harm to the environment, demonstrate **sustainable development**. Many people regard sustainable development as one of the most important ideas of our time because it is like a crossroad—the place where pressing ecological, societal, and economic issues all meet.

> **non-sustainable:** incapable of being maintained at length due to interruption, weakening, or loss of essential characteristics (such as matter and energy)

> **sustainable development:** the development of industrial and natural resources that meets the needs of the present generation without compromising the ability of future generations to meet their own needs

Practice

1. Two next-door neighbours utilize very different strategies when it comes to landscaping their front yards. One neighbour plants a front lawn of lush green grass that requires regular watering and fertilizer application. The other neighbour uses stone pathways that wind through a variety of drought-resistant wildflowers and shrubs that are native to the area.

   a. Explain which neighbour has the more sustainable front yard.

   b. Describe the cumulative effects of many people utilizing non-sustainable landscaping practices on both the local environment and the biosphere.

2. To some people, Earth is considered to be a fragile spaceship that is the home for humans and many other life forms. Use the notion of "spaceship Earth" to explain the importance of sustainable development.

Demonstrating Sustainable Development

One example of how a community can move in the direction of sustainable development can be found in the town of Okotoks, Alberta. Like many communities surrounding Calgary, Okotoks has experienced rapid population growth. What makes this community different is that its administrators have made a conscious decision to control the growth of the town—keeping it in step with the ability of the environment to support the population. In addition, the creative use of renewable-energy technologies within the community has attracted national and international attention. You will learn more about the sustainable development occurring in Okotoks in the next activity.

Utilizing Technology

Okotoks—Moving Toward Sustainable Development

Purpose

You will watch a video to identify and analyze examples of sustainable development that have been utilized by the town of Okotoks, Alberta.

Science Skills

✓ Performing and Recording
✓ Analyzing and Interpreting

Procedure

Before you begin, read the Analysis questions and determine strategies you will use to identify parts of the video where useful information is located. View the video "Road Stories: Green Cities" on the Science 30 Textbook CD.

Analysis

1. Identify the natural resource that was chosen when the town of Okotoks established limits on its maximum size.

2. Describe some of the strategies used to ensure the long-term sustainability of the resource identified in your answer to question 1.

3. Identify the renewable-energy technologies used to meet the energy needs of municipal buildings in Okotoks.

4. Describe how the design of municipal buildings has allowed for renewable-energy technologies to be used.

5. Drake Landing Solar Community in Okotoks has taken a unique approach to utilizing the Sun's energy. Obtain the "Drake Landing Solar Community" handout from the Science 30 Textbook CD. Match the labels provided on the handout with locations on the diagram of the energy capture and distribution system used at Drake Landing.

6. Describe other features of the homes in Drake Landing Solar Community that enable them to reduce annual greenhouse emissions by 83%.

7. Sustainable development involves consideration of other aspects of human activity in addition to energy. Communities like Drake Landing Solar Community can be rated in terms of how close they come to perfectly illustrating sustainable development. A score of 10 out of 10 represents the ideal sustainable-development community, and a score of 0 represents the complete opposite.

   a. List the activities designed to reduce environmental impact in which the citizens of Okotoks participate.

   b. Determine a score out of 10 for the Drake Landing Solar Community in terms of its ability to incorporate sustainable development. Justify your score.

   c. Determine a score out of 10 for the community where you live in terms of its ability to incorporate sustainable development. Justify your score.

Evaluating Energy Technologies for Sustainability

As you saw in the preceding activity, if a community like Okotoks pursues a community plan to promote sustainable development, access to sustainable sources of energy must be part of the strategy. How are decisions made when choosing one energy source—or a technology that uses that energy source—over another? What criteria could be used to compare different technologies and their sustainability?

The overall sustainability of an energy source is determined by examining its

- ecological sustainability
- societal sustainability
- economic sustainability

Ecological Sustainability

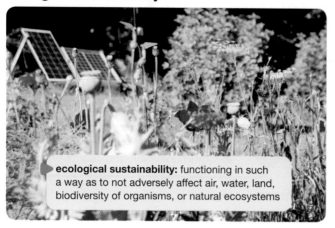

ecological sustainability: functioning in such a way as to not adversely affect air, water, land, biodiversity of organisms, or natural ecosystems

An energy technology demonstrates **ecological sustainability** if its use enables the protection of the three key components of the biosphere: land, water, and air. In addition, the use of the technology should maintain biodiversity, promote the survival of species at risk, and protect fragile ecosystems. It follows that environmental sustainability involves protecting organisms from the harmful effects of pollution and ionizing radiation. The following list of statements describes an energy source that supports ecological sustainability.

An energy technology that demonstrates ecological sustainability

- is based on a renewable energy source
- maintains the quantity of surface water
- maintains the quality of surface water
- does not contribute to acid deposition
- does not contribute to the presence of persistent organic pollutants in water, soil, or air
- does not contribute to the presence of heavy metals in water, soil, or air
- recycles liquid and/or solid waste products
- does not contribute to deforestation or habitat destruction
- does not contribute to greenhouse gas emissions
- does not contribute to emissions of ozone-depleting materials
- does not contribute to emissions of particulate matter
- does not contribute to photochemical smog
- does not threaten the survival of species at risk
- does not contribute to the destruction of fragile ecosystems
- does not contribute to the release of ionizing radiation
- does not contribute to the mass of radioactive waste produced

Societal Sustainability

In your studies throughout this course, you examined many technologies that convert energy from one form into other forms. Coal-fired power plants and nuclear power plants are two examples of energy technologies that generate electricity that, in turn, supports communities. Human communities can maintain themselves only if their populations have their needs met in terms of health and education. Sustainable societies ensure that people can support themselves with a reasonable standard of living so that families have access to affordable housing. A sustainable society is one that shows respect for the diversity of the cultural values within the community. The following statements describe aspects of **societal sustainability** in reference to how energy is provided.

societal sustainability: the ability of a group to support adequate living standards for its members; includes housing, health care, and respect and maintenance of cultural values

An energy technology that demonstrates societal sustainability

- does not decrease life expectancy through exposure to pollution
- stimulates a healthy economy, enabling adequate health care
- requires a highly trained workforce
- requires the workforce to adapt to change through continuous training
- reduces excessive land use (e.g., urban sprawl)
- encourages per capita energy consumption to be reduced
- stimulates a healthy economy, enabling affordable housing
- requires co-operation of diverse cultural groups in decision making

Economic Sustainability

Just as individuals need to provide for themselves economically, communities of people must be able to maintain economic activities over time. Indicators of **economic sustainability** include adequate employment opportunities for the population and opportunities for economic growth, which include goods and services that can add to the GDP. The following list of statements describes energy sources that support economic sustainability.

> ▶ **economic sustainability:** the ability to provide employment opportunities and have access to goods and services in a manner that does not decrease the availability of natural resources

An energy technology that demonstrates economic sustainability

- supports full-time employment for the population
- enables a higher proportion of the workforce to be paid reasonable wages
- has a relatively low cost per megajoule (MJ)
- enables development of other industry or opportunity
- reduces the import of energy, contributing positively to the GDP
- enables the export of energy, contributing positively to the GDP
- can be used in a variety of locations that are well-suited to industry
- allows for continuous, around-the-clock production
- does not decrease the availability of natural resources

In the next activity you will have an opportunity to evaluate an energy resource for ecological, societal, and economic sustainability.

Try This Activity

Determining the Sustainability of Coal-Fired Power Plants

Science Skills

✓ Analyzing and Interpreting
✓ Communication and Teamwork

Purpose

You will use a detailed checklist to determine the sustainability of generating electricity using coal as a source of energy. You will then compare your results with other students.

Background Information

From your previous work in Units B and C, you are already quite familiar with coal as an energy source. In this activity you will rely on your knowledge of key concepts covered in this course to complete a checklist outlining criteria that are essential for ecological, societal, and economic sustainability. Completing the checklist will enable you to determine the sustainability of this technology.

Procedure

Obtain the document "Determining Sustainability of Technologies" from the Science 30 Textbook CD. Follow the instructions in the document to determine the overall sustainability of coal-fired power generation. **Note:** Keep your completed checklist because you will be asked to refer to it throughout this chapter.

Analysis

1. Justify the weightings you chose for each type of sustainability. Given the results of other students, would you revise your weightings if you were to repeat this activity?

2. Identify the sources responsible for the variability in the overall score for sustainability in this activity. Include an explanation as to why there is no "right answer" in terms of the overall score for sustainability for a given energy resource.

Making Sense of Sustainability Scores

You just determined the sustainability of coal-fired electricity generation. The point of the activity was not to arrive at a pre-determined "right answer," but rather to stimulate discussions with others and to validate the use of the checklist. These skills will be beneficial when determining the sustainability of other energy technologies. Even though individual students may not completely agree with the weightings for the categories of ecological, societal, and economic sustainability, the common sets of criteria shown in the checklist allow you and your classmates to compare various energy sources. Is it possible for other technologies to score higher than coal-fired power plants? Which technologies show the greatest potential for providing human communities with a sustainable future? The rest of this chapter will largely be focused on helping you answer these questions.

Practice

In Chapter 1 you discovered that CANDU reactors use nuclear fission to generate electrical energy.

Before completing questions 3 and 4, review the energy conversions and processes involved in the operation of a CANDU reactor.

3. Obtain the document "Determining Sustainability of Technologies" from the Science 30 Textbook CD. Follow the instructions in the document to determine the overall sustainability of nuclear fission as a source of electricity. **Note:** Keep your completed checklist for nuclear fission because you will be asked to refer to it throughout this chapter.

4. Compare your assessment of the sustainability of nuclear fission as a source of electricity with your evaluation for coal-fired electricity generation from the "Determining the Sustainability of Coal-Fired Power Plants" activity.

   a. Identify which technology is more sustainable. Justify your selection.

   b. Compare your answer to question 4.a. with other students. Did other students agree with your answer and your justification? Identify any major differences between conclusions and justifications.

Earth's Heat—Geothermal Energy

You may recall from previous science courses that geothermal energy is responsible for the movement of Earth's tectonic plates, in addition to other spectacular displays, like volcanic eruptions and geysers. The plumes of hot rock and lava sent into the air from active volcanoes or the periodic blasts of high-temperature water and steam from geysers originate from nuclear decay reactions that occur thousands of kilometres below Earth's surface.

Figure D2.2: Volcanoes and geysers are examples of the large quantity of energy available from geothermal sources.

Evidence suggests that the radioactive decay of unstable isotopes within Earth's core helps maintain the temperature of Earth's inner-most layer at about 5000°C. Heat from the nuclear reactions in the core drives convection currents within the molten rock of the mantle—Earth's middle layer. These convection currents cause the crustal plates to move. **Geothermal energy** tends to collect at the boundaries between these plates where Earth's crust is thin or fractured. The condition of the crust at these boundaries often provides pathways for geothermal energy to reach the surface.

> **geothermal energy:** heat that originates from radioactive decay in Earth's core

Geothermal Energy—Heat from Within Earth

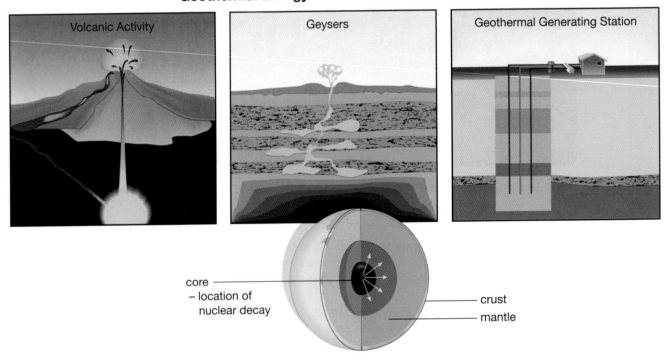

DID YOU KNOW?

The decay of the isotopes potassium-40, thorium-232, uranium-235, and uranium-238 produce geothermal energy.

For individuals, industries, and governments around the world looking for ways to diversify energy and fuel production, geothermal energy may be an alternative. Despite the fact that the nuclear isotopes responsible for the production of heat are limited, current estimates predict they will not be depleted for millions of years.

Figure D2.3: Bathers in Iceland relax in natural hot water, which is the result of geothermal energy from deep within Earth reaching the surface. In the background is a large power plant that uses the geothermal energy to generate electricity.

Figure D2.4: Iceland's largest city, Reykjavik, uses sustainable geothermal energy to heat its buildings and generate its electricity.

Geothermal energy is used either for heating or generating electricity in over 30 countries around the world. In the Philippines, geothermal energy provides 27% of the country's electricity. In Iceland's capital city, Reykjavik, geothermal energy heats over 80% of the buildings and is used to generate nearly all of the electricity. In the United States, geothermal energy provides approximately $1 billion worth of electricity in California, Hawaii, Nevada, and Utah each year. In 2000, the United States' government set a goal to increase geothermal energy use from 0.45% to at least 10% of the electricity production in the western United States by 2020.

? **DID YOU KNOW?**

Geothermal Electricity in Canada

Canada does not currently use geothermal energy to generate electricity. Areas with the greatest potential are found in British Colombia's coastal mountains. To date, the Meager Mountain area appears to hold the greatest potential for geothermal electricity. A 100-MW facility may eventually be built in this area.

Using Geothermal Energy

At first blush, geothermal energy seems to have some significant advantages as an energy source. Since Earth's energy can be used to produce pressurized steam, the need for fuels to heat water is eliminated. If it is possible to construct a generating station close to the fissure and to the source of hot water, electricity generation can be relatively inexpensive to set up and can be very efficient.

However, since geothermal generating stations often utilize steam from deep within Earth's crust, emissions of hydrogen sulfide, $H_2S(g)$, and carbon dioxide, $CO_2(g)$, often occur. Even though these emissions come from a natural source, they represent only a fraction of those from comparably sized fossil fuel-fired installations. As you determined in Unit B, $H_2S(g)$ and $CO_2(g)$ can react to form acids, causing corrosion of metals used in a geothermal facility and acid deposition within the surrounding area.

Perhaps the greatest drawback of geothermal energy is that it is a localized resource. It is only cost-effective in areas where geological hot spots already exist. Since many populated areas in the world are not located along the boundaries of crustal plates, geothermal energy is not a practical alternative.

The exception to this trend occurs in California. As you may recall, a large portion of California's population lives near the San Andreas Fault, close to the border between the North American Plate and Pacific Plate—which contains many geothermal hot spots. The transformation of geothermal energy in California made the United States the world's largest producer of electricity from geothermal sources in 2003. Other countries that are major users of this energy source include Iceland, the Philippines, Mexico, Indonesia, Italy, Japan, and New Zealand. In spite of what seems to be an ample supply of heat, geothermal hot spots can decrease in temperature if they are not properly managed and, thus, reduce the energy available for transformation.

Practice

5. Identify a way geothermal energy is used other than to generate electricity.

6. Identify which part of Canada is believed to have the greatest potential to exploit geothermal energy on a large scale. Concisely explain why.

7. Identify two advantages and two disadvantages of geothermal energy.

8. Obtain the document "Determining Sustainability of Technologies" from the Science 30 Textbook CD. Follow the instructions in the document to determine the overall sustainability of geothermal energy as a source for producing electricity. **Note:** Keep your completed checklist for geothermal energy because you will be asked to refer to it throughout this chapter.

Tidal Energy

Figure D2.5: It's low tide at Alma Harbor, New Brunswick, on the Bay of Fundy. The highest tides in the world occur in the Bay of Fundy, located between New Brunswick and Nova Scotia.

Although it may appear that some form of natural disaster has left these fishing boats stranded, their position is due to the cycle of the **tide** in the Bay of Fundy. The extreme tides in this area are due to the way water moves—because of the unique shape of the bay and the natural cycle of the tides. The result is an effect similar to pushing a child on a swing, amplifying the energy of the original movement. Oceanographers have determined that the energy within a wave entering the Bay of Fundy returns to the mouth of the bay in just under 13 hours.

▶ **tide:** the deformation of land and water due to the gravitational fields of the Moon and Sun acting on every part of Earth

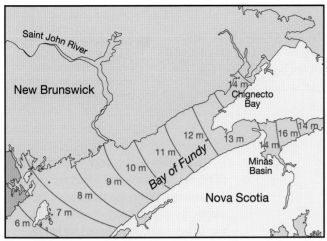

Figure D2.6: This map of the Bay of Fundy shows the difference between high tide and low tide for various locations.

Since the time between one high tide and the next is 12 hours 25 minutes, the rhythm of Earth's tides is precisely tuned to this particular bay. The natural frequency of the movement of water in the bay becomes amplified by the energy in the pulse of the tides. Why is the time between adjacent high tides exactly 12 hours 25 minutes?

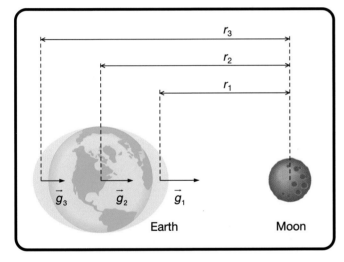

Tides are the result of the gravitational fields of both the Sun and Moon acting on every part of Earth. Recall from Unit C that the gravitational field of a source weakens as the distance from the source increases. Since the Moon is closest to Earth, it accounts for most tidal effects. The explanation provided in this course will focus only on the effects of the Moon on tidal patterns.

As mentioned in Unit C, a field is defined by the behaviour of a test object within it. In a tidal system, the Moon is the source of the gravitational field and the test object is Earth's water. Since approximately 70% of Earth's surface is water, two portions of Earth are considered when analyzing tides: the water on the side of Earth closest to the Moon and the water on the side of Earth farthest from the Moon. Also, the mass of Earth must be considered when analyzing this system.

The water on Earth's surface closest to the Moon is subjected to the strongest gravitational field, $\vec{g}_1$. The centre of Earth is farther from the Moon, so the Moon's gravitational field, $\vec{g}_2$, is weaker compared to the force $\vec{g}_1$. The slight difference between these two forces distorts Earth's shape and causes the water to form a tidal bulge on the side closest to the Moon.

The difference between the gravitational field acting on the far side of Earth, $\vec{g}_3$, and the field acting on the centre of Earth, $\vec{g}_2$, accounts for the bulge on the side of Earth farthest from the moon. Since the centre of Earth experiences a gravitational attraction to the Moon larger on the far side, the difference between these two forces distorts Earth's shape. In a sense, the centre of Earth is "pulled away" from the water on the far side leaving a tidal bulge.

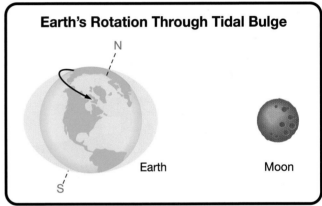

As Earth spins on its axis, each part of the planet along a sea coast moves through two areas of high tide and two areas of low tide every 24 hours 50 minutes. The extra 50 minutes is needed to make up for the Moon's motion. The Moon takes an extra 50 minutes each day to return to its highest point in the night sky (as observed from a location on Earth).

Figure D2.7: In Nova Scotia, tidal bore rafting has become a popular recreational experience. The rapids are created when incoming tidal water collides with outgoing river water.

Using Tides to Generate Electricity

At all locations around the Bay of Fundy, massive amounts of water move in and then retreat. As the water reaches its higher level in the daily tidal cycle, it possesses increased gravitational potential energy, in contrast to its kinetic energy when it flows between high and low tide. The potential and kinetic energy associated with the rise and fall of water during ocean tides is known as **tidal energy**.

> **tidal energy:** the gravitational potential energy and the kinetic energy of ocean water generated by tidal effects

Cross Section of Tidal Station

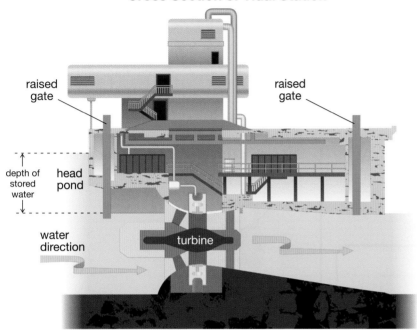

To harness tidal energy, a special type of barrier—often called a barrage—is constructed. When the tide comes in, electricity is generated as water flows through the turbines housed within the barrage. Water that has passed through the barrage is held in the estuary behind the barrage by gates. The gates act like valves in veins, preventing a backflow of water until it can be used to generate electricity. To generate electricity after high tide, the water held in the estuary is released through channels, flowing past the turbines connected to the generators. The Annapolis Tidal Station (seen in the photo below), located in the Bay of Fundy, generates 20 MW of electricity daily.

Assessing Tidal Energy

Like geothermal energy, tidal energy is a renewable resource. The energy of the water flowing through the turbine within the barrage is due to the potential and kinetic energy of the Earth-Moon system. Appropriate conditions for the conversion of tidal energy—a 5-m difference between low tide and high tide—only occur in a few localized areas. Even if these conditions can be met, the fact that high tides are spaced over 12 h apart means that energy from tides is only available at certain times; it is not available on a constant basis.

From an ecological point of view, tidal energy may appear to be a strong option because it does not involve the combustion of a fuel or produce harmful emissions. However, the presence of the barrage across the estuary could affect the ecology of the estuary—for example, it could interfere with the migration routes of fish.

Practice

9. Explain why the Bay of Fundy is one of the world's most promising tidal energy sites.

10. Obtain the document "Determining Sustainability of Technologies" from the Science 30 Textbook CD. Follow the instructions in the document to determine the overall sustainability of tidal energy as a source for producing electricity. **Note:** Keep your completed checklist for tidal energy because you will be asked to refer to it throughout this chapter.

2.1 Summary

Many people think that it is imperative for human communities to move in the direction of sustainable development. A cornerstone of this approach is for people to seek energy sources that ensure ecological, societal, and economic sustainability. Although there may be consensus that each of these categories is important, there is considerable variability in terms of the weightings that should be assigned to each category. This leads to a wide spectrum of opinions when it comes to evaluating conventional energy sources, like coal, as well as alternative energy sources, like geothermal and tidal energy.

2.1 Questions

Knowledge

1. Define the following terms.
   a. sustainable development
   b. geothermal energy
   c. tidal energy

2. Describe the energy transformations that occur to produce electricity from each of the following sources. Begin with the original source of the energy and finish with the electricity produced.
   a. geothermal energy
   b. tidal energy

3. Explain the classification of each of the following processes as being either renewable or non-renewable.
   a. combustion of coal
   b. fission of uranium-235
   c. fission of isotopes in Earth's core
   d. movement of water in ocean tides

Applying Concepts

4. When energy is converted from one form into another, some of the energy is always lost. Use this idea to comment on the efficiency of a geothermal electrical generating station as compared to a coal-fired electrical generating station.

Earlier in this chapter you completed the "Determining Sustainability of Technologies" checklist to determine the sustainability of generating electricity using the following energy sources: coal energy, nuclear energy (fission), geothermal energy, and tidal energy. Review your completed checklists; then answer question 5.

5. Prepare a table that ranks the four methods from most sustainable to least sustainable. Support your ranking by writing a brief summary.

Every second, nuclear fusion reactions in the Sun convert about 4 billion kilograms of mass into energy. Only a tiny fraction of that energy from the Sun strikes Earth (about 1 billionth of the energy produced per year). Some of this energy reaching Earth is trapped by photosynthesis. As you have learned in previous science courses, solar energy is required either directly or indirectly by nearly all the organisms on Earth, including humans. Although only a small fraction of solar energy is captured as chemical potential energy, society's current outlook on energy involves a reliance on the combustion of fossil fuels.

Larger percentages of incoming solar energy are absorbed by land, water, and the atmosphere. Might it be possible to utilize solar energy converted into other energy forms? Could sources of solar energy eliminate the use of non-renewable energy sources (e.g., fossil fuels)? Can solar energy help make sustainable development a reality? In this lesson you will have an opportunity to survey some of the technologies that harness energy from the Sun.

> **passive solar energy:** thermal energy derived from the Sun's radiant energy, absorbed by massive materials, and then transferred naturally to other areas by conduction, convection, and radiation

Passive Solar Energy

Have you ever noticed how a family pet seems to know where the warmest location is in its home? Often, it is near a window, where the pet can nap in the warmth provided by a sunbeam. A home's windows, walls, and floors can be designed to capture and store solar energy in the form of heat. The heat that is transferred to other areas of the building can be referred to as **passive solar energy**, since it is distributed without the need of a mechanical device. This captured energy is distributed by conduction, convection, and radiation.

During winter, the position of the Sun allows electromagnetic radiation to enter a passive solar home through the south-facing window and be absorbed by the concrete floor, as shown in Figure D2.8. When the radiation strikes the floor, the energy of the incoming photons is absorbed by the floor's molecules and transformed into thermal energy. Thermal energy within the floor is then transferred by conduction to regions of the interior space that are at a lower temperature. Thermal energy from the floor can also be transferred to the overlying air. The warmer air over the floor rises and is replaced by denser, cooler air. This creates convection currents in the room. To increase the efficiency of passive solar energy, materials used in a home's construction are designed to enhance the ability to absorb solar radiation. To prevent overheating in the summer, certain home designs (e.g., roof overhangs) help reduce the quantity of solar radiation directly entering the house.

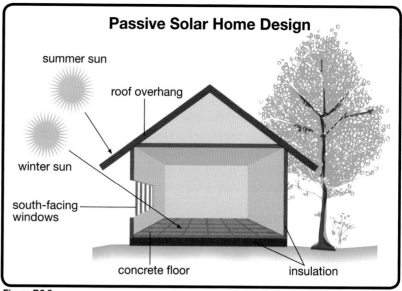

Passive Solar Home Design

summer sun

roof overhang

winter sun

south-facing windows

concrete floor

insulation

Figure D2.8

Active Solar Energy Technologies

Have you ever boarded a bus on a sunny day and found the seats to be hot to the touch? When solar radiation is absorbed (especially by a black surface), the result is heat. You may have noticed one popular solar technology—a **solar heat collector**—on some buildings. How does this device work to heat buildings? Earlier in this chapter, you saw how solar collectors are used on the roofs of garages in the Drake Landing Solar Community. In fact, over two million homes in North America are equipped with this technology.

> **solar heat collector:** a device that absorbs radiant solar energy and converts it into thermal energy that is carried by a fluid pumped through the collector

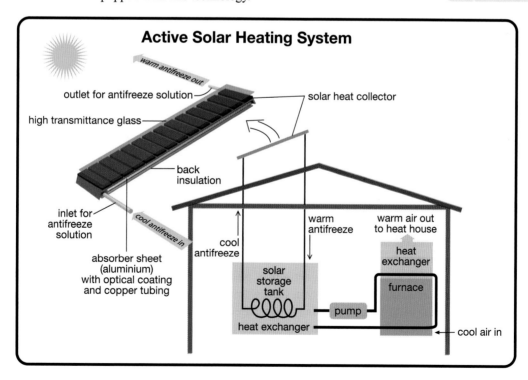

Active Solar Heating System

warm antifreeze out

outlet for antifreeze solution

high transmittance glass

solar heat collector

back insulation

inlet for antifreeze solution

cool antifreeze in

absorber sheet (aluminium) with optical coating and copper tubing

cool antifreeze

warm antifreeze

warm air out to heat house

heat exchanger

solar storage tank

furnace

pump

heat exchanger

cool air in

Solar heat collectors typically consist of a flat, black box. Inside the box is a series of pipes that contains an antifreeze solution. As in Drake Landing, rooftop solar heat collectors absorb solar radiation striking the box, allowing a transfer of energy to the fluid inside the pipes. The transfer of energy heats the fluid. The fluid in the system is pumped through the collector and to a heat exchanger, where it releases thermal energy to water in a short-term storage tank. This tank could be located below the collector in the building.

In Drake Landing Solar Community, the short-term storage tank is located in the neighbourhood's energy centre. Recall that for long-term energy storage, the community has a borehole thermal-energy storage system. Warm fluid is pumped into the deep boreholes to make an underground storage system for thermal energy. Since Drake Landing is a new community, it is expected to take years for the ground surrounding the boreholes to become fully charged with thermal energy. Once operational, the thermal energy stored from the summer months should enable the long-term storage system to meet most of the community's heating needs during the winter season.

Earth Energy Systems

Earth's surface absorbs over half of the incoming solar energy it receives. This is a huge amount of energy that, until recently, remained largely untapped. **Earth energy systems** work much like rooftop solar collectors except they use the ground like a single giant solar heat collector. Incoming solar radiation and heat radiated from inside Earth absorbed by the ground is converted into thermal energy. As you saw in your investigation of the Drake Landing renewable energy systems, warmed earth can act as an energy-storage reservoir. Weather changes that cause the atmosphere's temperature to fluctuate do not affect the temperature below ground, which remains much more constant year-round.

▶ **earth energy system:** a heating system that uses a loop of piping through the ground to absorb thermal energy

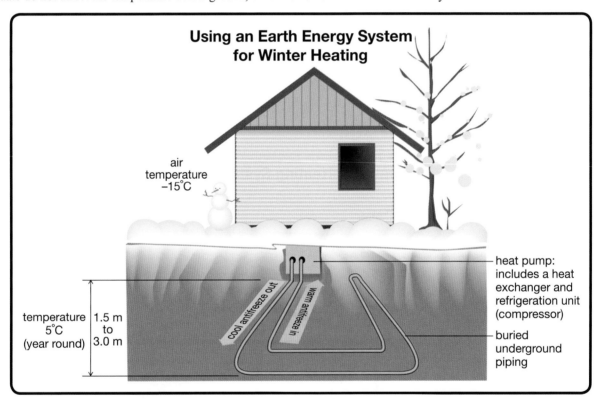

The design of an earth energy system consists of a network of pipes installed underground to collect heat. These pipes can be arranged vertically in deep holes or horizontally in shallow trenches. The pipes are filled with a circulating antifreeze solution. During winter, thermal energy from the ground is transferred to the antifreeze where it can be extracted and used to heat the building. Although the temperature of the earth on the prairies is around 5°C, a heat-pump system similar to that used in a refrigerator, except run in reverse, concentrates the heat from the earth, allowing it to be delivered throughout the house. Earth energy systems are a proven technology, with some systems having been in operation since the 1940s. According to Natural Resources Canada, over 30 000 Canadian buildings are now heated and/or cooled using earth energy systems. Earth energy systems are expensive to install, but they require very little additional energy to operate, eventually providing a cost savings and reduced reliance on fossil fuels.

11. Explain how passive solar heating and other solar-energy systems involve the use of a renewable energy source.

12. Explain how earth energy systems are technology based on a renewable source of energy.

Use the following information to answer questions 13 and 14.

Users of natural gas in Canada often encounter price fluctuations from month to month. Due to its finite supply, the price of natural gas is undergoing an upward trend.

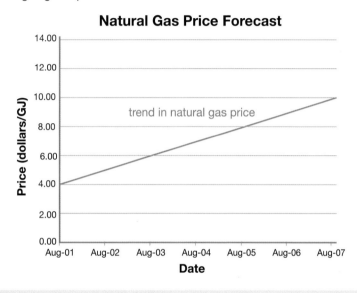

Natural Gas Price Forecast

13. State two reasons why natural gas prices fluctuate.

14. Many consumers are concerned about increasing heating costs. Do you think that the cost of an earth energy system would fluctuate in a manner similar to natural gas prices? Provide a reason for your answer.

Photovoltaic Cells—Electricity Directly from EMR

In Unit C, a **photovoltaic cell** was used in many of the investigations that explored the properties of electromagnetic radiation (EMR). Photovoltaic cells convert radiant energy in a manner quite similar to what occurs in photosynthesis. When a photon of electromagnetic radiation is absorbed by a photovoltaic cell, atoms of the light-sensitive material within the cell eject electrons. Brighter light sources provide the cell with a larger population of photons, resulting in a larger number of electrons that are ejected. Recall that moving electrons form an electric current (Unit C). Since the energy given to each of the electrons is relatively small, the current is weak (as shown in Figure D2.9, where the cell tested has a voltage output of less than half a volt). The low energy efficiency of photovoltaic cells can restrict their use to low-power devices, such as calculators. Connecting many photovoltaic cells together, forming an array, produces more energetic electric currents; but this requires a large area.

> **photovoltaic cell:** a device that converts electromagnetic radiation into electrical energy

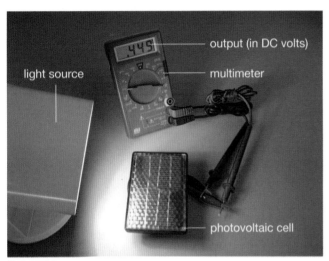

Figure D2.9

Figure D2.10: An array of photovoltaic cells can provide sufficient electrical energy for electrical devices.

Photovoltaic Cells for Home and Business

Given that photovoltaic cells are renewable sources of energy that produces no emissions during their operation, it is natural to wonder why photovoltaic cells have yet to be used on a large scale for homes and businesses.

One reason photovoltaic cells aren't used on a large scale is that they don't work in the dark. That means batteries are needed for use at night or on overcast days. Second, photovoltaic cells produce direct current (DC) electricity. Most appliances used in homes and businesses use alternating current (AC) electricity, meaning that an inverter is needed to convert the DC current into an AC current. Third, photovoltaic cells are not very efficient. Heavy-duty applications, like operating large appliances, require huge arrays of cells that cover an enormous area. This is not practical. Finally, photovoltaic cells are expensive to produce and require toxic heavy metals, like arsenic and cadmium. Strict adherence to safety guidelines is necessary to produce photovoltaic cells without harming humans or the environment.

Despite these challenges, photovoltaic cells are being used in an increasing number of applications: as energy sources for small devices and as supplemental or back-up power to primary power systems. As further improvements are made to the manufacturing process, the cost of photovoltaic cells, batteries, and inverters may decrease. This low cost will most likey make photovoltaic cells a more attractive alternative.

Figure D2.11: This garden lantern uses a photovoltaic cell to charge a small battery pack during the day so it is able to light a walkway at night.

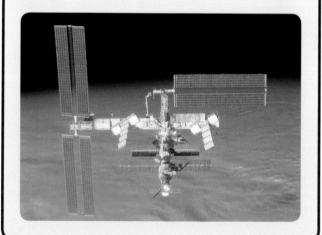
Practice

15. When white light lands on the surface of a photovoltaic cell, photons from all regions of the visible spectrum deliver energy to the light-sensitive materials.

    a. Sketch a diagram to show red, green, and violet photons landing on the surface of a photovoltaic cell.

    b. Which type of photon—a photon of red light or a photon of violet light—delivers the most energy to the photovoltaic cell.

16. Obtain the document "Determining Sustainability of Technologies" from the Science 30 Textbook CD. Follow the instructions in the document to determine the overall sustainability of photovoltaic cells as an energy source. **Note:** Keep your completed checklist for photovoltaic cells because you will be asked to refer to it throughout this chapter.

Hydroelectric Power

Moving water possesses kinetic energy. One of the oldest technologies to utilize water's energy is the water wheel. Earliest records of water wheels date back to 400 BC, when they were used by Greeks to grind grain. Later, in Europe, water wheels powered the saws, pumps, and machinery in a variety of mills.

Kinetic energy of flowing water is an important energy source that is often used to generate electricity. Hydroelectric power supplies about 19% of the world's electricity. Over 95% of Quebec's electrical energy production comes from the energy of flowing water—the largest percentage of any province. The ability to produce excess electricity beyond provincial demand enables Quebec to sell much of the electricity it generates to cities in the United States.

Figure D2.12: Water wheels have been used throughout history to power a variety of machines. As water falls from a higher elevation to a lower elevation, the wheel converts the water's gravitational potential energy into kinetic energy.

Original Source of Hydroelectric Power

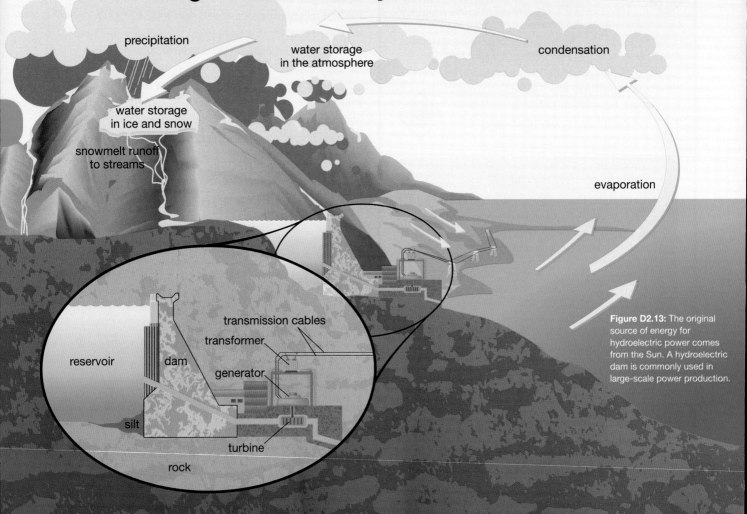

Figure D2.13: The original source of energy for hydroelectric power comes from the Sun. A hydroelectric dam is commonly used in large-scale power production.

In Lesson 2.1 you prepared process maps for some technologies that convert energy. What would a process map for hydroelectric energy look like? Is hydroelectric power a renewable energy? It may surprise you to know that the original energy source for hydroelectric power is the Sun. Water heated by solar radiation at lower elevations evaporates, allowing it to rise and be carried by air currents in the atmosphere, often over great distances. Eventually, water vapour condenses, forming clouds and precipitation. Precipitation that falls at higher elevations has gained gravitational potential energy, which can be converted into kinetic energy once it begins to run downhill. Since the energy from the Sun is inexhaustible, hydroelectric power, like other solar-based technologies, are processes providing renewable energy.

Dams are commonly used to convert gravitational potential energy of water into electricity. Dams can concentrate and control the energy in moving water by storing it in a large reservoir. In some dams, the difference in height between the reservoir and the turbines is over 200 m. The higher the water level, the faster the water flows through the turbine (increasing the kinetic energy). The force of the flowing water pushes against turbine blades, causing them to turn. As with other technologies you have evaluated, the turbines are attached to generators that convert the kinetic energy into electrical energy. The electrical energy from the generators is transferred to transformers that increase the voltage so that energy loss due to resistance in the transmission lines is minimized.

Hydroelectricity in Alberta

Hydroelectric dams in Alberta currently supply about 5% of the province's electricity. This low value, which is less than many other provinces, may be the result of the plentiful supply of coal in Alberta, which is used to generate over 75% of Alberta's electrical energy. Although some people suggest that Alberta should be utilizing more hydroelectric power, as you'll see in the next activity, the development of large-scale hydroelectric projects requires careful consideration of ecological, societal, and economic risks and benefits.

Assessing Hydroelectric Power

As an energy source, hydroelectric power has many strengths:

- The underlying energy source is the Sun, making it a renewable source of energy.
- Power production does not release any harmful emissions into the environment.
- The water used is not polluted or consumed as it passes through the turbines and is able to re-enter the water cycle.
- Very little waste heat is generated, meaning that this is a very efficient process. (Over 80% of the gravitational potential energy of the water is transformed into electrical energy.)
- The high energy efficiency enables the cost per kilowatt-hour of energy produced to be relatively low.

Major criticisms of hydroelectric power focus on the environmental impact resulting from the reservoir of water held behind the dam. As the reservoir fills, large areas of land are covered with water. This may include usable farmland, forests, and even cities. The action of flooding such areas may have an impact on the natural aquatic ecosystem. Dams impede the movement of nutrient-rich silt carried by the flow of the river that is important to the fertility of land downstream. In some situations, leaching of metal ions occurs from soils in the flooded area, affecting the quality of water in the river. These factors can put enormous stresses on species living upstream and downstream of the reservoir. Societal concerns include the potential for the forced relocation of entire communities that may have inhabited the area for long periods of time, resulting in the loss of archaeological sites and cultural artifacts.

Any area to be developed for the collection of hydroelectricity must demonstrate suitable geography and rainfall patterns. In addition, the location should be geologically stable to reduce possible damage to the structure from the effects of earthquakes.

Figure D2.14: The Oldman Dam near Pincher Creek, Alberta, provides 25 MW of electrical energy as well as water for irrigating crops in southern Alberta.

Try This Activity

Making a Decision About Hydroelectric Dam Construction

Purpose

In this activity you will review a document summarizing a decision made in response to a proposal to build a hydroelectric dam on a river in northern Alberta. Many impacts of hydroelectric dams are identified within the decision.

Problem

What are the risks and benefits of hydroelectric dams? What perspectives are considered when making decisions regarding the development of hydroelectric projects?

Procedure

Read the "Hydroelectric Dam Construction" handout from the Science 30 Textbook CD.

Analysis

1. Prepare a risk-benefit analysis of hydroelectric dams.
2. Prepare a list of perspectives considered in the decision.
3. Evaluate the decision made regarding the proposed hydroelectric project. In your evaluation, comment on whether relevant risks and benefits was accurately assessed and whether a suitable range of perspectives was considered in making this decision.

17. In Figure D2.13 showing the original source of hydroelectric power, a large transformer is shown above the generator.

    a. Explain why a transformer is vital to the transmission of electricity from the hydroelectric plant to distant consumers.

    b. Determine whether a step-up transformer or a step-down transformer is required.

18. Obtain the document "Determining Sustainability of Technologies" from the Science 30 Textbook CD. Follow the instructions in the document to determine the overall sustainability of hydroelectric dams as an energy technology. **Note:** Keep your completed checklist for hydroelectric power because you will be asked to refer to it throughout this chapter.

Use the following information to answer questions 19 to 21.

The Three Gorges Dam spans the world's third-largest river, the Yangtze River in China. This project began in 1997 and, when completed, will be the largest dam in the world. The Three Gorges Dam will span 2 km, and the power plant will be capable of generating 18 000 MW of electrical energy.

ENERGY DATA FOR CHINA

Electricity Production (2006)	
2.83×10^5 MW	
Energy Source for Electricity Production	**Percentage of Energy Produced**
coal	83%
hydro	14%
nuclear	2%
other	1%

Four Criticisms of the Three Gorges Dam

    I. 1.3 million people have been displaced by the construction of the dam and flooding of the reservoir.

    II. The flooded reservoir area contains former factories, industrial centres, and garbage dumps, resulting in pollution to the Yangtze River.

    III. The construction of the dam could result in the extinction of some rare species of fish.

    IV. The location of the Three Gorges Dam is near six seismic faults that have demonstrated activity.

19. Calculate the percentage of China's electricity production that could be met once the Three Gorges Dam is operating at full capacity.

20. Identify the impact that power production from the Three Gorges Dam could have on China in terms of societal and ecological impact.

21. Respond to one of the criticisms of the Three Gorges Dam project listed, by defending the project.

Wind Energy

Have you ever been on the streets of a large city on a windy day? Tall buildings can dramatically intensify the speed of the wind, turning some streets into virtual wind tunnels. The effect that buildings have on wind is similar to the change to water flowing down a stream that suddenly narrows. Since the same volume of water is rushing through a narrower opening, its speed must pick up. You might be surprised to know that this same effect makes the southwestern corner of Alberta one of the best places on Earth to harness wind energy.

Figure D2.15: These wind turbines, along with hundreds of others, generate electricity by converting the energy from the steady, high winds in certain regions of Alberta.

Earlier you reviewed the effect that thermal energy has in creating air currents. Solar energy can be converted into thermal energy, which affects the kinetic energy and density of molecules in the air. As air molecules absorb thermal energy, they move faster and take up more space, thus decreasing in density. In Unit B you learned that the predominant direction of winds across the prairies is from the west, and that these winds are created by the combination of global convection currents and Earth's rotation. In some parts of Alberta, the westerly winds are especially strong and have become a source of energy.

Locations of Larger Wind Farms in Southern Alberta

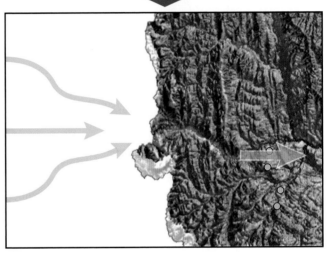

In western Canada, numerous ranges of mountains form natural barriers to these westerly winds. However, when the prevailing winds encounter a gap between mountains, like at Crowsnest Pass, the energy of the wind becomes concentrated as it is funnelled through the narrow opening between mountains. The wind follows the valleys and travels east into southern Alberta. Elevation drops as the mountains give way to the foothills and then to the prairies. Other atmospheric effects further intensify the kinetic energy of the wind. The end result is that places like Pincher Creek, Fort Macleod, and Lethbridge have wind conditions ideally suited to run wind turbines. The kinetic energy of the moving air pushes against the blades of a wind turbine and causes the blades to spin. As is the case with all electric generating apparatus, a spinning turbine connected to a generator converts the kinetic energy of the spinning blades into electrical energy.

Figure D2.16: Two technicians inspect the enormous blade of a wind turbine.

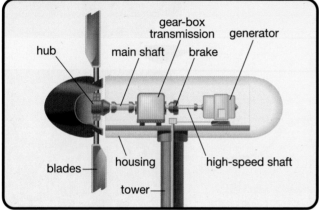

Figure D2.17: The kinetic energy of the spinning blades is transferred to the generator, which transforms it into electrical energy.

There is a great deal of interest in wind energy. Currently, wind energy is the fastest growing form of electricity generation in Canada. However, it provides only a small portion of Canada's electricity. As you learned earlier, the ultimate source of energy for wind power is the Sun, making wind energy a renewable resource. It is impossible for air to be "used up" during the process and there are no harmful emissions. Wind energy is also very versatile. Large wind farms—made up of hundreds of turbines—have the ability to supply electricity to communities; and single, smaller turbines can be used to meet the electricity demands for a single isolated home.

The limitations of wind energy are similar to those of other renewable sources. As you have learned, only certain locations have the proper conditions to allow for suitable, nearly constant winds. Wind energy also shares two drawbacks associated with photovoltaic cells: the energy source can be quite variable from day to day and the conversion into electrical energy is not very efficient. In the case of wind energy, only about 30% of the energy in the wind is transformed into electrical energy. This means that generating a significant amount of electrical energy requires many wind turbines that occupy a large area. Although the land used for a wind farm can also be used for grazing livestock or for other agricultural activities, it still must be set aside.

Other effects of wind energy have emerged since the technology has been used. In Alberta, scientists at the University of Calgary have been investigating the effect that the moving blades of the turbines have on bat populations. Similar concerns exist over the number of birds killed by the blades of wind turbines. Some landowners report that the noise produced by the rotating blades can be annoying and that the site of the giant turbines is a form of visual pollution—as it ruins the view of the landscape.

Practice

22. Describe the factors that make the area around Pincher Creek well-suited for harvesting wind energy.

23. Obtain the document "Determining Sustainability of Technologies" from the Science 30 Textbook CD. Follow the instructions in the document to determine the overall sustainability of wind energy as an energy source. **Note:** Keep your completed checklist for wind energy because you will be asked to refer to it throughout this chapter.

Biomass

You have learned that many energy sources used by society can be traced back to solar energy. Photosynthesis—the chemical reaction that converts the Sun's radiant energy into chemical potential energy—allows plant material to be used as an energy source either as food or as **biomass**. The chemical potential energy within recently living organic material such as wood, corn, or organic waste can be used as a source of renewable and potentially sustainable energy.

> **biomass:** plant matter or agricultural waste from recently living sources used as a fuel or as an energy source

Figure D2.18: Wood, an example of biomass, was likely the first fuel used by humans for heating and cooking.

Biomass Energy—Emission and Absorption of CO₂

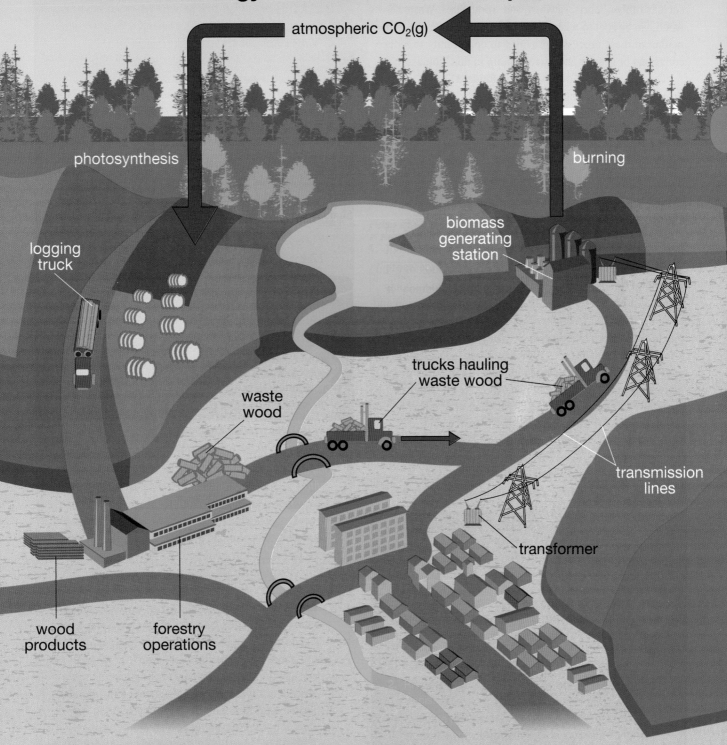

atmospheric CO_2(g)

photosynthesis

burning

logging truck

biomass generating station

trucks hauling waste wood

waste wood

transmission lines

wood products

forestry operations

transformer

? DID YOU KNOW?

Biomass refers to organic matter from living or recently living sources. Fossil fuels are not considered biomass because they were derived from plants and animals that died millions of years ago.

Direct Combustion—Generating Electricity Using Biomass

Modern forestry operations produce waste wood products, such as timber debris, sawdust, and wood chips. Waste wood can be sent to a landfill or be combusted on site, but neither of these processes provides an opportunity to reduce emissions or use the energy remaining in this biomass.

The generating station (shown in Figure D2.19) in Whitecourt uses waste wood from nearby forestry operations to produce electricity. The combustion of the waste wood within a furnace is used to heat boilers that produce the steam needed to drive turbines connected to generators. The Whitecourt Generating Station utilizes modern emissions-control technology to reduce the release of particulate matter and oxides of nitrogen.

Although the plant material is combusted, resulting in carbon dioxide emissions, biomass can be produced in a sustainable manner. Sustainability involves the absorption of carbon dioxide by the next generation of plant material. Earlier in this lesson you prepared a process map demonstrating the interrelationship between combustion and photosynthesis. The combination of combustion and crop planting to absorb carbon dioxide make biomass energy use a "carbon-neutral" process. When biomass fuels are used in place of fossil fuels, the carbon in the non-renewable fossil fuels stays in the ground. Estimates indicate that biomass power production is not exactly carbon-neutral, releasing just under 40 g of carbon dioxide per kilowatt-hour of electrical energy produced. As you discovered in Unit C, this value compares favourably to conventional coal-fired plants, which emit about 1000 g of carbon dioxide for every kilowatt-hour of electrical energy produced.

Figure D2.20: Waste wood piled outside a mill

Figure D2.19: The Whitecourt Generating Station uses waste wood products as a fuel to produce steam for electricity production.

Practice

24. Refer to the illustration "Biomass Energy—Emission and Absorption of CO_2" on page 547.

    a. Identify any activity depicted in the illustration that increases CO_2 emissions, affecting the ability of the process depicted to be carbon-neutral.

    b. The illustration focuses on the energy derived from waste wood products. Identify other sources of biomass that could also be used to generate electricity.

25. Obtain the document "Determining Sustainability of Technologies" from the Science 30 Textbook CD. Follow the instructions given in the document to determine the overall sustainability of generating electricity from biomass. **Note:** Keep your completed checklist for biomass because you will be asked to refer to it throughout this chapter.

Biofuels

Biomass as an energy source has many advantages. Usable sources of biomass tend to be readily available; and since most forms are combustible, complex technology is not required to use them. If society is to consider using biomass fuels to develop improved energy sustainability, the largest advantage of biomass is the ability to convert it into a **biofuel**. Methane, ethanol, and the mixtures in biodiesel are composed of high-energy molecules. This means that the biomass energy they produce can be applied to a great number of technologies including automobiles.

biofuel: a fuel produced from renewable biological resources, including biomass

?-DID YOU KNOW?-

The quantity of solar energy absorbed by photosynthesis is almost ten times greater than the current world energy demand. Using biomass makes some of this energy available for use.

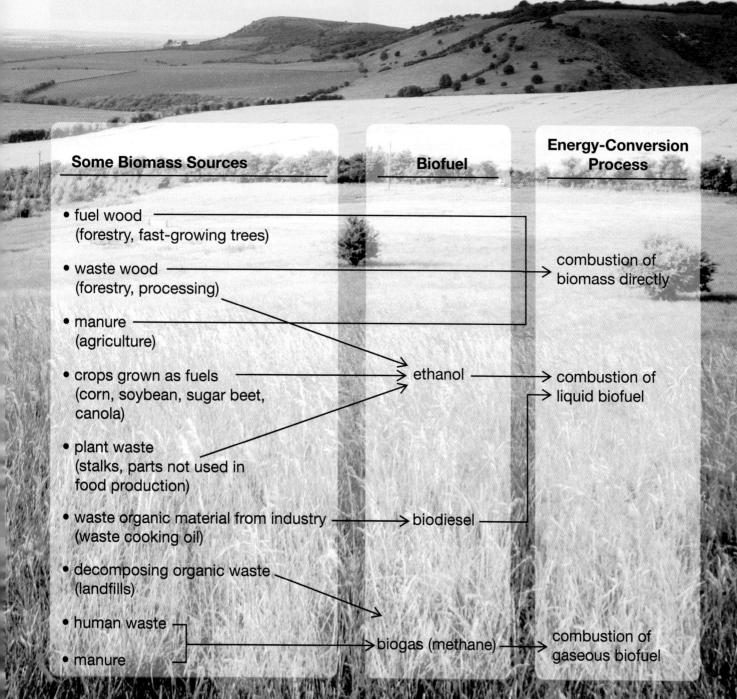

Some Biomass Sources	Biofuel	Energy-Conversion Process
• fuel wood (forestry, fast-growing trees)		combustion of biomass directly
• waste wood (forestry, processing)		
• manure (agriculture)		
• crops grown as fuels (corn, soybean, sugar beet, canola)	ethanol	combustion of liquid biofuel
• plant waste (stalks, parts not used in food production)		
• waste organic material from industry (waste cooking oil)	biodiesel	
• decomposing organic waste (landfills)		
• human waste	biogas (methane)	combustion of gaseous biofuel
• manure		

Ethanol in Gasoline

In Unit B you studied alcohols. Ethanol, an alcohol, is a highly usable biofuel that can be produced using yeast to ferment the sugars within organic matter like crop plants and even waste wood. Humans have used yeast to produce ethanol to make alcoholic beverages for thousands of years. As you learned, alcohols like ethanol are combustible, making them an excellent fuel.

Ethanol produced from biomass is currently blended with gasoline. New automobiles can operate with gasoline containing up to 10% ethanol, with some special models being able to use gasoline containing up to 85% ethanol. Small amounts of ethanol can also be added to diesel; but at high percentages, modifications to the engine are necessary.

Ethanol from biomass is considered to be a renewable energy source because it is derived from crops that can be continually grown. In Brazil, ethanol for gasoline is produced using sugar cane. The growth of new crops absorb carbon

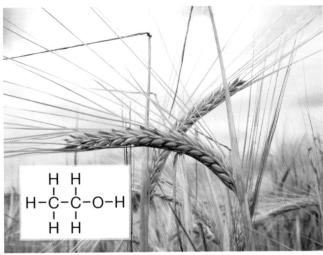

Figure D2.21: Ethanol, $C_2H_5OH(l)$, can be produced by fermenting grain, corn, wood, or other plant products. Ethanol can be combusted directly or blended with gasoline as a way to reduce the content of nonrenewable substances in gasoline.

dioxide from the atmosphere, enabling the production of new biomass and making the process sustainable. Brazil's use of biomass has significantly reduced the country's reliance on oil imports and has reduced its contribution to global climate change.

A major criticism of biomass energy focuses on the large amount of land needed for the growth of the crops and on the decision to use a potential food source as a fuel for transportation. Throughout your studies in Unit B, you discovered that current agricultural practices include the use of fertilizers, herbicides, and pesticides. These practices can have adverse effects on the environment. It is hoped that any increase in crop production for use in making biofuels will be accompanied by sustainable agricultural practices.

An additional concern involve the loss of efficiency in the making of a biofuel. You have learned in this unit that whenever energy is converted, there is a loss of some of the input. Critics of biofuel production cite two sources of inefficiency. First, biofuels produce methane and ethanol, which contain few carbons, making them low-energy molecules compared to the complex organic molecules from which they were derived. Second, high concentrations of ethanol are toxic to many organisms, including the yeast involved in the fermentation process. This toxicity means that it is difficult to produce sufficient ethanol to meet projected demands. Currently, scientists are working on developing strains of micro-organisms that will continue to ferment biomass at higher ethanol concentrations. It is hoped that efforts to develop these micro-organisms will improve the efficiency of biofuel production and increase the potential for biomass use.

Landfill Gas

Garbage in a landfill is sealed off from oxygen by the layers of garbage and dirt above it. Under these oxygen-free conditions, bacteria digest organic waste and release methane—the main component of natural gas. This biogas can be collected using a network of pipes and then used as a fuel for the production of electricity. Many major cities, like Calgary, Edmonton, and Grande Prairie, have constructed landfills to allow for the collection of biogas. At the Clover Bar Landfill in Edmonton, a 4.8-MW biogas facility produces enough electricity for 4600 Edmonton homes.

Biogas can also be collected from feedlots or other intensive agriculture operations where manure is allowed to decompose in the absence of oxygen.

Biodiesel

The chemical potential energy within waste oils can be a source of energy. In the "Determining Heat of Combustion" investigation on page 494, you learned that organic molecules containing many carbon atoms can store a large quantity of chemical potential energy. You also learned from your study in Unit B that fats and oils are esters of large organic acid molecules joined to a glycerol molecule. In some automobile engines, waste cooking oil can be used directly as a fuel. Biodiesel is a mixture of organic acids obtained from the conversion of waste cooking oil and diesel fuel. The reaction to produce biodiesel from waste cooking oil involves breaking the bonds within the molecules of the ester functional groups within the chemical structure of the waste cooking oil. Breaking the ester bonds helps maintain the proper viscosity of the resulting biodiesel. The blending of biodiesel with conventional diesel fuel is designed to maintain the energy content of the product and decrease the amount of fossil fuels consumed.

Practice

26. Burning ethanol releases carbon dioxide. Identify aspects of ecological sustainability associated with the production and combustion of the biofuels ethanol and biodiesel (formed from canola or other vegetable oils).

27. Biogas often contains impurities like hydrogen sulfide, $H_2S(g)$. Identify possible problems associated with the combustion of biogas containing hydrogen sulfide.

Hydrogen—Fuel of the Future?

Research into the use of biodiesel is one attempt to reduce the use of fossil fuels as the main energy source for transportation. Another approach is the development of the hydrogen fuel cell.

In many ways, a fuel cell is similar to an electrochemical cell. It consists of two electrodes separated by a membrane that allows ions to pass. Electrons extracted by the reaction of the fuel in the cell flow through an external circuit to any electrical device, like a car's electric motor. Without a constant supply of reactants, power production from a fuel cell immediately stops.

A variety of fuel cells exist, but one of the most tested types is the hydrogen fuel cell. Hydrogen enters the fuel cell at one electrode while its reactant—oxygen—enters the fuel cell at the other electrode. Within the fuel cell, the two reactants never come into direct contact; but each reactant is absorbed by opposite sides of a material containing a catalyst. The catalyst allows hydrogen to react in such a way that it provides electrons for the external circuit as well as positively charged ions that migrate through the membrane to complete the flow of charge. The changes during the operation of the fuel cell (as shown in Figure D2.22) result in a flameless combustion reaction between hydrogen and oxygen that produces an electric current rather than a flame.

In 2006, the use of hydrogen fuel cells in Canada was uncommon. Five buses equipped with hydrogen fuel cells in Victoria and Vancouver were some of very few examples where this technology was used. But with more research and development, fuel-cell automobiles may become an increasingly common sight. Currently, the application of the technology is limited by the high cost for the catalysts used in fuel cells and the size of the cells required limit application of the technology. Researchers are optimistic because the hydrogen fuel cell is a very energy-efficient device that has only one emission—water vapour.

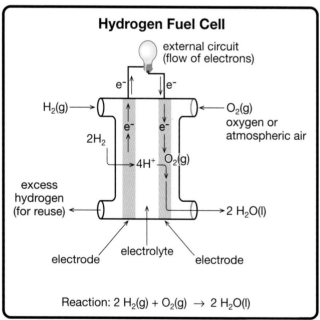

Hydrogen Fuel Cell

external circuit (flow of electrons)

$H_2(g)$ → $2H_2$

excess hydrogen (for reuse) ←

$4H^+$ $O_2(g)$

→ $O_2(g)$ oxygen or atmospheric air

→ $2 H_2O(l)$

electrode   electrolyte   electrode

Reaction: $2 H_2(g) + O_2(g) \rightarrow 2 H_2O(l)$

Figure D2.22

A major drawback to the wide-scale use of hydrogen fuels is the limited supply of hydrogen. Elemental hydrogen, $H_2(g)$, is not readily available; but it can be extracted from hydrocarbons or water, both energy-rich molecules. Hydrocarbons, for example CH_4, and water, H_2O, are possible hydrogen sources. The process of removing hydrogen from these two possible sources is not without controversy. Removing hydrogen from hydrocarbons can involve a process called steam reformation. Industrially, the reformation and additional reactions to produce hydrogen result in the formation of carbon monoxide, carbon dioxide, and coke ($C(s)$).

Decomposition of Water

$$2\ H_2O(l) \xrightarrow{\text{electrical energy}} 2\ H_2(g) + O_2(g)$$

In previous science courses, you may have observed the electrolysis of water, where an electric current is applied to water, resulting in the decomposition of water. In order for fuel cells to be a sustainable technology, the electricity used for electrolysis must come from a renewable source (e.g., wind, nuclear, solar, or hydro). In addition, the source of the water that is electrolyzed must also come from a renewable source. Concerns over drought and a decrease in drinkable water may cause seawater to become a likely source for hydrogen to power cars in the future.

Try This Activity

Producing Hydrogen Fuel

Purpose
You will examine an illustration depicting the transformation of water to produce the hydrogen needed to operate a hydrogen fuel cell, and you will identify the energy forms and transformations involved.

Science Skills

✓ Analyzing and Interpreting

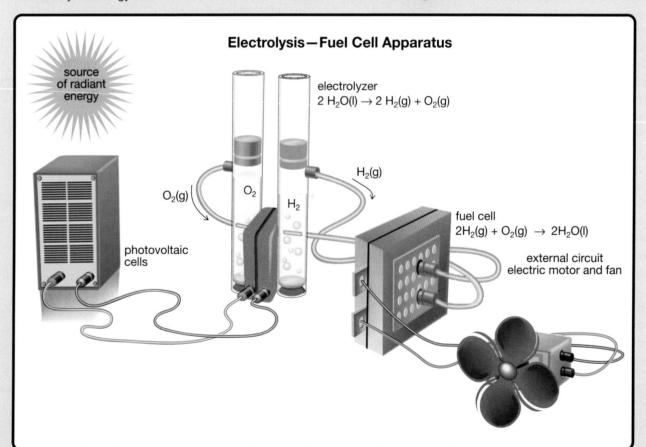

Analysis
Use an energy-flow diagram to describe the energy forms and transformations that occur during the operation of the apparatus shown in the illustration.

From the Carbon Economy to the Hydrogen Economy

Which energy sources do societies depend upon the most? Presently, particularly in Alberta, there is a heavy dependence on coal for electricity, natural gas for heating, and petroleum for transportation. All of these forms of energy are non-renewable and increase the levels of atmospheric carbon dioxide. A phrase used to describe this dependence on fossil fuels is the **carbon economy**. Due to the non-renewable nature of fossil fuels, the carbon economy is simply not sustainable.

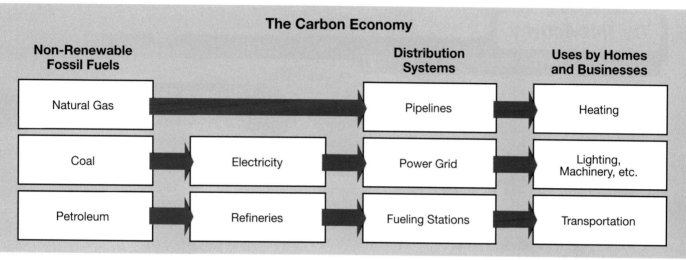

Many people think that within the next twenty years, hydrocarbons will no longer be primary sources of energy and that renewable energy sources will have increasing importance. One proposal calls for the use of renewable energy sources to generate electricity and for the use of hydrogen fuel cells in vehicles. Such a proposal would make hydrogen a primary fuel and result in the development of a **hydrogen economy**.

carbon economy: an economy that depends on fossil fuels as the primary source of energy, resulting in excessive emissions of carbon dioxide

hydrogen economy: an economy that depends on renewable sources of energy to generate electricity and depends upon hydrogen as the fuel for transportation

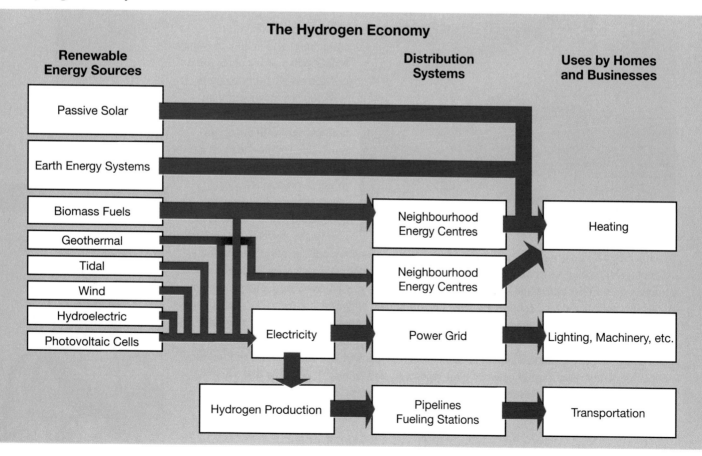

When comparing the diagrams of the carbon economy and the hydrogen economy, you can see that a greater variety of energy sources are required to support the increased use of hydrogen. To make the proposed hydrogen economy a success, creative combinations of many energy sources must be used, along with different distribution systems. In the Drake Landing Solar Community, the energy centre provides heat to the homes in the neighbourhood. For more remote dwellings, heating needs might be met by earth energy systems located in the homeowner's backyard.

Try This Activity

Converting to the Hydrogen Economy

Purpose

You will work with other students to identify changes to your home or community if it were to convert to the hydrogen economy.

Science Skills

✓ Analyzing and Interpreting
✓ Communication and Teamwork

Procedure and Analysis

1. Identify non-sustainable energy technologies used in your home or community.

2. Identify sustainable technologies and strategies that could be used to replace the non-sustainable technologies identified in question 1.

3. Indicate major differences between the current carbon economy and the hydrogen economy.

4. Predict problems and solutions that might occur within your home or community during the conversion to the hydrogen economy.

5. Some countries in Europe have adopted twenty- and thirty-year plans that will move them toward a hydrogen economy. To fund the conversion, tax rebates are given to people who make the necessary changes to their buildings, means of transportation, and energy infrastructure. These rebates are partially funded by "carbon taxes" on technologies that are based on the old carbon economy. For example, the use of large, inefficient vehicles (like SUVs) is discouraged by high gasoline taxes. Public transportation is heavily subsidized and rebates are offered to people who purchase more-efficient, smaller vehicles with new technology. Do you think these strategies would work in Alberta?

One Future, Many Paths

What do you think your community will be like in twenty years? Will you see photovoltaic cells on nearly every rooftop? Will you see neighbourhood energy centres providing homeowners with energy from renewable sources? As you have seen, choosing which technology to use to produce energy involves many perspectives and should address aspects of ecological, societal, and economic sustainability. Finding workable solutions to energy issues may not only involve overcoming technological challenges, it may also involve changing attitudes and behaviours. Behaviours and attitudes stem from culture: the beliefs, values, and symbols passed down from one generation to the next and shared by a community. This line of thought suggests that the greatest challenges ahead relate to the cultural dimension of sustainable development. Does this sound familiar?

Earlier in this course you were introduced to traditional ecological knowledge, which involves developing an understanding of human interactions with the environment and focusing on the inseparable relationship between land, resources, and culture. It could be that a holistic approach—which brings the human aspects of knowledge, spirit, and emotion into decision making—may prove to be very helpful in making sustainable development a reality.

2.2 Summary

The quantity of solar energy reaching Earth each day exceeds the world's energy demand. The main problem is finding a way to harness solar energy that is cost-competitive with fossil fuels. Unlike fossil fuels, solar technologies are renewable and avoid many of the negative effects to human health and the environment. Solar technologies can be high tech or low tech and large scale or small scale. They also can generate heat or electricity. Solar technologies have a wide range of applications and are likely to play an important role in the world's future energy production. As renewable technologies improve and fossil fuels become more expensive because of shrinking supplies, renewable forms of energy will become more commonly used throughout the world.

2.2 Questions

Knowledge

1. Define each of the following terms.

   a. passive solar energy

   b. earth energy system

   c. biomass

   d. hydrogen economy

2. Describe the energy conversions involved during the use of each of the following technologies.

   a. photovoltaic cells

   b. hydroelectric power

3. Describe one way you could use solar energy to reduce your household energy costs without purchasing any new equipment.

4. Identify the main limitations and benefits of solar-energy technologies.

Applying Concepts

5. Explain how the operation of an earth energy system is similar to your body's circulatory system.

6. List actions that you and your family perform that are consistent with sustainable development. In each case, identify whether the action addresses ecological sustainability, environmental sustainability, societal sustainability, or any combination of these.

7. Earlier in this chapter you evaluated six energy sources—coal, nuclear fission, photovoltaic cells, hydroelectric power, wind energy, and biomass—for sustainability as sources of energy. You will need these six completed evaluations to answer questions 7.a. and 7.b.

   a. Summarize your findings by producing a table that compares the weighted scores for each category of sustainability as well as the overall score for each source of energy.

   b. Refer to your table to discuss the overall rankings, from highest to lowest, of the sources of energy. Support your findings by describing the overall reasons for your ranking.

Alberta relies heavily on non-renewable energy sources. Hydrocarbons provide the main fuels for transportation, heating, and electricity. Because these sources will eventually run out and because their continued use has associated environmental costs, more sustainable energy sources and technologies are needed. Renewable technologies include hydroelectricity, tidal, wind, solar, biomass fuels, geothermal, and hydrogen fuel cells. Switching to more renewable technologies will be necessary to meet Alberta's future energy needs. Other strategies, such as increasing efficiency and reducing waste, will also be important in reducing Alberta's growing energy demand.

Summarize Your Learning

In this chapter you examined a number of new terms, concepts, and techniques for problem solving. You will have a much easier time recalling and applying the information you learned if you take some time to organize it into some sort of pattern. Now that you have come to the end of the chapter, this is an appropriate time to focus on the patterns within the things that you have learned.

Since the pattern has to be in a form that is meaningful to you, you have some options as to how you can create this summary. Each of the following summary techniques is described in "Summarize Your Learning Activities" in the Reference section.

Option 1: Draw a concept map or a web diagram.	Option 2: Create a point-form summary.	Option 3: Write a story using key terms and concepts.	Option 4: Create a colourful poster.	Option 5: Build a model.	Option 6: Write a script for a skit (a mock news report).

Chapter 2 Review Questions

Knowledge

1. The following table summarizes the important renewable technologies studied in this chapter. Copy and complete the table in your notebook.

Renewable Technology	Original Energy Source	Main Use (e.g., heating, electricity)	Key Advantages	Key Disadvantages
hydroelectric				
tidal				
wind				
solar				
earth energy system				
photovoltaic cell				
geothermal				
biomass				
hydrogen fuel cell				

2. The title of this chapter is "Dreams of a Sustainable Future."

   a. Explain the meaning of the term *sustainable development*.

   b. A sustainable source of energy must satisfy criteria in three broad categories of sustainability. Describe the key characteristics that describe each of these categories.

3. Describe two renewable ways an individual household can generate electricity.

4. Describe the energy transformations that occur when electricity is produced from geothermal energy. Begin with the original source of the energy and finish with electricity.

5. Identify one way geothermal energy is used other than to generate electricity.

6. Identify the range of materials classified as biomass. Explain how each of the materials listed can be used as a source of energy.

7. Describe the energy changes associated with a hydrogen fuel cell. Identify limitations to the use of the fuel cell.

8. The "pop test" is commonly used to identify the presence of hydrogen. In a "pop test" a very small quantity of hydrogen is brought into contact with a burning splint. The combustion of the hydrogen produces a flame and a small explosion, resulting in a popping sound. Compare the reactions for hydrogen in a fuel cell with the combustion of hydrogen in a "pop test." Which process has the greatest energy efficiency? Support your reason.

9. Describe the two main ways hydrogen can be produced for use in hydrogen fuel cells.

10. Describe how a hydrogen economy might work in the future. Identify two challenges and two benefits associated with developing a hydrogen economy.

Applying Concepts

11. Compare hydroelectric energy with tidal energy. List the similarities and differences.

12. Iceland is a country that has officially committed to switching from a carbon economy to a hydrogen economy. Briefly describe how this hydrogen economy could best be supported by sources of renewable energy in Iceland.

13. Note that nuclear fission does not appear as an entry in the hydrogen economy or in the carbon economy. Yet many people think that nuclear power could play a critical role in a period of transition between the current carbon economy and the proposed hydrogen economy.

   a. Suggest a reason why nuclear fission does not appear on the flowchart for the carbon economy or on the flowchart for the hydrogen economy.

   b. Explain the role that nuclear fission could play during a period of transition between these two economies.

Unit D Conclusion

Earth's population continues to grow. More countries are becoming industrialized, and the world's energy demand is climbing higher and higher. Yet, the world continues to rely mostly on non-renewable and ecologically damaging energy technologies.

Renewable and sustainable technologies are needed. Some renewable technologies, such as hydroelectricity and geothermal heat, have long been providing sustainable energy. More recent technologies, like tidal energy, wind power, biomass, and photovoltaic cells, are increasing their share in the world's energy market. Also, emerging technologies, such as hydrogen fuel cells, may even facilitate a global transition to sustainable economies.

The long-term health of the planet depends upon moving toward the goal of sustainable development. It will take action from regular citizens, industry, the scientific community, and governments to reconcile dreams of limitless energy with dreams of a sustainable future.

Career Profile

Welder

Destiny Golosky definitely doesn't fit the stereotypical view of a blue-collar trades person, but that doesn't bother the confident, well-spoken, 23-year-old steamfitter/pipefitter or her employer, Clearwater Welding. Given the shortage of skilled people in Alberta, Clearwater was delighted when Destiny decided to return to her hometown of Fort McMurray after spending four years learning her craft at NAIT.

Given the shortage of skilled trades people in the northeastern Alberta city, most employers would be delighted if more young people decided to follow Destiny's path into the trades. Her father, Richard, a welder, encouraged Destiny after she started to show an interest as a teenager. "My parents were very supportive," she said. "I wanted to do something that was interesting and challenging, and that paid well. And because I grew up in Fort McMurray, I got to see and meet a lot of very successful people in the trades."

Given the problems in recruiting skilled labour to northeastern Alberta, oil sands companies became forerunners in forging partnerships with Aboriginal communities to train and hire Aboriginal employees as well as conducting business with Aboriginal contractors. NAIT has also taken steps to engage these communities through its Aboriginal Student Success Initiative. "It's important to know that you can succeed if you are Aboriginal," Destiny said. "At the end of the day, I don't think anybody expects any special treatment. Most people just want a chance to prove they can do the job, whether they are a man or a woman, Aboriginal or not."

1. The following list summarizes some of the important terms and concepts used in this unit. In a table, define each item (including relevant symbols and equations) in one column and state any related terms and applications (e.g., examples or diagrams) in a second column. If you prefer, a table has been set up in a Microsoft® Word file titled "Unit D Key Terms" on the Science 30 Textbook CD.

- energy
- energy efficiency
- fossil fuel (hydrocarbon)
- hydrocarbon combustion
- heat of combustion
- energy change for a reaction
- standard heat of formation

- first law of thermodynamics
- second law of thermodynamics
- radioactivity
- nucleon
- isotope
- ionizing radiation

- conservation of nucleons
- nuclear fission
- nuclear fusion
- mass-energy equivalence
- sustainable development
- biosphere

2. In this unit you studied a variety of energy technologies. Copy and complete the following table in your notebook. Remember to leave enough room for your answers.

Technology	Energy Conversions (original source to final use)	Renewable or Non-renewable	Negative Aspects	Positive Aspects
coal-fired power plant				
CANDU nuclear power plant				
hydroelectric power generating facility				
tidal power generating facility				
wind turbine				
solar collector				
earth energy system				
photovoltaic cell				
geothermal heating				
geothermal electricity generating facility				
ethanol fuel				
hydrogen fuel cell (automobile)				

Use the following information to answer questions 3 to 8.

Projections concerning energy use in the future are important because they impact the research and development of alternative fuels. The following graph shows projections of the world's use of various energy types from 2003 to 2030.

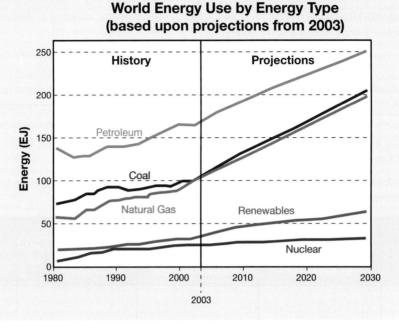

**World Energy Use by Energy Type
(based upon projections from 2003)**

History | Projections

Petroleum

Coal

Natural Gas | Renewables

Nuclear

Energy (EJ): 0, 50, 100, 150, 200, 250

1980, 1990, 2000, 2010, 2020, 2030

2003

3. Suggest a possible reason for the small proportion of world energy coming from nuclear power.

4. The world's supply of coal is much more plentiful than that of natural gas, yet natural gas use could surpass that of coal. Provide a possible reason for this.

5. Calculate the percentage of the world's total use of energy that was supplied by renewable sources in 2003.

6. Calculate the percentage of the world's total use of energy that will be supplied by renewable sources in 2030.

7. Use your answers to questions 5 and 6 to determine whether the authors of this graph are anticipating a switch to the hydrogen economy.

8. Buses that use hydrogen as a fuel emit only water and heat in their exhaust. Some buses in Edmonton are electric (powered by high-voltage cables suspended above the street). At first glance, neither bus appears to generate harmful emissions. Is this impression correct? Suport your answer.

9. List some factors affecting energy use in Canada. Describe practices that could be used to reduce the need for fossil fuels as an energy source. In your answer, identify technologies that could be used, and explain how they could be used in a way that demonstrates sustainable development.

SCIENCE 30

Appendix

Glossary

A

abiotic factor: a physical, non-living part of the environment

absorption spectrum or dark-line spectrum: a spectrum that has a pattern of dark lines due to the light passing through an absorbing medium; can be used to identify a material

acid: the substance that donates or loses a hydrogen ion to another substance during a chemical reaction

acid deposition: airborne particles containing acids or acid-forming substances contained within precipitation (wet deposition) or that absorb directly into parts of Earth's surface (dry deposition)

acid rain: any form of precipitation (wet deposition) containing an excess amount of dissolved acids; wet deposition with a pH of 5.6 or less

acquired traits: traits acquired during a person's lifetime because of experiences, education, and upbringing, such as a scar from a cut or the ability to speak a particular language

algal bloom: a rapid increase in the population of algae

alkaline: having the properties of a base

allele: an alternative form of a gene responsible for a trait

alpha particle: a positively charged particle consisting of two neutrons and two protons, which is a helium nucleus

alpha radiation: a stream of alpha particles emitted from unstable nuclei; one of the three principal types of nuclear radiation

alternating current (AC): a flow of charges that reverses directions at regular intervals

amino acid: one of the 20 possible building blocks of proteins determined by the genetic code of DNA

ammeter: an instrument that measures the electric current flowing through a component in a circuit

amniocentesis: a prenatal test done to look at the karyotype of an unborn child

anaphylactic reaction: a life-threatening, severe reaction of the immune system to an antigen that results in severe swelling and may affect the muscles involved in breathing

aneurysm: a widening or bulging of a blood vessel due to a weakening of the vessel wall

angina: chest pain caused by a narrowing of vessels that supply blood to the heart tissue

antenna: a transmitter or receiver of electromagnetic energy

anthropogenic: coming from human activity

antibiotic: a drug that fights bacterial infections

antibody: a protein molecule produced by a B-cell designed to bind to a specific antigen to facilitate its destruction

antigen: a complex molecule on the surface of an invading pathogen that triggers an immune response

It is short for antibody generator.

antioxidant: a substance that prevents the oxidation of another substance; a substance present within the body or other materials that reacts with free radicals to protect important components

antiseptic: a solution or substance that prevents or inhibits the growth of micro-organisms

antiviral drug: a type of medication that controls or cures an infection from a virus

aorta: the largest artery in the body; carries oxygen-rich blood from the left ventricle of the heart

Branches of the aorta form the body's main arteries, delivering oxygenated blood to all parts of the body.

aqueous solution: a solution in which water is the solvent

armature: the section of a motor or generator that rotates, consisting of a coil of wire, a rotating shaft, and a commutator

aromatic ring: another name for a benzene ring

arteriole: a small artery that joins a larger artery to a capillary

artery: a thick-walled blood vessel that carries blood away from the heart

asexual reproduction: the production of genetically identical offspring from one individual

astronomy: the science of objects and phenomena that originate outside Earth's atmosphere

atherosclerosis: a hardening of the arteries due to the accumulation of fatty deposits

atomic number: the number of protons in the nucleus of an atom; determines the identity of an element

e.g., All atoms with an atomic number of 6 are carbon atoms.

atrium: the smaller upper chamber that receives blood returning to the heart

autoimmune disease: a disorder in which the immune system produces antibodies against the body's own cells

autosomal cell: a cell of the body not involved in sexual reproduction

autosomal inheritance: traits controlled by genes found on the 22 pairs of autosomal chromosomes

B

B-cell: a type of white blood cell that produces antibody molecules when stimulated by helper T-cells

bacteria: microscopic, single-celled organisms that lack a membrane-bound nucleus and membrane-bound organelles; reproduction is chiefly by cell division to produce identical daughter cells

base: the substance that accepts or gains a hydrogen ion from another substance during a chemical reaction

base pair: the two nucleotides connected on opposite sides of complementary strands of the DNA molecule

Complementary base pairings for DNA are adenine with thymine and cytosine with guanine.

beaming: the communication of data between wireless devices using a beam of infrared light

benzene ring: the hexagonal-ring-shaped chemical structure formed by six carbon atoms and six hydrogen atoms or other atoms

beta decay: a spontaneous change in which an unstable nucleus emits beta radiation

It is impossible to predict when this process will occur in an individual atom.

beta particle: a high-speed electron emitted from an unstable nucleus; the result of the change of a neutron to a proton during a nuclear reaction

beta radiation: a stream of beta particles emitted from unstable nuclei; one of three principle types of nuclear radiation

bias: a preference for one particular point of view that interferes with neutral or objective decision making

biconcave: the distinctive shape of red blood cells where the cells are flat but dip inwards at the centre on both the top and bottom

biochemical (biological) oxygen demand (BOD): a measure of the amount of oxygen required for the decomposition of organic matter

biodegradable: ability to be broken down by natural mechanisms

biodiversity: the variety of life in all its forms, including the genetic diversity and numbers and types of organisms within an ecosystem

biofuel: a fuel produced from renewable biological resources, including biomass

biogeochemical cycle: a diagram representing the movement of elements and compounds between living and non-living components of an ecosystem

biomagnification: the tendency of a pollutant to appear at higher concentrations at higher levels in a food chain

biomass: plant matter or agricultural waste from recently living sources used as a fuel or as an energy source

bioplastic: an organic polymer produced by plants or bacteria that can be used in place of synthetic polymers to form materials

biotic factor: a living organism in the environment

bioweapons: genetically modified disease-causing organisms designed to infect people and either make them sick or kill them

black hole: an area in space with a gravitational field so strong that neither matter nor EMR can escape; formed as the last stage in the evolution of high-mass stars

blood clot: a jellylike, solid mass consisting mainly of red blood cells trapped in a net of fibrin fibres

blood pressure: the pressure exerted by blood against the walls of blood vessels such as arteries

blue shift: an increase in frequency due to a source of EMR moving toward an observer, due to the Doppler effect

broad-spectrum pesticide: a chemical substance that can control the population of a large variety of organisms

brush: a stationary part of a motor or generator that makes electrical contact with the rotating commutator

buffering: a chemical reaction to minimize a change to the hydronium-ion concentration in soil or water

buffering capacity: the relative ability of a substance to resist change to its pH despite the addition of an acid or base

calorimeter: a device that measures energy changes

CANDU: Canadian Deuterium Uranium Reactor; a nuclear reactor technology developed in Canada and now operating in Canada and six other countries

capillary: a tiny blood vessel that connects the smallest branch of an artery to the smallest branch of a vein

A capillary delivers nutrients to the cell and removes waste.

capillary bed: a network of capillaries in a particular area or organ of the body

carbon economy: an economy that depends on fossil fuels as the primary source of energy, resulting in excessive emissions of carbon dioxide

carbonyl functional group: the functional group formed by the joining of an oxygen atom to a carbon atom by a double bond

carboxyl functional group: the organic chemical structure composed of a carbonyl functional group and a hydroxyl functional group chemically joined to the same carbon atom

carcinogen: any agent that causes the likelihood of cancer to increase

Many carcinogens are also mutagens.

cardiac output: the volume of blood pumped by the heart in one minute, which is equal to the product of stroke volume and heart rate

cardiovascular disease: one of many disorders—coronary heart disease, strokes, and varicose veins—that affect the heart and/or the blood vessels

High levels of cholesterol can lead to cardiovascular disease.

carrier: an individual who possesses a form of a gene (allele) that results in a disease but does not demonstrate, exhibit, show, or have the symptoms of that disease

However, this individual can pass the disease-causing allele to his or her offspring.

catalyst: a substance used in a chemical process that increases the speed of the reaction and is not affected by the process

catalytic converter: an emission-control device used to remove NO_x, carbon monoxide, and hydrocarbons from vehicle exhaust

cellular respiration: the process by which cells convert the chemical energy stored in organic molecules (sugars) into energy that cells can use

centriole: the source of the spindle microtubules that form during mitosis and meiosis

centromere: the region on a replicated chromosome that attaches the two identical copies during cell division

chain reaction: a nuclear reaction that perpetuates itself; the release of neutrons during nuclear fission that initiates the fission of other atoms

chemical potential energy: the energy present within the chemical bonds of a substance

chlorofluorocarbon (CFC): a synthetic organic molecule in which hydrogen atoms are replaced with chlorine and fluorine atoms; also called Freon

cholesterol: a waxy, fat-like substance present in the cell membrane of every body cell and in food from animal sources

High levels of cholesterol can lead to cardiovascular disease.

chromatid: one of two identical strands of DNA joined at the centromere

chromosome: a strand of DNA that contains the instructions for making proteins

Chromosomes become X-shaped before cells divide.

circulatory system or cardiovascular system: the system consisting of the heart, blood vessels, and blood that circulates through the body

combustion: a chemical reaction that occurs in the presence of oxygen and results in the release of energy

commutator: a part of a motor or generator found on the armature that provides electrical contact, allowing current to flow to the rotating coil

concentration: the ration of the quantity of solute to the quantity of solution

conductor: a material in which some of the electrons can move freely, allowing the material to conduct an electric current

conjugate acid: an acid formed in an acid-base reaction when a base accepts a hydrogen ion (or proton); a product of an acid-base reaction that may behave like an acid in subsequent reactions

conjugate base: a base formed in an acid-base reaction when an acid donates a hydrogen ion (or proton); a product of an acid-base reaction that may behave like a base in subsequent reactions

constellation: a group of stars perceived as being in the shape of a figure or a design

continuous spectrum: a spectrum having no distinct lines that is distributed over an unbroken band of wavelengths

coronary arteries: the vessels that supply the heart muscle with oxygen-rich blood

coronary heart disease: a disease in which blood flow through the coronary arteries is restricted, possibly resulting in chest pain and/or a heart attack

cosmic rays: a stream of high-speed, ionized particles ejected from the objects beyond the solar system, consisting mainly of atomic nuclei

coulomb: an SI unit for charge; one coulomb is equivalent to the transfer of 6.25×10^{18} electrons

cross-pollinate: transferring pollen between genetically different plants

crossing over: the exchange of corresponding segments of DNA between maternal and paternal chromosomes during meiosis

cycle: one complete vibration of a wave

daughter cells: the two identical cells produced during mitosis

deoxyribonucleic acid (DNA): the twisted ladder-shaped molecule that contains the genetic information of cells

deuterium: a heavy isotope of hydrogen with one proton and one neutron in the nucleus

diastole: the phase of the heart's cycle where a chamber of the heart, either an atrium or a ventricle, relaxes and fills with blood

diastolic pressure: the residual pressure exerted on the artery walls when the heart's ventricles are relaxing

diffraction: the bending of a wave as it passes by obstacles or by the edges of an opening

diffraction grating: a piece of glass or plastic with thousands of tightly spaced lines etched on its surface; used to produce spectra

diffraction pattern: a pattern produced by waves that have undergone diffraction

diploid cells: cells with pairs of homologous chromosomes

direct current (DC): a flow of charges that does not increase or decrease and flows in a single direction

direct exposure: contact with a chemical substance that occurs while using it or by being present in an area where it has been used

direct variation: a relationship between two related variables where an increase in the magnitude of one variable results in an increase in the magnitude of the related variable

dissociation: the separation of a chemical substance into its individual ions in a solution

DNA fingerprint: a unique pattern of bands created when DNA is processed by running it through a special gel

A DNA fingerprint can be used to match individuals to biological remains.

DNA profile: see DNA fingerprint

DNA triplet code: three adjacent nitrogen bases found on a gene that codes for the amino acid to be produced, begin, or end the reading of a gene

dominant: referring to a dominant allele that overpowers a recessive allele—an individual only needs one dominant allele for the dominant trait to be expressed

Doppler effect: a change in the observed frequency of a wave due to motion between the source and the observer

drift: the transfer of a pesticide by wind or air currents from the location where it is sprayed

dry deposition: gases or particles that are transported by winds and absorbed by Earth's surface

E

earth energy system: a heating system that uses a loop of piping through the ground to absorb thermal energy

ecological sustainability: functioning in such a way as to not adversely affect air, water, land, biodiversity of organisms, or natural ecosystems

economic sustainability: the ability to provide employment opportunities and have access to goods and services in a manner that does not decrease the availability of natural resources

electrical energy: the energy made available by the movement of charge

electric current: the flow of electric charge from one point to another

electric field: a property of the space around a source charge that enables the source charge to exert forces on other charges that enter this region

electric field strength: the number of newtons per coulomb that a test body will experience at a given location from a source charge

electric force: the force exerted on a charged test body by an electric field; calculated by multiplying the electric field strength by the charge on the test body

electric potential difference: the change in potential energy per unit of charge

electrolytic solution: an aqueous solution that conducts an electric current

electromagnetic radiation (EMR): a wave that consists of a changing electric field and a changing magnetic field travelling at right angles to one another

electromagnetic spectrum: the wide band of different types of electromagnetic radiation ranging from radio waves to gamma rays

electrostatic attraction: a force that acts to pull oppositely charged objects toward each other

electrostatic precipitator: a device that uses electric fields to collect fly ash from emissions

emission: a substance discharged into the atmosphere or into surface water

emission spectrum or bright-line spectrum: a spectrum that has a pattern of separate bright lines that is emitted from an excited gas under low pressure; can be used to identify a material

empirical: a result of an observation

energy: the capacity to do work

energy efficiency: the percentage of input energy that has been transformed into useful output energy

energy intensity: the ratio of energy input (in joules) to economic output (in US\$); commonly expressed in terajoules (TJ) per billions of US\$ of GDP

erythrocyte: a term for a red blood cell that contains hemoglobin and transports oxygen from the lungs to the body's cells

essential fatty acid: a fatty acid that the body cannot synthesize itself and must be obtained from food

eutrophic: of a body of water having excessive plant growth due to a rich supply of nutrients

exothermic change: a chemical change that involves a release of energy, usually in the form of heat, to the surroundings

extremely low frequency (ELF): electromagnetic radiation with a frequency between 3 and 300 Hz; emitted from power distribution cables

false-colour image: an image that depicts an object in colours that differ from how a person would see the same object using only his or her eyes; often used to produce images using EMR outside of the visible spectrum

fertilizer: a substance containing one or more nutrients required by plants

fibrin: a thread-like insoluble protein formed from fibrinogen

The threads of fibrin mesh to form the fabric of a blood clot.

fibrinogen: a soluable protein present in blood plasma that converts to fibrin when blood clots

field lines: lines that describe the direction of a field by the way they point, and the strength of a field by their density

first law of thermodynamics: a law stating that energy cannot be created or destroyed

Energy is always conserved.

fly ash: small particles of sand and other unburned material that remain suspended in the exhaust gases when pulverized coal is combusted

fossil fuel: a hydrocarbon deposit (e.g., petroleum, coal, and natural gas) derived from plants and animals that lived millions of years ago that is used for fuel

frameshift mutation: the deletion or addition of a nucleotide during DNA replication

This change causes the three-letter groupings or frames in DNA to be read in an alternate pattern.

frequency: the number of cycles per second

fuel: a substance that releases energy when involved in a chemical reaction (often combustion) or a nuclear reaction

functional group: an arrangement of single atoms or groups of atoms, other than carbon or hydrogen, attached to an organic molecule

fungi: organisms that absorb food in solution directly through their cell walls and do not conduct photosynthesis; reproduction occurs through spores

gamete: a sex cell, such as a sperm and an egg, produced during meiosis with only one copy of each chromosome type

gamma radiation: the highest energy form of electromagnetic radiation with frequencies above 10^{18} Hz; emitted from the nuclei of radioactive materials

Geiger counter: a device that detects and measures the intensity of ionizing radiation

gene: a segment of DNA that carries instructions that result in the production of proteins

gene therapy: the technique of using a vector, such as a virus, to repair or replace defective genes in the treatment and possible cure of genetic diseases

genetic disease: a disease caused by a mutation of one or more genes that can be inherited by future generations

genetic engineering: the modification of genetic material through the actions of people, including selective breeding and modern techniques outside the normal reproductive process of organisms

genetically modified organism (GMO): an organism whose genetic material has been deliberately altered through transgenics

genetics: the science of gene function and inheritance

genotype: a description of the alleles that an individual possesses

This is communicated by using letters to represent the different allele versions.

geothermal energy: heat that originates from radioactive decay in Earth's core

grasshopper effect: the transport of pesticides that results from their evaporation in warmer climates and condensation and deposition in colder climates

gravitational field: a property of the space around a source mass that enables the source mass to exert forces on other masses that enter this region

gravitational field strength: the number of newtons per kilogram a test body will experience at a given location from a source mass

gravitational force: the force exerted on a test body by a gravitational field; calculated by multiplying the mass of the test body by the gravitational field strength

gross domestic product (GDP): the total market value of all goods and services produced by the country in one year; often considered as an indication of a country's economic output

grounded: connected to the ground; providing a safe conducting path for stray or excess charges; having zero electric potential energy

halogenated hydrocarbon: a hydrocarbon molecule that has one or more hydrogen atoms replaced by atoms of chlorine, fluorine, bromine, or iodine

haploid cell: a cell that has only one member from each pair of homologous chromosomes

heart attack: the death of heart cells due to a blockage in the coronary arteries that supply oxygenated blood to the heart

heart valves: thin flaps of tissue in the heart that open and close to ensure the proper direction for blood flow

heat: the transfer of energy from molecules or atoms at a higher temperature to those at a lower temperature

heat of combustion ($\Delta_c H°$): the amount of heat released when a substance undergoes combustion

heavy water: water composed of two atoms of the heavier isotopes of hydrogen and one atom of oxygen

helper T-cell: a type of T-cell that co-ordinates the actions of other cells involved in the immune response

It sends chemical messages to activate the antibody producing B-cells and killer T-cells.

hemoglobin: an iron-containing pigment that binds oxygen to facilitate its movement in the circulatory system

hemophilia: a blood disorder involving the blood's reduced ability to clot, which can lead to excessive bleeding

hertz (Hz): the unit for frequency

heterozygous: referring to an organism that has a dominant allele and a recessive allele for a given trait—*Pp*

high-density lipoprotein (HDL): a blood protein that carries cholesterol in the bloodstream from the body cells to the liver

High levels of HDL in the blood means it is less likely that deposits will form on the walls of arteries, so this is referred to as "good cholesterol."

histone: a protein that acts like a spool for DNA to wind around—it helps to compact and package the DNA in the nucleus

homologous chromosomes: a pair of chromosomes that would be matched during karyotyping because they have the same length, centromere position, and staining pattern

homozygous: referring to an organism that has two copies of the same allele for a given trait—*pp* or *PP*

hydrocarbon: an organic compound containing only carbon and hydrogen atoms

hydrogen economy: an economy that depends on renewable sources of energy to generate electricity and depends upon hydrogen as the fuel for transportation

hydronium ion: an ion created when a water molecule combines with a hydrogen ion; $H_3O^+(aq)$

hydroxyl functional group: a chemical structure found in organic molecules that consists of an oxygen atom bonded to a hydrogen atom; often represented as R–OH, where R represents a hydrocarbon or an organic molecule

hypertension: chronic, abnormally high blood pressure, characterized by values greater than 140/90

I

indicator: a substance that changes colour in response to the change in pH of a system

indoor air quality: an evaluation of the air within a room or structure

infrared light or infrared radiation: a type of electromagnetic radiation, with a frequency between 3.0×10^{11} Hz and 4.3×10^{14} Hz, that increases the vibrations between molecules, resulting in heating effects

inherited traits: traits genetically passed on from one generation to the next, such as a particular blood type or eye colour

inoculation: a process of producing immunity by introducing antigens of an infectious agent through a cut in the skin's surface

input energy: the form of energy entering into a process involving a transformation of energy

insulator: a material in which none of the electrons can move freely, preventing the material from being able to conduct an electric current

intranuclear potential energy: energy stored within the nucleus of atoms

inverse variation: a relationship between two related variables where an increase in the magnitude of one variable results in a decrease in the magnitude of the related variable

ionic compound: a chemical substance formed from the mutual attraction of positive and negative ions

ionizing radiation: high-energy radiation capable of ionizing the material through which it passes, leading to the formation of free radicals

isotope: a particular variety of an element as defined by its atomic mass

e.g., Carbon-12, $^{12}_{6}C$, has 6 protons and 6 neutrons, whereas carbon-14, $^{14}_{6}C$, has 6 protons and 8 neutrons

J

K

karyotype: an image that organizes the chromosomes of a cell in relation to number, shape, and size

killer T-cell: a type of T-cell that recognizes and destroys body cells by releasing proteins that create large holes in the target cell's membrane

kilowatt-hour: the traditional unit for electrical energy used by utility companies; 1 kW•h = 3.6 MJ

L

LC_{50}: the concentration of a chemical substance in air or water that kills half (50%) the population tested within a specified time

LD_{50}: the dosage of a chemical substance, given all at once, that kills half (50%) the population tested within a specified time

leaching: extracting a substance from a solid by dissolving it in a liquid; the removal of metal ions from topsoil that allows for their movement into lower levels of soil or into surface water

leukocytes: a term for white blood cells

liming: adding a basic compound to soil or a body of water to neutralize acid deposition

low-density lipoprotein (LDL): a blood protein that carries cholesterol in the bloodstream from the liver to the rest of the body

Too much LDL in the blood leads to deposits on the walls of arteries, so this is referred to as "bad cholesterol."

macrophage: a type of white blood cell that engulfs dead cells, cellular debris, and foreign cells

It presents pathogenic antigens to T-cells in the immune response.

magnetic field: a property of the space around a magnet or an electric current that enables the magnet or electric current to exert forces on other magnets, such as compass needles, and electric currents that enter this region

magnetic resonance imaging (MRI): a method of obtaining internal images of objects, especially living organisms, by using radio waves and strong magnetic fields

mass number: the total number of protons and neutrons in an atom; frequently written after the name of an element to identify a specific isotope (e.g., carbon-14)

mechanical energy: the energy possessed by an observable object due to motion or its position; the sum of the kinetic energy and potential energy of an object

meiosis: a two-stage form of cell division that produces gametes with only half of the number of chromosomes as the original cell

memory B-cell and memory T-cell: specialized white blood cells that persist in the bloodstream to provide future immunity to invaders bearing a specific antigen

microwaves: a type of electromagnetic radiation with a frequency between 1 GHz and 100 GHz; used for radar, satellite communications, and cooking food

millimetres of mercury: a unit for measuring pressure in terms of the height of a column of mercury that can be supported by that pressure

mineral: a solid, inorganic chemical compound produced by natural chemical processes

mitosis: the division of an autosomal cell into two identical daughter cells

mmHg: the symbol for millimetres of mercury

moderator: a substance of low molecular mass capable of reducing the speed of neutrons during the operation of a nuclear reactor

molecular compound: a chemical substance formed by elements sharing valence electrons

multiwavelength astronomy: the study of objects in space using the principle that these objects reveal different aspects of their behaviour through the many wavelengths of EMR they emit

mutagen: any agent that causes the likelihood of mutations to increase

mutation: a heritable change in the sequence of nitrogen bases along a DNA molecule

nebula: an interstellar cloud of gas and dust

negatively charged: having more electrons than protons, creating an imbalance

neutron: a component of an atomic nucleus with a mass of 1 atomic mass unit and no net charge

neutron star: a super-dense star consisting mainly of neutrons formed as the last stage in the stellar evolution of intermediate-mass stars

non-renewable: can only be used once within the scope of human timescales

It is not replenished by the biosphere, nor is it inexhaustible.

non-renewable energy: energy derived from sources that will become depleted because they are not able to be replenished in a short period of time

non-sustainable: incapable of being maintained at length due to interruption, weakening, or loss of essential characteristics (such as matter and energy)

no relationship: a situation where no recognizable pattern is demonstrated between two variables

nuclear fission: a nuclear reaction in which a large nucleus splits into smaller nuclei or particles with the simultaneous release of energy

nuclear fusion: a process in which two smaller nuclei join to form a larger nucleus, releasing energy

nuclear meltdown: the result of improper control of a nuclear reaction within a reactor; the increase in the temperature of the core of a nuclear reactor, resulting in damage and increasing the risk of releasing radioactive substances into the environment

nuclear notation: representation of an atom, $_{Z}^{A}X$, that lists the chemical symbol for the element (X), its atomic number (Z), and its mass number (A)

e.g., Carbon-14 is represented as $_{6}^{14}C$.

nucleon: the name applied to protons and neutrons (the parts of an atom's nucleus)

nucleotide: a chemical unit consisting of a phosphate molecule, a deoxyribose sugar molecule, and one of the four nitrogen-base molecules—adenine, cytosine, thymine, or guanine

Two complementary nucleotide chains combine to form DNA.

off-gassing: the release of volatile organic compounds from building materials

ohmmeter: an instrument that measures the resistance across two points in a circuit

organic matter: waste or decaying material from plants or animals

oxyhemoglobin: a hemoglobin bound with oxygen that appears bright red in colour

ozone layer: the portion of the stratosphere, between 15 km and 20 km above Earth's surface, where the highest concentrations of ozone occur

parallel connection: more than one path available for electric current, where the electric current divides, allowing each portion of the current to simultaneously pass through separate devices

passive solar energy: thermal energy derived from the Sun's radiant energy, absorbed by massive materials, and then transferred naturally to other areas by conduction, convection, and radiation

pathogen: an agent, especially a virus or a bacterium, that causes disease

pedigree: a set of standard symbols used as a tool for geneticists to trace a particular trait

It is like a genetic family tree.

per capita: for each person

persistence: the resistance of a chemical substance being broken down by biological or chemical means

persistent organic pollutant (POP): an organic compound that is resistant to being broken down by biological or chemical means

pesticide: a substance used to kill fungi, insects, animals, or plants considered as pests

petroleum: liquid hydrocarbons formed over millions of years from the remains of ancient microscopic marine organisms

pH: a value that represents the concentration of dissolved hydronium ions, $H_3O^+(aq)$, within a solution

phenotype: the physical and physiological traits of an organism

phenyl ring: another name for a benzene ring

photochemical smog: a brownish-red haze produced by the reaction of sunlight and the components in automobile exhaust

photon: a small bundle of electromagnetic energy

photovoltaic cell: a device that converts electromagnetic radiation into electrical energy

plaque: a semi-hardened accumulation of substances originally suspended in a fluid

plasma: the pale yellow fluid portion of blood where the cells are suspended

plasmid: a self-replicating circular piece of DNA that can be transferred between bacteria

Plasmid transfer allows for the sharing of genes on the plasmids between bacteria.

plastic: material that can be shaped or moulded with or without the application of heat

platelet: a particle found in the bloodstream that begins the blood-clotting process at the site of a wound

point mutation: the substitution of one nucleotide base for another during DNA replication

polarity: the presence of different regions of charge on a molecule

polarization: confining a wave to vibrate in one direction

polycyclic aromatic hydrocarbon (PAH): a compound that contains multiple benzene rings produced by the incomplete combustion of organic substances, like oils, gasoline, diesel, wood, garbage, and plastics

polyester: a polymer containing many ester functional groups

polymer: a large molecule formed by the chemical joining of many smaller molecules

positively charged: having fewer electrons than protons, creating an imbalance

power: the rate of doing work or transforming energy

primary coil: the coil to which the input voltage is applied in a transformer

protein: a large organic molecule consisting of a chain of amino acids: an essential building block of all that plays a key role in the functioning of body systems

proton: a component of an atomic nucleus with a mass of 1 atomic mass unit and a charge of 1+

protozoan: a group of microscopic, single-celled organisms that each have a nucleus

Many disease-causing protozoans can only divide within a host organism.

pulmonary artery: the large blood vessel that carries oxygen-poor blood from the heart's right ventricle to the lungs

pulmonary vein: the large blood vessel that carries oxygenated blood from the lungs to the heart's left atrium

pulsar: a rotating neutron star that emits radiation in regular pulses

Punnett square: a table that uses the alleles of the parents to indicate all possible outcomes resulting from gamete fertilization

qualitative data: a description of a substance by identifying its properties, characteristics, or attributes

quantitative data: a description of a substance that involves a measurement and a numerical magnitude

radiant energy: the energy of electromagnetic waves

radiation: energy emitted in the form of particles or waves

radiation therapy: the medical use of ionizing radiation to treat disease, especially forms of cancer

radioactive: a term used to describe substances that spontaneously emit radiation from unstable nuclei

radioactive decay: a spontaneous change in which an unstable nucleus emits radiation

It is impossible to predict when this process will occur in an individual atom.

radio wave: a type of electromagnetic radiation with a frequency less than 3000 GHz; used primarily for communications

recessive: referring to a recessive allele that is not expressed when the dominant allele is present—two recessive alleles need to be present for the recessive trait to be expressed in an individual

reclamation: restoring an area to its original form or some other usable form

recombinant DNA: DNA containing the genes spliced from two or more organisms

red giant: a star of great size and age that has a relatively low surface temperature

red shift: a decrease in frequency due to a source of EMR moving away from an observer, due to the Doppler effect

reflection: a return of a wave from a boundary

refraction: a bending in the direction of a wave that occurs when the wave changes speed

remediation: the removal of pollutants from soil, groundwater, or surface water

renewable energy: energy derived from continuously available sources that can be replenished in a short period of time

replicate: to produce an exact copy of a DNA strand

replication: the process of making two DNA molecules from one original molecule prior to cell division

resistance: the ratio of the voltage across a device to the current flowing through it

resistant population: a group of organisms not affected by a pesticide

resistor: an electronic component that resists the flow of electric current in a circuit

resolution: the amount of small detail visible in an image; low resolution means only large features can be seen, while high resolution means that small details can be seen

resonance: a concept used to describe the true structure for certain compounds that cannot be accurately represented using any one type of bonding structure

royalty: money paid to the government that is a share of the profits made from the development of a natural resource

S

schematic diagram: a sketch that uses symbols to detail the components of a system such as an electrical circuit

scrubbing: a process used to remove one or more components from a mixture of gases by passing it through substances that absorb and separate unwanted components

secondary coil: the coil that supplies the output voltage of a transformer

second law of thermodynamics: a law stating that when energy is transferred or changed from one form into another, some of the energy is always transferred to the surroundings (usually as waste heat)

selective breeding: choosing individuals with useful characteristics to produce a more desirable plant or animal stock

self-pollinate: transferring pollen from one plant to the female part of the same plant or to another plant with the same genetic makeup

septal defect: a condition where the opening between the left and right halves of the heart fails to close before birth, causing excess blood to be pumped to the lungs

septum: a thick wall of muscle that divides the left and right sides of the heart

series connection: a single path available for electric current, where the charges flow through one device before passing through to the next

sewage: waste matter often carried in sewers

sex-linked inheritance: traits not directly related to primary or secondary sexual characteristics that are coded by the genes located on the sex chromosomes

shaft: a part of a motor or generator that supports the coil of the armature, providing an axis for the rotation of the armature

societal sustainability: the ability of a group to support adequate living standards for its members; includes housing, health care, and respect and maintenance of cultural values

solar heat collector: a device that absorbs radiant solar energy and converts it into thermal energy that is carried by a fluid pumped through the collector

solar wind: a stream of high-speed, ionized particles ejected from the Sun, consisting mainly of electrons, protons, and helium nuclei

solute: a substance in a solution whose bonds are broken by a solvent; a substance that dissolves

sour gas: natural gas that contains greater than 1% hydrogen sulfide

spectra: plural form of *spectrum*

spectrometer: an optical instrument that is used to measure the wavelengths of light

sphygmomanometer: an instrument for measuring blood pressure

spindle microtubule: fibre that helps to separate chromosomes during mitosis and meiosis

standard heat of formation ($\Delta_f H°$): the energy change for a chemical reaction that involves the formation of a compound from its elements determined at standard conditions

standard solution: a solution that has a known concentration

stratosphere: the portion of the atmosphere between 10 km and 50 km above Earth's surface

stroke: a sudden loss of brain function caused by an interruption in the blood flow to the brain

strong nuclear force: an attractive force between nuclear particles that acts over short distances

supernova: a stellar explosion that produces a very bright cloud of ionized gas that remains a very bright object in the sky for weeks or months

suppressor T-cell: a type of T-cell that sends chemical messengers to stop the immune response to an antigen

sustainable: capable of being maintained at length without interruption, weakening, or loss of essential characteristics (such as matter and energy)

sustainable development: the development of industrial and natural resources that meets the needs of the present generation without compromising the ability of future generations to meet their own needs

synthetic organic molecule: a human-made compound containing carbon

systole: the phase of the heart's cycle when the ventricles contract to eject blood from within the chamber

systolic pressure: the pressure exerted on the artery walls when the heart's ventricles are contracting

T

T-cell: a type of white blood cell that matures in the thymus gland

It recognizes and destroys invaders or releases chemical messengers to co-ordinate the immune response.

target specificity: the range of organism(s) affected by a pesticide

temperature: a measure of the average kinetic energy of the atoms or molecules of a substance

test body: an observable object that can experience a force due to the presence of a field

tidal energy: the gravitational potential energy and the kinetic energy of ocean water generated by tidal effects

tide: the deformation of land and water due to the gravitational field of the Moon and Sun acting on every part of Earth

titration: a technique used to determine the concentration of a substance in a solution by adding measured quantities of another substance that it is known to react with until an endpoint is reached

toxicity: the ability of a substance to cause damage to living tissue, impair the function of a body system, or cause death when ingested, inhaled, or absorbed through the skin

toxin: a substance that can have harmful effects

traditional ecological knowledge: the accumulated observations and understanding of the people living within an area, acquired over many hundreds of years through direct contact with the environment

Incorporating traditional ecological knowledge involves developing an understanding of human interactions with the environment and focusing on the inseparable relationship among land, resources, and culture.

transformation: the process by which free DNA is incorporated into a bacterial cell

transformer: a device that transforms the AC voltage of one circuit into a different AC voltage for another circuit using separate coils of wire wound around a common iron core

transgenics: a type of genetic modification in which the gene or genes from one species are transferred and spliced into the DNA of another species

transverse wave: a wave in which the vibrations are perpendicular to the direction the wave is travelling

troposphere: the lowest region of the atmosphere that extends to approximately 18 km above Earth's surface; the region of the atmosphere where all weather occurs

ultraviolet light, ultraviolet radiation, or UV: a type of electromagnetic radiation that is emitted by very hot objects; frequencies range from 7.5×10^{14} Hz to 1×10^{18} Hz

useful output energy: the desired energy form resulting from a process involving a transformation of energy

vaccination: an injection that exposes the body to the antigens from a disease-causing pathogen so that memory cells and antibodies can be made to provide immunity

varicose vein: an enlarged, twisted vein near the surface of the skin resulting from poorly functioning valves

vector: an organism, such as a mosquito or a flea, that carries disease-causing pathogens from one person to another

vein: a thin-walled blood vessel with valves that carries blood toward the heart

vena cavae: the largest veins in the body that carry oxygen-poor blood to the heart

The body's major veins flow into each of the vena cavae before returning to the right atrium.

ventricle: the larger v-shaped bottom chamber that pumps blood from the heart

venule: a small vein that joins a larger vein to a capillary

very large array: a group of radio telescopes distributed over many kilometres along the arms of a Y-shaped track

virus: a non-cellular particle consisting of a protein coat surrounding genetic material that multiplies only within the cells of a living organism

visible spectrum: the complete range of all colours of light that can be seen by the human eye; red, orange, yellow, green, blue, indigo, and violet; frequencies range from 4.3×10^{14} Hz to 7.5×10^{14} Hz

volatile organic compound (VOC): a hydrocarbon or other organic molecule that vapourizes and exists as a gas in the air; sources include gasoline, solvents, paints, and other petroleum-based materials that vapourize

volt: the unit for electric potential difference; 1 V = 1 J/C

voltage: another term for *electric potential difference*

voltmeter: an instrument that measures the voltage across two points in a circuit

wavelength: the distance from a point on one wave to the corresponding point on the next wave: the length of one cycle

wet deposition: gases or particles that are removed from the atmosphere by water (liquid or solid) and deposited as precipitation

white blood cell: a colourless blood cell that acts to defend the body against diseases and other foreign invaders

white dwarf: a compact star found as the last stage in the evolution of low-mass stars

winterkill: the death of water organisms caused by the depletion of oxygen in an ice-covered body of water

X-rays: high-energy electromagnetic radiation with a frequency between 10^{18} and 10^{21} Hz; can be produced when fast-moving electrons strike a metal target

Reference

Contents

1 Safety in the Laboratory

Students share the role when ensuring that science activities are conducted in a safe and responsible manner. This section deals with actions you can take to help promote your own personal safety and the safety of others during lab activities.

Before Starting This Course

1) Inform your teacher of any health concerns and circumstances that may affect your personal safety, such as allergies, medication you are currently taking, whether you wear contact lenses, and any medical or physical condition that may affect your ability to participate.

2) Familiarize yourself with the lab you will use. Your teacher may ask you to draw a map of the lab and to indicate the location of various safety equipment, including lab aprons, safety glasses, protective gloves, eyewash stations, fire extinguishers, fire blankets, fire alarms, first-aid kit(s), chemical-spill kit(s), the chemical disposal area, and the broken glass disposal. Your teacher may also ask you to label other important areas in the room. At the bottom of your map, indicate the location of the nearest exit—in the event of a fire—from the lab and the building.

Before Each Activity

1) For days when you know you will be doing a lab activity, arrive appropriately dressed. For example, wear close-toed shoes, no loose clothing, and no dangling jewellery. Also, if applicable, tie your hair back.

2) Learn about the hazards posed by the materials and equipment you will be using in the activity. If your teacher asks you to read over the activity the day before, remember to do so! Read the activity not only for what you will do, but for what it instructs you not to do, and for other safety concerns. Pay particular attention to WHMIS symbols and other safety information.

3) Take only the materials you will need (e.g., textbook, laboratory instruction sheet, paper, pencil or pen, calculator) into the lab.

4) Listen carefully to your teacher's instructions. If you do not understand how to perform a step, ask for clarification.

5) Ensure that you understand the safety precautions associated with the procedure of the activity and what to do in the event of an accident.

6) Obtain your teacher's approval before starting any activity or investigation you designed yourself.

7) Wear safety glasses and a lab apron, and ensure that you have all other safety equipment required for an activity before proceeding.

During the Activity

1) In the event of a chemical spill (or any other unsafe situation), immediately report the situation to your teacher.

2) Dispose of all chemicals, specimens, and other materials in the manner instructed by your teacher.

3) Follow all instructions and safety procedures. When manipulating equipment and materials, do so in a way that shows concern for your own safety and the safety of others in the lab.

4) If you are uncertain about an issue involving safety, ask your teacher for clarification.

5) Do not eat or drink while in the laboratory.

6) Use only the amount of material needed to complete the activity. Taking additional chemicals does not increase the accuracy of your efforts; it only increases the amount of waste.

7) Do not taste substances or draw them into your mouth (e.g., mouth pipetting).

8) Use two hands to carry lab equipment. One hand should always be used to support the piece from the bottom.

9) If any part of your body comes into contact with a chemical, immediately inform your teacher. Quickly and thoroughly wash the contacted skin with water. In the event that chemicals get into your eyes, immediately flush your eyes with water for a minimum of 15 minutes.

At the End of Each Activity

1) Ensure that all materials and equipment are cleaned and returned to their proper place in the laboratory.
2) Place all chemical wastes into the appropriate containers or disposal areas in the lab as instructed by your teacher.
3) Ensure that you have cleaned your workstation by checking the tabletop, shelves, drawers, and floor.
4) Report any problems regarding broken, cracked, chipped, or unsafe equipment to your teacher.
5) Return lab aprons and safety glasses to their proper places.
6) Wash your hands thoroughly before leaving the lab.

2 WHMIS

Workplace Hazardous Materials Information System

Every day, people are exposed to materials that may be potentially harmful. To communicate information about the possible risks associated with the use of these materials and to convey information regarding proper use, the WHMIS system was developed. Eight symbols are used to depict the hazard classes in this system. For each symbol, a brief description of the materials, the possible risks associated with them, and the safety considerations regarding their handling and storage are given. It is possible for some substances to be categorized into more than one WHMIS category. For such substances, both sets of safety considerations should receive attention. Other systems for labelling and communicating safety information related to chemical compounds exist. Canada is taking steps to implement the Globally Harmonized System of Classification and Labelling of Chemicals (GHS). The GHS will allow for clearer communication of information related to chemicals used in the workplace and those that are transported within and between countries.

Class A: Compressed Gas

Description: compressed pure gases (e.g., helium and oxygen), dissolved gases (e.g., aqueous carbon dioxide), and gases liquified when compressed or refrigerated (e.g., propane)

Possible Risks: Containers may explode if heated or dropped.

Safety Considerations: Handle containers with care, ensuring not to drop or place them in a manner that they can be easily upset. Keep containers away from sources of heat and from substances that may ignite.

Class B: Flammable and Combustible Material

Description: solids, liquids, or gases capable of catching fire or exploding in the presence of a source of ignition (e.g., ethanol, propane, and group 1 metals like sodium and potassium) **Note:** Flammable materials are defined as materials that may be easily ignited or are capable of burning readily. Combustible materials are defined as substances that may burn, but do not readily ignite.

Possible Risks: These substances will burn and, therefore, are a potential fire hazard. Flammable materials will burn at low temperatures. Some substances may spontaneously burst into flames in air or may release a flammable gas when coming into contact with water.

Safety Considerations: Keep these materials away from sources of heat, sparks, or flames. Some materials must be stored in special containers to prevent exposure to air or water.

Class C: Oxidizing Material

Description: substances that provide oxygen when they react (e.g., hydrogen peroxide and sodium hypochlorite) **Note:** The production of oxygen increases the risk of fire if the substances contact Class B materials.

Possible Risks: These materials may ignite or explode if they come into contact with flammable or combustible materials. These materials may burn skin or eyes upon contact.

Safety Considerations: Wear proper protective equipment, including eye, face, and hand protection. Keep these substances away from sources of ignition and combustible materials. Store these materials in appropriate containers.

Class D: Poisonous and Infectious Material
Division 1: Materials Causing Immediate and Serious Toxic Effects

Description: materials that can cause the death of a person if exposed to small amounts

Possible Risks: These materials may result in death or serious harm, even if exposed to small amounts of the substance, and may enter the body by inhalation, ingestion, or through the skin.

Safety Considerations: Handle these materials with extreme caution. Avoid contact with eyes and skin, and avoid inhalation. Wear safety glasses, a face shield, and gloves. Work in well-ventilated areas. Store materials in proper containers and in appropriate areas. Wash thoroughly after handling these materials.

Class D: Poisonous and Infectious Material
Division 2: Materials Causing Other Toxic Effects

Description: exposure does not result in immediate effects, but may result in long-term effects to individuals who are repeatedly exposed to these materials in small amounts (e.g., asbestos, acetone, and chromium oxide)

Possible Risks: These materials may be poisonous in the long term if repeatedly exposed. They may irritate skin or eyes, may cause chemical sensitivities, allergies, cancer, and/or result in birth defects.

Safety Considerations: Avoid contact with skin by wearing proper protection for eyes and skin. Avoid inhalation by working in well-ventilated areas or by using appropriate respiratory equipment. Store in proper containers.

Class D: Poisonous and Infectious Material
Division 3: Biohazardous Infectious Material

Description: harmful micro-organisms, including bacteria, fungi, and viruses

Possible Risks: These micro-organisms may infect other organisms and cause illness or disease.

Safety Considerations: Handle material only in appropriate areas (can be sterilized) with appropriate techniques (e.g., aseptic technique) and equipment (e.g., biosafety hoods) to avoid contamination.

Class E: Corrosive Material

Description: materials that can destroy the skin and/or eat through metals [e.g., acids and caustic (basic) substances]

Possible Risks: These materials can cause severe irritation to eyes or skin upon contact. If there is prolonged contact, more serious tissue damage can result. These materials may be harmful if inhaled.

Safety Considerations: Keep materials in tightly sealed containers. Avoid contact with skin and eyes by using appropriate protection. Avoid inhalation by working in well-ventilated areas.

Class F: Dangerously Reactive Material

Description: materials that can undergo reaction when subjected to heat, pressure, and shock or when allowed to contact water [e.g., butadiene (plastic monomer) and group I metals like sodium and potassium]

Possible Risks: These materials may explode or release toxic or flammable gases when they react.

Safety Considerations: Store in a cool, flame-proof area. Exercise extreme caution when moving and opening containers.

3 Measurements and Significant Digits

Numerical information is communicated in terms of exact values (defined quantities or quantities that are counted) and measurements (readings from a measuring instrument).

EXAMPLES OF NUMERICAL INFORMATION

Exact Values	Measurements
• 1 h = 3600 s • 5 of the 10 seeds germinated.	• 37.64 g of NaCl • The marble rolled 16.7 cm.

Accuracy and Precision

Since measurements always involve taking a reading from a measuring instrument, all measured quantities have some degree of uncertainty. The source of this uncertainty has to do with the two types of measurement errors:

1) **Errors Due to Precision**—Errors due to precision occur when the person reading the instrument has to estimate the last digit of the measurement. Using the ruler at the top of the upper photo, the leaf would measure 2.1 cm or 2.2 cm. Because the markings on this ruler are 0.5 cm apart, the first digit past the decimal must be estimated.

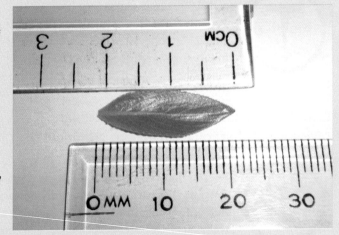

The ruler on the bottom of the upper photo has greater precision because the markings on this ruler are 0.1 cm or 1.0 mm apart. A measurement of the same leaf with this ruler suggests that the length of the leaf could be 21.0 mm, 21.1 mm, or 21.2 mm.

2) **Errors Due to Accuracy**—These errors are the result of problems with the measuring system used. The bottom photo shows the same leaf measured with a ruler that has a rounded end. Although this ruler is just as precise as the one at the bottom of the top photo, it is not as accurate. In this case, the leaf appears to have a length of 22.2 mm.

Significant Digits

If a leaf is measured to be 21 mm long, it is said to have two significant digits. The last digit is the uncertain or estimated digit. The precision of the measurement does not change with the choice of units, since precision is determined by the measuring instrument used. All of the following measurements have two significant digits:

length of leaf = 21 mm = 2.1 cm = 0.021 m = $2.1 \times 10^4 \ \mu m$

Zeros in front of the value when expressed in metres are not significant, they are just place holders. Zeros at the end of a number (trailing zeros) are used to indicate precision of measurement and are considered significant digits. The length of the page of this textbook was measured and found to be 27.50 cm, a value with four significant digits.

Logarithmic values, such as pH, have special conditions regarding significant digits. For the purpose of the Science Diploma Examinations in Alberta, digits to the left of the decimal are not considered significant. A solution with a measured pH of 10 has no significant digits, 10.0 has one significant digit, and 10.57 has two significant digits. Further information and examples of calculations involving pH appear in Unit B of this resource.

Calculations with Significant Digits

Rounding

Expressing calculated values to the correct number of significant digits requires skills in rounding. There are only two rules to rounding:

1) If the first digit to be dropped is 0, 1, 2, 3, or 4, the digit preceding it does not change. For example, to round 6.2547 to three significant digits, look at the fourth digit. Since the digit to be dropped is 4, this value is rounded to 6.25.

2) If the first digit to be dropped is 5, 6, 7, 8, or 9, the digit preceding it increases by 1. For example, to round 6.2547 to two significant digits, look at the third digit. Since the digit to be dropped is 5, this value is rounded to 6.3.

Exact Values

All exact values have an infinite number of significant digits. Recall that exact values represent defined quantities or quantities that are counted. For example, consider the statement, "5 of 10 seeds germinated." Because the number of seeds germinated is counted and, therefore, considered to be exactly known, the value 5 has an infinite number of signficant digits.

Conversion factors, like $\frac{3600 \ s}{1 \ h}$ and $\frac{1 \ km}{1000 \ m}$, are also considered to be exact values. Because conversion factors are considered to be exactly known, they, too, have an infinite number of significant digits. Therefore, when you convert a measurement, the converted measurement must have the same number of signficant digits as the original measurement.

Example Problem 1

Convert 1.50 h into seconds.

Solution

There are 3600 s in 1 h.

$$1.50 \ h \times \frac{3600 \ s}{1 \ h} = 5.40 \times 10^3 \ s \quad \leftarrow 3 \text{ significant digits}$$

Adding and Subtracting

When adding and subtracting values of varying precision, first carry out the operation without rounding any of the values. Then round the final answer to the same precision as the least precise value.

Example Problem 2

Students recorded measurements while performing a titration. Their measurements are recorded in the following table.

Trial	Volume of Standard Solution (mL)		
	Final	Initial	Added
1	13.44	3.42	
2	23.43	13.44	
3	33.5	23.43	

Calculate the volume of solution added in each trial. Identify which measurement has the least precision.

Solution

Trial	Volume of Standard Solution (mL)		
	Final	Initial	Added
1	13.44	3.42	10.02
2	23.43	13.44	9.99
3	33.5	23.43	10.1

Answers are reported to the precision of the least precise measured value used in the calculation. The least precise measured value is 33.5 (one decimal place).

Multiplying and Dividing

When multiplying values with varying numbers of significant digits, first carry out the operation. Then answer to the least number of significant digits in the original values.

Example Problem 3

Calculate the gravitational field strength for Mercury and Mars. The values for mass and radius are provided in the table.

Planet	Mass (kg)	Average Radius (m)
Mercury	3.3×10^{23}	2.439×10^{6}
Mars	6.4219×10^{23}	3.397×10^{6}

Solution

Mercury

$$g = \frac{Gm}{r^2}$$
$$= \frac{\left(6.67 \times 10^{-11}\ \text{N} \cdot \text{m}^2/\text{kg}^2\right)\left(3.3 \times 10^{23}\ \text{kg}\right)}{\left(2.439 \times 10^{6}\ \text{m}\right)^2}$$
$$= 3.700\,123\,102\ \text{N/kg}$$
$$= 3.7\ \text{N/kg}$$

Mass is reported with two significant digits; therefore, the gravitational field strength is rounded to two significant digits.

Mars

$$g = \frac{Gm}{r^2}$$
$$= \frac{\left(6.67 \times 10^{-11}\ \text{N} \cdot \text{m}^2/\text{kg}^2\right)\left(6.4219 \times 10^{23}\ \text{kg}\right)}{\left(3.397 \times 10^{6}\ \text{m}\right)^2}$$
$$= 3.711\,917\,189\ \text{N/kg}$$
$$= 3.71\ \text{N/kg}$$

Gravitational constant is reported with three significant digits; therefore, the gravitational field strength is rounded to three significant digits.

(4) Graphing Skills and Graphical Analysis

You will see a number of different types of graphs as you work through this course. As the following examples indicate, graphs should always include a title.

Bar Graphs

A bar graph can compare the effect of a specific variable within a particular category. Each category—in this case the region of Canada—becomes the manipulated variable. The value being compared—percentage of lakes categorized as either improving, stable, or deteriorating—is the responding variable. It is important for both axes to be labelled and for each of the bars to be the same width.

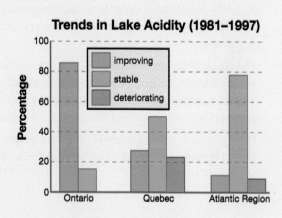

Circle Graphs

Circle graphs, sometimes called pie charts, show the contributions of different categories to the whole.

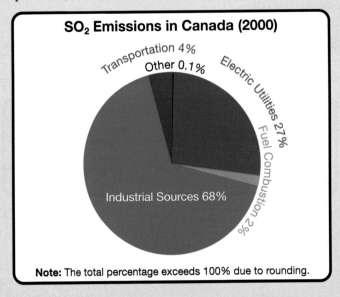

SO₂ Emissions in Canada (2000)

Transportation 4%
Other 0.1%
Electric Utilities 27%
Fuel Combustion 2%
Industrial Sources 68%

Note: The total percentage exceeds 100% due to rounding.

Scatterplots

Scatterplots are most useful when both the manipulated and responding variables are changing throughout the experiment. Consider the following data, which was collected by a group of students measuring voltage and gathering current data for a circuit containing cells, as an energy source, and a resistor.

Number of Cells	1	2	3	4
Voltage (V)	1.54	3.08	4.61	6.14
Current (mA)	1.47	2.93	4.40	5.88

How to Produce a Scatterplot from Sample Data

step 1: Labelling

Place the manipulated variable on the horizontal axis (x-axis) and the responding variable on the vertical axis (y-axis). Include units in the label.

The students defined the number of cells to use before starting the experiment, making voltage the manipulated variable (x-axis). The students then measured the current that corresponds with each setting, making current the responding variable (y-value).

Once you have labelled the axes, title your graph. One common format to follow is "Responding Variable Versus Manipulated Variable."

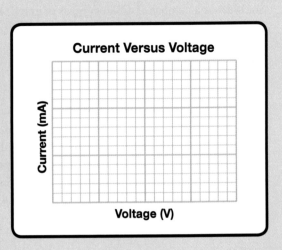

Current Versus Voltage

Current (mA)

Voltage (V)

step 2: Scaling the Axes

Choose a scale that is convenient and that uses as much of the available space as possible. The values for voltage range from 1.54 V to 6.14 V. When determining an appropriate scale, the range should go beyond the range of the data. For this grid, the voltage data can be spread over 20 gridlines. So, an appropriate scale would be 2.00 V every five gridlines. The values for current range from 1.47 mA to 5.88 mA. For this grid, the current can be spread over 15 gridlines. An appropriate scale would be 2.00 mA every five gridlines.

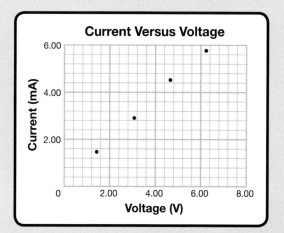

step 3: Plotting the Data

Each pair of values represents a point on the graph. Plot each point by moving along the horizontal axis to the specified voltage value and then up to the corresponding value for current.

step 4: Drawing a Best-Fit Line or Curve

Data points usually do not line up perfectly due to experimental error. So, a best-fit line or curve is needed to show a trend (if one appears) in the data.

If the trend is a straight line, use a ruler. If the trend is a curved line, draw a smooth curve that best represents the trend of the data. **Do not draw a jagged line by simply connecting the points, and do not force the best-fit line or curve through the origin.** The line should be drawn so that the same number of data points appears slightly above and below the best-fit line.

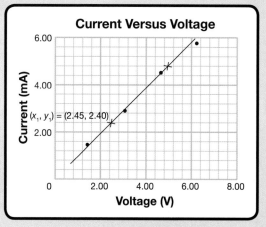

Calculating the Slope of a Best-Fit Line

The formula for determining slope is

$$slope = \frac{rise}{run} = \frac{y_2 - y_1}{x_2 - x_1}$$

Slope is determined through a calculation involving measurements. Therefore, slope has units and should be expressed with the same number of significant digits as the least precise measurement from the original data. Follow these steps to determine slope:

step 1: Select two points on the best-fit line. Ideally, these points should be as far apart as possible, easy to read, and not a part of the original data.

step 2: Substitute the values, with units, into the slope equation; then calculate the slope.

$$\begin{aligned} slope &= \frac{rise}{run} \\ &= \frac{y_2 - y_1}{x_2 - x_1} \\ &= \frac{4.80 \text{ mA} - 2.40 \text{ mA}}{5.07 \text{ V} - 2.45 \text{ V}} \\ &= \frac{2.40 \text{ mA}}{2.62 \text{ V}} \\ &= 0.916\ 035\ 344 \text{ mA/V} \\ &= 0.916 \text{ mA/V} \end{aligned}$$

The slope is 0.916 mA/V.

5 Science Skills

The activities and investigations described in this textbook are designed to improve a variety of skills essential for all learners. When you are asked to critically read an article about an environmental issue, perform an experiment, use the Internet to find information on a topic, format a spreadsheet to make predictions, or prepare a presentation to communicate a message, you are using and developing the skills associated with academic inquiry.

Alberta Education has divided science skills into four categories: initiating and planning, performing and recording, analyzing and interpreting, and communication and teamwork. Throughout this resource, science skill visual cues are shown along with each activity. When asked to complete an activity where any of these skills are identified, it may be helpful to refer to this Science Skills table to clarify what is expected.

SCIENCE SKILLS

Category	Description
Initiating and Planning	• Identify and state questions that could be investigated. These questions may arise from practical problems or from issues related to the application of science and technology. • Propose and assess alternative solutions to practical problems, and develop a plan to address them. • Design an experiment, identifying and controlling major variables. • State a prediction and a hypothesis based on available evidence, background information, or theories. • Evaluate, select, and develop a plan for the use of appropriate methods, procedures, and equipment for collecting evidence or information.
Performing and Recording	• Research, integrate, and synthesize information on a scientific question, practical problem, or technology from various print and electronic sources. Evaluate the strategy for the collection of information. • Select and use appropriate instruments for collecting data safely and accurately. • Carry out procedures in a manner to control variables or adapt and extend procedures where applicable. • Compile and organize findings and data by hand or computer using diagrams, tables, or graphs. • Apply WHMIS standards when handling and disposing of materials used in experiments.
Analyzing and Interpreting	• Interpret patterns or trends in data using appropriate scientific terminology. • Estimate and calculate values. Compare empirical and theoretical values, and account for discrepancies. • Identify limitations of data and measurements, explain sources of error, and evaluate their importance to the overall result. Determine the reliability and adequacy of the data and the methods used to collect the data. • Identify new questions that arise from an investigation. • State a conclusion based on the data obtained. Explain how the evidence gathered supports or refutes the hypothesis, prediction, or theory. • Evaluate designs or technologies on the basis of criteria, including function, reliability, cost, safety, efficient use of materials, and impact on the environment. • Identify potential strengths and weaknesses (risks and benefits) of a solution to a problem based on the data collected. Use the analysis of the strengths and weaknesses (risks and benefits from a variety of perspectives) to recommend a possible course of action.
Communication and Teamwork	• Work co-operatively with others to develop and carry out investigations, troubleshoot problems, or develop prototypes. • Select appropriate numeric, symbolic, and graphical modes to communicate findings and conclusions. • Communicate in a persuasive and engaging manner using appropriate forms of multimedia. • Evaluate processes used both individually and as a group to complete the investigation.

6 Evaluating Sources of Information

You are bombarded with information on a daily basis. Whether you watch it on television, hear it on the radio, see it in a magazine or a newspaper, or find it on the Internet, the information you collect may not be authentic.

Research not only involves the collection of information; it also involves a careful analysis of the information collected. Can it be useful to you? Since your research usually includes finding information regarding a certain topic, you want this information to be credible, accurate, reasonable, and supported. The Criteria for Evaluating Sources of Information table may assist you in evaluating sources of information you collect; it may also help you improve not only the quality of your research, but your confidence in understanding and expressing your own ideas using the information.

CRITERIA FOR EVALUATING SOURCES OF INFORMATION

Criteria	Indicators That Source . . .	
	May Be Valuable	**May Not Be Valuable**
Credibility	• author knowledgeable and respected (**Hint:** Do a search using the author's name. See what other information he or she has published on the topic or what others have said about him or her.) • has been reviewed by others who are knowledgeable in the area (peer review)	• lists no author • has negative reviews regarding information • poor grammar and spelling
Accuracy	• includes up-to-date information as well as important historical information about the topic • provides a complete, well-rounded story (includes important facts, qualifications, and alternative explanations) • presents appropriate information for the type of research you are conducting	• lacks dates • descriptions vague • presents large generalizations • fails to mention recent information regarding topic • views expressed from only one (or very few) perspective • claims made that may not be supported by reasonable evidence
Reasonableness	• presents information in a thoughtful and balanced tone • presents and argues alternative opinions • presents believable information • contains no contradictions or gaps in logic	• terms indicating inappropriate criticism (e.g., How could any intelligent person not believe this?) • exaggerates (e.g., Join the thousands of satisfied customers.) • contains a conflict of interest (Authors of the information have a vested interest in swaying your opinion.)
Support	• data, values, or statistics from reliable sources • explains how data was collected • experiments used to collect data described and performed in appropriate scientific manner • information consistent with other information gathered from other sources • author describes information in a manner that you agree with	• presents statistics or data without identifying sources or how it was collected • lacks other sources that present or acknowledge information in the same manner

7 Internet Searching Skills

The Internet is a vast source of information on a variety of topics. Although it is extremely easy to find many websites that contain information on a topic, there are often only a few that have the most relevant information you require and have time to read. There are a number of different tools, called search engines, available to assist you in finding information on the Internet. These engines organize and sort information by topic or key word. Alta Vista Canada (**www.altavista.com**), Google Canada (**www.google.ca**), and Yahoo! Canada (**www.yahoo.ca**) are just a few of the search engines available.

When using the Internet, there are two things to keep in mind:

1) **Do not believe everything you read.** The Internet is filled with information. Unfortunately, not all of it is correct. Anyone can put information on the Internet. The important thing is that you take a close look at the source to determine who is credited with supplying the information. The web address or URL—short for Uniform Resource Locator—can provide key pieces of information about the website that is supplying the information. As an example, a student searching the Internet for information related to the use of bicycle helmets was directed to the following site:

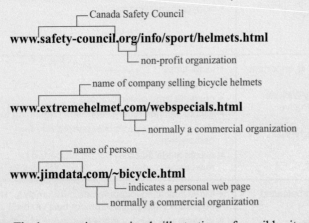

The first part of the URL, up to the first solitary forward slash, describes the "publisher"—the person or agency operating the server computer that is making this information available. In this case, the site is operated by the Faculty of Medicine and Dentistry at the University of Alberta. This indicates that the information is provided by a trustworthy source. The last part of the URL following the first solitary forward slash describes the specific folders and files for locating a particular document on this site.

As you examine the following three sites that could have resulted from the Internet search on bicycle safety, use the URL as an indicator of the trustworthiness or reliability of the information provided.

Note: The last two sites are simply illustrations of possible sites.

The point is to use a critical eye and not believe everything you read. If you are uncertain about something, it is wise to double-check the information on one or two other sites or with other resources. For more information on assessing the credibility of information, read "Evaluating Sources of Information" on page 583.

2) **Websites can change or disappear.** You should keep in mind that the Internet is constantly changing. Sometimes you will discover that after typing in an address, a note will appear on the screen indicating that the site has moved or disappeared. If you find that an address does not work, you should go back to one of the search engines and do a general search using a key word or phrase.

Internet searching strategies can assist you in targeting your search toward finding relevant information and, then, refining your search to improve the relevance of the information you collect. They can be used to narrow (reduce), expand (increase), or identify connections (associations) between the websites identified during a search. The following table lists search operators (terms or keystrokes), their function, the expected result for your search, and the possible instance for its use. Use these strategies whenever you search for information on the Internet to increase the precision of your searches and your efficiency.

Operator	Description	Expected Result	Example
AND +	All terms joined by "AND" must appear in the document in any order.	• narrows a search • requires information on both search terms	• birds AND bioaccumulation • birds + bioaccumulation
OR	Either term joined by "OR" must appear in the document.	• expands a search • requires information on either search term	• bioaccumulation OR biomagnification
NOT AND NOT -	The term following "NOT" must be excluded from the document.	• narrows a search • helps locate specific information	• bioaccumulation NOT PCB • bioaccumulation AND NOT PCB • bioaccumulation-PCB
" "	The phrase inside the quotation marks must appear in the document.	• narrows a search • useful for phrases and associations between phrases	• "global warming" • "global warming" AND arctic • "global warming" AND "arctic food chains"
NEAR	The term following "NEAR" is to be within a certain number of words of the term in front of "NEAR."	• narrows a search • identifies documents that most likely link both search terms	• mercury NEAR bioaccumulation
( )	The terms inside the brackets are to be searched for first.	• narrows a search • can be used with other search operators (e.g., AND, OR, and NEAR) • useful for phrases and associations between phrases	• (global warming) NEAR (arctic food chains)
site:	Search within a defined site.	• narrows a search • searches within a site using a specific search term or terms	• quirks site:cbc.ca • "quirks and quarks" site:cbc.ca

domain:	Search for websites from a certain domain or place of origin.	• narrows a search
		• obtains information from locations that may have distinct or unique perspectives
		• adds specific search terms to further target search
			• domain:uk
			• other domains:
			  – .com (commercial)
			  – .org (organizations)
			  – .ca (Canada)
			  – .uk (United Kingdom)
			  – .gov (government)

url:	Search for websites with specific words or terms in their title.	• narrows a search • uses synonyms as other search terms as they may appear in the url name for sites on the subject	url:WHMIS
link:	Find sites that have links to a specific site or search term.	• expands a search • useful for identifying sites with a related purpose • substantiates information or opinions expressed on one site	• link:policynut.com • link:"quirks and quarks"
title:	Identify pages that contain the search term in their title.	• narrows a search • identifies specific information within a general search	• title:mercury • title:bioaccumulation canada AND mercury

8　Reading for Understanding

An essential skill of science is to be able to read for understanding. Information must be processed before it can be made useful. Useful information might confirm or add support to ideas you already have by expanding on ideas or adding new arguments; or it might present alternate data or points of view you must consider before making your final decision. Since you use information to demonstrate your level of understanding, it is essential that you develop skills to read for understanding.

Points to Remember

- Reading is an active process. You must be thinking while you are reading.
- You need to break the information down into smaller bits and re-organize it.
- Try recalling what you already know about the topic before you start reading.
- Reading for understanding often requires multiple readings of the same document. Although it is not a quick process, it is thorough and efficient.
- Reading for understanding is a skill. With practice, you get better and quicker at it.

Note: The method described in this section may be similar to strategies you have already heard about or used. For example, one technique called SQ3R may have been introduced to you in other courses. If you already use a method to improve your level of reading for understanding, read this section over to see if there are any new aspects you can apply.

Steps to Follow

step 1: Prepare a table summarizing what you already know about the topic.

step 2: Skim through the reading to get a general idea of what the author is trying to communicate.

Pay attention to titles and subtitles, opening paragraphs, illustrations, conclusions, and vocabulary.

Rationale:　• organizes the major points being presented

　　　　　　 • often contains summaries or overviews

　　　　　　 • often restates the major points being made

　　　　　　 • allows you to look up the meaning of unfamiliar words (Are they important to what is being said?)

At this point, identify any questions you have. Then use the information in the document to find answers to these questions before going on to the next step.

step 3: Thoroughly read the document with the conclusion in mind.

Pay attention to information used to support the conclusion.

Rationale: enables you to identify how the author connects the information presented (facts, data, opinions, etc.) to the conclusions made

step 4: Does the information agree, disagree, expand, or present other perspectives on what you already know? If it is useful information, add it to a new column in your table.

Pay attention to information and conclusions.

Rationale:　• enables you to organize and incorporate the new information into what you already know to deepen and strengthen your level of understanding

　　　　　　 • helps you identify areas where your level of understanding is weak and where further information is needed

Here's what your chart might look like as you read for understanding.

Step 1:
Divide a page into three columns. Title the first column "What I Already Know About…"; and list the major points you already know.

Step 2:
Skim through the first document. Focus on titles, subtitles, illustrations, and new vocabulary, as well as the opening and closing paragraphs.

Step 3:
Thoroughly read the first document with the conclusion in mind.

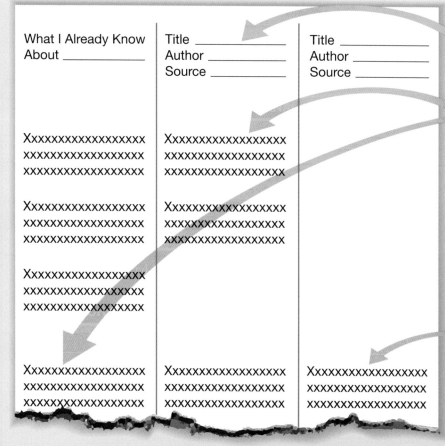

Step 4:

A Write the title, author, and source of the first article.

B Place information from the document that agrees, disagrees, expands on, or presents other perspectives to the points you have already listed. Align the information with the same points beside each other in the columns.

Step 5:
Repeat steps 2, 3, and 4 with the other documents collected in your research.

What I Already Know About _____

Title _____
Author _____
Source _____

Title _____
Author _____
Source _____

Xxxxxxxxxxxxxxxxx
xxxxxxxxxxxxxxxxx
xxxxxxxxxxxxxxxxx

Xxxxxxxxxxxxxxxxx
xxxxxxxxxxxxxxxxx
xxxxxxxxxxxxxxxxx

Xxxxxxxxxxxxxxxxx
xxxxxxxxxxxxxxxxx
xxxxxxxxxxxxxxxxx

Xxxxxxxxxxxxxxxxx
xxxxxxxxxxxxxxxxx
xxxxxxxxxxxxxxxxx

Xxxxxxxxxxxxxxxxx
xxxxxxxxxxxxxxxxx
xxxxxxxxxxxxxxxxx

Xxxxxxxxxxxxxxxxx
xxxxxxxxxxxxxxxxx
xxxxxxxxxxxxxxxxx

Xxxxxxxxxxxxxxxxx
xxxxxxxxxxxxxxxxx
xxxxxxxxxxxxxxxxx

Xxxxxxxxxxxxxxxxx
xxxxxxxxxxxxxxxxx
xxxxxxxxxxxxxxxxx

⑨ Citing Sources of Information

The research you undertake leads you to sources that contain information about a topic. Although the information contained in sources is vital to the completion of your assignment, your performance and level of understanding is determined by how you connect and develop the ideas and facts contained in the information. A poorly completed assignment simply states or lists a great deal of information on a topic; it does not demonstrate that the writer spent the time to understand, explain, and connect the information into ideas in his or her own way. Any information collected by other people, or ideas that come from what others have written, must be acknowledged in a bibliography or a list of references.

The following table provides sample formats for citing important information or ideas you have collected in your research and have used in your own writing.

Source of Information	Example of Appropriate Format
Books	
with one author	Burlingame, R. *Scientists Behind the Inventors*. New York: Avon Books, 1960.
with more than one author	Black, P., C. Harrison, C. Lee, B. Marshall, and D. William. *Assessment for Learning*. Maidenhead, Berkshire: Open University Press, 2003.
Print Articles	
from a magazine	Dewar, E. "Nuclear Resurrection." *Canadian Geographic, 125 (3)*. May/June 2005: 68–84.
from a journal	Pearson, E. "Weekly Molecules: A Cure for the 8:30 a.m. Blues." *Journal of Chemical Education, 82 (6)*. 2005: 850.
from a newspaper	McLean, A. (2005 June 21). "River City Likely to Escape Deluge." *The Edmonton Journal*. 21 June 2005: A3.
Online Articles	
from an online journal	Williams, Kathryn R. "Don't Forget the Units!" Electronic version. *Journal of Chemical Education, 76*. 1999: 313. Internet. Retrieved from http://jchemed.chem.wisc.edu/Journal/Issues/1999/Mar/abs313.html 27 September 2005.
from an online newspaper	Hotz, R. "Brain Development Rate Linked to IQ." *Los Angeles Times*. 30 March 2006. Internet. Retrieved from http://www.latimes.com 31 March 2006.
full-text article obtained from a database	Linn, M. "Technology and Science Education: Starting Points, Research Programs, and Trends." *International Journal of Science Education, 25 (6)*. 2003: 727. 32 p. Internet. Retrieved from EBSCO database 15 June 2005.
Websites	
	"Ecology of Grazed Ecosystems." *The Macaulay Land Use Research Institute*. Internet. 2005. Retrieved from http://www.mluri.sari.ac.uk/grazedecos 15 May 2005.
Government Documents	
	"Science 20-30 Program Outcomes." *Alberta Education*. June 2007.

A variety of websites exist that can provide additional information on the formats for other sources of information you may use.

10 Self-Assessment Rubric

Throughout your study in Science 30, your teacher will use rubrics or scoring guides to judge your work. Rubrics contain descriptions of what your work should look like in order to receive a particular mark. The descriptions listed in rubrics are useful for helping you to gain a better understanding of what is expected of you in your finished work.

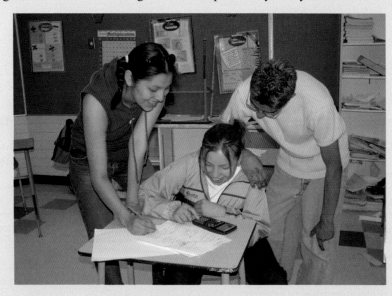

A series of generic rubrics for Knowledge; Skills; and Science, Technology, and Society (STS) are shown on the back cover of the *Science Data Booklet* for your reference. Your teacher may also provide you with individual rubrics for assignments and activities you complete in this course.

Here is a rubric for self-assessment or for assessing the effort of other students in terms of their participation during group activities or activities in this textbook where communication and teamwork skills are checked.

Score	Scoring Description
Standard of Excellence (4 marks)	The student effectively participates in discussions and activities, and encourages group members to get started and keep focused on the task. Practical solutions are offered to problems that arise, and the student actively seeks the input of others, initiating the sharing of ideas inside and outside of his or her group. The student is highly skilled in the use of technology and with the manipulatives used in the experiment or activity. The student routinely completes work that is required out of class time and often goes beyond requirements.
(3 marks)	The student contributes to discussions and activities and aids in keeping group members focused on the task. Practical solutions are offered to problems that arise, and the student listens to the input of others and shares ideas inside and outside of his or her group. The student is skilled in the use of technology and with the manipulatives used in the experiment or activity. The student routinely completes work that is required out of class time.
Acceptable Standard (2 marks)	The student participates in discussions and activities and usually focuses on the task. Some solutions may be offered to problems that arise, and the student usually listens to the input of others and is usually willing to share ideas inside and outside of his or her group. The student possesses adequate skill in the use of technology and with the manipulatives used in the experiment or activity. The student usually completes work that is required out of class time.
(1 mark)	The student doesn't contribute much to discussions and activities and has difficulty keeping focused on the task. Practical solutions are seldom offered to problems that arise, and the student does not listen to the input of others or share ideas inside and outside of his or her group. The student lacks skill (or doesn't participate) in the use of technology and with the manipulatives used in the experiment or activity. The student often does not complete work that is required out of class time.
(0 marks)	The assignment is not done at an appropriate level for a 20-level student.

11 Decision-Making Skills and Risk-Benefit Analysis

Many processes can be used to arrive at a decision. What is common to all these processes is the assessment of the possible impact that a solution will have before any action is taken. Problems do not occur in isolation; nor do they involve only one group of people. As a result, the perspectives of the groups of people involved must be considered. The decision-making model described in this section requires a number of steps to be completed.

step 1: Define the issue. Clearly state the problem, conflict, or issue, and state its source.

step 2: Make a table that identifies the groups of people involved (stakeholders), and identify their possible perspectives on the issue.

PERSPECTIVES AND THEIR FOCUS

Perspective	Focus
scientific	bases decisions on observation of natural phenomena, development of experiments to determine relationships, and theories
technological	advocates development of practical uses for scientific discoveries
ecological	bases decisions on concerns for environment and balance between biotic and abiotic factors within
economic	relates decisions to trade, industry, or money
political	bases decisions around actions of government or organizations involved with government that attempt to influence way a country is governed
legal	bases decisions on existing laws or their interpretation
ethical	bases decisions around accepted beliefs of group that acts to control its behaviour
societal	focuses on ways in which society functions and the way people interact and carry out their lives

SCORING RUBRIC FOR IDENTIFYING PERSPECTIVES

Score	Scoring Description
Standard of Excellence (4 marks)	The response demonstrates that at least three stakeholders have been identified and that a range of perspectives has been considered.
Acceptable Standard (2 marks)	The response demonstrates that more than one stakeholder has been identified and that more than one perspective was considered.

Note that this rubric, as well as the others shown in this section, are concise rubrics. Scores of 3, 1, and 0 can be inferred by the criteria for the scores of 4 and 2.

step 3: Research the issue. Conduct research to collect and assess information for all the perspectives of the stakeholders you identified. Assemble the relevant information as points in a table.

SCORING RUBRIC FOR RESEARCHING THE ISSUE

Score	Scoring Description
Standard of Excellence (4 marks)	The response demonstrates that at least four searches using different combinations of key words have been attempted and that a rich base of information related to the issue was developed.
Acceptable Standard (2 marks)	The response demonstrates more than one search attempt was made and that some information related to the issue was discovered.

step 4: Analyze the issue. Identify the risks and benefits of all the information relevant to the problem or issue. Determine a possible reaction for each of the stakeholder groups to the information you collected.

SCORING RUBRIC FOR RISK-BENEFIT ANALYSIS AND REACTIONS OF THE STAKEHOLDERS

Score	Scoring Description
Standard of Excellence (4 marks)	The response lists a variety of risks and benefits. The items listed demonstrate that thorough research was conducted by the student. The response demonstrates that most of the risks and benefits have been cited as the student considered the question from the point of view of at least three stakeholders.
Acceptable Standard (2 marks)	The response lists more than one entry in each column. The items listed demonstrate that some research was conducted by the student. The response demonstrates that some of the risks and benefits have been cited as the student considered the question from the point of view of more than one stakeholder.

step 5: Take a stand and defend your position. Review your analysis, and clearly state and defend a logical solution or an action to take.

SCORING RUBRIC FOR TAKING A STAND AND DEFENDING YOUR POSITION

Score	Scoring Description
Standard of Excellence (4 marks)	The response indicates that the student has taken a clear position that is supported by the body of the research and has considered the question from more than one point of view.
Acceptable Standard (2 marks)	The response indicates that the student has taken a position that is supported by some of the research.

step 6: Evaluate. Share your decision with others. How do their decisions differ from yours? How do the arguments differ? What have you learned from listening to their decisions? Comment on how their decisions have affected yours. Do the decisions shared completely address the initial question posed?

SCORING RUBRIC FOR EVALUATING

Score	Scoring Description
Standard of Excellence (4 marks)	The response indicates that the student considered the positions of other students and that these alternative viewpoints have each been addressed.
Acceptable Standard (2 marks)	The response indicates that the student considered the position of at least one other student and that this alternative viewpoint has been addressed.

12 Mathematics and Science Directing Words

When you receive an assignment to complete, the first question you will probably ask yourself will be, "What am I being asked to do?"

To determine what you need to do, you must identify and have a correct understanding of the directing words used in the assignment instructions. Directing words are terms that describe the actions you will need to take to complete the task.

The list of mathematics and science directing words given are used in questions, activities, and laboratory exercises throughout this textbook. This same list is used in examination questions—including the diploma examinations in mathematics and science—to provide you with specific directions of what to do in completing your response. It is important that you become familiar with the meanings of these words so you can increase the accuracy and efficiency of your work.

Algebraically

Use mathematical procedures that involve letters or symbols to represent numbers.

Analyze

Make a mathematical, chemical, or methodical examination of parts of the whole; determine the nature, proportion, function, interrelationship, etc., of those parts.

Compare

Examine the character or qualities of two things by providing characteristics of both that point out their similarities and differences.

Conclude

State a logical end based on reasoning and/or evidence.

Contrast/Distinguish

Point out the differences between two things that have similar or comparable natures.

Criticize

Point out the demerits of an item or issue.

Define

Provide the essential qualities or meaning of a word or concept; make distinct and clear by marking out the limits.

Describe

Give a written account or represent the characteristics of something by a figure, model, or picture.

Design/Plan

Construct a plan (e.g., a detailed sequence of actions for a specific purpose).

Determine

Find a solution, to a specified degree of accuracy, to a problem by showing appropriate formulas, procedures, and calculations.

Enumerate

Specify one by one or list in concise form according to some order.

Evaluate

Give the significance or worth of something by identifying the good and bad points or advantages and disadvantages.

Explain

Make clear what is not immediately obvious or entirely known; give the cause of or reason for; make known in detail.

Graphically

Use a drawing produced electronically or by hand that shows a relation between certain sets of numbers.

How

Show in what manner or way and with what meaning.

Hypothesize

Form a tentative proposition intended as a possible explanation for an observed phenomenon (e.g., a possible cause for a specific effect). The proposition should be logically and/or empirically testable.

Identify

Recognize and select as having the characteristics of something.

Illustrate

Make clear by giving an example. The form of the example must be specified in the question (e.g., word descriptions, sketches, and diagrams).

Infer

Form a generalization from sample data; arrive at a conclusion by reasoning from evidence.

Interpret

Tell the meaning of something; present information in a new form that adds meaning to the original data.

Justify/Show How

Show reasons for or give facts that support a position.

Model

Find a model that effectively represents a situation. (In mathematics, a model of a situation is a pattern that is supposed to represent or set a standard for a real situation.)

Outline

Provide the essential parts of something in an organized fashion. The form of the outline must be specified in the question (e.g., list, flowchart, and concept map).

Predict

Tell in advance on the basis of empirical evidence and/or logic.

Prove

Establish the validity of a statement for the general case by providing factual evidence or a logical argument.

Relate

Show a logical or causal connection between things.

Sketch

Provide a drawing that represents the key features of an object or graph.

Solve

Provide a solution for the problem (e.g., an explanation in words and/or numbers).

Summarize

Give a brief account of the main points.

Trace

Provide a step-by-step description of the development.

Verify

Establish the truth of a statement by substitution for a particular case or by geometric comparison.

Why

Show the cause, reason, or purpose.

(13) Summarize Your Learning Activities

At the end of a chapter, unit, or any substantial amount of material, it is important to identify the most important concepts and determine why they are important and how they relate to each other. There are six options listed. They are intended to help you review, connect, and associate the concepts and information you studied in unique ways that will engage your thinking and promote higher levels of understanding. Your teacher may choose to assess your work. So, use the rubric given on page 595 to guide your efforts and to assess your work before its completion.

Drawing a Concept Map or Web Diagram

Here's a challenge for you. Show yourself how much you've learned by using a concept map. Creating a concept map allows you to turn on the other parts of your brain to see how the concepts are organized, how the concepts can be interconnected to each other, and how to interpret large amounts of information in a new way.

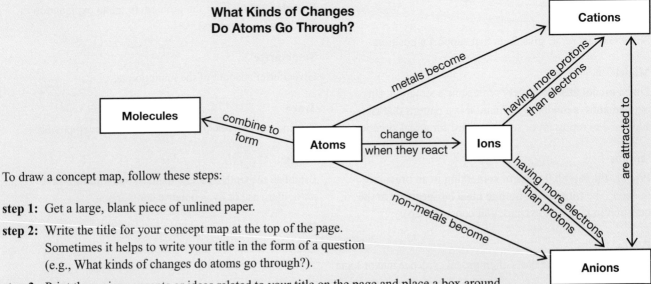

To draw a concept map, follow these steps:

step 1: Get a large, blank piece of unlined paper.

step 2: Write the title for your concept map at the top of the page. Sometimes it helps to write your title in the form of a question (e.g., What kinds of changes do atoms go through?).

step 3: Print the major concepts or ideas related to your title on the page and place a box around them. Don't worry about where you place them, just get those important ideas down on the page.

step 4: Identify boxes that contain related concepts. If they are related, connect them with a line.

step 5: Using a maximum of five words, describe how the two concepts are related. Print this linking statement on the line. (It may help to use an arrow rather than a line so that your linking statements read easier; for example, Atoms *combine to form* Molecules.

step 6: Try connecting each concept on your map as many times as possible.

step 7: Place new concepts on your map when needed. You may be surprised just how much you remember from the lessons in the chapter, or other parts of the course, and how they relate to each other. Don't forget to include examples of things you saw or did that connect to the concepts as well.

A concept map is never finished; so don't be afraid to come back to it from time to time to read it, to remember what you've learned, and to revise and add to it as you learn more.

Keep it creative! You can use colours to organize the information on your concept map to show the organization of the concepts around related themes. Make lots of links between concepts; they show how well you understand how the concepts are related.

Add in personal events or examples you can think of that relate to the concepts. These might be observations from labs and demonstrations and examples from what you have read and seen.

Creating a Point-Form Summary

Summaries are an effective way to review the notes you have made for the information from articles or textbooks. Good summaries include key terms, and they briefly describe why the key terms are important.

Lesson 1.4: Point-Form Summary

Key Term	Why Term Is Important
radiation	• alpha particles – particle composed of 2 protons and 2 neutrons • beta particles – particle composed of 1 electron • gamma photons – electromagnetic wave, not a particle

Writing a Story Using Key Terms and Concepts

Let your imagination flow. Think of a situation that would provide a great opportunity for you to use your knowledge of the concepts in the chapter to tell a scientifically accurate story. It could be a personal event, or you may want to base your story on an extension of one of the situations mentioned in the chapter.

Creating a Colourful Poster

Be visual in demonstrating what you've learned. Portray not only the main knowledge concepts, but other important aspects related to the topic, such as political, economic, or social issues and technologies. Display these aspects in a way that invites people to look at the poster and see what you have learned.

Building a Model

Sometimes the best way to explain all the parts or events occurring in a situation is with a model. Models provide a chance to identify the important parts or events and show how they contributed to the overall effect or end result.

Writing a Script for a Skit or a Mock News Report

If your news report is to make it onto the nightly newscast, it has to get across all the essential information as clearly, accurately, and briefly as possible. Remember the 5 Ws of journalism: What happened? Where did it happen? When did it happen? Why did it happen? Who was affected?

Write your news report to answer the 5 Ws for a situation that relates to the chapter information. Think of who should be interviewed to provide insight into the story (e.g., experts, observers, and people affected). Remember to include the key terms and concepts and their correct interpretation in your script.

SCORING RUBRIC FOR SUMMARIZING YOUR LEARNING ACTIVITIES

Score	Scoring Description
Standard of Excellence (4 marks)	The sample of work is well organized and addresses many major points. Relevant scientific, technological, and/or societal concepts and examples are identified and interrelationships are explicit. The descriptions and/or explanations of these concepts are correct, well organized, and reflect thorough understanding and logical consistency of thought. The student makes effective use of scientific vocabulary where appropriate. When appropriate, suitable metaphors, similes, diagrams, and/or sketches are used to illustrate descriptions and/or explanations.
Acceptable Standard (2 marks)	The sample of work addresses most major points. Relevant scientific, technological, and/or societal concepts and examples are identified, and interrelationships are shown. The descriptions and/or explanations of concepts may be disorganized but demonstrate correct understanding. The student inconsistently uses appropriate scientific vocabulary. Diagrams and sketches may demonstrate a correct, but sketchy, level of understanding.

Lesson Answers

Unit A
Maintaining Health

Chapter 1: Circulation and Immunity

Practice, page 9

2. 4.1 L/min.

3. 2.1×10^6 L/a.

5. 13 L/min.

6. a. 4.3 L/min.

Practice, page 23

12. a. pulmonary arteries

   b. aorta

   c. coronary arteries

   d. pulmonary veins

   e. venae cavae

Practice, page 24

15. a. vein   b. capillary

   c. venule   d. arteriole

   e. artery

16. artery, arteriole, capillary, venule, vein

Practice, page 29

20. b. millimetres of mercury

Practice, page 36

24. a. plasma

   b. red blood cells

   c. platelets and white blood cells

Practice, page 38

25. a. red blood cells

   b. centrifuge

Practice, pages 40 and 41

28. plasma

29. platelets

1.3 Questions, page 41

1. a. plasma, red blood cells, white blood cells, platelets

Practice, page 45

34. peanut butter

35. a. millimoles per litre

   b. person B

1.4 Questions, page 54

1. a. angina   b. stroke

   c. septal defect   d. atherosclerosis

   e. plaque   f. heart attack

   g. aneurysm

Practice, page 62

47. particles extremely small

Practice, page 69

51. not an ethical practice

1.5 Questions, page 70

6. a. memory cells produced

   b. bacteria growth inhibited

   c. most disease-causing agents destroyed

Chapter 2: Genetics

2.1 Questions, page 92

1. a. chromosome   b. karyotype

   c. protein   d. DNA

   e. gene

3. female

6. factor

Practice, page 96

14. 75%

15. a. no   b. 50%

Practice, page 97

16. a. *RR*   b. *Rr*   c. *rr*

17. b. 100%   c. 0%   d. 100%

Practice, page 98

18. a. fuzzy skin   b. fuzzy skin

   c. smooth skin

19. a. *nn*   b. *Nn*   c. *NN*

20. d. 100%

22. b. 100%

Practice, page 101

23. b. 50%

24. b. 50%   c. 50%   d. 50%

26. males

2.2 Questions, page 104

2. a. *M*   b. *m*

   c. heterozygous   d. black

3. a. $X^G Y$

   b. black male cat

   c. ginger female cat

4. 50%

7. b. 100%   c. 0%   d. 100%

Practice, page 109

28. a. adenine with thymine; cytosine with guanine

29. a. TTTACAGCGGA

   b. ATCAGAT

   c. CTAACTAAGGCCCGATT

2.3 Questions, page 115

1. a. False   b. True   c. False

   d. True   e. True   f. False

   g. False   h. True   i. False

   j. False

2. sequence III

Practice, page 118

35. a. point mutation   b. tyrosine

36. a. frameshift mutation

   b. Glycine-Leucine-Glutamate

   c. Glycine-Isoleucine-Arginine

Practice, page 121

38. b. 25%   c. 50%   d. 25%

39. b. *Hh* and *hh*   c. 50%   d. 50%

40. b. 25%   c. 0%   d. 50%

Practice, page 124

42. a. two females and two males

2.4 Questions, pages 128 to 130

4. a. colour-blind

   b. three males and two females

   c. seven females

   d. six males, one female

9. b. *SS*, *Ss*, and *ss*   c. 50%

   d. 25%

10. a. mutation

2.5 Questions, pages 140 and 141

1. a. genetic modification

   b. DNA fingerprinting

   c. gene therapy

   d. recombinant DNA

   e. transgenics

5. most similar to suspect 2

Unit B
Chemistry and the Environment

Chapter 1: Acid Deposition

Practice, page 157

1. a. 1, 8, 5, 6

   b. 1, 6, 4, 4

   c. 2, 13, 8, 10, or 1, 6.5, 4, 5

Practice, page 160

8. a. increase   **b.** increase

   c. increase

1.1 Questions, page 164

5. a. 1, 2, 1, 2

   b. 2, 7, 4, 6 or 1, 3.5, 2, 3

   c. 1, 5, 3, 4

Practice, page 166

9. a. ionic compound

   b. acid

   c. molecular compound

   d. base

Practice, page 183

22. a. 3.000, acidic

   b. 3.699, acidic

   c. 5.82, acidic

   d. 7.870, neutral or slightly basic

   e. 11.812, basic

23. a. 1.0×10^{-7} mol/L

   b. 1.0×10^{-3} mol/L

   c. 1.22×10^{-9} mol/L

   d. 8×10^{-14} mol/L

Practice, page 186

27. a. between 1.2 and 1.4

   b. between 0.04 mol/L and 0.06 mol/L

28. green

1.2 Questions, page 187

4. a. 2.903, acidic   **b.** 8.64, basic

   c. 12.355, basic   **d.** 1.25, acidic

   e. 7.092, neutral

5. a. 7.2×10^{-3} mol/L

   b. 8×10^{-8} mol/L

   c. 3.66×10^{-10} mol/L

   d. 1.0×10^{-11} mol/L

9. a. blue   **b.** blue

   c. yellow   **d.** yellow

Practice, page 193

29. no

31. yes, sedimentary rock

33. yes; volcanic, intrusive, and metamorphic

34. no

36. a. Quebec, 82%

   b. Alberta, 6%

   c. yes

Practice, page 198

37. a. chlorosis

39. a. 1.6×10^{-4} μg/g body mass

   b. 1.6×10^{-7} μg/g body mass

1.3 Questions, page 201

3. a. sedimentary rock

   b. calcium carbonate or magnesium carbonate

5. no

Practice, page 211

42. a. **Burette I:** 4.34 mL
   Burette II: 20.55 mL
   Burette III: 25.11 mL
   Burette IV: 45.94 mL

   b. 16.21 mL

   c. 20.83 mL

43. 1.24×10^{-4} mol/L

44. a. 0.0742 mol/L   **b.** 1.130

Practice, page 215

46. ethanoic acid: 0.003 mol/L or 3×10^{-3} mol/L

   hydrochloric acid: 1 mol/L

Practice, page 217

49. 7.10×10^{-3} mol/L

50. 0.0269 mol/L

51. 1.33 L

1.4 Questions, page 221

4. a. 0.167 mol/L   **b.** 0.777

5. 1.03 L

6. 0.0815 mol/L

7. a. 11.9 mL   **b.** 0.0677 mol/L

8. Titration 1

Practice, page 222

52. 300 million tonnes

Chapter 2: The Chemical Legacy of Human Activity

Practice, page 245

1. a. ethane

   b. prop-1-ene or propene

   c. methane

Practice, page 247

4. aromatic ring, phenyl ring

Practice, page 257

10. 56.7%

11. Antarctica, Greenland, and Baffin Island

Practice, page 258

15. a. Total Ozone Mapping Spectrometer

   b. Ozone Monitoring Instrument

Practice, page 273

23. c. ethanol

Practice, page 289

30. a. A, C, B

   b. raw sewage: B

   river water upstream: A

   river water downstream: C

Practice, page 293

35. **a. agriculture:** 8 100 000 kg

    domestic: 65 000 kg

    b. 125

2.3 Questions, page 299

5. organochlorines or halogenated hydrocarbon compounds

Unit C
Electromagnetic Energy

Chapter 1: Electric and Magnetic Fields

Practice, page 314

3. **a.** negatively charged

   b. 2.2×10^{-9} C

Practice, page 316

4. **a.** 2.3×10^{9} J

Practice, page 334

12. **Location II:** 0.997 N/kg

    Location III: 0.0399 N/kg

    Location IV: 0.009 97 N/kg

    Location V: 0.003 34 N/kg

13. **Location V:** 0.003 34 N/kg

    Location VI: 1.45 N/kg

Practice, page 338

16. **a.** 7.2×10^{6} N/C

1.2 Questions, page 346

1. **a. Mars:** 3.70 N/kg

   Io: 1.80 N/kg

   c. Mars: 370 N

   Io: 180 N

2. **a. van de Graaff generator:** 9.7×10^{5} N/C

   Balloon: 1.5×10^{3} N/C

   c. van de Graaff generator: 3.4×10^{-6} N, toward the van de Graaff generator

   Balloon: 5.1×10^{-9} N, away from the balloon

Practice, page 357

24. 6.2 A

1.3 Questions, page 364

1. AC generator, DC motor, DC generator

2. **a.** rotating coil

   b. brush

   c. voltmeter

   d. permanent magnet

   e. slip rings

   f. split-ring commutator

   g. voltage source

   h. split-ring commutator

Practice, page 370

32. **a.** AC   **b.** 4.8×10^{2} Ω

33. **a.** DC   **b.** 0.75 A

Practice, page 376

34. 14.4 V

35. 14.4 V

Practice, page 381

36. **a.** 12.0 V

    b. 60 Ω

    c. 0.20 A

    d. resistor 1: 4.0 V

    resistor 2: 8.0 V

37. **a.** 6.0 V   **b.** 13 Ω

    c. 0.45 A

Practice, page 383

38. **a. Blender:** 2.0 A

    Toaster: 10 A

    Kettle: 12 A

    b. 24 A

    c. 5.0 Ω

    d. 24 A

1.4 Questions, page 384

7. 9.00×10^{-2} A

8. 0.900 A

9. **a.** 24.0 V   **b.** 12.0 V

10. **a.** 100.0 Ω   **b.** 25.0 Ω

11. **b.** **i.** 130.0 Ω

    ii. 0.138 A

    iii. R_1: 6.92 V

    R_2: 11.1 V

12. **b.** **i.** 333 Ω

    ii. 1.50 V

    iii. 4.50×10^{-3} A or 4.50 mA

Practice, page 387

39. **a. First Model:** 1.5×10^{7} J

    Second Model: 1.1×10^{7} J

Practice, page 389

40. 16 W

41. $V = 18$ V

    $P = 81$ W

42. **b.** 4.0 Ω

    c. 1.0×10^{2} W

    d. Method 1: 20 V

    Method 2: 20 V

43. **b.** 16.0 Ω   **c.** 1.25 A

    d. 25.0 W

Practice, page 392

46. **a.** 7.6×10^{2} kW•h   **b.** about \$71

Practice, page 394

47. **a.** CO_2(g): 1.1×10^{4} kg or 11.0 t

    SO_x(g): 20 kg

    NO_x(g): 15 kg

    particulate matter: 1.5 kg

    b. \$924

48. **a.** 7.5×10^{2} kW•h   **b.** 7.1%

Practice, page 402

50. **a.** step-down transformer

    b. 3.00×10^{3}

    c. 6.00 A

51. **a.** step-up transformer

    c. 5.2 A

d. 60 A

e. $P_p = 1.2 \times 10^6$ W

$I_p = 60$ A

1.5 Questions, page 403

4. $V = 8.57$ A

$P = 1.03 \times 10^3$ W

5. $E = 43.8$ kW•h

cost of energy = \$3.81

6. a. $V_s = 1.20 \times 10^3$ V

$I_s = 1.00$ A

b. 1.20×10^3 W

Chapter 2: The Electromagnetic Spectrum

Practice, page 417

5. a. 28.8 μm   b. 81.6 km

Practice, page 419

6. a. 7.40×10^5 Hz or 740 kHz

b. 2.45×10^9 Hz or 2.45 GHz

Practice, page 421

7. a. 313 m

b. three city blocks

8. a. 1.82×10^9 Hz or 1.82 GHz

b. 11.2

Practice, page 422

11. 4.73×10^{17} m

Practice, page 423

12. 0.122 m

Practice, page 424

14. b. 3.0×10^{13} Hz

Practice, page 432

24. 4.2×10^{-11} m

2.1 Questions, page 434

2. a. 4.2×10^{-11} m

3. **first signal:** 1.58×10^9 Hz or 1.58 GHz

second signal: 1.23×10^9 Hz or 1.25 GHz

Unit D
Energy and the Environment

Chapter 1: Dreams of Limitless Energy

Practice, page 472

1. 14%

Practice, page 473

4. Kenya: 20 EJ/trillion US\$

Sweden: 7.4 EJ/trillion US\$

Canada: 18.3 EJ/trillion US\$

5. Kenya's

6. decrease

Practice, page 477

9. 28%

10. 8.9 MJ

Practice, page 478

11. 28%

12. 18 towns

1.1 Questions, pages 479 and 480

2. exponential trend

10. exponential growth

Practice, page 483

15. approximately 70% (coal and renewables)

30% (petroleum and hydroelectricity)

Practice, page 485

16. a. 1.0×10^5 years   b. no

17. a. charcoal

Practice, page 486

18. a. petroleum and natural gas

b. increased from 20% to 63%

1.2 Questions, page 490

1. coal, petroleum, and natural gas

2. coal

Practice, page 498

22. a. −1234.8 kJ   b. −5314.6 kJ

c. −42 500.0 kJ

1.3 Questions, page 501

1. coal

2. chemical potential energy

3. combustion

9. a. 52%

10. b. −5074.1 kJ

Practice, page 503

27. a. over 1800 times larger

28. a. $_{92}^{235}\text{U}$

b. $_{92}^{238}\text{U}$

c. $_{84}^{210}\text{Po}$

d. $_{84}^{218}\text{Po}$

Practice, page 511

36. a. yttrium-96

b. lanthanum-143

Practice, page 516

38. a. 1.81×10^{13} J

b. 1.90×10^{13} J

39. 2.2×10^{-3} kg

Practice, page 517

40. a. helium-4, $_2^4\text{He}$

b. oxygen-15, $_8^{15}\text{O}$

41. a. 1.80×10^{12} J

b. 7.05×10^{11} J

1.4 Questions, page 519

1. a. 36   b. +36

c. 92   d. 92

7. non-renewable

8. a. $_2^3\text{He} + _1^2\text{H} \rightarrow _1^1 p + _2^4\text{He}$

b. 1.92×10^{12} J

Chapter 2: Dreams of a Sustainable Future

Practice, page 554

17. b. step-up transformer

19. 6.36%

Index

A

Aboriginal people. *See* First Peoples
absorption spectrum, 448
AC (alternating current), 361–62, 364, 403
ACE satellite, 347–48
acids
  about acids, 168, 173
  about acidic solutions, 169–70
  Arrhenius's theory of, 170–72, 176
  Brønsted-Lowry theory of, 172–73, 175–77
  buffering capacity, 194, 217–19
  comparing two acids, 204, 213
  concentrated, 180
  conductivity of, 170
  natural sources, 184
  proton hopping, 177
  strong and weak, 214–15
  table of acids and bases, 173, 214
  See also acid-base reactions; carboxylic acids;
    household products; hydronium ions; pH
    scale; titrations
acid deposition
  about acid deposition, 178, 201
  about effects of, 188, 192–96, 199
  acid rain, 179, 234
  biomagnification, 197–98, 260, 285, 298
  buffering capacity, 194, 217–19
  calcium carbonate and, 192–95
  effects on ecosystems, 199–200, 231
  effects on lake water, 191
  effects on plants, 195–96
  effects on rainwater, 189
  leaching, 196–97, 199, 201, 287–88
  recovery from, 231
  wind patterns and, 190–91
  See also emissions
acid deposition, management of
  catalytic converters, 227, 229, 233
  individual and group actions, 233–34
  reducing deposition, 223
  reducing emissions, 224–27, 233
acid-base reactions
  about acid-base reactions, 173
  Brønsted-Lowry theory, 172–73, 175–77
  conjugate acids and bases, 173
  indicators to estimate pH, 184–85
  proton hopping, 177
  table of acids and bases, 173, 214
  See also conjugate acids and conjugate bases;
    pH scale; titrations
acquired traits, 93, 103
actin, as protein, 83
activity, economic, 475
adenine, in DNA, 106–8, 113–14
adenovirus in gene therapy, 136–37
aerobic exercise, 15–16, 51
aerosol sprays, 255, 259
agriculture
  biofuels, 549–50
  fertilizers, 287–88
  genetically modified foods, 139, 294
  organic farming, 299
  use of organic compounds, 242, 284–85
  See also pesticides; plants
air monitoring stations, 219

air quality
  air monitoring, 162, 219
  Alberta Environment website, 228
  indoor air quality, 279–81
  international agreements, 234, 258–59, 298
  ozone, 228–29
  peroxyacetyl nitrate (PAN), 229
  photochemical smog, 228–30
  VOCs (volatile organic compounds), 229,
    279–80
ALARA (as low as reasonably achievable),
  431, 508
Alberta Environment, 162, 219, 228
albinism pedigree, 124
alcohols, 249, 263–65, 277
algae and algal bloom, 157, 288
alkaline, 192
  See also bases
alleles, 94–95, 128
allergic reactions, 263, 268, 280
alpha radiation, 504–6, 509–10
aluminium ions, 196
amino acids, in DNA, 113–14, 136–37
ammeters, 367–69, 373–74
ammonia, 122, 249–50, 252
amperes (electric current), 356
amylase, as protein, 83
anaphylactic reaction, 268
Anasazi People, 455
anemia, 37
aneurysm, 44, 52
angina, 45, 53
answers to lesson questions, 596–99
Antarctic, 256–57, 261
antennae, 422
antibiotics, 61, 126–28, 278
antibodies, 66–69, 83
anticoagulants, 289
antifreeze, 263–64
antigens
  about immune system response, 64–65, 69
  anaphylactic reaction, 268
  blood types and, 99, 147
  vaccinations and inoculations, 66–69
antioxidants, 256
antiseptics, 59–60
antiviral drugs, 62
aorta (heart), 11–12, 20, 22
aqueous solutions
  about aqueous solutions, 166–67
  acidic solutions, 169
  Arrhenius's theory, 170–71, 176
  See also acids; bases; hydronium ions; neutral
    solutions
Arctic
  astronomy, 436–37
  biomagnification in, 198, 260, 285, 298
  grasshopper effect, 285–86, 296
  polar vortex, 261, 298
  pollution in, 242, 296–98
  sundogs, 440
armature, 351–56, 358–59
aromas, synthetic, 270, 273
aromatic compounds, 245–47
Arrhenius's theory, 170–72, 176
arsenic, 122

arteries, 22–23, 44–45
  See also blood vessel diseases
arterioles, 23–24, 28
artrioventricular valves, 11–13, 44, 53
asthma, 162, 280
astronomy
  about astronomy, 437, 454
  constellations, 436–37
  deep-space probes, 453–54
  multiwavelength astronomy, 445, 455
  traditional ecological knowledge, 436–37, 455
  use of absorption spectrum, 448
  See also cosmic rays; stars and starlight; Sun;
    telescopes
atherosclerosis
  about atherosclerosis, 44–45, 53
  aneurysms and, 52
  nutrition and, 49, 51
atmosphere, as radiation shield, 345, 439
atomic number, 503
atoms, 503
atria (heart), 11–13, 19, 20, 52
autoimmune diseases, 69
automobiles. See vehicles
autosomal cells, 84, 92
autosomal inheritance, 100, 103, 120, 123–24

B

bacteria
  about bacteria, 60–61
  acid deposition and, 179, 199
  antibiotic-resistant bacteria, 126–27, 128
  as pathogens, 56–59, 61
  asexual reproduction of, 84
  Bacillus thuringiensis (Bt), 294
  E. coli (*Escherichia coli*), 58, 288
  recombinant DNA and, 137, 140
  sulfur and, 231, 233
  in transgenics, 134–35, 140
  See also immune system
balloon sondes, 257
bar graphs, 579
base pairs, in DNA, 107–8, 113–14
bases
  about bases, 168, 173
  about basic solutions, 169–70
  Arrhenius's theory of, 170–72, 176
  Brønsted-Lowry theory, 172–73, 175–77
  buffering capacity, 194, 217–19
  concentrated, 180
  natural sources, 184
  table of acids and bases, 173, 214
  See also acid-base reactions; household
    products; pH scale; titrations
Bay of Fundy tidal energy, 532–35
B-cells, 64–65, 69, 137
beaming, 425
benzene, 122, 245–48, 291
benzocaine, 273
benzopyrene, 247
beryllium, 503–4, 506, 514
beta radiation, 506–7, 509–10
bias, 489
Big Dipper constellation, 436–37

pacemakers, 10
size of, 10
stroke volume, 8
See also circulatory systems
heart disease
angina, 45, 53
blood clots, 39, 46, 51, 53
coronary heart disease, 42, 44–46
heart attacks, 44, 46, 53, 75
septal (fetal) heart disease, 44, 52, 147
valvular heart disease, 44, 53
See also cardiovascular diseases
heart rates
about heart rates, 5, 15–16
blood pressure and, 32
dinosaur heart rates, 72
heart rate vs. mass, 71
impact of aerobic exercise on, 15–16, 51
maximum (target) heart rate, 16
resting heart rate, 5, 8, 15–16
heat
as non-useful output energy, 498–99
as transfer of energy, 492–95, 499
calorimeters to measure, 496, 499
standard heats of formation, 497–98
heavy metals. *See* metals and metal oxides
heavy water, 512
helper T-cells, 64–65, 69
hemoglobin molecules, 36–37, 41, 114, 158
hemophilia, 39, 41, 120, 130, 137
hepatitis C virus, 58
herbicides
about herbicides, 282–83
2,4-D, 283–85
2,4-D opinions, 295
See also pesticides
hertz (Hz), 418
Hess's Law, 497–98
heterozygous organisms, 97, 103
HHPS (Household Hazardous Products Symbols), 180
high blood pressure, 28, 32, 50, 52
high-density lipoprotein (HDL), 45, 48
histones as spools for DNA, 109–10
HIV particles, 56, 58
homologous chromosomes, 84–85
homozygous organisms, 97, 103
hormones
about hormones, 82–83
compounds that mimic, 292–93
n plasma, 40
host organisms, 61
household products
aerosol sprays, 255, 259
biodegradable, 269
bioplastics, 276–78
choosing household devices, 477–78
cleaning products, 269
direct exposure, 269
disinfectants, 282
energy efficient appliances, 408
energy use of products, 480
grasshopper effect, 285–86, 296
labels, 180, 280, 285, 477
light bulbs, 386, 414, 477–78
paints, 279–80
risk-benefit analysis, 281
waste disposal of, 295

See also air quality, indoor; pesticides
Hubble Space Telescope, 445
human beings, reproduction of, 84–88
Huntington disease, 120, 124
hydrocarbons
about hydrocarbons, 156, 243, 489
aromas, synthetic, 270–73
aromatic compounds, 246–47
building models of, 243–44
effects on DNA, 247–48
functional groups, 249, 264, 266–67
naming, 244–45
nitrogen oxides as combustion products, 160
PAHs (polycyclic aromatic hydrocarbons), 247, 482
photochemical smog, 228–30
resonance in bonding structure, 247
saturated hydrocarbons, 243–44
synthetic organic molecules, 249
unsaturated hydrocarbons, 243–44
VOCs (volatile organic compounds), 229
See also aromatic compounds; benzene; chlorofluorocarbons (CFCs); halogenated hydrocarbons
hydrocarbons, combustion of. *See* combustion of hydrocarbons
hydrocarbons, saturated and unsaturated
about, 48–49
healthy food choices, 48–49, 51, 53
See also fats and fatty acids
hydrochloric acid, 214
hydroelectric power, 541–44, 553
hydrofluoric acid, 175
hydrogen
about hydrogen, 171, 552
Brønsted-Lowry theory, 172–73, 175–77
proton hopping, 177
hydrogen carbonate, 218
hydrogen economy, 553–54
hydrogen fuel cells, 233, 551–52
hydrogen sulfide
acid deposition management, 230–31
chemical reaction with water, 174, 231
Claus process, 164, 231
from geothermal reactions, 531
in sour gas, 159, 165, 231
See also sour gas
hydronium ions
about hydronium ions, 172, 177
Arrhenius's theory of, 170–71, 176
buffering capacity, 194
concentration of, 180–82
pH meters, 186
pH scale and, 180–81
proton hopping, 177
See also pH scale
hydrosulfuric acid, 174, 231
hydroxides and hydronium, 208
hydroxyl functional group, 264
hypertension, 28, 32, 50, 52

I

immune system
about immune systems, 56–57, 69
about immune responses, 64–65
anaphylactic reaction, 268
autoimmune diseases, 69

immunodeficiency (SCID), 137
pathogens, 56–62
vaccinations and inoculations, 66–69
vectors, 58–59, 61, 137, 140
indicators, acid-base, 184
See also pH scale
inferior vena cava (heart), 11–12
inflammation and omega-3 fatty acids, 51
influenza, 57, 62
See also pathogens
infrared light or radiation
about infrared light, 421, 424–26, 434
false-colour images, 444
infrared astronomy, 445
inheritance
about inheritance, 78, 93, 103
dominant and recessive alleles, 94–97, 103
genetic crosses, 97
genotypes and phenotypes, 98–99, 102–3
heterozygous and homozygous, 97, 103
sex-linked inheritance, 100–101, 103
of traits, 102–3
See also genetics; Punnett squares
inoculations, 68–69
insecticides, 282
See also pesticides
insulin, 83, 135, 140
international agreements
management of acid deposition, 234
management of POPs, 298
Montreal Protocol, 258–59, 262
International Space Station (ISS), 541
Internet searching skills, 584–85
intranuclear potential energy, 511
Inuit
astronomy, 436–37, 456
pollution in Arctic, 296–97
traditional diets, 42–43, 47–48, 51, 53
traditional energy sources, 501
See also traditional ecological knowledge
inverse variation, 189
iodine, 250–51
ionic compounds, 169
ionizing radiation
about ionizing radiation, 429, 434
alpha, beta and gamma, 504–9, 519
effects on living tissues, 429, 434
gamma radiation, 421, 432
safety precautions, 430–31
shielding of, 508–10, 516
ultraviolet radiation (UVC), 421, 428–30
X-rays, 421, 430–32, 438
See also cosmic rays; solar wind
iron (hemoglobin), 36–38, 41, 114
Iroquois (Haudenosaunee) people, 89
isopropanol, 264
isopropyl alcohol, 265
isotopes, 503, 530–31

J

jet stream, 191
See also wind patterns
joule (electric potential difference), 315–16, 471

impact on ozone layer, 253, 255
nitrogen dioxide and monoxide, 178, 227
photochemical smog, 228–30
power plant emissions, 392–93
reaction with water, 178, 186
sources of, 161, 177, 230
See also acid deposition
Nobel Prize, for DNA discovery, 108
non-renewable energy resources, 489, 518, 556
See also fossil fuels
non-sustainable development, 525
See also sustainable development
North Pole
monitoring of ozone layer, 256–57
polar vortex, 261, 298
northern lights, 309, 345
nuclear energy
about nuclear energy, 503, 519
about nuclear fission, 510–13, 515–17, 519
about nuclear fusion, 438, 517–19
Earth, nuclear reactions in, 530–32
Einstein's theory (E=mc2), 514–16, 519
how to balance nuclear equations, 505
intranuclear potential energy, 511
nuclear notation, 503
process maps, 523
Sun, nuclear reactions, 514, 517–18
nuclear radiation
about radiation, 504, 519
alpha, 504–6, 510, 519
beta, 506–7, 510, 519
damage to living tissues, 508–10
gamma, 508, 510, 519
Geiger counter for detection, 509
radiation therapy, 508, 513
shielding of, 508–10, 516
nuclear reactors
CANDU reactors, 502, 510–13, 515
nuclear fission in, 515–16
nuclear meltdown, 513
nuclear waste, 516
shielding in, 510, 516
sustainability of, 529
use of, 502, 516, 560
nucleons, 503
nucleotides, 106–8, 114, 117–18
nutrition
analyzing labels, 50
free radicals, reducing exposure to, 256
high-fat diets, 42
Inuit traditional diets, 42–43, 47–48, 51, 53
iron requirements, 37–38
See also fats and fatty acids

O

odours, synthetic. *See* esters
off-gassing, 279–80
ohmmeters, 371–72
Ohm's law, 369–71, 383
oil and gas. *See* natural gas; petroleum
oil sands, 159, 473, 487
Okotoks solar community, 525–26, 537–38
oleic acid, 47
olive oil, fats in, 47
omega-3, omega-6, and omega-9 fatty acids, 47–48, 51
organic compounds, 243

See also benzene; halogenated hydrocarbons; hydrocarbons
organic farming, 299
organic matter, 287–88
output energy, non-useful, 498–99
output energy, useful, 477
oxides
from combustion, 156, 157–60
reactions with water, 178, 186
See also acid deposition; carbon dioxide; carbon monoxide; metals and metal oxides; nitrogen (nitrous) oxides; sulfur oxides
oxygen
antioxidents and, 256
See also ozone
oxygen, in combustion. *See* combustion of hydrocarbons
oxygen-poor and oxygen-rich blood, circulation of, 11–12, 20, 22–23, 37
oxyhemoglobin, 36–37, 41, 114
ozone
about ozone, 228–30
about ozone cycle and ozone layer, 253–57
impact of CFCs on, 249, 253–56
Montreal Protocol, 258–59, 262
ozone depletion process, 254–55
ozone layer, 249, 256–57, 302
protection from UV radiation, 430
ozone sonde, 257

P

PABA (para-aminobenzoic acid), 268, 273, 278
pacemaker, heart, 10
PAHs (polycyclic aromatic hydrocarbons), 247, 482
paints, 279–80
PAN (peroxyacetyl nitrate), 229
parallel connections
about parallel connections, 367, 383
cells in series and parallel, 374–75
circuits as both series and parallel, 382–83
energy sources in series or parallel, 375–76
light bulbs in parallel, 377–78
multimeters, 367–69, 371
See also resistors and resistance (electricity)
partially hydrogenated fats, 48–49
particulate matter
about particulate matter, 162
emissions removal and reduction, 224, 247
pollutants in Canada, 305
power plant emissions, 392–93
sources of, 482
parts per billion/trillion, 198
pathogens
about, 56–62, 66, 69
bacteria, 56–59, 61
fungi, 60–61
immune response to, 64–65
protozoans, 61
vaccinations and inoculations, 66–69
See also immune system; viruses
PCBs (polychlorinated biphenyl)
about PCBs, 259–60
as POPs, 246, 298, 303
PDA computers, 425
peaches and nectarines, 98
pedigree charts, 123–24, 128, 130

peer review, 172–73
penicillin, as antibiotic, 61
persistence, 285, 290
perspectives (stakeholders), 590
pesticides
about pesticides, 282, 285, 298
biomagnification of, 260
broad-spectrum pesticides, 283–84
database of, making a, 283
disposal of, 295
grasshopper effect, 285–86, 296
halogenated compounds as, 259
insecticides, 282
LD_{50} and LC_{50}, 284
persistence of, 285, 290
pest-control strategies, 293–94
POPs, 246, 298
resistant populations, 289–90
safety precautions, 285, 292–95
sales by sector, statistics, 292–93
target specificity, 283
toxicity, 283
water quality, 287
See also herbicides
petroleum
about petroleum, 486–87
in carbon cycle, 157–58
in carbon economy, 553–54
future supply, 489
geological processes, 486–88
nuclear energy, comparison, 514
oil sands, 473, 487
sulfur in, 159
use of, 486, 489, 490, 560
pH meters, 186
pH scale
about pH scale, 180–81
about pH scale indicators, 184
acid deposition and pH, 189
acid deposition impact on, 179, 192, 194–96
buffering capacity, 194, 217–19, 267
comparing two acids, 213
estimating pH using indicators, 184–86
measuring using indicators, 183
measuring using pH meters, 186
significant digits and calculations, 182
See also titrations
phenols, 60
phenotypes, 98, 102–3
phenyl ring, 245
See also benzene
phosphorus, 195
photochemical smog, 228–30
photon model of light
about photon model, 426–28, 434
EMR from Sun, 438
photon and wave properties, 446
photosynthesis
about photosynthesis, 427–28, 481
biomass energy from, 547
in carbon cycle, 157–58
process maps, 523
total energy from, 549
photovoltaic cells, 415, 540–41, 553
PKU (phenylketonuria), 124
plague, 58

Photo Credits and Acknowledgements

All photographs, illustrations, and text contained in this book have been created by or for Alberta Education, unless noted herein or elsewhere in this Science 30 textbook.

Alberta Education wishes to thank the following rights holders for granting permission to incorporate their works into this textbook. Every effort has been made to identify and acknowledge the appropriate rights holder for each third-party work. Please notify Alberta Education of any errors or omissions so that corrective action may be taken.

Legend: t = top, m = middle, b = bottom, l = left, r = right

front cover (main) © Ron Hilton/shutterstock (cells) © Sebastian Kaulitzki/shutterstock (plane) © Kevin Webb/shutterstock (lightning) Photodisc/Getty Images (dam) Alberta Economic Development (Unit B) (Unit C) (Unit D) **back cover** (hikers) Alberta Economic Development (harvest) Digital Images/Getty Images (northern lights) Alan Heartfield/Dreamstime (wind farm) Alberta Economic Development **title page** © Ron Hilton/shutterstock **IV** (t) Alberta Economic Development (b) Courtesy NASA **V** (t&b) © Ron Hilton/shutterstock (b) © Sebastian Kaulitzki/shutterstock, © Kevin Webb/shutterstock, Photodisc/Getty Images, Alberta Economic Development **VII** (tl) Photodisc/Getty Images (tr) © Courtesy of iStockphoto (bl) Wyle Laboratories/NASA–JSC **2–3** Alberta Economic Development **4–5** © Stacey Lynn Brown/shutterstock **6** © 2006 Jupiterimages Corporation **7** (br) www.general-anaesthesia.com/images/galen.html **8** (mr) © 2007 Jupiterimages Corporation **14** © iofoto/shutterstock **15** (both) © 2007 Jupiterimages Corporation **16** (tl) © Image courtesy of Dreamstime.com (br) © Tomaz Levstek/iStockphoto **19** (t) © Rod Ferris/shutterstock **20** (t) © Vera Bogaerts/shutterstock **27** (top main) Digital Vision/Getty Images (top inset) © Chin Kit Sen/shutterstock **33** © 2006 Jupiterimages Corporation **34** © Millanovic/iStockphoto **35** (tl) © Leah Groisberg/shutterstock (mr) Copyright © 2006 Dennis Kunkel Microscopy, Inc. (bl) © uzinusa/iStockphoto (bm) © Nancy Louie/iStockphoto (br) © Courtesy of iStockphoto **36** (ml) © Sebastian Kaulitzki/shutterstock **38** Copyright © 2004, 2006 Dennis Kunkel Microscopy, Inc. **40** © Anthony Hernandez/iStockphoto **42** (t) Copyright © 2007 Alberta Education and its licensors. All rights reserved. (br) Copyright © 2006 PolarHusky.com. All Rights Reserved **43** (tr) © 2007 Jupiterimages Corporation (b) Courtesy Library of Congress **47** (t) Copyright © 2007 Alberta Education and its licensors. All rights reserved. **49** (ml) © 2007 Jupiterimages Corporation (mr&b) Photodisc/Getty Images **51** (tl) Copyright © 2007 Alberta Education and its licensors. All rights reserved. (bl) © 2007 Jupiterimages Corporation (r) Copyright © 2007 Alberta Education and its licensors. All rights reserved. **55** (t) © Phil Johnson/Dreamstime (b) © Jim Lopes/shutterstock **56** (tr) Copyright © 2004 Dennis Kunkel Microscopy, Inc. (br) © J. Tan/iStockphoto **57** (bl) © fred goldstein/shutterstock (br) © Niels Laan/iStockphoto **58** (bl) © yuksel reklam/iStockphoto (br) Copyright © 2007 Alberta Education and its licensors. All rights reserved. **61** (tl) Copyright © 2005 Dennis Kunkel Microscopy, Inc. (b) © sgame/iStockphoto (tr) © 2007 Jupiterimages Corporation **66** (tr) Brendan Byrne/Digital Vision/Getty Images **68** (tl) © Patrick Roherty/iStockphoto **73** (b) © 2007 Jupiterimages Corporation **74** © Jan Daly/shutterstock **75** Michael Stoppings/Artville/Getty Images **76–77** (large photo) © Ronnie Comeau/iStockphoto **77** (br) © Mateusz Kopyt/shutterstock **78** (t) Brendan Byrne/Digital Vision/Getty Images **79** (bl) © Sean Locke/iStockphoto (r) Eyewire/Getty Images **88** Eyewire/Getty Images **89** (bl) Courtesy of Richard I. Ford (br) © The Snowgoose Ltd. (snowgoose.ca) **93** (t) © Ronnie Comeau/iStockphoto (bottom photo everything but screen image) Photodisc/Getty Images **94** (tl) © Pascale Wowak/shutterstock **96** © Melissa King/shutterstock **98** (left photo illustration) (l) © Jenny Home/shutterstock (r) © Laitr Keiows/shutterstock (br) © Philip Date/shutterstock **100** (r) Courtesy of U.S. Army Forces Strategic Command **104** (tl) © Sascha Burkard/shutterstock (bl) © Davier Yoon/shutterstock **105** © sagayago/iStockphoto **106** Courtesy of "Genetic Science Learning Center," University of Utah, http://gslc.genetics.utah.edu (bl) © R.D. Sherwood/iStockphoto.(bm) Photodisc/Getty Images **108** (tr) Courtesy U.S. National Library of Medicine (bl inset) Courtesy U.S. Department of State (br) © Javiermontero/Dreamstime (bottom background) Photodisc/Getty Images/ **112** (bl) © Bluestocking/Dreamstime (bm) © Rolffimages/Dreamstime (br) © 2007 Jupiterimages Corporation **113** (tr) © Longshots/Dreamstime **116** (t) © Larry St. Pierre/shutterstock **121** Photodisc/Getty Images **122** (tr) © alexander briel perez/iStockphoto

(m) © Andriy Doriy/shutterstock (b) © Vegard Berget/iStockphoto **124** (b) © Tim Osborne/iStockphoto **125** (mr) © Ana Kelecevic/shutterstock (tr) © J. Norman Reid/shutterstock (bl) © Natalia Sinjushina/Dreamstime (br) © Marilyn Barbone/Dreamstime **130** (tr) © Peter Spiro/iStockphoto **131** © Courtesy of the City of Ottawa **133** (tr) © 2005 Trustees of the University of Pennsylvania (bl and bm) © cjmckendry/iStockphoto (br) © gary milner/iStockphoto **134** (l) © Ladanov Sergey Valentinovic/shutterstock (r) © Andrei Tchernovi/iStockphoto **137** Courtesy Hadassah-Hebrew University Medical Center **138** (l) © Heather L. Jones/shutterstock (r) © Irena Ivanova/iStockphoto **139** © David Elfstrom/iStockphoto **140** © Baloncici/shutterstock **141** (b) © 2007 Jupiterimages Corporation **142** © Mark Goldman/shutterstock **144** Courtesy of Dr. Malcolm King **146** (t) © Karina Maybely Orellana Rojas/shutterstock **147** © Francois Etienne du Plessis/shutterstock **150–151** Digital Vision/Getty Images **152–153** © 2007 Jupiterimages Corporation **154** © AioK/shutterstock **156** © Brian McEntire/shutterstock **159** (tl) © Jack Dagley Photography/shutterstock (bl) © 2007 Jupiterimages Corporation (br) © Fred W. Paget www.fredpagetphotography.com **160** © 2007 Western Wordsmith and World of Stock **160–161** Photodisc/Getty Images **162** (tr) © Courtesy Alberta Environment (mr) © Dena Steiner/iStockphoto (bl) © Nick Cowie/iStockphoto **163** Copyright © 2007 Alberta Education and its licensors. All rights reserved. **165** (t) Copyright © 2000–2001 ATCO Ltd. Photo used with permission. (b) © L. Kragt Bakker/shutterstock **166** © Edyta Pawlowska/iStockphoto **168** © Hazlan Abdul Hakim/iStockphoto **169** Photodisc/Getty Images **170** (tr) © Popovici Ioan/shutterstock **177** (br) © Florea Marius Catalin/shutterstock **179** (tl) Copyright © 2007 Alberta Education and its licensors. All rights reserved. **180** (tl) © Greg Nicholas/iStockphoto **181** (b) © Stanislav/shutterstock **184** © USDA Forest Service - Ogden Archives **188** (t) © Bryce Kroll/iStockphoto (br) © Courtesy of iStockphoto **192** (bl) NASA (br) © Jim White/shutterstock **194** (br) © Cesair/shutterstock (b) © Ewa Brozek/shutterstock **195** © sierpniowka/shutterstock **196** (t) Reid Frederick, USDA, ARS, Ft. Detrick, MD **198** (tl) David B. Langston, University of Georgia, United States (br) © Roberto Bottazzi/iStockphoto **199** (tl) © Mike Norton/shutterstock (br) © Joan Kimball/iStockphoto **201** Photodisc/Getty Images **205** (l) © Laurence Gough/iStockphoto **208–209** © Mark Yuill/shutterstock **212** © Mrloz/CanStockPhoto **213** © Olivier/CanStockPhoto **215** (br) © Razvan Photography /CanStockPhoto **216–217** © Trout55/shutterstock **219** (br) © Alberta Environment **220** © Alexander Iotzov/shutterstock **223** (tr) © 2001 Queens Printer for Ontario (m) © Gary Unwin/iStockphoto **226** (tr) © 2004 LEHIGH INLAND CEMENT LIMITED. All rights reserved. (br) © 2007 Jupiterimages Corporation **227** (bl) © Edwin Verin/shutterstock **228** (tr) © Jess Wiberg/iStockphoto (br) © Laura Aqui/shutterstock **230** (b) © Hazlan Abdul Hakim/iStockphoto **231** © Stephen Aaron Rees/shutterstock **233** (tl) © 2006 CUTE CONGRESS All rights reserved. (bl) © Salvador Hernandez/iStockphoto **234** © Canstockphoto **236** © Edmonton Transit **237** © Steve Greenberg **242** (t) Photodisc/Getty Images (br) © Greg Thiemann **243** (l) © 2007 Jupiterimages Corporation (r) © 2007 Jupiterimages Corporation **246** (tr) © Tim Pleasant/Shutterstock (b) © EBA Engineering Consultants Ltd. Used with permission. **247** (tr) © Grag Nicholas/iStockphoto (bl) © Thomas Mounsey/iStockphoto **249** © fred goldstein/shutterstock **251** © Frances Twitty/iStockphoto **252** Courtesy National Institute of Science and Technology **254–255** (Earth) Photodisc/Getty Images **255** (t) NASA (b) © Juan Manuel Ordóñez/shutterstock **257** (l) © NASA/Goddard Space Flight Center **258** © VisualField/shutterstock **261** (Earth) Copyright © 2007 Map Resources, All rights reserved. (bl) © Earth Tech Canada Inc., Operators of the Swan Hills Treatment Centre. **266** (bl) © Photogirl/Dreamstime **267** © Eric Skorupa/iStockphoto **271** Courtesy of Italian Center Shops **275** © Wayne Johnson/shutterstock **276** (b) © J. Breedlove/shutterstock **277** ©

Edwin Parr Composite School